INFORMATION TRANSMISSION, MODULATION, AND NOISE

McGRAW-HILL ELECTRICAL AND ELECTRONIC ENGINEERING SERIES

FREDERICK EMMONS TERMAN, *Consulting Editor*
W. W. HARMAN AND J. G. TRUXAL,
Associate Consulting Editors

AHRENDT AND SAVANT · Servomechanism Practice
ANGELO · Electronic Circuits
ASELTINE · Transform Method in Linear System Analysis
ATWATER · Introduction to Microwave Theory
BAILEY AND GAULT · Alternating-current Machinery
BERANEK · Acoustics
BRACEWELL · Transform Methods in Linear Systems
BRENNER AND JAVID · Analysis of Electric Circuits
BROWN · Analysis of Linear Time-invariant Systems
BRUNS AND SAUNDERS · Analysis of Feedback Control Systems
CAGE · Theory and Application of Industrial Electronics
CAUER · Synthesis of Linear Communication Networks
CHEN · The Analysis of Linear Systems
CHEN · Linear Network Design and Synthesis
CHIRLIAN · Analysis and Design of Electronic Circuits
CHIRLIAN AND ZEMANIAN · Electronics
CLEMENT AND JOHNSON · Electrical Engineering Science
COTE AND OAKES · Linear Vacuum-tube and Transistor Circuits
CUCCIA · Harmonics, Sidebands, and Transients in Communication Engineering
CUNNINGHAM · Introduction to Nonlinear Analysis
EASTMAN · Fundamentals of Vacuum Tubes
EVANS · Control-system Dynamics
FEINSTEIN · Foundations of Information Theory
FITZGERALD AND HIGGINBOTHAM · Basic Electrical Engineering
FITZGERALD AND KINGSLEY · Electric Machinery
FRANK · Electrical Measurement Analysis
FRIEDLAND, WING, AND ASH · Principles of Linear Networks
GEPPERT · Basic Electron Tubes
GHOSE · Microwave Circuit Theory and Analysis
GREINER · Semiconductor Devices and Applications
HAMMOND · Electrical Engineering
HANCOCK · An Introduction to the Principles of Communication Theory
HAPPELL AND HESSELBERTH · Engineering Electronics
HARMAN · Fundamentals of Electronic Motion
HARMAN · Principles of the Statistical Theory of Communication
HARMAN AND LYTLE · Electrical and Mechanical Networks
HARRINGTON · Introduction to Electromagnetic Engineering
HARRINGTON · Time-harmonic Electromagnetic Fields
HAYASHI · Nonlinear Oscillations in Physical Systems
HAYT · Engineering Electromagnetics
HILL · Electronics in Engineering
JAVID AND BRENNER · Analysis, Transmission, and Filtering of Signals
JAVID AND BROWN · Field Analysis and Electromagnetics
JOHNSON · Transmission Lines and Networks
KOENIG AND BLACKWELL · Electromechanical System Theory
KRAUS · Antennas

Kraus · Electromagnetics
Kuh and Pederson · Principles of Circuit Synthesis
Ledley · Digital Computer and Control Engineering
LePage · Analysis of Alternating-current Circuits
LePage and Seely · General Network Analysis
Ley, Lutz, and Rehberg · Linear Circuit Analysis
Linvill and Gibbons · Transistors and Active Circuits
Lynch and Truxal · Introductory System Analysis
Lynch and Truxal · Principles of Electronic Instrumentation
Lynch and Truxal · Signals and Systems in Electrical Engineering
Millman · Vacuum-tube and Semiconductor Electronics
Millman and Seely · Electronics
Millman and Taub · Pulse and Digital Circuits
Mishkin and Braun · Adaptive Control Systems
Moore · Traveling-wave Engineering
Nanavati · An Introduction to Semiconductor Electronics
Pettit · Electronic Switching, Timing, and Pulse Circuits
Pettit and McWhorter · Electronic Amplifier Circuits
Pfeiffer · Linear Systems Analysis
Reza · An Introduction to Information Theory
Reza and Seely · Modern Network Analysis
Rogers · Introduction to Electric Fields
Ryder · Engineering Electronics
Schwartz · Information Transmission, Modulation, and Noise
Seeley · Electromechanical Energy Conversion
Seely · Electron-tube Circuits
Seely · Electronic Engineering
Seely · Introduction to Electromagnetic Fields
Seely · Radio Electronics
Seifert and Steeg · Control Systems Engineering
Siskind · Direct-current Machinery
Skilling · Electric Transmission Lines
Skilling · Transient Electric Currents
Spangenberg · Fundamentals of Electron Devices
Spangenberg · Vacuum Tubes
Stevenson · Elements of Power System Analysis
Stewart · Fundamentals of Signal Theory
Storer · Passive Network Synthesis
Strauss · Wave Generation and shaping
Terman · Electronic and Radio Engineering
Terman and Pettit · Electronic Measurements
Thaler · Elements of Servomechanism Theory
Thaler and Brown · Analysis and Design of Feedback Control Systems
Thaler and Pastel · Analysis and Design of Nonlinear Feedback Control Systems
Thompson · Alternating-current and Transient Circuit Analysis
Tou · Digital and Sampled-data Control Systems
Tou · Modern Control Theory
Truxal · Automatic Feedback Control System Synthesis
Valdes · The Physical Theory of Transistors
Van Bladel · Electromagnetic Fields
Weinberg · Network Analysis and Synthesis
Williams and Young · Electrical Engineering Problems

BROOKLYN POLYTECHNIC INSTITUTE SERIES

ANGELO · Electronic Circuits

LYNCH AND TRUXAL · Signals and Systems in Electrical Engineering
Combining Introductory System Analysis
Principles of Electronic Instrumentation

MISHKIN AND BRAUN · Adaptive Control Systems

SCHWARTZ · Information Transmission, Modulation, and Noise

STRAUSS · Wave Generation and Shaping

INFORMATION TRANSMISSION, MODULATION, AND NOISE

A Unified Approach to Communication Systems

MISCHA SCHWARTZ

Professor of Electrical Engineering
Polytechnic Institute of Brooklyn

McGRAW-HILL BOOK COMPANY, INC.
New York Toronto London
1959

INFORMATION TRANSMISSION, MODULATION, AND NOISE

 Library of Congress Catalog Card Number 59-9993

IX

55760

THE MAPLE PRESS COMPANY, YORK, PA.

To my wife

Lillian

and son

David

PREFACE

This book is intended to serve as a textbook for a senior-level systems course in electrical engineering. It emphasizes the fundamental role of system bandwidth and noise in limiting the transmission of information and stresses the unifying principles underlying modern information-transmission systems.

Many engineering schools have traditionally offered a radio-engineering type of course in the senior year, stressing the actual circuitry and details of design of different kinds of radio systems. The communications field has expanded explosively, however, since the early 1940s. In addition to the commonly used amplitude-modulation and frequency-modulation systems we now have pulse-modulation systems, pulse-code modulation (PCM), servo systems, and sampled-data servo systems, to name a few. Both time-multiplexing and frequency-multiplexing techniques have been widely adopted. Television and radar and the circuitry required for their operation have become important in the electrical-engineering field. Data-processing systems play an ever-increasing role in our lives.

Obviously all these different systems can no longer be treated individually and in detail in one senior electrical-engineering course. With an ever-increasing necessity for assimilating and understanding vast amounts of new material and the difficulty of expanding an already hard-pressed electrical-engineering curriculum the emphasis has begun to shift to a common unifying approach to the study of modern communication systems. The pioneering studies of Wiener and Shannon in the area of communication theory have served to focus attention since 1948 on the unifying principles of information transmission. It is hoped that this textbook, in stressing the principles common to all information-transmission systems, will enable both the student and the practicing engineer better to understand the myriad communication systems which he may encounter.

Most of the material of the first five chapters of the book has been taught for several years in a one-semester course required of all electrical-engineering senior students at the Polytechnic Institute of Brooklyn. As prerequisites to this course the students have had one-year courses in electronics and networks at the junior level and a one-semester course in pulse circuits at the senior level. Many of the students also take a communication electronics course parallel with this course which treats the actual design of such devices as power amplifiers, modulators, oscillators, etc.

The stress in this course is therefore placed on block diagrams embodying the actual circuitry treated either in the previous courses or in the parallel course. This course thus serves to unify and apply material studied previously in the electrical-engineering curriculum.

The material of the last two chapters of the book has been taught as part of a first-year graduate course in communication theory at Adelphi College and the College of the City of New York.

In schools where the Fourier integral and the frequency analysis of networks are studied as part of a networks course, Chaps. 1 and 3 to 6 could be covered in a one-semester senior course, with Chap. 2 assigned for home reading. Alternatively, a one-year course combining both the systems approach and circuit design might be offered, with design sessions used to treat in more detail the actual circuitry mentioned in passing in the book.

The order of presentation of the material in the book has been made as logical as possible. The book begins in Chap. 1 by developing in a qualitative way a measure of information capacity of a system. Limitations in information capacity are shown to be due to the presence of energy-storage devices in the system and to unavoidable noise fluctuations. The major portion of the book is devoted to an exploration of the significance of these limitations. The energy-storage or time-response limitation is shown in Chap. 2 to be expressible as a bandwidth limitation. For this purpose the Fourier series, Fourier integral, and concept of the frequency spectrum are developed and related to time response. The response of idealized linear systems is discussed and the relation of amplitude and phase distortion to time response developed.

Some practical information-transmission systems are then studied in Chaps. 3 and 4 as applications of the previous material. The process of modulation is treated for two different types of carrier: sinusoidal and pulse. A study of balanced modulators and the analysis of time switching serves to unify the treatment. Conventional AM, single-sideband, and FM systems are studied, then double-sideband modulation is introduced, leading to a discussion of sampled-data systems. The sampling theorem develops naturally out of the discussion. Pulse-modulation systems are then considered, with particular reference made to a typical pulse-amplitude modulation (PAM) system and pulse-position modulation (PPM) system.

Chapter 5 introduces the second system limitation—noise. Sources of noise, shot effect and thermal noise, are discussed, and simple noise models for vacuum tubes, transistors, and semiconductor diodes are introduced. Mean-squared noise voltages and currents are calculated for simple circuits, and the concepts of noise figure, signal-to-noise ratio, available gain, etc., are introduced.

The two system limitations, noise and bandwidth, are tied together in Chap. 6. Here comparisons are made in a simple manner between the different types of modulation systems introduced previously. The comparisons utilize the ideas of bandwidth and signal-to-noise ratio developed previously. Pulse-code modulation is introduced as an example of a coded form of signal transmission, and coded transmission systems are compared with noncoded wideband systems such as FM and PPM.

Any further discussion of modern communication systems must of necessity utilize statistical concepts. To make the book as self-contained as possible, Chap. 7 introduces the necessary elements of probability theory. These are applied to a further discussion of PCM and in dealing with radar-system analysis. The statistics of fluctuation noise are included. The book concludes by introducing the concept of the correlation function and its relation to the system power spectrum. An example of the calculation of the power spectrum of a random-type signal is included.

The multiple-section system of teaching required courses to large numbers of students at the Polytechnic Institute of Brooklyn has enabled the author to profit immensely from the searching criticism of the other instructors teaching the course.

Particular acknowledgment should be made to Professor A. George Schillinger, who subjected the entire manuscript to close scrutiny and who suggested innumerable ways of making the presentation more understandable to the student. A special debt of gratitude is also due the late Professor Maurice V. Joyce, with whose untimely passing the author lost an esteemed colleague and friend. Professor Joyce helped considerably in clarifying the author's understanding of various points throughout the book and was particularly helpful in the writing of Chap. 5 on Noise.

Mischa Schwartz

CONTENTS

CHAPTER 1

INTRODUCTION TO INFORMATION TRANSMISSION

This book is devoted to a study of communication systems, or systems used to transmit information. In the course of the development we shall emphasize the limitations imposed on the information transmitted by the system through which it was passed and shall attempt some comparison of different systems on the basis of information-handling capabilities.

A complete system will generally include a transmitter, a transmission medium over which the information is transmitted (wires in the case of telegraphy or telephony, and air in the case of radio), and a receiver which produces at its output a recognizable replica of the input information.

In most communication work information transmission is closely related to the modulation or time variation of a particular sinusoidal

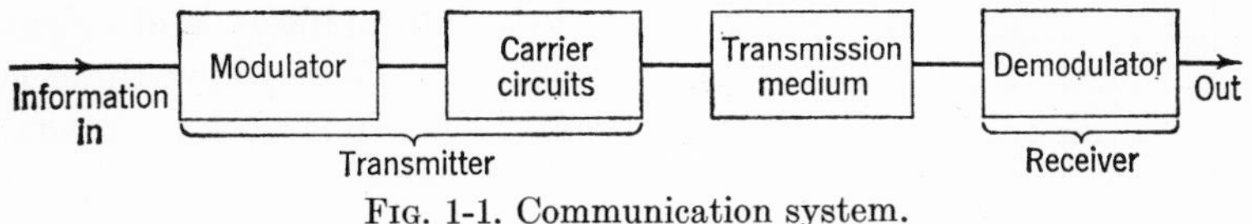

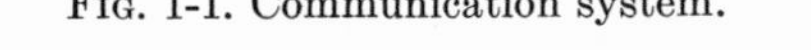
FIG. 1-1. Communication system.

signal called the *carrier*. A typical system diagram would thus appear as in Fig. 1-1.

Note that we have used the word *information* many times in the previous sentences. We shall have occasion to use this word many times in the future. Although a precise mathematical definition can be set up for this concept, we shall rely on our intuitive sense in this introductory text.

Consider a student attending a class in which the teacher spends the entire time whistling one continuous note. Obviously, attending such a class would be a waste of time. What could one possibly learn from the one note? (Even if it were important for the student to repeat the sound exactly, he would be better off staying at home listening to a recording.) Perhaps in the next class the teacher chooses to devote the entire hour to a reading, word for word, from the text: no time for questions, no pauses, no original thoughts. Again why come to class (aside from the irrevelant fact that many persons might not then take the opportunity to read the book for themselves)?

What is the point to these hypothetical and obviously made-up stories?

A student comes to class to receive *information.* That is, the teacher and student are in class to discuss new material or, at least, review old material in a new way.

The words and phrases used should thus be *changing* continuously; they should, in most cases, be *unpredictable* (otherwise—why come to class?).

The key word here is *change:* If information is to be conveyed, we must presumably have sounds or, more generally, *signals changing with time.* A continuous trilling of one note conveys no information to you. If the note is varied in a manner that you can interpret, however, the "signal" begins to convey meaning and information.

So the transmission of information is related to signals changing with time, and changing in an unpredictable way. (For a well-known melody or old story conveys no new information although made up of changing notes or words.)

Why is it so important to stress these points? Obviously if we, as engineers, are to design systems to transmit information and are interested in the best possible type of system, given practical equipment and a limited budget, we must know (at least intuitively) what it is we are transmitting and the effect of the system on this quantity.

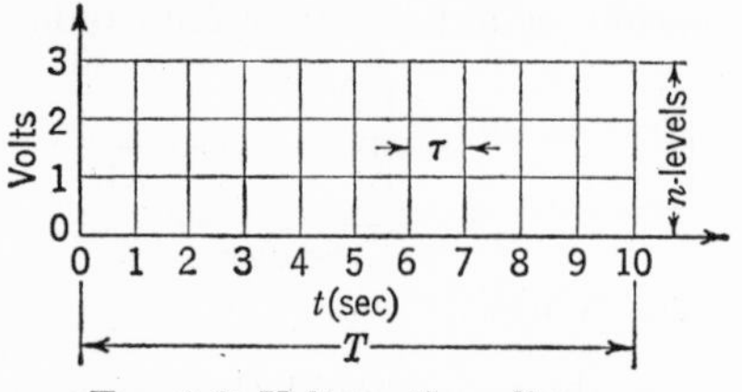

FIG. 1-2. Voltage-time diagram.

1-1. Information and System Capacity. To see how these concepts fit into our work in communication, consider the voltage-time diagram of Fig. 1-2.

Assume that we have an interval of time T sec long in which to transmit information and a maximum voltage amplitude (because of power limitations) that we can use. (In Fig. 1-2 T is 10 sec, and the maximum voltage is 3 volts.) A natural question to ask is: How much information can we transmit in this interval? Can we put a tag on the amount, and how does it depend on our system? (Note that the system has already introduced one limitation—that of power.)

The next question is: Why a limit to the amount of information? If information transmission is related to signals changing unpredictably with time, why not just change the signal as rapidly as we like and over as many subdivisions of the maximum amplitude as we like? This would imply increasing the information content indefinitely.

We deal with physical systems, however, and these systems do not allow us to increase indefinitely the rate of signal change and to distinguish indefinitely many voltage amplitudes, or levels:

1. All our systems have energy-storage devices present, and changing

the signal implies changing the energy content. There is a limit on the rate of doing this determined by the particular system.

2. Every system provides inherent (even if small) variations or fluctuations in voltage, or whatever parameter is used to measure the signal amplitude, and we cannot subdivide amplitudes indefinitely. These fluctuations of a parameter to be varied are called *noise*.

There is thus a *minimum* time τ required for energy change and a minimum detectable signal-amplitude change. As an example, τ is given as 1 sec in Fig. 1-2. If the inherent voltage fluctuations of the system may be assumed as an example to vary within ± 1 volt most of the time, then the minimum detectable voltage change due to the signal is 1 volt. With a maximum voltage amplitude of 3 volts, there are thus four detectable levels of signal (0 voltage being assumed to be a possible signal value). For if the signal were to change by less than 1 volt, it could not be distinguished from the undesired noise fluctuations introduced by the system.

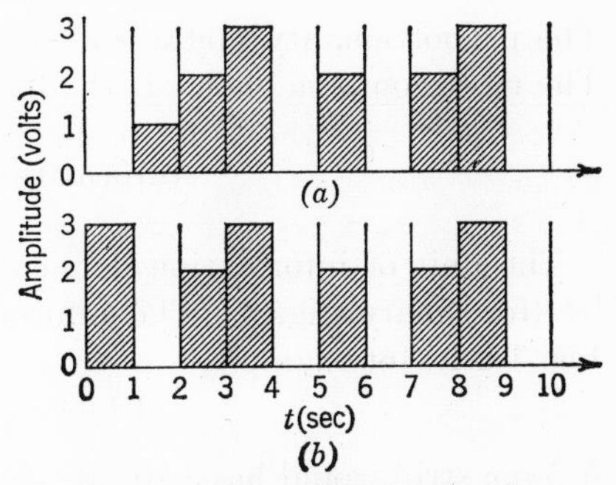

FIG. 1-3. Two different signals.

If the "amount of information" transmitted in T sec is related to the number of different and distinguishable signal-amplitude combinations we can transmit in that time—as we might intuitively feel to be the case—then it is apparent that the information capacity of the system is limited.

The system capacity, or maximum rate at which it can transmit information, should be measurable in terms of τ and n, the number of distinguishable amplitude levels. (Both limitations may be produced anywhere in the system of Fig. 1-1. We talk of the effect of the *over-all* system.)

We can derive a more quantitative measure of system capacity in the following manner: We assume that the information transmitted in the 10-sec interval of Fig. 1-2 is directly related to the number of different signal-amplitude combinations in that time. For example, two different signals that might be transmitted are shown in Fig. 1-3. They differ over the first two intervals and have the same amplitudes over the remaining 8 sec. How many such combinations can we specify? There are 4 different possibilities in the first interval, and corresponding to each such possibility there are 4 more in the second interval, or a total of $4^2 = 16$ possibilities in two intervals. (The reader should tabulate the different combinations to check this result.) Repeating this procedure, we find that there are 4^{10} combinations of different signal amplitudes in 10 sec.

If, instead of 4, we had had n levels and, instead of 1-sec, τ-sec intervals, the number of combinations in T sec would have been

$$n^{T/\tau}$$

Under our basic assumption the information transmitted in T sec is related to this number of signal combinations. We might feel intuitively, however, that information should be proportional to the length of time of transmission. Doubling T (10 sec here) should double the information content of a message. The information content can be made proportional to T by taking the logarithm of $n^{T/\tau}$, giving us

$$\text{Information transmitted in } T \text{ sec} \propto \frac{T}{\tau} \log n \tag{1-1}$$

The proportionality factor will depend on the base of logarithms used. The most common choice is the base 2, or

$$\text{Information} = \frac{T}{\tau} \log_2 n \tag{1-2}$$

The unit of information defined in this manner has been named the *bit* (for *b*inary dig*it*). The information content of the 10-sec strip of Fig. 1-2 is, for example,

$$10 \log_2 4 = 20 \text{ bits}$$

A 5-sec strip would have 10 bits of information. If there had been only two possible voltage levels (say 0 and 1), the information conveyed in 10 sec would have been 10 bits.

The system capacity can be defined as the maximum *rate* of transmitting information. From Eq. (1-2) this is simply

$$C = \frac{\text{information}}{T} = \frac{1}{\tau} \log_2 n \tag{1-3}$$

and the units are given in bits per second.

System capacity is thus inversely proportional to the minimum interval τ over which signals can change and proportional to the logarithm of n.

We shall show in the next chapter, reviewing some simple concepts of networks, that there is an intimate inverse relationship between time response and frequency response. This will enable us to relate information transmitted and system capacity to the system "bandwidth."

These two parameters of system behavior, τ (or its inverse, bandwidth) and n (or, as we shall see, the signal-to-noise ratio in a system), are basic in any study of communication systems. Much of the material of this book will thus be devoted to a study of the time (or frequency) and noise characteristics of different networks and the frequency-noise characteristics of various practical communication systems.

1-2. Binary Digits in Information Transmission. The information content of a signal was defined in the previous section by Eq. (1-2),

$$\text{Information} = \frac{T}{\tau} \log_2 n \qquad \text{bits}$$

The use of the logarithm to the base 2 in defining the unit of information can be justified in an alternative and instructive way. Assume that a signal to be transmitted will vary anywhere from 0 to 7 volts with any one voltage range as likely as the next. Because of the system limitations described in Sec. 1-1 the signal can be uniquely defined only at the integral voltage values and will not change appreciably over an interval τ sec long. (The noise fluctuations are assumed to have the same magnitudes on the average as in the example of Sec. 1-1.)

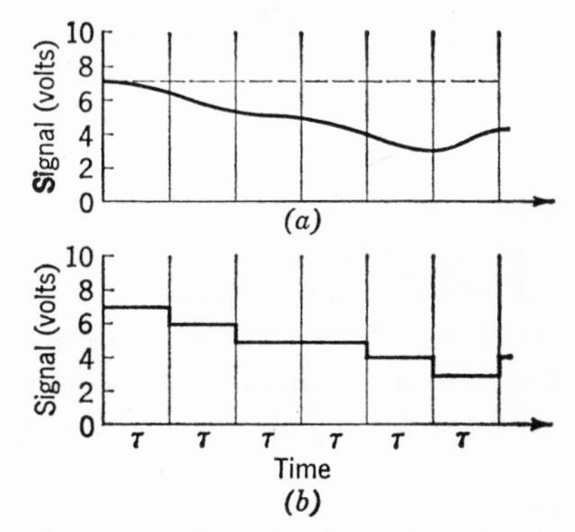

FIG. 1-4. Quantization of a signal. (a) Original signal; (b) quantized signal.

The signal can thus be replaced by a signal of the type shown in Fig. 1-3; during any interval τ sec long it will occupy one of eight voltage levels (0 to 7 volts), each one equally likely to be occupied.

The process of replacing a continuous signal by such a discrete signal is called the *quantizing process.* A typical signal and its quantized equivalent are shown in Fig. 1-4.

The signal can of course be transmitted by simply sending the successive integral voltage values as they appear. In any one interval any one of eight different voltages must be sent. The informational content of the signal is thus related to these eight different voltage levels (i.e., one of eight choices).

We ask ourselves, however: Is there another way of sending this information so that fewer than eight numbers are needed completely to specify the signal in any one interval? The informational content will then be assumed equal to the smallest number needed. The answer is yes: the simplest way uniquely to label a particular level and to indicate its selection is by means of a series of yes-no instructions. For this particular type of signal with eight levels three such yes-no instructions are needed.

To indicate the procedure followed, assume that the signal is at 7 volts during a particular instant. We first decide whether the proper level lies among the first four or the last four levels. If "yes," we use a designating symbol 1 for each level in the group of four; if "no," a designating symbol 0. In this case, then, levels 0 to 3 are labeled 0, and levels 4 to 7 are labeled 1 (see Fig. 1-5*a*). We can thus immediately reject the 0 levels and concentrate on choosing one of the remaining four. Our area of choice has been reduced considerably.

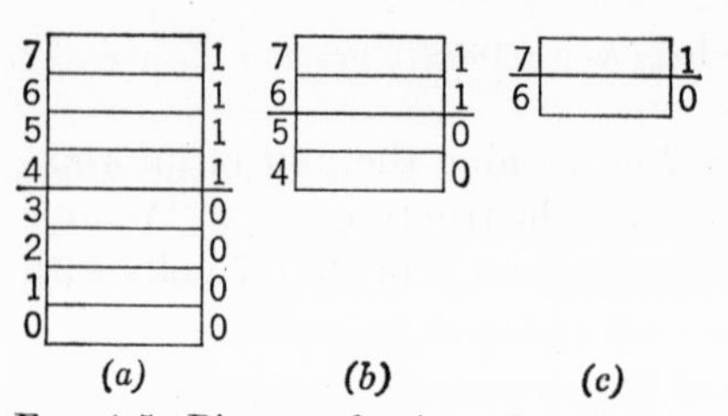

FIG. 1-5. Binary selection of a signal. (*a*) First choice; (*b*) second choice; (*c*) third choice.

Again we separate the remaining levels into two parts: That half which does not contain the desired level (7 in this case) is labeled no, or 0; the other yes, or 1. This is shown in Fig. 1-5*b*. Again half the levels are eliminated, leaving only 6 and 7. This time we find level 7 uniquely singled out.

Note that this method required three consecutive yes-no responses.

Proceeding in a similar way, we could single out any one of the eight possible voltages. They can thus be uniquely identified by means of three 0 or 1 labels. This method of identification is called *binary coding*. A typical identification table would appear as follows:

	Binary coding
7	111
6	110
5	101
4	100
3	011
2	010
1	001
0	000

Instead of transmitting this signal as one of eight different voltage levels, we need transmit only three successive yes-no (voltage–no voltage) voltages during a particular interval. Any one yes-no label is called a binary digit, or bit for short. Three bits are thus required to transmit the desired information as to a particular voltage level occupied for the eight-level signal under discussion.

This process of binary coding is the simplest one that can be devised for uniquely tagging a signal. With binary selection only three consecutive numbers, or 3 bits, are needed to transmit the informational content of this particular signal in any one time interval. For 16 levels 4 bits are required, for 32 levels 5 bits, and so on. For n levels $\log_2 n$ bits are required.

If the information in three successive intervals, each containing eight possible levels, is to be transmitted, then 3 bits for each interval, or 9 in all, are required for the signal transmission.

For T/τ intervals and n levels, $T/\tau \log_2 n$ bits must be transmitted. The information content of a signal is defined to be equal to the number of bits, or binary choices, needed for transmission.

1-3. Relation between System Capacity and Information Content of Messages. In Sec. 1-1 we pointed out that the capacity (or ability) of a system to transmit information depended on the system time response and its ability to distinguish among different levels of a signal.

The capacity of a given system is defined as the maximum amount of information per second (in bits per second) that the system can transmit. The following chapters of this book will be devoted to relating the system limitations on information transmission to bandwidth and system noise properties. Here we take time to consider the relation between system capacity and the information content of signals to be transmitted.

Being able to measure the ability of a particular system to transmit information is not enough. The more basic question in information transmission should perhaps be phrased: Which system or group of systems will have sufficient capacity to transmit a specified class of signals or information-bearing messages? In order to answer this question, we must be able to measure the information content of a signal.

For example, assume that we are interested in transmitting a speech delivered in the English language. In order to choose a system for transmission, we must be able to determine the information content of the speech and the rate at which it is to be transmitted. The system chosen will then obviously have to accommodate the rate of information to be transmitted, or will have to possess a capacity greater than the rate of information transmission desired. The system must thus be "matched" to the class of signals being transmitted.

(Once a group of systems possessing the desired capacity is selected, a further choice of a particular system can be made on the basis of minimum power required, minimum complexity and cost of equipment, minimum bandwidth, etc. Not all the different criteria of selection may be compatible so that some compromises may eventually have to be made. Some of these points will be considered in passing in Chaps. 3 and 4 on typical modulation systems, while the actual comparison of different communication systems as to information capacity will be taken up in Chap. 6.)

In order to choose a system or group of systems with the proper information capacity, we first determine or measure the information content of the signals that are to be transmitted. The detailed consideration of this point is in the realm of information theory, and the reader is referred to the ever-growing literature on this subject for thorough discussions.[1]

[1] The basic material is contained in the classic paper by C. E. Shannon, A Mathematical Theory of Communication, *Bell System Tech. J.*, vol. 27, pp. 379–423, July, 1948, pp. 623–656, October, 1948.

We shall, however, indicate the approach used, and we shall find some of the material of value in our later work.

We have already shown, in Secs. 1-1 and 1-2, that, where different values of a signal are *equally likely* and where the signal appears at discrete voltage levels, the information content of a signal is readily evaluated. It is simply the logarithm of the number of equally likely signal combinations possible in a given interval. (In the example we considered, $n^{T/\tau}$ was the number of equally likely signal combinations in T sec, since each signal level was as likely to be occupied as any other. The information content of the strip T sec long was thus $\log_2 n^{T/\tau} = T/\tau \log_2 n$.)

The equally likely case is a very restricted one, however. For example, if we were transmitting a speech in the English language by transmitting the different letters in the successive words uttered, this would correspond to assuming that each letter was equally likely to occur. This assumption is obviously not true, since we know, for example, that the letter *e* occurs much more frequently than the letter *z*, or any other letter for that matter. We could guess that a particular letter to come would be an *e* and be much more sure that we were right than if we had guessed *q*, *z*, or *u*.

But this prior knowledge of the greater chance of *e* rather than *z* occurring reduces the information content of the speech being transmitted. For, as we noted in Sec. 1-1, the amount of information transmitted depends on the *uncertainty* of the message. In particular, if *e* were known to be the only letter occurring in this speech, no information at all would be transmitted, since all uncertainty as to the message would vanish.

Thus, although the different number of signals in any one interval is still the gamut of all letters from *a* to *z*, the fact that some occur more frequently than others reduces the information content of the message. In T sec the different signal combinations possible occur with differing relative frequencies, and the information content of the T-sec message is reduced as compared with the equally likely case.

The same considerations obviously hold true in our representation of different signals by different voltage levels in Sec. 1-1. If a 3-volt signal were to be the only signal transmitted, it would carry no information and transmission might just as well cease. If the 3-volt signal were to be expected more often than any other, a message T sec long would carry information but the *information content* of the message would be less than if all voltage levels were equally likely. (Those signal combinations containing the 3-volt level would be expected to occur more frequently than any of the others.)

The information content of a message thus relates not only to the number of possible signal combinations in the message but also to their *relative frequency of occurrence.* This in turn depends on the source of the message. The information content of a message in the English language depends on a knowledge of the structure of the language and its alphabet: the relative frequency of occurrence of each letter, of different combinations of letters, of word combinations, of sentence combinations, etc. All these structural properties of English affect the different possible signal combinations and their relative frequency of occurrence, and hence the information content of a particular signal.

The decrease in the information content of a message due to unequally likely signals results in the requirement of a correspondingly reduced system capacity for information transmission. Telegraph transmission of messages in the English language has long taken this into account by coding the letter e with the shortest telegraph symbol. This thus reduces the average time required for transmission of a message.

But how do we *quantitatively* measure the information content of a message in this more general case of signals with differing frequencies of occurrence? To study this case, we shall first assume that successive signals (the individual letters in the case of English) are independent of one another and then attempt some further generalization. The assumption of *independence* implies that the occurrence of any one signal does not affect in any way the occurrence of any other signal. In the case of a message in the English language the occurrence of one letter does not affect the occurrence of any other. (A q coming up could then be followed by an x or a z, as well as by a u. This assumption of independence is thus an oversimplification of a much more complicated situation in the case of English, but it does serve to simplify the analysis.)

To develop a quantitative measure of the information content of a message, we shall first rewrite our result for the equally likely case in a different form. We recall that we showed that $n^{T/\tau}$ was the total possible number of signal combinations in T sec if each signal lasted τ sec and there were n possible levels in each interval.

If we were to look at many messages, each T sec long, we would find that on the average each possible signal combination would occur with a relative frequency of $1/n^{T/\tau}$. For example, with $\tau = 1$ sec and $n = 4$, 64 different combinations are possible in an interval 3 sec long. The relative frequency of occurrence of each 3-sec message would be $\frac{1}{64}$. In 10,000 such 3-sec messages there would be approximately 10,000/64 messages of each of the 64 possibilities. The greater the number of 3-sec messages we were to look at, the more closely any one signal combination would approach a relative frequency of $\frac{1}{64}$.

The relative frequency of occurrence of any one combination, or *event,* we define to be its probability of occurrence, or, symbolically, P. Thus

$$P \equiv \frac{\text{number of times event occurs}}{\text{total number of possibilities}} \tag{1-4}$$

where the total number of possibilities must be very large compared with the number of possible events (10,000 as compared with 64 in the example just cited) if we are to have an accurate measure of the relative frequency.

For example, if we were interested in the probability of occurrence of a letter in the English alphabet, we would pick letters at random (say, from words on successive pages of a book to ensure independence of choice) and determine the number of times a given letter showed. We would have to pick many more than 26 total letters for our results to be valid, however.

If n possible events are specified to be the n possible signal levels, at any instant, of Sec. 1-1, then $P = 1/n$ for equally likely events. The information carried by the appearance of any one event in one interval is then

$$H_1 = \log_2 n = -\log_2 P \qquad \text{bits/interval} \tag{1-5}$$

Over m intervals of time (an interval is τ sec long) we should have m times as much information, assuming that each signal or event in time is independent. Therefore

$$H = mH_1 = -m \log_2 P \qquad \text{bits in } m \text{ intervals} \tag{1-6}$$

The information available in T sec is thus ($m = T/\tau$)

$$H = -\frac{T}{\tau} \log_2 P = \frac{T}{\tau} \log_2 n \qquad \text{bits in } T \text{ sec} \tag{1-7}$$

as in Sec. 1-1.

Now consider the case where the different signal levels (or events) are not equally likely. For the sake of simplicity we first assume just two levels to be transmitted, 0 or 1, the first with probability p, the second with probability q. Then

$$p \equiv \frac{\text{number of times 0 occurs}}{\text{total number of possibilities}} \tag{1-8}$$

and

$$q \equiv \frac{\text{number of times 1 occurs}}{\text{total number of possibilities}} \tag{1-9}$$

Since either a 0 or a 1 must always come up, $p + q = 1$. (The number of times 0 comes up plus the number of times 1 comes up equals the total number of possibilities.)

For example, say that the message to be transmitted by this two-level signal device represents the birth of either a boy or a girl in the United States; 1 corresponds to boy, 0 to girl. After counting 1,000,000 births we find that 480,000 boys and 520,000 girls were born. Then $p = 0.52$, $q = 0.48$, and $p + q = 1$.

What is now the information content of a particular message consisting of a group of 0's and 1's? Each time a 0 appears, we should gain $-\log_2 p$ bits of information, and each time 1 appears we gain $-\log_2 q$ bits. If p and q are approximately each 0.5, either event occurring (0 or 1) carries almost the same amount of information. The two events are nearly equally likely. This is of course the case in the births of boys and girls in the United States to which we referred. But now assume $p \gg q$ (0 occurs more frequently, on the average). Since $-\log_2 q \gg -\log_2 p$, the occurrence of a 1, the more *rarely occurring* event, carries *more* information.

This seems to agree with our previous discussion, where we pointed out that, the greater the uncertainty of an event occurring, the more the information carried. Does this again agree with intuition? We use births as an example once more but this time consider the case of a family with five sons and no daughters. The father has given up all hope of a daughter, especially since both his family and that of his wife have a long history of a preponderance of male children. The father, waiting expectantly for his wife to give birth again, receives word that his wife has given birth to—a *boy*. So? That is nothing new. A boy was expected. But had his wife given birth to—a *girl!* This news would be something tremendously different, it would carry much more information, it would be the completely unexpected!

More rarely occurring events thus carry more information than frequently occurring events in an intuitive sense, and our use of the $-\log_2 p$, $-\log_2 q$ formulation for information agrees with the intuitive concept.

The information carried by a group of 0 or 1 symbols should now be the sum of the bits of information carried by each appearance of 0 or of 1. If $p = 0.8$ and $q = 0.2$ and if p occurs 802 times in 1,000 possibilities, q occurring 198 times, the information content of the 1,000 appearances of a 0 or 1 is

$$
\begin{aligned}
H &= -(802 \log_2 0.8 + 198 \log_2 0.2) \\
&\doteq -1{,}000(0.8 \log_2 0.8 + 0.2 \log_2 0.2) \\
&= -1{,}000(p \log_2 p + q \log_2 q)
\end{aligned}
$$

The information content of a longer message made up of many 0's and l's thus depends on $p \log_2 p + q \log_2 q$, the information in bits per occurrence of a 0 or 1, times the relative frequency of occurrence of 0 or 1.

Generalizing for this case of two possible signals, we again consider a time interval T sec long, subdivided into intervals τ sec long. There are then $m = T/\tau$ possibilities for a 0 or 1 to occur. On the average ($m \gg 1/p$ and $1/q$) the 0 will appear $mp = (T/\tau)p$ times, the 1, $mq = (T/\tau)q$ times in the T-sec interval. (Remember again that q and p represent, respectively, the probability or relative frequency of occurrence of a 1 and a 0.)

The information content of a message T sec long is thus, on the average,

$$H = m(-p \log_2 p - q \log_2 q) \qquad \text{bits in } T \text{ sec} \tag{1-10}$$

The average information per interval τ sec long is

$$H_{av} = \frac{H}{m} = -p \log_2 p - q \log_2 q \qquad \text{bits/interval} \tag{1-11}$$

A communication system capable of transmitting this information should thus have an average capacity

$$C_{av} \geq \frac{H_{av}}{\tau} = \frac{1}{\tau}(-p \log_2 p - q \log_2 q) \qquad \text{bits/sec} \tag{1-12}$$

As a check consider the two possibilities, 0 or 1, equally likely. Then $p = q = 0.5$, and

$$H_{av} = \log_2 2 = 1 \text{ bit/interval}$$

or

$$\frac{T}{\tau} \log_2 2 = \frac{T}{\tau} \qquad \text{bits in } T \text{ sec}$$

(Note that $n = 2$ here.)

As a further check $p = 1$, $q = 0$ or $q = 1$, $p = 0$ gives $H_{av} = 0$. This corresponds to the case of a completely determined message (all 0's or 1's), which should carry no information according to our previous intuitive ideas.

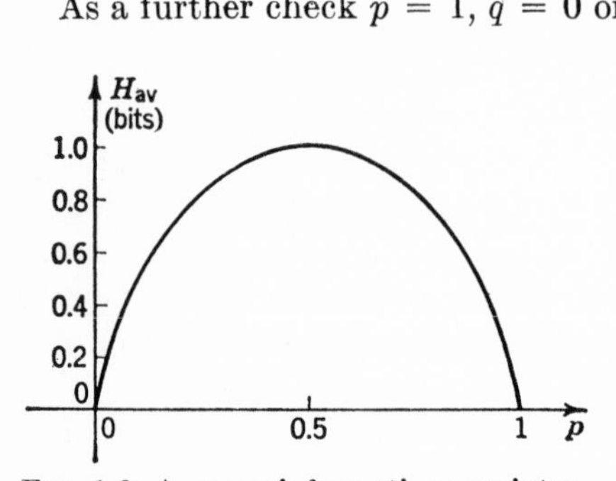

FIG. 1-6. Average information per interval, with two possible signals. (*From C. E. Shannon, A Mathematical Theory of Communication, Bell System Tech. J., vol. 27, p. 394, fig. 7, July, 1948, by permission.*)

Since $q = 1 - p$ in this simple case, H_{av} may be plotted as a function of p to give the curve of Fig. 1-6.[1] H_{av} reaches its maximum value of 1 bit per interval when $p = q = \frac{1}{2}$, or the two possibilities are equally likely. This is of course also in accord with our intuitive ideas that the maximum information should be transmitted when events are completely random, or equally likely to occur.

We can now generalize to the case of n possible signals or signal levels in any one signal interval τ sec long. This could be the n levels of Sec. 1-1, the 26 possible letters in the English alphabet, any group of symbols or numbers of which one appears at a time, etc. We again seek an expression for the information content of a message T sec long ($T > \tau$) and the average information in bits for the interval τ sec long.

[1] Shannon, *op. cit.*

Let the relative frequency of occurrence, or probability, of each possible signal level or symbol be $P_1, P_2, \ldots, P_n$, respectively,

$$P_1 + P_2 + \cdots + P_n = 1$$

and, for the jth symbol, $0 \le P_j \le 1$. If we again assume that occurrences in adjacent intervals are independent (i.e., that any particular symbol occurring in any one interval does not affect the relative rate of occurrence of any of the symbols in any other interval), we can find the information carried by a particular selection in any one interval, the total information (on the average) in T sec or $m = T/\tau$ intervals, and the average per τ-sec interval, as before.

As previously, if level (or symbol) j appears in any interval, it carries $-\log_2 P_j$ bits of information. In m intervals j will appear, on the average, mP_j times. The information in bits contributed, on the average, by each symbol appearing mP_j times in m intervals is then summed to give

$$\begin{aligned} H &= -m \sum_{j=1}^{n} P_j \log P_j \qquad \text{bits in } m \text{ intervals} \\ H &= -\frac{T}{\tau} \sum_{j=1}^{n} P_j \log P_j \qquad \text{bits in } T \text{ sec} \end{aligned} \tag{1-13}$$

The *average* information per single symbol interval (τ sec long) of a message with n possible symbols or levels, of probability P_1 to P_n, respectively, is then

$$H_{av} = -\sum_{j=1}^{n} P_j \log P_j \qquad \text{bits/interval} \tag{1-14}$$

With τ-sec intervals the rate of transmission of information is $1/\tau$ symbols per second. The capacity required of a system to transmit this information would thus be

$$C_{av} \ge -\frac{1}{\tau} \sum_{j=1}^{n} P_j \log P_j \qquad \text{bits/sec} \tag{1-15}$$

As a check let $P_1 = P_2 = \cdots = P_n = 1/n$ (equally likely events). Then

$$H = m \log_2 n \qquad \text{bits in } m \text{ intervals} \tag{1-16}$$

as before.

As an example of the application of these results, we again consider the problem of determining the information content of a typical message of English speech. This is of course important knowledge required in determining the capacity of a communication system to be used for transmission of messages in English.

If we assume that the occurrence of any letter in the English alphabet is independent of preceding letters or words (a gross approximation), we may use a table of the relative frequency of occurrence of letters in the English alphabet to get an approximate idea of the information content of English speech or writing. This in turn can give us some estimate of the system capacity needed to transmit English at any specified rate (letters or words per second). Such a table appears in a book by Fletcher Pratt[1] and has been reprinted by S. Goldman[2] in his book "Information Theory." C. E. Shannon[3] in the article already referred to reproduces some of the information available.

The relative frequency of occurrence of the letter *e* is found to be 0.131 (131 times in 1,000 letters), *t* occurs 0.105 of the time, *a* 0.086 of the time, etc., all the way down to *z* with a probability of 0.00077 (0.77 times in 1,000 letters). Equation (1-14) then gives, as a first approximation to the information content of English, 4.15 bits per letter. Had the letters been equally likely to occur ($P_j = 1/26$ for all 26 letters), we would have had $H_{av} = \log_2 26 = 4.7$ bits per letter. The fact that some letters are more likely to occur than others has thus *reduced* the information content of English from 4.7 bits to 4.15 bits per letter. If six letters are to be transmitted every second, we require a system with a capacity of at least $6 \times 4.15 = 25$ bits/sec. Doubling the number of letters to be transmitted doubles the required capacity as well.

The information content of English is actually much less than the 4.15 bits per letter figure because there is of course some dependence between successive letters, words, and even groups of words. Thus, if the letter *q* occurs, it is almost certain to be followed by a *u*. These two occurrences (*q* and then *u*) are thus not independent, and the uncertainty of a message with a *q* occurring is reduced, and with it the message information content. Similarly, *t* is frequently followed by an *h*, *r*, or *e* and almost never by a *q* or an *x*. Certain patterns of letters in groups of two thus occur much more frequently than others. The same holds true for groups of three letters. (The group *ter* frequently occurs in that order, while *rtn*, as an example, rarely appears.) Patterns also exist for four- and even five-letter combinations (*mani-*, *semi-*, etc.). In addition, there is dependence between successive words. The word *the* is almost

[1] Fletcher Pratt, "Secret and Urgent," Garden City Books, New York, 1942.

[2] S. Goldman, "Information Theory," Prentice-Hall, Inc., Englewood Cliffs, N.J., 1953.

[3] Shannon, *op. cit.*

always followed by a noun or adjective, a noun is frequently followed by a verb, etc. Various other words commonly occur together.

All these constraints on different letter and word combinations in English tend to reduce its information content. This reduction in information content of a message from the maximum possible (equally likely and independent symbols) is called the *redundancy* of the message.

To calculate the information content of English more accurately, one would have to consider the influence of the different letters and words on one another. This requires additional knowledge of the statistics of the language, for example, the probability that *e* occurring would be followed by *a* or *b* or any of the other letters, the probability that a *th* would be followed by *a* or *b*, etc. These probabilities can also be calculated from the relative frequencies of occurrence of the different combinations. They are called *conditional probabilities* because they relate the occurrence of an event to the previous occurrence of another event. We shall have occasion to discuss these probabilities in a later chapter in the book.

The existence of redundancy in message transmission can also be demonstrated very simply in the case of TV pictures. Here one signal element or interval corresponds to one spot on the screen, and the time taken for the electron beam to move one element corresponds to the time interval τ in our previous example. n, the number of levels, then corresponds to the number of intensity levels from white to gray to black that can be distinguished. In the case of TV one does not expect adjacent elements to change drastically very often from black to white as the beam sweeps across the screen (usually there is a gradual change from black through gray to white). In addition, a particular element will not be expected to change very much from one sweep interval to the next ($\frac{1}{30}$ sec). More than likely a given picture will persist for a while, backgrounds may remain the same for long intervals, small areas of black will remain black for a while, etc. The signal message considered as a time sequence, with various voltage levels corresponding to the different brightness levels and τ to the time to move across one element, will thus not consist of equally likely voltage levels, with the possibility of completely independent changes from one τ interval to the next. These constraints reduce the different number of signal combinations possible and thus quite markedly the average information content of a TV picture. (The limiting case again corresponds to the one in which the picture remains unchanged indefinitely. This implies no information content: you might as well turn off your set and go to bed.) Television scenes have a high percentage of redundancy and for this reason require (at least theoretically) much less system capacity than under the assumption of equally likely and independently varying signal levels.

PROBLEMS

1-1. In facsimile transmission, 2.25×10^6 square picture elements are needed to provide proper picture resolution. (This corresponds to 1,500 lines in each dimension.) Find the maximum information content if 12 brightness levels are required for good reproduction.

1-2. An automatic translator, with a capacity of 15×10^3 bits/sec, converts information from one coding system to another. Its input is a train of uniformly spaced variable-amplitude pulses, 2.71×10^5 pulses occurring each minute. Its output is another uniformly spaced variable-amplitude pulse train, with one-fifth the number of possible amplitude levels as in the input. Find the repetition rate of the output pulses.

1-3. (*a*) Find the capacity in bits per second that would be required to transmit TV picture signals if 500,000 picture elements were required for good resolution and 10 different brightness levels were specified for proper contrast. Thirty pictures per second are to be transmitted. All picture elements are assumed to vary independently, with equal likelihood of occurrence.

(*b*) In addition to the above requirements for a monochrome system a particular color TV system must provide 30 different shades of color. Show that transmission in this color system requires almost $2\frac{1}{2}$ times as much capacity as the monochrome system.

1-4. Refer to Prob. 1-3*b*. If 10 of the 30 color shades require only 7 brightness levels instead of 10, what is the capacity of the system? How many times greater is this capacity than that required for the monochrome system described in Prob. 1-3*a*?

1-5. Express the following decimal numbers in the binary system of notation: 6, 16, 0, 33, 1, 63, 127, 255, 117.

1-6. A system can send out a group of four pulses, each of 1 msec width, and each equally likely to have a height of 0, 1, 2, or 3 volts. The four pulses are always followed by a pulse of height -1, to separate the groups. A typical sequence of groups is

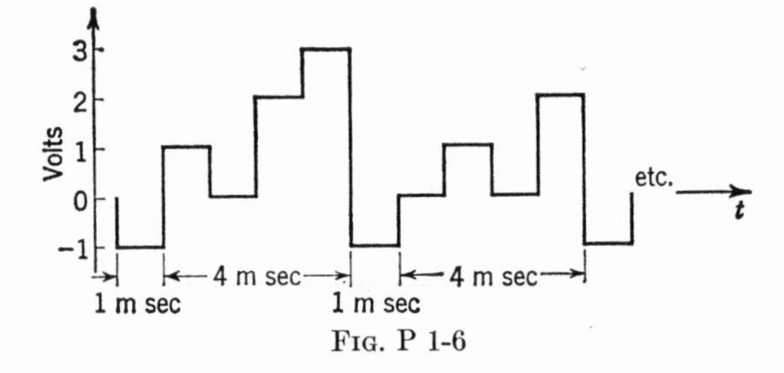

FIG. P 1-6

shown in Fig. P 1-6. What is the average rate of information in bits per second that is transmitted with this system?

1-7. In the system of Prob. 1-6 the zero voltage level occurs one-half the time on the average, the 1-volt level occurs one-fourth the time on the average, and the remaining two levels occur one-eighth the time each on the average. Find the average rate of transmission of information.

1-8. An alphabet consists of the letters *A*, *B*, *C*, *D*. For transmission each letter is coded into a sequence of two binary (on-off) pulses. The *A* is represented by 00, the *B* by 01, the *C* by 10, the *D* by 11. Each individual pulse interval is 5 msec.

(*a*) Calculate the average rate of transmission of information if the different letters are equally likely to occur.

(*b*) The probability of occurrence of each letter is, respectively, $P_A = 1/5$, $P_B = 1/4$, $P_C = 1/4$, $P_D = 3/10$. Find the average rate of transmission of information in bits per second.

1-9. Repeat Prob. 1-8 with the letters coded into single pulses of 0, 1, 2, or 3 volts amplitude and of 10 msec duration.

1-10. A communication system is used to transmit one of 16 possible signals. Suppose that the transmission is accomplished by encoding the signals into binary digits.

(*a*) What will be the pulse sequence for the thirteenth symbol? For the seventh symbol?

(*b*) If each binary digit requires 1 μsec for transmission, how much information in bits does the system transmit in 8 μsec? Asssume that the signals are equally likely to occur.

(*c*) If the symbols are sent directly without encoding, it is found that each symbol requires 3 μsec for transmission. What is the information rate in bits per second in this case?

CHAPTER 2

TRANSMISSION THROUGH ELECTRIC NETWORKS

We indicated in the previous chapter that the system capacity, or rate of information transmission through a communication system, is related to the rapidity with which signals may change with time. From studies of the transient behavior of networks we know that in all networks with energy-storage elements (L and C) currents, or voltages as the case may be, cannot change instantaneously with time. A specified length of time is required (depending on the network) to reach a desired amplitude level.

In all networks inherent capacitance and inductance limit the time response. In many networks additional limitations are purposely imposed by adding filtering circuits which include inductance and capacitance. From our previous studies we also know that the time, or transient, response is inherently related to the familiar frequency, or steady-state sine-wave, response.

Since frequency concepts are widely used in radio and communication practice, and since frequency analysis of networks frequently simplifies the study of a system, we shall review and extend, in detail, the relation between frequency and time response. The importance of these concepts can be seen from some typical examples:

1. Radio-broadcasting stations are required to operate at their assigned frequency with very tight tolerances. Channels are spaced every 10 kc in the amplitude-modulation (AM) broadcast band. This 10-kc spacing is specified in order to prevent overlapping of stations and to allow as many stations as possible to be "squeezed into" the available frequency spectrum. As we shall see later on, these severe restrictions limit the maximum rate of information transmission.

2. Telephone cables are limited in their transient response (or, alternatively, in their frequency response). For a given cable to accommodate as many signal channels as possible, a limitation must be placed upon the frequency extent, or bandwidth, of each channel. This again limits the rate of information transmission in a specified channel.

3. Television stations are limited to 6 Mc bandwidth, again to conserve available frequency space. This in turn imposes limitations on information-transmission capabilities.

Note that in all these simple examples it is the *frequency response* of the network that is specified. This has become common practice, and so it is important to study in detail the relation between frequency and time response, relating both in turn to the particular networks involved.

Consider the simplest set of examples of familiar time functions,

$$f(t) = a_1 \sin \omega_0 t,\ a_2 \sin 2\omega_0 t,\ a_3 \sin 3\omega_0 t,\ \ldots,\ a_n \sin n\omega_0 t \qquad (2\text{-}1)$$

As n increases, the rates of variation with time become more rapid. This may also be seen easily by comparing the different derivatives,

$$\frac{df(t)}{dt} = a_n n\omega_0 \cos n\omega_0 t \qquad (2\text{-}2)$$

As n increases, the maximum rate of change of $f(t)$ increases.

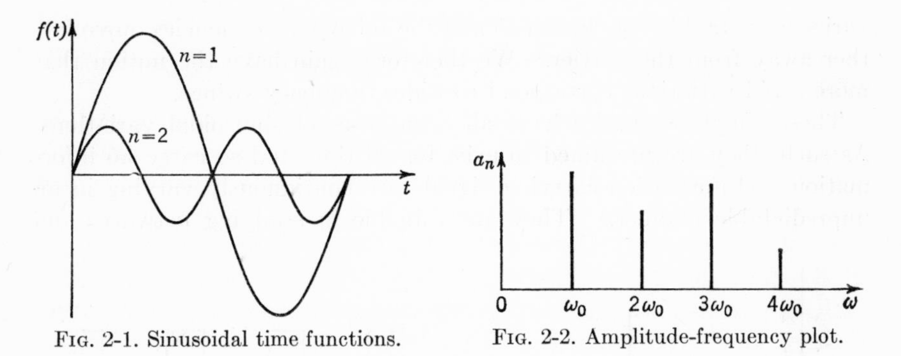

FIG. 2-1. Sinusoidal time functions.

FIG. 2-2. Amplitude-frequency plot.

We can represent these functions in a different way by plotting the amplitude a_n versus angular frequency, as in Fig. 2-2. As the frequency increases, the time function varies more rapidly.

Now consider a simple example of an amplitude-modulated signal,

$$f(t) = A(1 + \cos \omega_m t) \cos \omega_0 t \qquad \omega_m \ll \omega_0 \qquad (2\text{-}3)$$

The amplitude varies slowly (as compared with $\cos \omega_0 t$ time variations) between 0 and $2A$. Its rate of variation is given by ω_m, the modulating frequency. ω_0 is the carrier frequency. Figure 2-3 is a plot of one cycle of this function. The amplitude variations form the envelope of the complete signal and represent any information being transmitted. (In a practical situation the envelope would actually be a more complex function of time.)

A simple trigonometric manipulation of Eq. (2-3) gives

$$A(1 + \cos \omega_m t) \cos \omega_0 t = A \cos \omega_0 t + \frac{A}{2}[\cos (\omega_0 - \omega_m)t + \cos (\omega_0 + \omega_m)t] \qquad (2\text{-}4)$$

The complete function can thus be represented as the sum of three sinusoidal functions and be plotted on an amplitude-frequency graph (Fig. 2-4). The two smaller lines are called the sideband frequencies; the larger, central line, the carrier. As the amplitude-modulating signal

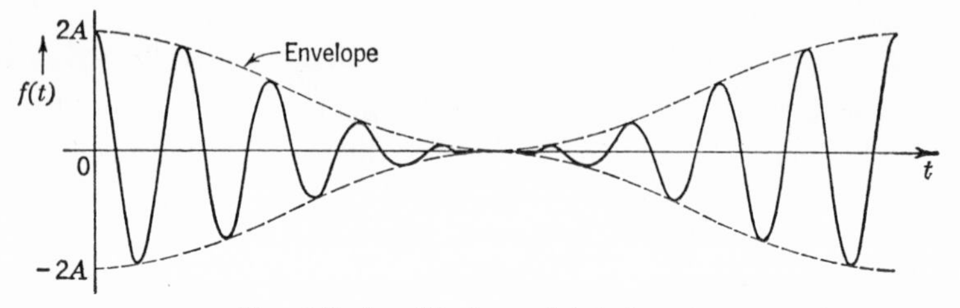

FIG. 2-3. Amplitude-modulated wave.

varies more rapidly, ω_m increases and the sideband frequencies move farther away from the carrier. We therefore again have the notion that more rapid variations correspond to wider frequency swings.

These simple examples have all been cases of sinusoidal variations. As such, they are presumed to exist for all time and so carry no information. (Information-carrying signals are continuously varying in an unpredictable manner.) They are valuable in studying networks and

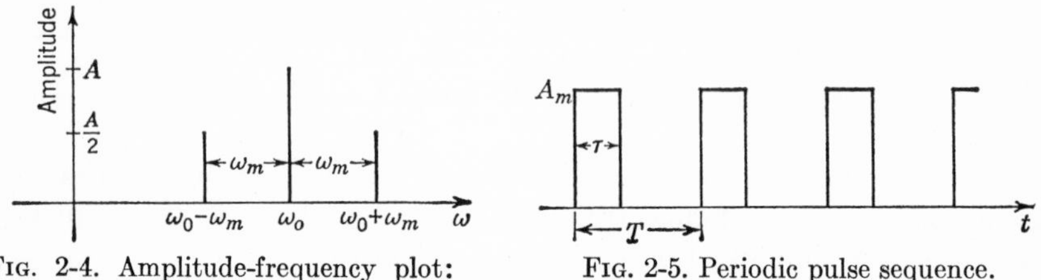

FIG. 2-4. Amplitude-frequency plot: modulated carrier.

FIG. 2-5. Periodic pulse sequence.

systems, however, since any physical time function existing over a finite time interval can be expanded into a Fourier series of sinusoidal functions. Such a series will then represent that function over the interval desired.

It is this concept that makes the frequency approach so useful in all electrical work. We are quite familiar with the steady-state sinusoidal response of networks. It is also a fact that sinusoidal analysis is frequently much simpler than a time, or transient, analysis. The ability to relate time to frequency response will thus simplify the solution of many problems.

The two examples previously discussed indicated that as the rate of time variation increased the frequency increased also. To generalize this concept somewhat, consider the series of periodic rectangular pulses shown in Fig. 2-5. Such a sequence of pulses can of course be expanded into a Fourier series. We ask the question: What is the amplitude-frequency plot of this sequence? This will further fix the time-frequency connection and will then enable us to go further into an examination of the effect of networks on time functions. Before treating this particular problem we review the Fourier-series concept.

2-1. Review of Fourier Series. Let $f(t)$ be a periodic function of time with period T. Then $f(t)$ may be expanded into the following Fourier series[1] (we shall not deal here with the mathematical conditions necessary):

$$f(t) = \frac{a_0}{T} + \frac{2}{T}\sum_{n=1}^{\infty}(a_n \cos \omega_n t + b_n \sin \omega_n t) \qquad \omega_n = \frac{2\pi n}{T} \tag{2-5}$$

To find the constants a_n, we multiply through by $\cos \omega_n t$ and integrate over the period. All terms on the right-hand side vanish except the a_n term,

$$\int_{-T/2}^{T/2} \cos \omega_j t \cos \omega_n t \, dt = 0 \qquad j \neq n$$

$$\int_{-T/2}^{T/2} \sin \omega_j t \cos \omega_n t \, dt = 0 \qquad \text{all } j$$

This gives us

$$\int_{-T/2}^{T/2} f(t) \cos \omega_n t \, dt = \frac{2a_n}{T}\int_{-T/2}^{T/2} \cos^2 \omega_n t \, dt = \frac{2a_n}{T}\frac{T}{2} = a_n \tag{2-6}$$

[Remember that $\cos^2 \omega_n t = (1 + \cos 2\omega_n t)/2$.] Thus

$$a_n = \int_{-T/2}^{T/2} f(t) \cos \omega_n t \, dt \qquad n = 0, 1, 2, 3, \ldots \tag{2-7}$$

Similarly

$$b_n = \int_{-T/2}^{T/2} f(t) \sin \omega_n t \, dt \qquad n = 1, 2, \ldots \tag{2-8}$$

The amplitude-frequency plot is proportional to a plot of $\sqrt{a_n^2 + b_n^2}$ versus ω_n. [The phase-frequency characteristic is a plot of $\tan^{-1}(-b_n/a_n)$ versus ω_n.] This plot of $\sqrt{a_n^2 + b_n^2}$ versus frequency will be referred to as the amplitude *spectrum* of the function.[2]

We know from our circuit analysis that, if the voltage across a 1-ohm

[1] Many forms of the series may be written. For example,

$$f(t) = A_0 + \sum_{n=1}^{\infty}(A_n \cos \omega_n t + B_n \sin \omega_n t)$$

is commonly used. This is the same as Eq. (2-5) with

$$A_0 = \frac{a_0}{T} \qquad A_n = \frac{2a_n}{T} \qquad B_n = \frac{2b_n}{T}$$

[2] Note that this differs from the amplitude-frequency plot by the constant T.

resistor is given by

$$v_n(t) = A_n \cos \omega_n t + B_n \sin \omega_n t$$

the average power dissipated in the resistor is $(A_n^2 + B_n^2)/2$ watts. Alternatively, if $A_n = 2a_n/T$ and $B_n = 2b_n/T$, the average power dissipated can be written as $\left(\frac{2}{T}\right)^2 \frac{a_n^2 + b_n^2}{2}$. The square of the amplitude spectrum is thus a measure of the power dissipated in a 1-ohm resistor at the different frequencies ($n = 0, 1, 2, \ldots$). By adding the power dissipated at each frequency we get the total average power dissipated when a periodic voltage is impressed across a resistor.

In our work to follow we shall be more interested in the amplitude spectrum $\sqrt{a_n^2 + b_n^2}$ and the phase angle $\tan^{-1}(-b_n/a_n)$ than in the individual Fourier coefficients a_n and b_n. (Note that in general two quantities must be specified at each frequency in order completely to specify the Fourier series.) This implies writing our Fourier series in the form

$$f(t) = \frac{a_0}{T} + \frac{2}{T} \sum_{n=1}^{\infty} \sqrt{a_b^2 + b_n^2} \cos(\omega_n t + \theta_n) \qquad \theta_n = \tan^{-1} \frac{-b_n}{a_n} \tag{2-9}$$

Equation (2-9) can of course be obtained from Eq. (2-5) by a simple trigonometric manipulation.

Since we shall frequently be interested in the amplitude and phase characteristics $\sqrt{a_n^2 + b_n^2}$ and θ_n of a periodic function, it would be much simpler to obtain these directly from $f(t)$, rather than by first finding a_n and b_n. We shall show that this can be done very simply by using yet another form of the Fourier series, the complex exponential form. This alternative form of the series may be written as

$$f(t) = \frac{1}{T} \sum_{n=-\infty}^{\infty} c_n e^{j\omega_n t} \tag{2-10}$$

The Fourier coefficient c_n is then a complex number defined as

$$c_n \equiv a_n - jb_n = \sqrt{a_n^2 + b_n^2}\, e^{j\theta_n} = \int_{-T/2}^{T/2} f(t) e^{-j\omega_n t}\, dt \tag{2-11}$$

$|c_n| = \sqrt{a_n^2 + b_n^2}$ is thus the desired amplitude spectrum and

$$\theta_n = \tan^{-1} \frac{-b_n}{a_n}$$

represents the phase characteristic. The coefficient c_n gives the complete frequency spectrum.

Equations (2-10) and (2-11) are completely equivalent to Eqs. (2-5), (2-7), and (2-8). Not only does Eq. (2-11) give the amplitude and phase characteristics directly, but Eqs. (2-10) and (2-11) represent a much more compact form of the Fourier series,

$$f(t) = \frac{1}{T} \sum_{n=-\infty}^{\infty} c_n e^{j\omega_n t} \tag{2-10a}$$

$$c_n = \int_{-T/2}^{T/2} f(t) e^{-j\omega_n t}\, dt \tag{2-11a}$$

In rewriting Eqs. (2-5), (2-7), and (2-8) in this new form use has been made of the exponential form for the sine and cosine. Thus, in Eq. (2-5) let

$$\cos \omega_n t = \frac{e^{j\omega_n t} + e^{-j\omega_n t}}{2}$$

$$\sin \omega_n t = \frac{e^{j\omega_n t} - e^{-j\omega_n t}}{2j}$$

Regrouping terms in Eq. (2-5),

$$f(t) = \frac{a_0}{T} + \frac{1}{T} \sum_{n=1}^{\infty} [e^{j\omega_n t}(a_n - jb_n) + e^{-j\omega_n t}(a_n + jb_n)] \tag{2-12}$$

If $c_n \equiv a_n - jb_n$, $c_n^* \equiv a_n + jb_n$, where c_n^* is the complex conjugate of c_n. But

$$a_n - jb_n = \int_{-T/2}^{T/2} f(t)(\cos \omega_n t - j \sin \omega_n t)\, dt = \int_{-T/2}^{T/2} f(t) e^{-j\omega_n t}\, dt \tag{2-13}$$

from Eqs. (2-7) and (2-8). Since $\omega_n = 2\pi n/T$, $e^{-j\omega_n t} = e^{-j(2\pi n t/T)}$ and

$$e^{+j\omega_n t} = e^{-j(2\pi/T)(-n)t} = e^{-j\omega_{-n} t}$$

Therefore

$$c_n^* = a_n + jb_n = \int_{-T/2}^{T/2} f(t) e^{j\omega_n t}\, dt = \int_{-T/2}^{T/2} f(t) e^{-j\omega_{-n} t}\, dt \tag{2-14}$$

Remember again that $\omega_n = 2\pi n/T$, $\omega_{-n} \equiv 2\pi[(-n)/T]$. From Eq. (2-14), then, $c_n^* = c_{-n}$ (that is, replacing n by $-n$ in c_n gives c_n^*). Equation (2-12) can now be rewritten as

$$f(t) = \frac{a_0}{T} + \frac{1}{T} \sum_{n=1}^{\infty} (e^{j\omega_n t} c_n + e^{j\omega_n t} c_{-n}) \tag{2-15}$$

But summing over $-n$ from 1 to ∞ is the same as summing over $+n$ from

-1 to $-\infty$ ($c_{-3} \equiv c_n$, $n = -3$). Also

$$c_0 = \int_{-T/2}^{T/2} f(t)e^{j0}\, dt = a_0$$

Equation (2-15) can thus be further simplified to

$$f(t) = \frac{1}{T} \sum_{n=-\infty}^{\infty} c_n e^{j\omega_n t} \tag{2-10}$$

$$c_n = \int_{-T/2}^{T/2} f(t)e^{-j\omega_n t}\, dt \tag{2-11}$$

Although "negative" frequencies seem to appear in Eq. (2-10), they are actually fictitious. For if Eq. (2-10) is rewritten in real form, Eq. (2-9) is obtained, in which the only frequencies appearing ($\omega_n = 2\pi n/T$) are positive. This is very simply shown by writing $c_n = |c_n|e^{j\theta_n}$. Then Eq. (2-10) becomes

$$\begin{aligned} f(t) &= \frac{1}{T} \sum_{n=-\infty}^{\infty} |c_n|e^{j(\omega_n t + \theta_n)} \\ &= \frac{1}{T} \sum_{n=1}^{\infty} [|c_n|(e^{j(\omega_n t+\theta_n)} + e^{-j(\omega_n t+\theta_n)})] + \frac{c_0}{T} \\ &= \frac{a_0}{T} + \frac{2}{T} \sum_{n=1}^{\infty} |c_n| \cos(\omega_n t + \theta_n) \end{aligned}$$

(Remember again that $-\omega_n = \omega_{-n}$, $-\theta_n = \theta_{-n}$.)

As an example of the utility of this complex form of the Fourier series,

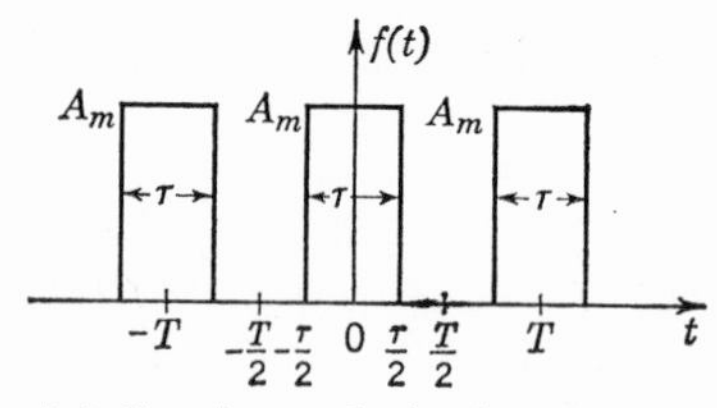

FIG. 2-6. Fourier analysis of periodic pulses.

consider the series of pulses of Fig. 2-6. (The origin has been chosen to coincide with the center of one pulse.) Then

$$\begin{aligned} c_n &= \int_{-\tau/2}^{\tau/2} A_m e^{-j\omega_n t}\, dt = -\frac{A_m}{j\omega_n} e^{-j\omega_n t}\Big]_{-\tau/2}^{\tau/2} \\ &= A_m \frac{e^{j\omega_n \tau/2} - e^{-j\omega_n \tau/2}}{j\omega_n} = \frac{2A_m}{\omega_n} \sin \frac{\omega_n \tau}{2} \end{aligned}$$

This may be written in the form

$$c_n = \tau A_m \frac{\sin (\omega_n \tau/2)}{\omega_n \tau/2} \tag{2-16}$$

If we define a normalized and dimensionless variable, $x = \omega_n \tau/2$,

$$c_n = \tau A_m \frac{\sin x}{x}$$

The $(\sin x)/x$ function will be occurring in many problems in the future

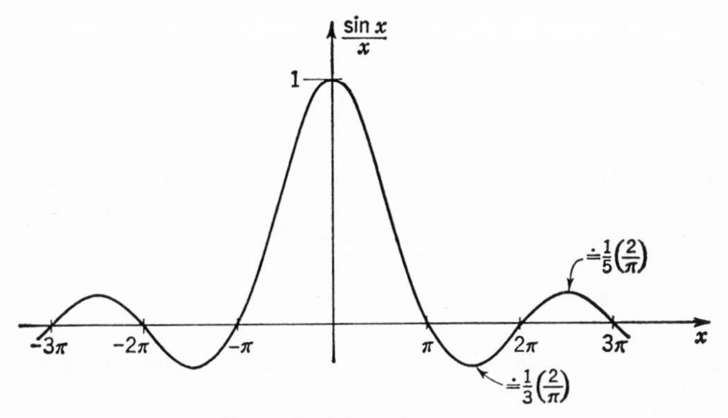

FIG. 2-7. $(\sin x)/x$ versus x.

and should be carefully studied. Note that it has its maximum value at $x = 0$, where $\sin x \rightarrow x$, $(\sin x)/x \rightarrow 1$. It approaches zero as $x \rightarrow \infty$, oscillating through positive and negative values. If x is a continuous variable, $(\sin x)/x$ has the form of Fig. 2-7.

In our particular problem n has discrete values only, ω_n takes on discrete values (harmonics of $\omega_1 = 2\pi/T$), and the normalized parameter x is thus also defined only at discrete points. The *envelope* of the plot of c_n will be exactly the curve of Fig. 2-7. The plot of c_n itself is shown in Fig. 2-8 ($\tau \ll T$). Since c_n is for this example a real number (alternately positive and negative), there is no need to find $|c_n|$ and θ_n and plot each separately. (Note again that the "negative" frequencies shown are just a mathematical artifice, since $\omega_n = 2\pi n/T$ and $\omega_{-n} = -2\pi n/T$.) The spacing between the successive lines is

$$\Delta\omega_n = \frac{2\pi}{T}(n + 1) - \frac{2\pi n}{T} = \frac{2\pi}{T}$$

or just the fundamental angular frequency. All lines of the frequency spectrum shown thus occur at multiples of this fundamental frequency.

The "d-c component" ($\omega_n = 0$) is of course just T times the average value.

Time-Frequency Correspondence. Although the periodic function of Fig. 2-6 contains frequency components at all integral multiples of the fundamental frequency, the envelope of the amplitude decreases at higher frequencies. Note, however, that, as the fundamental period T *decreases* (more pulses per second), the frequency lines move out farther.

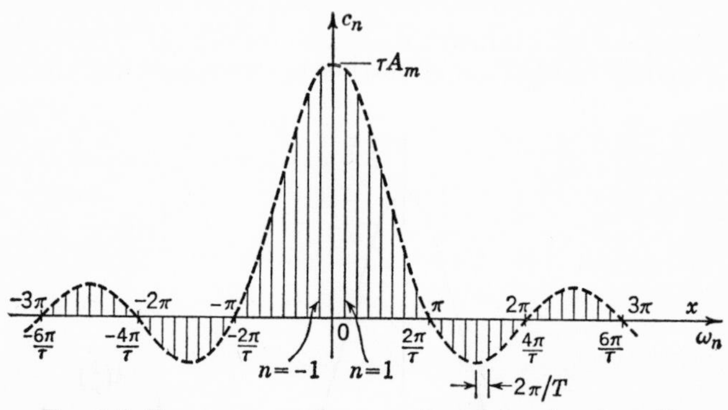

FIG. 2-8. Frequency spectrum, rectangular pulses ($\tau \ll T$).

Again a *more rapid variation* in the time function corresponds to *higher-frequency* components. Alternatively, as T increases, the lines crowd in and ultimately approach an almost smooth frequency spectrum. Since the lines concentrated in the lower-frequency range are of higher amplitude, we note that most of the energy associated with this periodic wave is confined to the lower frequencies. As the function varies more rapidly (T decreases), the relative amount of the energy contained in the higher-frequency range increases.

Figure 2-8 and Eq. (2-16) emphasize another interesting phenomenon that will be very useful to us in later work: as the pulse width τ *decreases,* the frequency content of the signal extends out over a larger frequency range. The first zero crossing, at $\omega_n = 2\pi/\tau$, moves out in frequency. There is thus an *inverse relationship between pulse width, or duration, and the frequency spread of the pulses.*

If $\tau \ll T$ (that is, very narrow pulses), most of the signal energy will lie in the range

$$0 < \omega_n < \frac{2\pi}{\tau}$$

The first zero crossing is frequently considered a measure of the frequency spread of a signal (assuming, of course, that the envelope of the amplitude spectrum decreases with frequency). In keeping with the notation for networks we can talk of the *bandwidth* of the signal as being a measure of its frequency spread.

As in the case of the frequency response of networks the bandwidth occupied by the signal cannot be uniquely specified unless the signal is "band-limited" (i.e., occupies a finite range of frequencies with no frequency components beyond the range specified). However, some arbitrary (and frequently useful) criterion for bandwidth may be chosen to specify the range of frequencies in which most of the signal energy is concentrated. As an example, if the bandwidth Δf is specified as the frequency extent of the signal from zero frequency to the first zero crossing,

$$\Delta f = \frac{1}{\tau} \tag{2-17}$$

where $\tau \ll T$. Any other criterion for bandwidth would still retain the inverse time-bandwidth relation, and, in general,

$$\Delta f = \frac{k}{\tau} \tag{2-18}$$

with k a constant depending on the choice of criterion.

2-2. Signal Transmission through Linear Networks.[1] We have just shown that a series of rectangular pulses has an amplitude-frequency spectrum whose bandwidth is inversely proportional to the pulse width. Let us assume that these pulses will ultimately carry the information to be transmitted. In Chap. 1 it was pointed out that increased information transmission would correspond to narrowing these pulses down as much as possible. But this implies increasing the bandwidth—an intolerable situation in many communication systems. There is thus a minimum pulse width allowable in any particular case, depending on the system requirements. For example, if these pulses were to be used for TV transmission with a 6-Mc bandwidth specified, the minimum allowable pulse width would be $\frac{1}{6}$ μsec. As noted previously, these pulses contain considerable energy in the frequency range outside the bandwidth defined. This would likewise be intolerable in those systems in which different signals would be required to occupy different frequency channels, with no overlapping between channels. Frequency-selective filters must thus be utilized to sharpen the frequency characteristics of the signal (the series of pulses in this case). This will change the signal time response and, of course, the allowable information content of the signal. In addition, parasitic capacitance and inductance in any electrical system

[1] Although the emphasis throughout will be on electric networks, the conclusions drawn and analyses made will hold for all types of linear physical systems, assuming that the proper electrical analogues are found.

(the analogous quantities in nonelectrical systems) serve to alter the frequency characteristics of the signal and, correspondingly, the time response and information-handling capacity.

As a simple example of these interrelated concepts, consider a periodic series of pulses passed through the simple RC filter of Fig. 2-9 ($\tau \ll T$). An analysis of the output voltage of this filter will enable us to draw simple conclusions as to the effect of the circuit on the time and frequency properties of the input pulses.

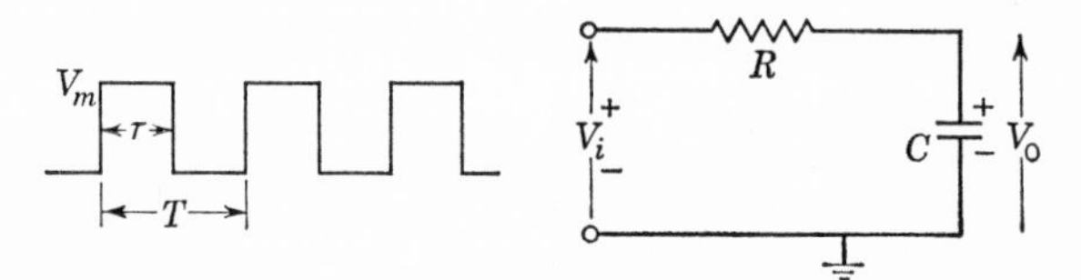

FIG. 2-9. Simple RC filter.

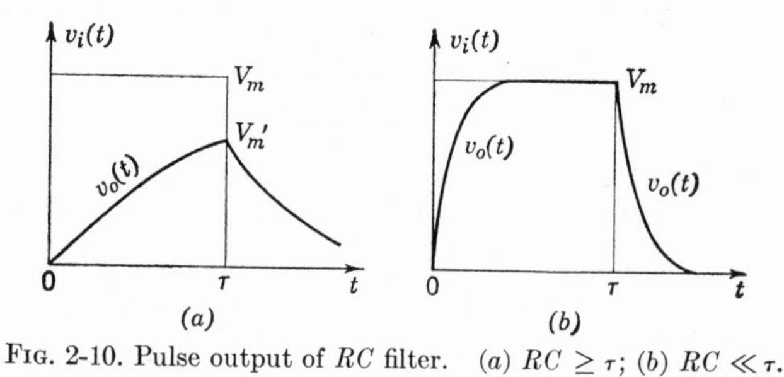

FIG. 2-10. Pulse output of RC filter. (a) $RC \geq \tau$; (b) $RC \ll \tau$.

Assume that $RC \ll T$. The output voltage v_o will then also be a series of nonoverlapping pulses. The spacing between successive pulses is so great that only the output due to one pulse at a time need be considered. (This is the practical situation, since large time constants RC lead to an overlapping of the output pulses and consequent jumbling of any information carried by the signal.) We know from transient analysis that the output and input waveshapes have the forms shown in Fig. 2-10. In Fig. 2-10a, with $RC \geq \tau$

$$\begin{aligned} v_o(t) &= V_m(1 - e^{-t/RC}) & 0 < t < \tau \\ v_o(t) &= V'_m(e^{-(t-\tau)/RC}) & \tau < t \quad V'_m = V_m(1 - e^{-\tau/RC}) \end{aligned} \tag{2-19}$$

In this case the RC network has considerably broadened the pulse, decreased its amplitude, and distorted its shape. But, provided that $RC \ll T$, we still obtain a unique output for each pulse input, with no mixing of the input pulses. (With $RC \ll T$ the output is negligibly small T sec later when the next pulse appears.)

The output in the case of Fig. 2-10b, with $RC \ll \tau$, differs considerably from that of Fig. 2-10*a*. Note that the output pulse is very much like the input, appearing almost rectangular in shape. The one notable difference between the input and output pulses, however, is the nonzero time required to reach the maximum output V_m, as well as the nonzero decay time as compared with the input.

The nonzero time required to reach a specified fraction of the peak voltage value V_m is commonly called the *rise time*. It is due, of course, to the presence of capacitance (the energy-storage element) in the circuit. The given input pulses were assumed to increase instantaneously from zero to maximum value—a highly idealized situation. The output pulses require a definite time to rise to any specified value. The rise time, as in the case of the bandwidth concept, is not uniquely defined (the rise here is exponential) but is frequently defined to be the time required for the pulse to rise from 10 to 90 per cent of the final value.

As can be seen from Fig. 2-10*b*, the rise time is related to the time constant of the RC network. Very short rise times require small time constants. Figure 2-10*a* and *b* emphasizes two concepts that are extremely useful in all communication work. These concepts involve the relation between the input-pulse width and the time constant of the network through which the pulse is transmitted. (Later the time constant will be shown to be inversely proportional to the network bandwidth.) The two concepts may be phrased as follows:

1. If the pulse shape itself carries no information so that a somewhat "smeared-out" version of the pulse is allowable at the filter output (Fig. 2-10*a*), then the filter time constant need be only approximately equal to the input-pulse width. Thus

$$RC \geq \tau \tag{2-20}$$

in order to reproduce a pulse at filter output. But we still have $RC \ll T$ (interval between pulses) so that there will be no overlap between successive pulses.

2. If fidelity is required so that the output closely resembles the input (Fig. 2-10*b*), the filter time constant must be much less than the pulse width,

$$RC \ll \tau \tag{2-21}$$

This implies rise times which are small compared with pulse width.

In more complicated filter networks it becomes difficult to talk of the network *time constant*. In these cases the filter-bandwidth concept becomes much more useful. We shall see very shortly that Eqs. (2-20) and (2-21) may be generalized to

$$\Delta f_t \leq \frac{1}{\tau}$$

for simple pulse reproduction with no special requirements for fidelity, and

$$\Delta f_f \gg \frac{1}{\tau}$$

where high fidelity (small rise time) is required. Δf_f is the normally defined 3-db filter bandwidth in cycles per second (i.e., the frequency at which the voltage amplitude is 0.707, or 3 db below the peak value in the case of a low-pass filter; for a bandpass filter the bandwidth would be the frequency difference between two 3-db points).

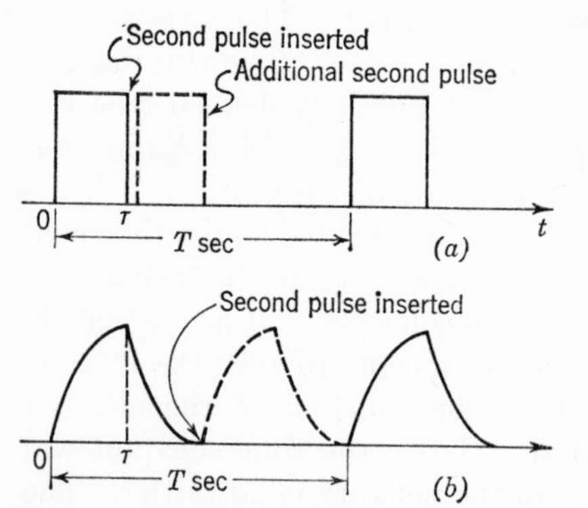

FIG. 2-11. Pulse lengthening due to RC filter. (a) Rectangular pulse train; (b) at filter output.

What effect does passing a series of pulses through a filter network have on the possible information content of the pulses, or, alternatively, how is the system information capacity (bits per second) limited by the network?

At the input to the filter the pulses were assumed rectangular, of duration τ sec, and appearing at intervals T sec apart. Additional pulses could thus have been inserted between the existing pulses. In particular, if a given pulse begins at $t = 0$ sec, a second pulse may begin and be inserted at $t = \tau$ sec. At the output of the filter this is no longer the case. The time insertion of the second pulse must be delayed somewhat in order to prevent overlap between two successive pulses. This is shown pictorially in Fig. 2-11.

The number of pulses that could have been included, in a given time interval, has thus been limited by the network (containing an energy-storage device), limiting the corresponding amount of information that could have been transmitted in that interval. (Compare with the discussion in Sec. 1-1.)

Alternatively we can say that the bandwidth of the output set of pulses has been decreased by action of the RC filter. The RC network may be looked upon as either a band-limiting device or as an energy-storage device slowing down possible time changes.

2-3. Filter-bandwidth Requirements. To demonstrate the band-limiting effect of the RC network, let us determine the frequency spectrum of the resultant output pulses. We shall do this formally by determining the complex Fourier coefficient c_n for the periodic series of output pulses.

As the time origin is taken at $t = 0$, as shown in Fig. 2-12, the Fourier series and complex coefficients are then defined as follows:

$$v_o(t) = \frac{1}{T} \sum_{n=-\infty}^{\infty} c_n e^{j\omega_n t} \qquad \omega_n = \frac{2\pi n}{T} \tag{2-22}$$

$$c_n = \int_0^T v_o(t) e^{-j\omega_n t}\, dt \tag{2-23}$$

The evaluation of c_n is somewhat "messy" algebraically but quite straightforward.

$$c_n = \int_0^\tau V_m(1 - e^{-t/RC}) e^{-j\omega_n t}\, dt + \int_\tau^T V'_m e^{-(t-\tau)/RC} e^{-j\omega_n t}\, dt \tag{2-24}$$

with $V'_m = V_m(1 - e^{-\tau/RC})$. Since $RC \ll T$ (to prevent pulse overlapping), the second integral may be extended to an infinite limit without

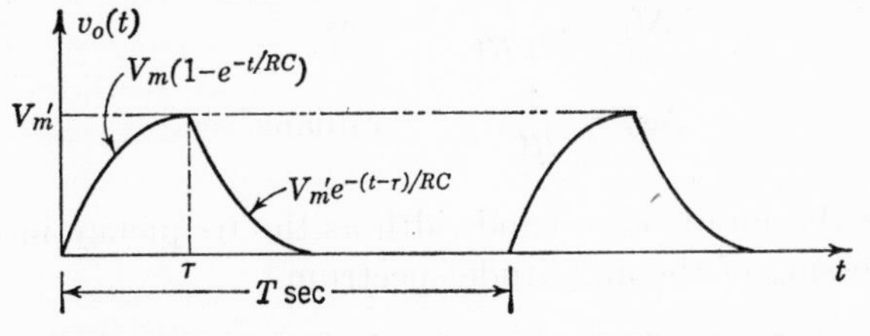

FIG. 2-12. Periodic pulsed output of RC network.

changing its value appreciably [$v_o(t)$ is assumed very nearly zero at $t = T$]. Then

$$c_n \doteq \int_0^\tau V_m(1 - e^{-t/RC}) e^{-j\omega_n t}\, dt + \int_\tau^\infty V''_m e^{-t/RC} e^{-j\omega_n t}\, dt \tag{2-25}$$

with $V''_m \equiv V'_m e^{\tau/RC} = V_m(e^{\tau/RC} - 1)$. Combining exponents in t, integrating the resultant exponentials, and collecting terms,

$$c_n = jV_m \tau e^{-j\omega_n \tau/2} \frac{e^{-j\omega_n\tau/2} - e^{j\omega_n\tau/2}}{\omega_n \tau} + \frac{(V_m + V''_m) e^{-\tau(1/RC + j\omega_n)}}{j\omega_n + 1/RC} - \frac{V_m}{j\omega_n + 1/RC}$$

But $\qquad V''_m = V_m(e^{\tau/RC} - 1) \qquad V_m + V''_m = V_m e^{\tau/RC}$

Therefore

$$\frac{c_n}{V_m \tau} = e^{-jx} \frac{\sin x}{x} + \frac{e^{-j2x} - 1}{\tau/RC + j2x} \qquad x \equiv \frac{\omega_n \tau}{2} \tag{2-26}$$

After some manipulation we finally obtain the desired result,

$$\frac{c_n}{V_m \tau} = e^{-jx} \frac{\sin x}{x} \; \frac{1/RC}{1/RC + j\omega_n} \qquad x \equiv \frac{\omega_n \tau}{2} \tag{2-27}$$

Spectrum of input pulses (including delay factor) — Effect of filter

The spectrum of the output pulses is thus simply the input-pulse spectrum multiplied by a complex function dependent upon the circuit constants.

The amplitude spectrum is

$$|c_n| = V_m\tau \left| \frac{\sin x}{x} \right| \frac{1/RC}{\sqrt{\omega_n^2 + (1/RC)^2}} \qquad x = \frac{\omega_n \tau}{2} \tag{2-28}$$

$|c_n|$ drops off more rapidly at higher frequencies than the corresponding coefficient for the input pulses, because of the filter term. The bandwidth of the pulse spectrum has thus been reduced by passing the pulses through the RC filter.

We normally define the bandwidth of the RC filter itself as being the frequency interval between zero frequency and the amplitude 3 db, or half-power point. For the RC network the 3-db bandwidth is simply

$$\Delta f_f = \frac{1}{2\pi RC} \qquad \text{cps}$$

or

$$\Delta \omega_f = \frac{1}{RC} \qquad \text{radians/sec} \tag{2-29}$$

If we define the input-pulse bandwidth as the frequency interval to the first zero crossing of the amplitude spectrum,

$$\Delta f_p = \frac{1}{\tau} \tag{2-30}$$

Referring to Eq. (2-28), two special cases may be considered:

1. Assume $RC \gg \tau/\pi$. As ω_n increases from zero, the filter frequency term in Eq. (2-28) begins to decrease while the $(\sin x)/x$ term is still approximately equal to 1. When $\omega_n = 1/RC$, $\omega_n\tau/2 \ll \pi/2$, $(\sin x)/x \doteq 1$, and the over-all 3-db bandwidth of the output-pulse spectrum is approximately that of the filter itself. From Eqs. (2-29) and (2-30) this corresponds to

$$\Delta f_f \ll \Delta f_p$$

or

$$\Delta f_f \ll \frac{1}{\tau} \tag{2-31}$$

If the filter bandwidth is less than the reciprocal of the input-pulse width, the filter limits the frequency spectrum of the pulses. Only those input-frequency components (Fourier-series components) within the passband of the filter are selected, and the output signal emerges a distorted replica of the input. This, of course, corresponds to the conclusions drawn from Fig. 2-10*a* and agrees with Eq. (2-20), derived from the transient analysis of the same problem.

2. $RC \ll \tau/2\pi$. In this case the over-all bandwidth is dependent upon the original spectrum of the input pulses. For when $\omega_n = 2\pi/\tau$,

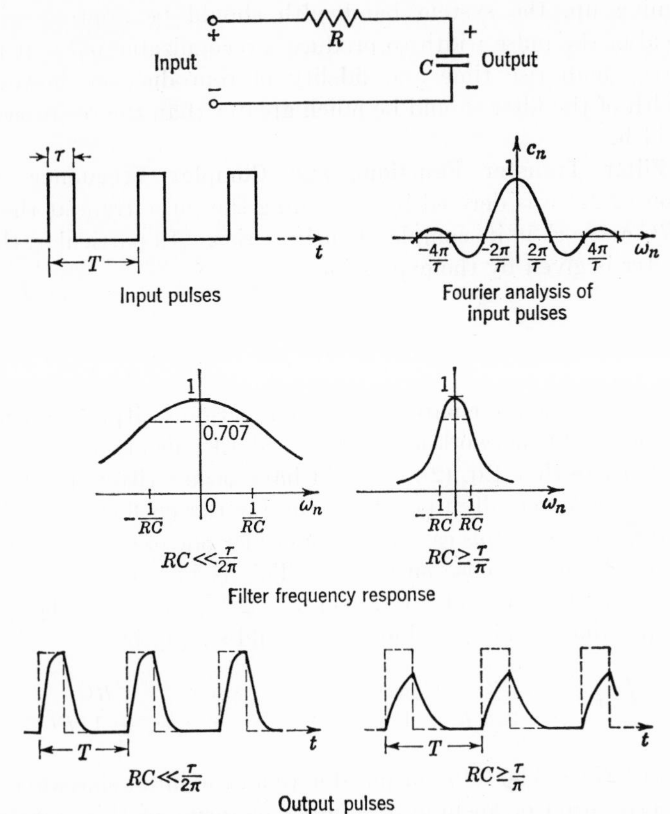

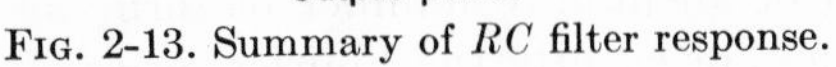
FIG. 2-13. Summary of RC filter response.

$(\sin x)/x = 0$, but $(1/RC)/\sqrt{\omega_n^2 + (1/RC)^2} \doteq 1$. The output amplitude spectrum is changed only slightly by the filter from that of the input. The output pulses will thus look very much like the input pulses. This corresponds to the case

$$\Delta f_f \gg \Delta f_p$$

or

$$\Delta f_f \gg \frac{1}{\tau} \tag{2-32}$$

The input pulses then appear as in Fig. 2-10*b*. This conclusion also agrees with that of Eq. (2-21), derived by the time analysis.

Conclusions as to system- (filter-) bandwidth requirements thus agree with the transient, or time, analysis. If $\Delta f_f \leq 1/\tau$, the output will be a distorted replica of the input, although the pulse character of the input will still be recognizable if Δf_f is not too small. Similarly, if $\Delta f_f \gg 1/\tau$, the output will be a reproduction of the input with high fidelity and the output rise time will be very much less than τ. These results are summarized pictorially in Fig. 2-13.

Summing up, the system bandwidth should be approximately the reciprocal of the pulse width to produce a recognizable pulse at the output. For small rise time and fidelity of reproduction, however, the bandwidth of the filter should be much greater than the reciprocal of the pulse width.

2-4. Filter Transfer Functions and Complex Frequency Spectra. Equation (2-27) was derived by expanding the pulse train at the output of the RC network in its complex Fourier series. In particular, the effect of the filter is given by the expression

$$\frac{1/RC}{1/RC + j\omega_n}$$

But this is just the a-c complex transfer function (output voltage/input voltage) of the RC network at any sinusoidal frequency ω_n.

This suggests that Eq. (2-27) might have been written down directly, without the need actually to evaluate the Fourier coefficients by integration (a difficult job in this case). For consider one of the frequency components of the input-pulse spectrum. This is just a sine wave of frequency ω_n and amplitude $V_m\tau\{[\sin(\omega_n\tau/2)]/(\omega_n\tau/2)\}$. The complex filter output due to this one sine wave would simply be

$$V_m\tau \frac{\sin \omega_n\tau/2}{\omega_n\tau/2} \frac{1/j\omega_n C}{R + 1/j\omega_n C} = V_m\tau \frac{\sin x}{x} \frac{1/RC}{j\omega_n + 1/RC}$$

as in Eq. (2-27). The total output due to all the input sine waves would be a superposition of an infinite number of terms of this type, one for each input frequency, or exactly the Fourier series of Eq. (2-22).

This result is a basic one in our work and is a direct consequence of the assumed linearity of our network. This is of course just one example of linear superposition (treating each Fourier component of the input wave separately) and gives rise to the following linear-network theorem.

Let c_n be the complex frequency spectrum of the periodic function $f(t)$,

$$c_n = \int_{-T/2}^{T/2} f(t)e^{-j\omega_n t}\, dt \qquad \omega_n = \frac{2\pi n}{T} \tag{2-33}$$

$f(t)$ is then passed through a linear network with complex frequency transfer response $H(j\omega_n)$ (output/input). $G(j\omega_n)$, the complex frequency spectrum of the periodic output $g(t)$, is then

$$G(j\omega_n) = c_n H(j\omega_n) \tag{2-34}$$

and

$$g(t) = \frac{1}{T} \sum_{-\infty}^{\infty} G(j\omega_n)e^{j\omega_n t} \tag{2-35}$$

In the example of the RC filter

$$c_n = V_m \tau e^{-j\omega_n\tau/2} \frac{\sin (\omega_n\tau/2)}{\omega_n\tau/2}$$

$$H(j\omega_n) = \frac{1/j\omega_n C}{R + 1/j\omega_n C}$$

$$G(j\omega_n) = c_n H(j\omega_n)$$

Thus

$$g(t) = \frac{1}{T} \sum_{n=-\infty}^{\infty} G(j\omega_n)e^{j\omega_n t} = \begin{cases} V_m(1 - e^{-t/RC}) & 0 \leq t \leq \tau \\ V'_m e^{-(t-\tau)/RC} & \tau \leq t \leq T \end{cases} \tag{2-36}$$

and at all integral multiples of T sec. (Implicit of course is the assumption that $RC \ll T$. The more exact expression for the output voltage contains an exponential term involving T/RC. This is left as an exercise for the reader.)

It is really quite remarkable that the complex Fourier series on the left-hand side of Eq. (2-36) should reduce to the real periodic time function on the right-hand side.[1]

2-5. Laplace Transform and Pole-Zero Plots. The close connection existing between frequency and time response that has been demonstrated in the previous pages is a familiar one to those readers acquainted with the Laplace-transform approach to network analysis and the associated pole-zero plots. For the frequency transfer function can be obtained simply from the transfer function in Laplace-transform form (or vice versa) by replacing p with $j\omega$. Thus, if the transfer function for a steady-state sinusoidal input is $H(j\omega)$, the Laplace-transform transfer function (output/input) is $H(p)$.

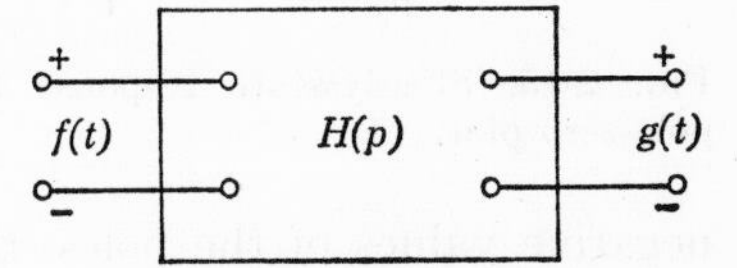

FIG. 2-14. Linear two-port network; transfer function $H(p) = G(p)/F(p)$.

Now assume the input time function to be $f(t)$ and its Laplace transform $F(p)$. Then the Laplace transform of the output, $G(p)$, is (Fig. 2-14)

$$G(p) = H(p)F(p) \tag{2-37}$$

Replacing p by $j\omega$ gives the over-all frequency response function as in Eq. (2-34). The output time function $g(t)$ may be found by determining the poles of $G(p)$ and expanding in a partial expansion about each pole. Thus, if the poles are $p_1, p_2, \ldots,$

$$G(p) = \frac{A_1}{p - p_1} + \frac{A_2}{p - p_2} + \frac{A_3}{p - p_3} + \cdots \tag{2-38}$$

and

$$g(t) = A_1 e^{p_1 t} + A_2 e^{p_2 t} + A_3 e^{p_3 t} + \cdots \tag{2-39}$$

[1] Those readers who disbelieve have only to sum the indicated Fourier series and show that it does indeed equal the indicated time function.

Large negative values of the poles (their real parts if complex) imply rapid time changes (small time constants).

The steady-state amplitude and phase characteristics (the complex frequency spectrum) of the network may be determined to within a constant from the poles and zeros of $H(p)$. For example, let

$$H(p) = \frac{K(p - p_0)}{(p - p_1)(p - p_2)(p - p_3)} \tag{2-40}$$

The poles and zeros of the transfer function are shown in Fig. 2-15. Since the frequency transfer function is obtained by replacing p by $j\omega$, $H(j\omega)$ will be K times the ratio of the product of zero vectors to the product of pole vectors, each vector drawn from the pole or zero to the particular value of ω chosen. The steady-state amplitude response is then given by K times the ratio of the products of vector magnitudes, and the phase response is simply $\theta_0 - \theta_1 - \theta_2 - \theta_3$.

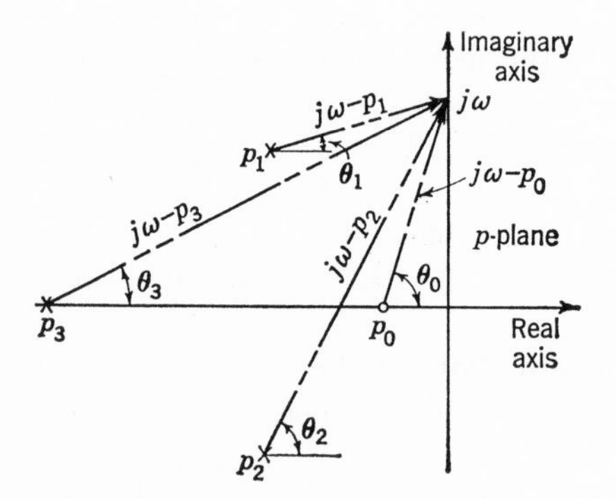

FIG. 2-15. Steady-state response from pole-zero plot.

Changes, or "breaks," in the amplitude spectrum occur at frequencies comparable in magnitude to the pole magnitude. For large negative values of the poles, then, variations in frequency do not occur until the higher frequencies. This implies *wide bandwidths,* corresponding to *rapid time variations.*

As a simple example, consider the RC network excited by a unit step,

$$f(t) = u(t) \qquad F(p) = \frac{1}{p} \tag{2-41}$$

$$H(p) = \frac{1/RC}{p + 1/RC} \tag{2-42}$$

$$G(p) = \frac{1/RC}{p(p + 1/RC)} = \frac{1}{p} - \frac{1}{p + 1/RC} \tag{2-43}$$

$$g(t) = 1 - e^{-t/RC} \tag{2-44}$$

Here a *long* time constant implies *slow* time variations, or a shorter time constant more rapid time variations.

The pole-zero plot of $H(p)$ is particularly simple, as shown in Fig. 2-16*b*: one pole at $p = -1/RC$. The amplitude-frequency response is inversely proportional to the length of the vector $j\omega - p_1 = j\omega + 1/RC$. The length of this vector is relatively constant for $\omega < 1/RC$. It begins to change in the vicinity of $\omega = 1/RC$ and increases asymptotically at the rate of 6 db/octave for $\omega > 1/RC$. The radian bandwidth is here $1/RC$ (Fig. 2-16c). As RC increases, the bandwidth decreases and the time variations become slower.

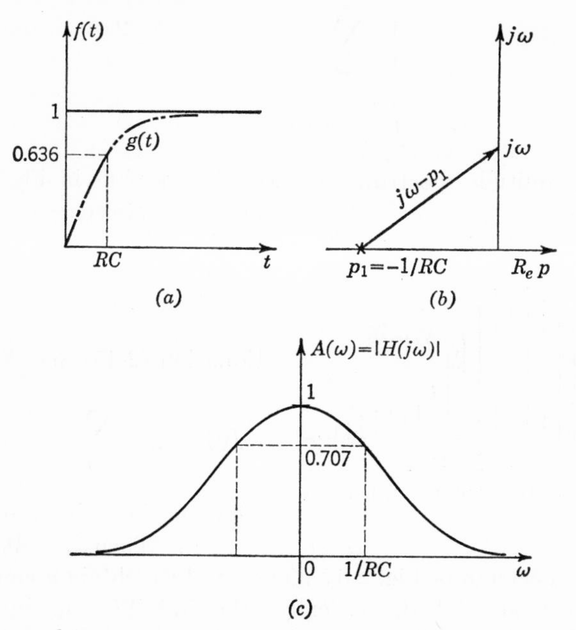

FIG. 2-16. Time and frequency-spectrum comparison, RC network. (a) Step-response RC network; (b) p-plane RC network; (c) amplitude-frequency spectrum.

2-6. Fourier Integral. Why is it that replacing p by $j\omega$ in the Laplace-transformed transfer function gives the steady-state frequency response? Why the close connection between the time and frequency response of linear networks?

The answers are apparent for the case of periodic time functions. The frequency spectra of periodic functions are obtained by expanding these functions in a Fourier series. The frequency-time correspondence is thus in a sense "built-in" once the Fourier-series expansion is chosen. This was of course demonstrated for the simple RC network.

An extension of these ideas to nonperiodic time functions requires the introduction of the Fourier integral. This is simply done by recognizing that any time function (subject of course to certain broad mathematical definitions and restrictions) defined only over a specified time interval T sec long may be expanded in a Fourier series of base period T. The time function is then artificially made to repeat itself outside the specified time interval. As the time interval of interest becomes greater, the Fourier period is correspondingly increased. Ultimately, as the region of interest is made to increase beyond bound, the resultant Fourier series becomes, in the limit, the Fourier integral.

Consider a periodic function $f(t)$,

$$f(t) = \frac{1}{T} \sum_{n=-\infty}^{\infty} c_n e^{j\omega_n t} \qquad \omega_n = \frac{2\pi n}{T} \tag{2-45}$$

$$c_n = \int_{-T/2}^{T/2} f(t) e^{-j\omega_n t}\, dt \tag{2-46}$$

A typical amplitude-spectrum plot would appear as in Fig. 2-17. The spacing between successive harmonics is just

$$\Delta\omega = \omega_{n+1} - \omega_n = \frac{2\pi}{T} \tag{2-47}$$

Equation (2-45) may be written as

$$f(t) = \frac{1}{2\pi} \sum_{n=-\infty}^{\infty} c_n e^{j\omega_n t}\, \Delta\omega \tag{2-48}$$

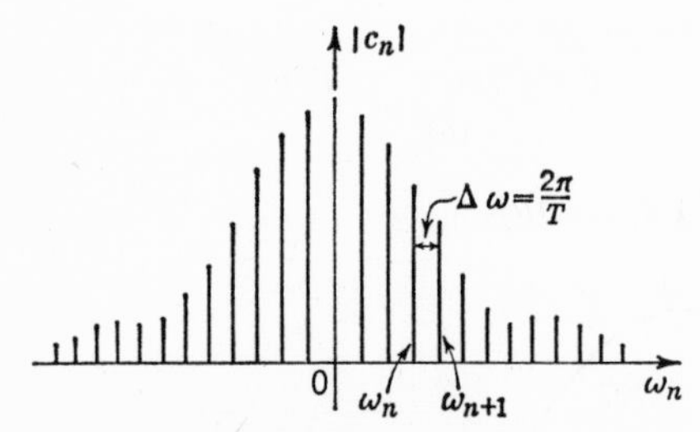

FIG. 2-17. Amplitude spectrum, periodic function.

Now consider the limiting case as $T \to \infty$. Then $\Delta\omega \to 0$, the discrete lines in the spectrum of Fig. 2-17 merge, and we obtain a continuous frequency spectrum. Mathematically, the infinite sum in Eq. (2-48) becomes the ordinary Riemann integral. c_n is now defined for *all* frequencies, not merely integral multiples of $2\pi/T$. In the limit, as $T \to \infty$, $\omega_n \to \omega$ and c_n becomes a continuous function $F(j\omega)$.

$$F(j\omega) = \lim_{T\to\infty} c_n \tag{2-49}$$

In the place of the Fourier series of Eq. (2-45) we now obtain as the Fourier-integral representation of a nonperiodic function $f(t)$

$$f(t) = \frac{1}{2\pi} \int_{-\infty}^{\infty} F(j\omega) e^{j\omega t}\, d\omega \tag{2-50}$$

with

$$F(j\omega) = \int_{-\infty}^{\infty} f(t) e^{-j\omega t}\, dt \tag{2-51}$$

from Eq. (2-46). $F(j\omega)$ is, in general, a complex function of ω and may be written

$$F(j\omega) = |F(j\omega)| e^{j\theta(\omega)} \tag{2-52}$$

A typical time function and its amplitude spectrum, $|F(j\omega)|$, are shown in Fig. 2-18. The periodic pulses previously considered serve as a good example of the transition from the Fourier series to the Fourier integral.

The pulses are shown in Fig. 2-19*a* and the corresponding spectrum in Fig. 2-19*b*.

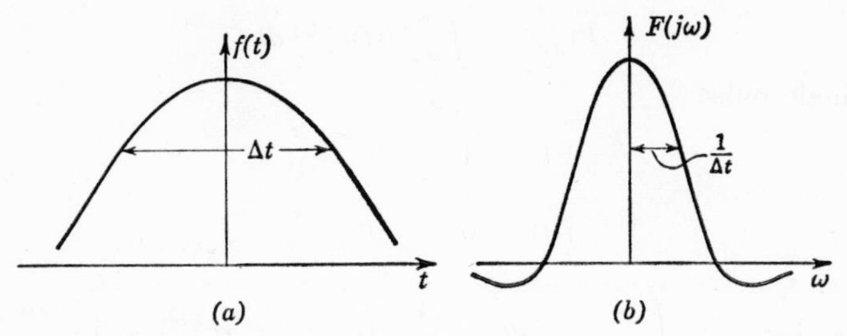

FIG. 2-18. A typical time function and its amplitude spectrum. (*a*) $f(t)$; (*b*) $F(j\omega)$.

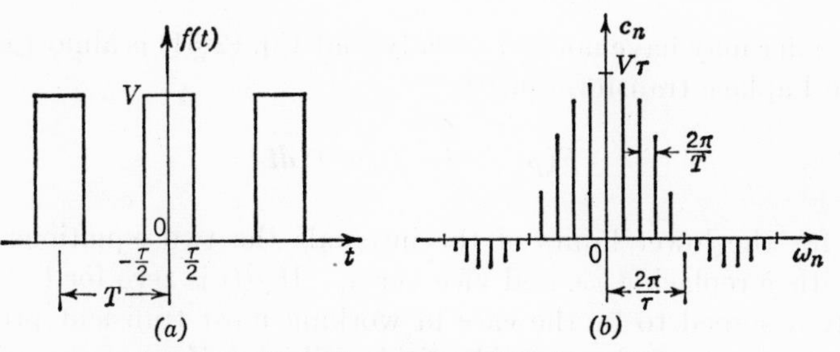

FIG. 2-19. Periodic pulses and their spectrum.

The frequency spectrum of the periodic pulses is of course a plot of the Fourier coefficient c_n (normally amplitude and phase plots).

$$c_n = V\tau \frac{\sin (\omega_n \tau/2)}{\omega_n \tau/2} \qquad \omega_n = \frac{2\pi n}{T} \tag{2-53}$$

As $T \to \infty$, all the pulses except for the one centered at $t = 0$ move out beyond bound and we are left, in the time plot, with a single pulse of amplitude V and width τ sec.

In the frequency plot $\omega_n \to \omega$ as $T \to \infty$, the lines move together and merge, and the spectrum becomes a continuous one (Fig. 2-20). Thus

$$F(j\omega) = \lim_{T\to\infty} c_n = V\tau \frac{\sin (\omega\tau/2)}{\omega\tau/2} \tag{2-54}$$

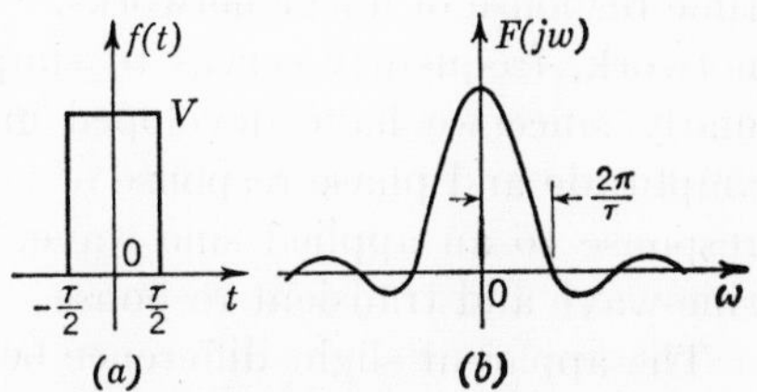

FIG. 2-20. Rectangular pulse and its spectrum. (*a*) Time plane; (*b*) frequency plane.

The single pulse of Fig. 2-20*a* has a continuous frequency spectrum of Fig. 2-20*b*, defined for *all* frequencies.

Equation (2-54) can of course be obtained directly from the defining relation for $F(j\omega)$ [Eq. (2-51)].

$$F(j\omega) = \int_{-\infty}^{\infty} f(t)e^{-j\omega t}\,dt$$

For a single pulse

$$\begin{aligned} f(t) &= V \qquad |t| < \frac{\tau}{2} \\ f(t) &= 0 \qquad |t| > \frac{\tau}{2} \end{aligned} \tag{2-55}$$

Then $$F(j\omega) = V\int_{-\tau/2}^{\tau/2} e^{-j\omega t}\,dt = \frac{V}{-j\omega}\left(e^{-j\omega\tau/2} - e^{j\omega\tau/2}\right) = V\tau\,\frac{\sin(\omega\tau/2)}{\omega\tau/2} \tag{2-56}$$

The reader may have noticed already that Eq. (2-51) is almost identical with the Laplace transform of $f(t)$,

$$F(p) = \int_{0}^{\infty} f(t)e^{-pt}\,dt \tag{2-57}$$

Except for the lower limits of the integrals the two equations are the same, with p replacing $j\omega$, and vice versa. If $f(t)$ is zero for $t < 0$ (as is normally assumed to be the case in working most transient problems), the two integrals do become identical. $F(j\omega)$ is frequently called the Fourier transform of $f(t)$.

The answers to the questions posed at the beginning of this section now become apparent.

The close connection between frequency and time response must exist because of the very definition of frequency response—given by the Fourier coefficients c_n and the integral of Eq. (2-51).

Although we talk of the "frequency properties" of networks and time functions as if they were physical entities in themselves, they are in reality mathematical abstractions that are utilized in determining the time response of linear networks. The concept, frequency response of a network, frequently serves to simplify many difficult problems, particularly since we have developed great facility in thinking in terms of amplitude and phase response of networks. It also gives us directly the response to an applied sine wave, thus serving to connect steady-state sine-wave and transient response.

The apparent slight difference between the Laplace transform and the Fourier transform due to the different lower limits in the integral may be eliminated by redefining either one of the two integrals. Thus, had we defined our original periodic function from 0 to T rather than from $-T/2$ to $T/2$, we would have obtained the so-called "one-sided" Fourier transform identical in form with the Laplace transform. This approach is useful in some cases and is discussed by S. Goldman.[1] Other authors have chosen to define the double-sided Laplace transform,[2] which has as its limits $-\infty$ and ∞.

Basically, however, the two transforms are the same, and both may be utilized in the solution of transient problems. Why, then, discuss the Fourier transform at all? Why not just use the Laplace transform?

In order to apply the Laplace transform to the solution of problems involving finite lumped-constant networks, we must be able to write the network transfer functions as ratios of polynomials in p. Otherwise there is no way of determining the zeros and poles. The Fourier transform enables us to talk of the amplitude and phase characteristics of networks rather than the poles and zeros (the two concepts are of course directly related). Using the Fourier transform, we shall be able to relate the time response and amplitude-phase characteristics of networks directly. This is of tremendous value in those systems where the amplitude and phase characteristics are readily known or approximated.

One word of caution, however. Not all time functions may possess a Fourier transform. The condition for the existence of the Fourier transform is that the Fourier integrals exist in the limit as $T \to \infty$. For absolute convergence of the integral of Eq. (2-51)

$$\int_{-\infty}^{\infty} |f(t)|\, dt < \infty \tag{2-58}$$

This is obviously not the case for such a simple time function as

$$\begin{aligned} f(t) &= t \qquad 0 < t \\ f(t) &= 0 \qquad t < 0 \end{aligned}$$

This integral does not even converge absolutely when $f(t)$ is a unit-step function, although the Fourier transform of the step may, under certain conditions, be defined and useful results obtained by its use. (Examples are given in the problems for this chapter.)

The Laplace transforms of many of these functions (i.e., those not possessing a Fourier transform) do exist, however, for the function e^{-pt} by which $f(t)$ is multiplied to obtain the Laplace transform of $f(t)$ can be made to provide suitable damping for the integral to converge. (The real part of p is chosen positive and large enough. In the case of the Fourier transform $p = j\omega$, and there is no damping.)

2-7. Response of Idealized Networks. Judicious use of both Fourier series and the Fourier-integral representation of time functions will

[1] S. Goldman, "Frequency Analysis, Modulation, and Noise," McGraw-Hill Book Company, Inc., New York, 1948.

[2] B. Van der Pol and H. Bremmer, "Operational Calculus Based on the Two-sided Laplace Integral," 2d ed., Cambridge University Press, New York, 1955.

enable us to solve many problems relating to the transmission of signals through linear networks. In particular, assume a system frequency transfer function of the form

$$H(j\omega) = A(\omega)e^{j\theta(\omega)} \tag{2-59}$$

$A(\omega)$ thus represents the amplitude characteristic and $\theta(\omega)$ the phase characteristic of the system. Some important questions we shall consider include: What relations must exist between $A(\omega)$, $\theta(\omega)$, and the frequency spectrum of the input signal in order to preserve the signal fidelity at the output of the system? What effect do variations of $A(\omega)$ (network amplitude characteristic) have on the shape of the output signal as compared with the input? How do variations in $\theta(\omega)$ manifest themselves so far as the output signal is concerned? How is signal distortion related to system bandwidth?

We have already answered some of these questions for the special case of the transmission of a series of narrow rectangular pulses through an RC network. We shall now attempt to extend these results and others to more complicated systems.

Assume an input time function $f(t)$ with its associated Fourier transform $F(j\omega)$. Then the Fourier transform of the output signal $g(t)$ is

$$G(j\omega) = H(j\omega)F(j\omega) \tag{2-60}$$

[Equation (2-60) may be considered an extension of Eq. (2-34) to include continuous frequencies. $F(j\omega)$ represents the amplitude and phase of a sinusoidal input of frequency ω. The network then introduces amplitude and phase changes given by $H(j\omega)$. Alternatively, Eq. (2-60) is merely Eq. (2-37), using Laplace transforms, with $p = j\omega$.]

The output signal $g(t)$ is then given by

$$g(t) = \frac{1}{2\pi}\int_{-\infty}^{\infty} \underbrace{H(j\omega)F(j\omega)}_{G(j\omega)} e^{j\omega t}\, d\omega \tag{2-61}$$

using Eq. (2-50).

Equation (2-61) will be the equation used to study the dependence of the output signal on network amplitude and phase characteristics. In using this equation many different kinds of practical circuits might be investigated. The mathematics would in most cases be quite cumbersome, however, and we would find it difficult to draw some general conclusions as to network amplitude and phase characteristics and their effect on signal transmission. We therefore resort to mathematical idealizations of practical circuits. Although these idealizations are physically unrealizable and therefore lead invariably to physically impossible results, they will serve to simplify the mathematics in many cases, will keep us from getting lost in a welter of algebraic quantities, and will produce results that can be interpreted quite usefully.[1]

As an example of such an idealization, consider the low-pass-filter characteristics of Fig. 2-21. Here the amplitude-frequency spectrum is a constant for all frequencies below the cutoff frequency ω_c. Thus, with $H(j\omega) = A(\omega)e^{j\theta(\omega)}$,

$$\begin{aligned} A(\omega) &= A \qquad |\omega| \leq |\omega_c| \\ A(\omega) &= 0 \qquad |\omega| > |\omega_c| \end{aligned} \tag{2-62}$$

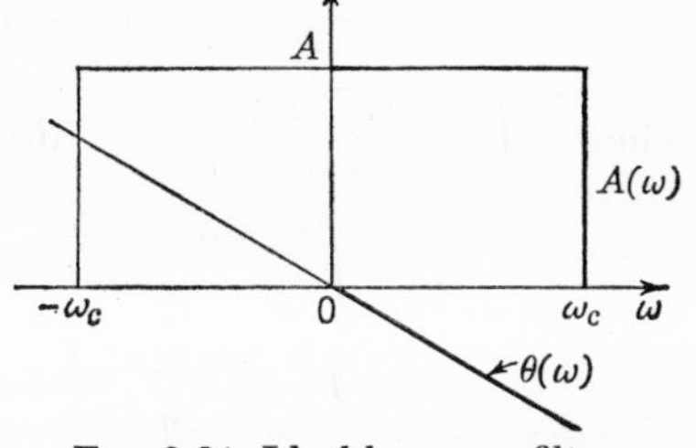

FIG. 2-21. Ideal low-pass filter.

The phase shift $\theta(\omega)$ is assumed linearly proportional to frequency.

$$\theta(\omega) = -t_0\omega \tag{2-63}$$

(t_0 is a constant of this ideal network. Negative frequencies must be introduced in order to use the Fourier integrals, defined also for negative ω.) This amplitude response is physically unattainable. The linear-phase-shift characteristic assumed is also physically impossible for finite lumped-constant networks. (Smooth transmission lines can have linear phase shift.) In addition, the amplitude and phase characteristics of a given network are connected together by the pole-zero plot of the network. They are thus normally not chosen independently, as was done here. (There do exist so-called "all-pass" networks, synthesized from lattice structures, which provide phase variation with constant-amplitude response. These networks have their poles and zeros symmetrically arranged on either side of the $j\omega$ axis. Such networks can be included in an over-all network to provide independent choice of amplitude and phase.)

The use of these idealizations to investigate the response of physical networks could thus lead to absurdities unless we are careful in interpreting our results.

If the input signal is a single rectangular pulse,

$$F(j\omega) = V\tau \frac{\sin(\omega\tau/2)}{\omega\tau/2} \tag{2-64}$$

(The time origin is chosen at the center of the pulse.) The transform of the output signal is

$$\begin{aligned} G(j\omega) &= V\tau \frac{\sin(\omega\tau/2)}{\omega\tau/2} Ae^{-jt_0\omega} \qquad -\omega_c < \omega < \omega_c \\ G(j\omega) &= 0 \qquad \text{elsewhere} \end{aligned} \tag{2-65}$$

[1] For many more examples than can be treated here see Goldman, *op. cit.;* T. Murakami and M. S. Corrington, Applications of the Fourier Integral in the Analysis of Color TV Systems, *IRE Trans. on Circuit Theory,* vol. CT-2, no. 3, September, 1955.

Then $g(t)$ will be

$$g(t) = \frac{AV\tau}{2\pi} \int_{-\omega_c}^{\omega_c} \frac{\sin(\omega\tau/2)}{\omega\tau/2} e^{j\omega(t-t_0)}\, d\omega \tag{2-66}$$

To evaluate this integral, we recall that

$$e^{j\theta} = \cos\theta + j\sin\theta$$

Then

$$\begin{aligned}\int_{-\omega_c}^{\omega_c} &\frac{\sin(\omega\tau/2)}{\omega\tau/2} e^{j\omega(t-t_0)}\, d\omega \\ &= \int_{-\omega_c}^{\omega_c} \frac{\sin(\omega\tau/2)}{\omega\tau/2} [\cos\omega(t-t_0) + j\sin\omega(t-t_0)]\, d\omega \\ &= \int_{-\omega_c}^{\omega_c} \frac{\sin(\omega\tau/2)}{\omega\tau/2} \cos\omega(t-t_0)\, d\omega \\ &\qquad + j\int_{-\omega_c}^{\omega_c} \frac{\sin(\omega\tau/2)}{\omega\tau/2} \sin\omega(t-t_0)\, d\omega \end{aligned} \tag{2-67}$$

The integrand of the first integral is an even function of ω. The integral is then just twice the integral from 0 to ω_c. The integrand of the second integral is an odd function, and the integral, between equal negative and positive limits, vanishes. Equation (2-67) can thus be written

$$\begin{aligned}2\int_0^{\omega_c} &\frac{\sin(\omega\tau/2)}{\omega\tau/2} \cos\omega(t-t_0)\, d\omega \\ &= \int_0^{\omega_c} \left[\frac{\sin\omega(t-t_0+\tau/2)}{\omega\tau/2} - \frac{\sin\omega(t-t_0-\tau/2)}{\omega\tau/2}\right] d\omega\end{aligned} \tag{2-68}$$

using the trigonometric relation for sum and difference angles.

Breaking the integral up into two integrals and changing variables [$x = \omega(t - t_0 + \tau/2)$ in the first integral, $x = \omega(t - t_0 - \tau/2)$ in the second], we get finally for $g(t)$

$$g(t) = \frac{AV}{\pi} \int_0^{\omega_c(t-t_0+\tau/2)} \frac{\sin x}{x}\, dx - \frac{AV}{\pi} \int_0^{\omega_c(t-t_0-\tau/2)} \frac{\sin x}{x}\, dx \tag{2-69}$$

Unfortunately $\int_0^a [(\sin x)/x]\, dx$ cannot be evaluated in closed form but must be evaluated by expanding $(\sin x)/x$ in a power series in x and integrating term by term. Tables are available for the integral,[1] however, and it is called the sine integral of x,

$$\text{Si}\, x \equiv \int_0^x \frac{\sin x}{x}\, dx \tag{2-70}$$

[1] Goldman, *op. cit.;* E. Jahnke and F. Emde, "Tables of Functions," Dover Publications, New York, 1945.

Equation (2-69) can thus be written

$$g(t) = \frac{AV}{\pi}\left\{\mathrm{Si}\left[\omega_c\left(t - t_0 + \frac{\tau}{2}\right)\right] - \mathrm{Si}\left[\omega_c\left(t - t_0 - \frac{\tau}{2}\right)\right]\right\} \quad (2\text{-}71)$$

This sine integral appears very frequently in the literature pertaining to pulse transmission through idealized networks. It represents the area under the $(\sin x)/x$ curve plotted previously and reproduced in Fig. 2-22, top. It thus has its maxima and minima at multiples of π (the points at which $\sin x$ changes sign). The first maximum is 1.85 at $x = \pi$. The curve is odd-symmetrical about $x = 0$ and approaches $\pi/2 = 1.57$ for large values of x.

Since $(\sin x)/x$ is an even function and has zero slope at $x = 0$, the initial slope of $\mathrm{Si}\, x$ is linear and $\mathrm{Si}\, x \doteq x$, $x \ll 1$. The sine integral is plotted in Fig. 2-22, bottom.

The response of an idealized low-pass filter to a rectangular pulse of width τ sec is given by Eq. (2-71) in terms of the sine integral. Figure 2-23 shows Eq. (2-71) plotted for different filter bandwidths.

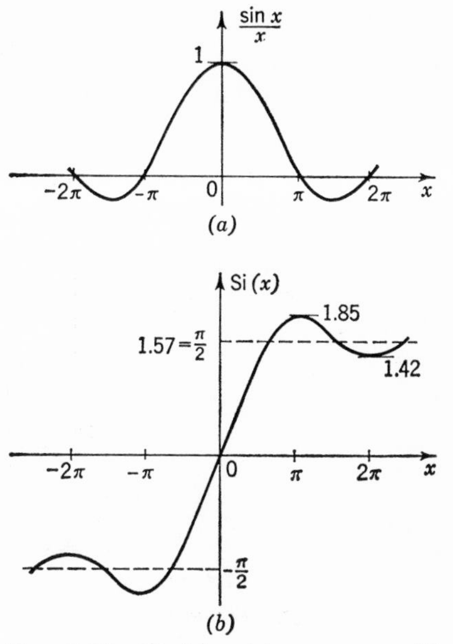

FIG. 2-22. (a) $(\sin x)/x$ versus x; (b) $\mathrm{Si}\, x$ versus x.

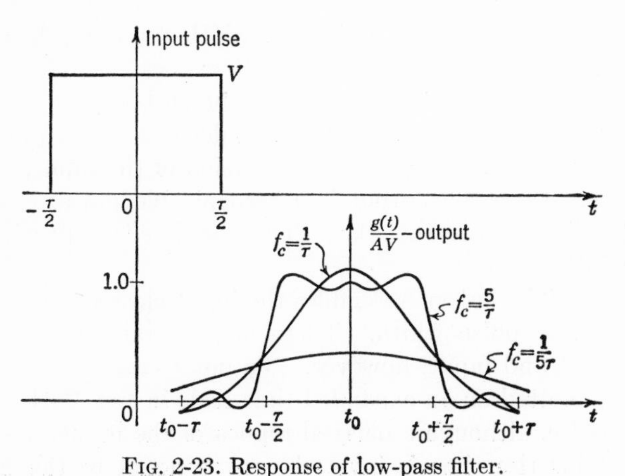

FIG. 2-23. Response of low-pass filter.

1: $$f_c = \frac{1}{5\tau} \qquad \left(f_c \ll \frac{1}{\tau}\right)$$

2: $$f_c = \frac{1}{\tau}$$

3: $$f_c = \frac{5}{\tau} \qquad \left(f_c \gg \frac{1}{\tau}\right)$$

The three cases are shown superimposed and compared with the rectangular-pulse input.

What conclusions can we draw from the curves of Fig. 2-23?

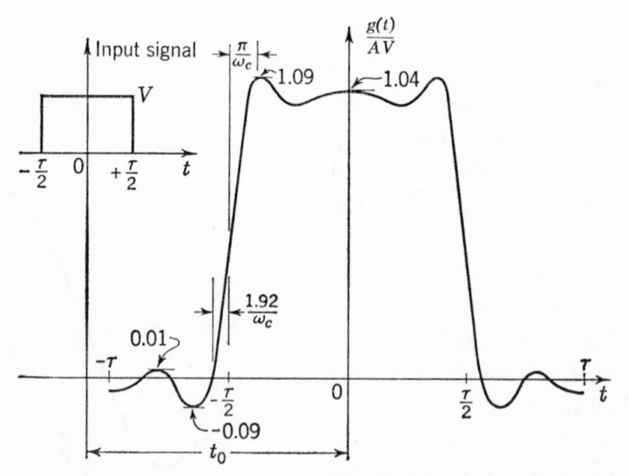

FIG. 2-24. Signal transmission through ideal low-pass filter ($f_c \gg 1/\tau$).

1. All three output curves are displaced t_0 sec from the input pulse and are symmetrical about $t = t_0$. The negative-linear-phase characteristic assumed for the filter has thus resulted in a *time delay* equal to the slope of the filter phase characteristic.

2. The curves bear out the filter-bandwidth–pulse-width relations we developed in the simple case of the *RC* filter:

a. $f_c \ll 1/\tau$. With the filter bandwidth much less than the reciprocal of the pulse width the output is much broader than the input and peaks only slightly, i.e., is a grossly distorted version of the input.

b. $f_c = 1/\tau$. Here the output is a recognizable pulse, roughly τ sec in width, but far from rectangular. The rise time is approximately half the pulse width.

c. $f_c \gg 1/\tau$. The output resembles the input closely and has approximately the same pulse width. There are several marked differences between output and input, however. To point these out, the curve for this case is replotted on an expanded time scale in Fig. 2-24. Note that the output pulse, although a delayed replica of the input, has a nonzero rise time. This rise time is inversely proportional to the filter bandwidth, as was to be expected. In particular, if the rise time here is defined as the time for a pulse to rise from zero to its maximum value of $1.09AV$,

$$\text{Rise time} = \frac{\pi + 1.92}{\omega_c} = 0.8\frac{1}{f_c} \tag{2-72}$$

Alternatively, if the rising curve is approximated by its tangent at the point $g(t) = 0.5AV$, the rise time of the resultant straight line (0 to AV) is

$$\frac{\pi}{\omega_c} = 0.5\frac{1}{f_c} \tag{2-73}$$

(Note that these results are valid only if $f_c \gg 1/\tau$, as is the case here.)

These results are in agreement with those obtained previously for the *RC* filter: If the object is merely to produce an output pulse which has about the same width as the input pulse, with fidelity unimportant, then the filter bandwidth required is approximately the inverse of the pulse width. This is the situation, for example, in a search radar system, where a recognizable signal pulse is required but its shape is of secondary interest.[1] If fidelity is required, then the bandwidth specified must be at least several times the reciprocal of the pulse width and is actually determined by rise-time considerations. For example, in tracking radars the time of arrival of individual pulses must be accurately known. The output pulse of the radar receiver must rise quite sharply so that the leading edge of the pulse may be accurately determined. The same considerations hold for loran navigational systems, where the time of arrival of each pulse, or its leading edge, must be accurately known. In pulse-modulation systems (to be considered in Chap. 4) the bandwidth is also determined by the specified pulse rise time. [Note that ordinarily i-f bandwidths, rather than a low-pass equivalent, are involved. As will be shown later, the i-f bandwidth is twice the low-pass equivalent; so $\Delta f = 2f_c$. From Eqs. (2-72) and (2-73), then, rise time is $1/\Delta f$ or $1.6/\Delta f$, depending on the rise-time definition in this case. Defining rise time as the time required for a pulse to rise from 10 to 90 per cent of its peak value leads essentially to the same result.]

These results, of course, account for the rule of thumb used in practice in most pulse system work that the system bandwidth should be the reciprocal of the pulse rise time. (Identical results are obtained, as is to be expected, from a transient analysis of typical wideband amplifier circuits.)

Some other interesting conclusions may be drawn from a study of

[1] Noise considerations lead to the same bandwidth requirement, as will be seen later on. Search radar specifications thus indicate that the over-all receiver bandwidth should be at least the reciprocal of the pulse width. (Actually the i-f bandwidth is normally specified and is $2f_c$.)

Fig. 2-24. Note that the output pulse *overshoots*, or oscillates with damped oscillations, about the flat-top section of the pulse. This phenomenon is characteristic of filters with sharply cut-off amplitude response. (It is of course encountered in simple double-energy circuits which are underdamped.)

Figure 2-24 indicates that the output pulse actually has nonzero value for $t < -\tau/2$, *before* the input pulse has appeared. In fact Eq. (2-71) gives nonzero values for negative time as well as positive time (although centered about $t = t_0$). This appearance of an output before the input producing it has appeared is obviously physically impossible and is due specifically to the nonphysically realizable filter characteristics assumed. Thus the rectangular amplitude characteristic of the idealized low-pass filter can never be realized with physical circuits. (It can be approached closely, but the number of elements required increases as the approximation becomes better. An exact fit requires an infinite number of elements theoretically. The filter phase-shift constant t_0 then becomes infinite, and the filter produces the amplitude of the pulse after infinite delay.) As pointed out previously, however, network idealizations are valuable since they frequently provide insight into system performance and enable general conclusions as to network response to be drawn.

2-8. Distortionless Transmission. The question may well be asked: Why were the "ideal" filter characteristics picked as constant amplitude and linear phase shift? These characteristics are of course rather simple to define and easy to talk about, but they are also important in a discussion of distortionless transmission.

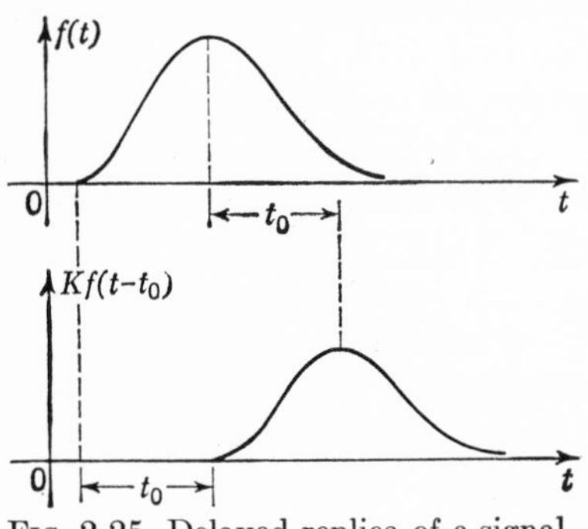

FIG. 2-25. Delayed replica of a signal.

Suppose that a given time function $f(t)$ is to be transmitted through a linear system and the resultant output is to "look" just like the input. Mathematically,

$$g(t) = Kf(t - t_0) \qquad K = \text{a constant} \tag{2-74}$$

The output $g(t)$ is a delayed replica of the input (delayed by t_0 sec) although of different magnitude (see Fig. 2-25).

The problem of distortionless transmission is a basic one in many fields of communication—telephony, radio, TV, etc.—in which the shape and appearance of the input must be retained after passage through electrical and electromechanical circuits, through wire or cable, through air, etc. A system producing such an output is said to be a "distortionless" system. This is indicated schematically in Fig. 2-26. What are the requirements for such a system in terms of frequency response?

Let $F(j\omega)$ be the Fourier transform of $f(t)$; then

$$F(j\omega) = \int_{-\infty}^{\infty} f(t)e^{-j\omega t}\,dt \qquad (2\text{-}75)$$

$$f(t) = \frac{1}{2\pi}\int_{-\infty}^{\infty} F(j\omega)e^{j\omega t}\,d\omega \qquad (2\text{-}76)$$

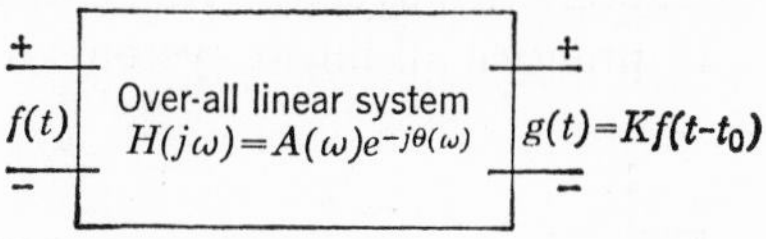

FIG. 2-26. Distortionless transmission.

$G(j\omega)$ is the Fourier transform of the output function $g(t)$,

$$G(j\omega) = \int_{-\infty}^{\infty} g(t)e^{-j\omega t}\,dt \qquad (2\text{-}77)$$

But $g(t) = Kf(t - t_0)$ by hypothesis. Therefore

$$\begin{aligned} G(j\omega) &= K\int_{-\infty}^{\infty} f(t - t_0)e^{-j\omega t}\,dt \\ &= K\int_{-\infty}^{\infty} f(x)e^{-j\omega(x+t_0)}\,dx \qquad x = t - t_0 \qquad (2\text{-}78) \\ G(j\omega) &= Ke^{-j\omega t_0}\int_{-\infty}^{\infty} f(x)e^{-j\omega x}\,dx \end{aligned}$$

But the integral in x is $F(j\omega)$ [see Eq. (2-75)], or

$$G(j\omega) = Ke^{-j\omega t_0}F(j\omega) \qquad (2\text{-}79)$$

We know, however, that $G(j\omega)$ and $F(j\omega)$ are related by the network frequency transfer function $H(j\omega)$,

$$G(j\omega) = H(j\omega)F(j\omega) \qquad (2\text{-}80)$$

Comparing Eqs. (2-79) and (2-80) gives us the simple result for distortionless transmission,

$$H(j\omega) = Ke^{-j\omega t_0} \qquad (2\text{-}81)$$

In words, if the signal is to be passed through a linear system without any resultant distortion, the over-all system response must have a constant-amplitude characteristic over the frequency spectrum of the input and its phase shift must be linear over the same range of frequencies.

The words *over-all* linear system are important here. A signal may well be distorted in passing through the different parts of the system, but phase- or amplitude-correction (equalization) networks may be introduced elsewhere to correct for distortion. It is the *over-all* characteristic that determines the ultimate output. The system is assumed linear throughout, however, for otherwise the Fourier relations used do not apply.

Much research on nonlinear networks has been carried out in recent years, but this work is beyond the scope of the book.

2-9. Effect of Phase Variation on Signal Transmission. We found in the previous section that a distortionless-transmission system would require flat (uniform- or constant-) amplitude and linear phase-shift characteristics over the range of frequencies covered by the signal.

In practice all linear systems introduce a certain amount of signal distortion because of bandwidth limitations and nonlinear phase characteristics. As pointed out previously, the amplitude and phase response of a given network are interrelated, and to treat the two characteristics separately in studying signal transmission could become an academic approach. We can gain some further insight into the effect of network characteristics on signal response, however, by treating amplitude and phase separately and attempting to superimpose the results.

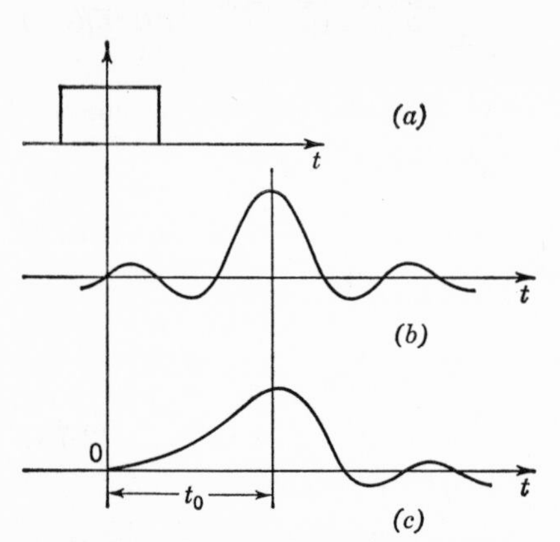

FIG. 2-27. Network amplitude and phase distortion. (*a*) Input pulse; (*b*) output response; amplitude distortion, linear phase shift (symmetrical); (*c*) phase distortion (nonsymmetrical). (*From C. Cherry, "Pulses and Transients in Communication Circuits," fig. 60, p. 147, Chapman & Hall, Ltd., London, 1949, Dover Publications, New York, 1950.*)

We considered previously the effect of amplitude limiting on pulse transmission and arrived at the basic relation between system bandwidth and pulse rise time. The phase characteristic assumed was a linear one, and it is of interest to explore the question of network phase response further.

Note first that, although the effect of bandwidth limiting on an input pulse was to distort the pulse, the *distortion* was found to be *symmetrical:* the output waves were symmetrical about a delayed time $t = t_0$ (Fig. 2-23). This symmetry in the output pulses is a direct consequence of the linear-phase-shift characteristic assumed for the network. It is a general property of networks that where amplitude distortion occurs (as in band limiting) the output transient is symmetrically related to the input if the network phase shift is linear. Phase linearity in networks thus gives rise to the symmetrical pulse response and symmetrical step response and is particularly desirable in TV and radar systems.[1]

Amplitude and phase distortion of a pulse input are illustrated in Fig. 2-27.[2]

[1] Murakami and Corrington, *op. cit.*

[2] C. Cherry, "Pulses and Transients in Communication Circuits," Chapman & Hall, Ltd., London, 1949, Dover Publications, New York, 1950.

The symmetrical-output property due to linear phase shift can be easily demonstrated. Assume an idealized linear network with frequency transfer function

$$H(j\omega) = A(\omega)e^{-jt_0\omega} \tag{2-82}$$

The phase-shift characteristic is thus linear, with the amplitude characteristic $A(\omega)$ arbitrary. The input signal is $f(t)$, and the output response is $g(t)$. Then

$$G(j\omega) = F(j\omega)H(j\omega) \tag{2-83}$$

with $F(j\omega)$ the Fourier integral of $f(t)$ and $G(j\omega)$ the Fourier integral of $g(t)$. We assume that $f(t)$ is a symmetrical function in time, either odd or even. Thus,

$$\begin{aligned} &\text{If } f(t) = f(-t) \qquad && f(t) \text{ is even} \\ &\text{If } f(t) = -f(-t) \qquad && f(t) \text{ is odd} \end{aligned}$$

Examples of even and odd functions are shown in Fig. 2-28.

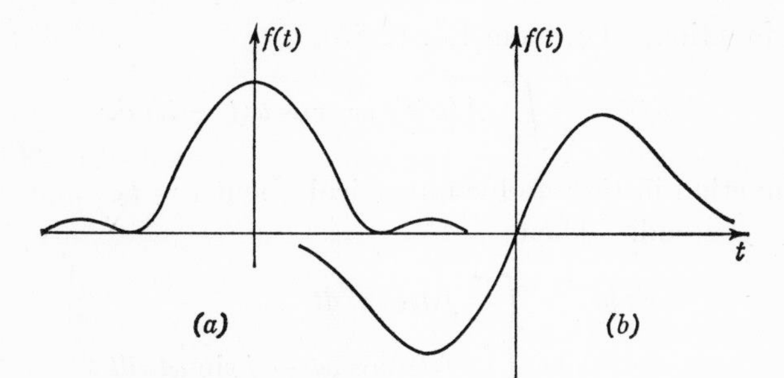

FIG. 2-28. Symmetrical time functions. (a) Even symmetry; (b) odd symmetry.

We should now like to prove that either type of symmetrical function produces a symmetrical function of the same type when passed through the idealized network with linear phase shift.

Case 1. $f(t)$ even. Then

$$\begin{aligned} F(j\omega) &= \int_{-\infty}^{\infty} f(t)e^{-j\omega t}\,dt \\ &= \int_{-\infty}^{\infty} f(t)(\cos \omega t - j \sin \omega t)\,dt \\ &= 2\int_{0}^{\infty} f(t) \cos \omega t\,dt \end{aligned} \tag{2-84}$$

since

$$\int_{-\infty}^{\infty} f(t) \sin \omega t\,dt = 0$$

$$\int_{-\infty}^{\infty} f(t) \cos \omega t\,dt = 2\int_{0}^{\infty} f(t) \cos \omega t\,dt$$

Equation (2-84) shows that $F(j\omega)$ must also be an even function in ω since

$\cos \omega t = \cos(-\omega t)$. The equation also indicates that $F(j\omega)$ must be a *real* function of ω since the $f(t)$ is real. A simple example is of course the rectangular pulse of width τ, amplitude V, and centered about $t = 0$. For this pulse we have $F(j\omega) = V\tau[\sin(\omega\tau/2)/(\omega\tau/2)]$, a real and even function of ω. Passing $f(t)$ through the idealized network, we obtain

$$\begin{aligned} g(t) &= \frac{1}{2\pi}\int_{-\infty}^{\infty} A(\omega)e^{-jt_0\omega}F(j\omega)e^{jt\omega}\,d\omega \\ &= \frac{1}{2\pi}\int_{-\infty}^{\infty} A(\omega)F(j\omega)[\cos\omega(t - t_0) + j\sin\omega(t - t_0)]\,d\omega \end{aligned} \tag{2-85}$$

But $A(\omega)$ must be an even function of ω since it represents the magnitude of $H(j\omega)$. [If $H(j\omega) = (1/RC)/(1/RC + j\omega)$, $A(\omega) = (1/RC)/\sqrt{(1/RC)^2 + \omega^2}$.] $F(j\omega)$ is even for $f(t)$ even. Therefore

$$A(\omega)F(j\omega)\cos\omega(t - t_0)$$

is an even function, and

$$A(\omega)F(j\omega)\sin\omega(t - t_0)$$

is an odd function. Or, from Eq. (2-85),

$$g(t) = \frac{1}{\pi}\int_0^{\infty} A(\omega)F(j\omega)\cos\omega(t - t_0)\,d\omega \tag{2-86}$$

an even function in *time* and symmetrical about $t = t_0$.

Case 2. $f(t)$ odd. Then

$$\begin{aligned} F(j\omega) &= \int_{-\infty}^{\infty} f(t)e^{-j\omega t}\,dt \\ &= \int_{-\infty}^{\infty} f(t)(\cos\omega t - j\sin\omega t)\,dt \\ &= -2j\int_0^{\infty} f(t)\sin\omega t\,dt \end{aligned} \tag{2-87}$$

$F(j\omega)$ is then also odd in ω, since $\sin\omega t$ is odd. [$\sin(-\omega t) = -\sin\omega t$; so $F(-j\omega) = -F(j\omega)$.] As an example, let

$$\begin{aligned} f(t) &= e^{-at} \qquad & t > 0 \\ f(t) &= -e^{-a|t|} \qquad & t < 0 \end{aligned}$$

Then

$$F(j\omega) = \frac{-2j\omega}{\omega^2 + a^2}$$

From Eq. (2-85)

$$\begin{aligned} g(t) &= \frac{1}{2\pi}\int_{-\infty}^{\infty} A(\omega)F(j\omega)[\cos\omega(t - t_0) + j\sin\omega(t - t_0)]\,d\omega \\ &= \frac{j}{\pi}\int_0^{\infty} A(\omega)F(j\omega)\sin\omega(t - t_0)\,d\omega \end{aligned} \tag{2-88}$$

$g(t)$ is thus symmetrical about $t = t_0$. [$\sin\omega(t - t_0) = -\sin\omega(t_0 - t)$.]

Any signal input $f(t)$ beginning at time $t = 0$ can be shown to be decomposable into a sum of an even and an odd function. The above results may then be superimposed. The odd component produces an odd component of the output, the even component an even component of the output. The over-all output function $g(t)$ is thus also symmetrical, although symmetrical about its average value. For example, if $f(t)$ is a step, it may be decomposed into the odd and even functions shown in Fig. 2-29*b*. The response of the filter with linear phase shift to the unit step is symmetrical about $g(t) = 0.5$ as shown in Fig. 2-29*c*.

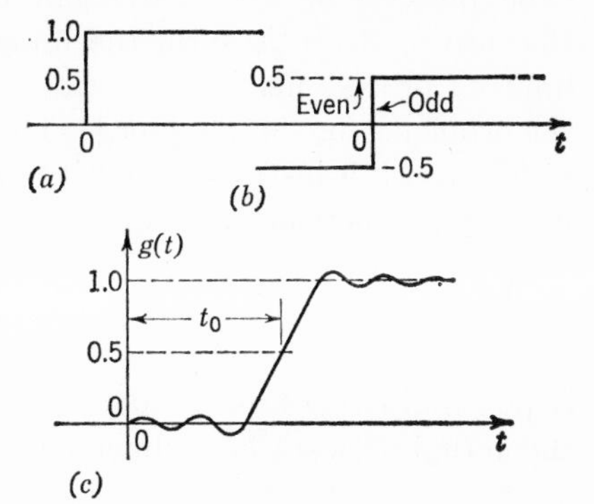

FIG. 2-29. Response of linear-phase network to a unit step. (*a*) Unit step; (*b*) even and odd components; (*c*) output response [symmetrical about $g(t) = 0.5$].

Although the linear-phase network is an idealization, the phase shift of a given network may be made very nearly linear by the addition of phase-correction networks. (The all-pass network mentioned previously may be used for this purpose.)

Murakami and Corrington, in the paper previously referred to, have investigated the relation between rise time and phase characteristics. They conclude that a simple *RC* low-pass filter will respond more rapidly to the step input if the phase characteristics are linearized. We reproduce here, in somewhat modified form, some of their work.

The network of Fig. 2-30 represents the high-frequency (h-f) model of the ordinary amplifier or may be a simple low-pass filter inserted into the system. The step response is

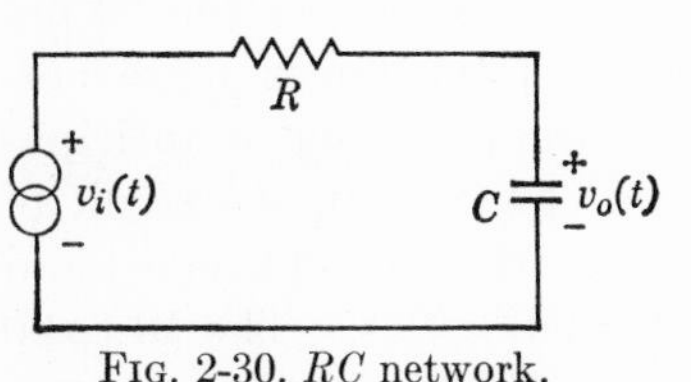

FIG. 2-30. *RC* network.

$$v_o(t) = 1 - e^{-t/RC} \qquad v_i(t) = u(t) \qquad \text{(2-89)}$$

The equation has of course been written by inspection from the network, but it is of interest to solve the same problem using Fourier-integral analysis.

Since the Laplace transform of a unit step is $1/p$, the Fourier integral, or complex frequency spectrum, of the unit step is $1/j\omega$. The output-voltage spectrum is then

$$\begin{aligned} V_o(j\omega) &= \frac{1}{j\omega} H(j\omega) = \frac{1}{j\omega} \frac{1}{1 + jRC\omega} \\ &= \frac{1}{j\omega} \frac{1}{\sqrt{1 + (\omega RC)^2}} e^{-j \tan^{-1} \omega RC} \end{aligned} \qquad \text{(2-90)}$$

Therefore
$$
\begin{aligned}
v_o(t) &= \frac{1}{2\pi}\int_{-\infty}^{\infty}\frac{1}{j\omega}\,\frac{1}{\sqrt{1+(\omega RC)^2}}\,e^{j\omega t}e^{-j\tan^{-1}\omega RC}\,d\omega \\
&= 1 - e^{-t/RC} \qquad t > 0 \\
v_o(t) &= 0 \qquad t < 0
\end{aligned}
\tag{2-91}
$$

[The integral of Eq. (2-91) can be found in Fourier-integral tables. Because of the $1/j\omega$ term the integral does not exist at the origin. A limiting process may be utilized, however, as is suggested in several of the problems for this chapter.] This is obviously the hard way of finding $v_0(t)$. But it is instructive, for it tells us how to evaluate the response to a linear-phase network with the same amplitude characteristics:

$$H(j\omega)_{\text{linear phase}} = \frac{1}{\sqrt{1+\omega^2R^2C^2}}\,e^{-jt_0\omega} \tag{2-92}$$

[Upon comparing Eqs. (2-90) and (2-92), it is apparent that for $\omega \ll 1/RC$ the actual network has a linear-phase response.]

$$v_o(t) = \frac{1}{2\pi}\int_{-\infty}^{\infty}\frac{1}{j\omega}\,\frac{1}{\sqrt{1+\omega^2R^2C^2}}\,e^{j\omega(t-t_0)}\,d\omega \tag{2-93}$$

This integral has been evaluated and the results plotted by Murakami and Corrington. The resulting curve is reproduced here in Fig. 2-31, together with the step response of the ordinary RC network. The slope of the phase-shift curve, t_0, is chosen so that both curves coincide at the 50 per cent point. Note the symmetrical response about the 50 per cent point of the linear-phase network and the precursor or anticipatory transient ($t < 0$), the result of "noncompatible" amplitude and phase characteristics. The 10 to 90 per cent rise time is 5 per cent better for the linear-phase case.

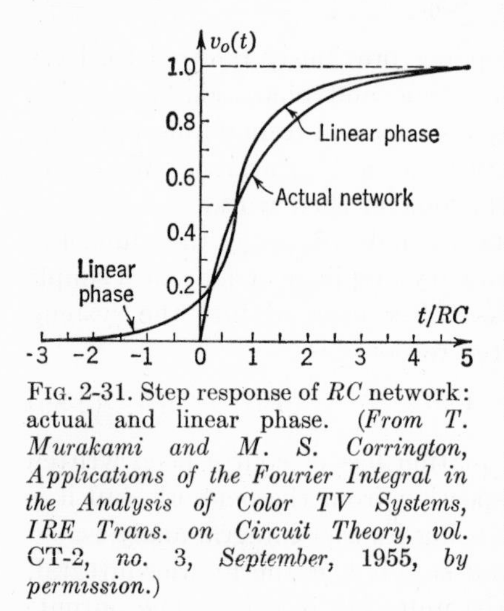

FIG. 2-31. Step response of RC network: actual and linear phase. (*From T. Murakami and M. S. Corrington, Applications of the Fourier Integral in the Analysis of Color TV Systems, IRE Trans. on Circuit Theory, vol.* CT-2, *no.* 3, *September,* 1955, *by permission.*)

2-10. Bandwidth-Time Inverse Relationship for Pulses of Arbitrary Shape. We have shown, by example, in the last few sections that there exists an inverse relationship between pulse width and bandwidth. Thus the frequency spectrum of a rectangular pulse has a "bandwidth" (as arbitrarily defined) inversely proportional to the pulse width (Fig. 2-20). In order to pass this pulse through a given network with a minimum of distortion, then, the network bandwidth must be greater than the pulse "bandwidth." Alternatively, if a pulse is passed through a network with a bandwidth smaller than the pulse "bandwidth," a distorted pulse will emerge. This pulse will itself have a "bandwidth" (as found from its frequency spectrum or Fourier integral) very nearly that of the network.

Any pulse of specified width in time can be viewed as having come from a network of bandwidth inversely proportional to the pulse width. The smallest bandwidth anywhere in a linear system will determine the width (in time) of pulses emerging from that system.

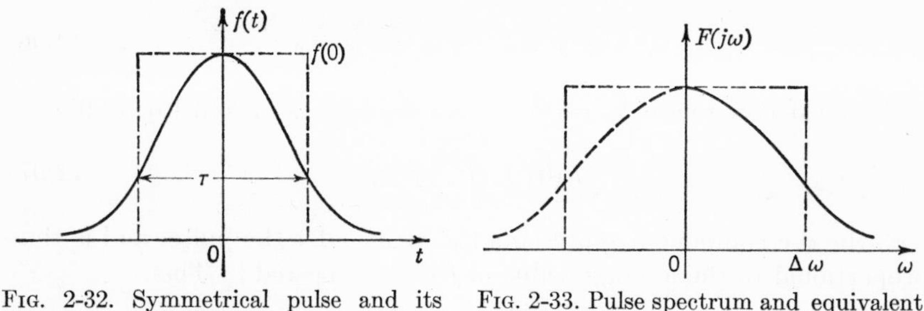

FIG. 2-32. Symmetrical pulse and its equivalent rectangular pulse.

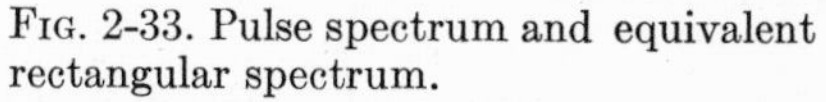

FIG. 2-33. Pulse spectrum and equivalent rectangular spectrum.

The inverse frequency-time relationship was discussed in Sec. 2-1 for the specific case of a periodic set of rectangular pulses. The inverse relationship was expressed there by Eq. (2-18). This inverse relationship is a specific property of the Fourier-series or Fourier-integral expansion of time functions and may be generalized to the case of a pulse of arbitrary shape. The exact relationship will again depend on the definition of pulse width (a unique quantity in the case of a rectangular pulse, but not so easily defined in the case of pulses with trailing edges) or bandwidth. But no matter what the definition, a relationship of the form of Eq. (2-18) will be found to hold.

A simple demonstration of the inverse pulse-width–bandwidth relationship may be carried out as follows: Assume that we have a *symmetrical positive pulse* $f(t)$ of arbitrary shape. (The only restriction on the shape is that the pulse have a definable width, i.e., that most of its energy be concentrated over a specified time interval. Any oscillations that are present are assumed to occur in the tail of the pulse.) We shall choose as our definition of pulse width (as the simplest choice and the one relating to our previous work) the width τ of an equivalent rectangular pulse of the same area and same amplitude, $f(0)$, at the point of symmetry, chosen to be $t = 0$. Figure 2-32 emphasizes this definition. Mathematically, we have

$$\tau f(0) = \int_{-\infty}^{\infty} f(t)\, dt \tag{2-94}$$

The frequency spectrum of $f(t)$ is found from the Fourier integral,

$$F(j\omega) = \int_{-\infty}^{\infty} f(t)e^{-j\omega t}\,dt \tag{2-95}$$

$F(j\omega)$ will be real and symmetrical since $f(t)$ is assumed symmetrical [Eq. (2-84)].

We now define the pulse bandwidth $\Delta\omega$ as the width of the equivalent rectangular spectrum having the same area and same value at $\omega = 0$. (Note that this differs from our previous definitions.) This is shown in Fig. 2-33. Mathematically

$$2\,\Delta\omega\,F(0) = \int_{-\infty}^{\infty} F(j\omega)\,d\omega \tag{2-96}$$

We must now relate $\Delta\omega$ (or $\Delta f = \Delta\omega/2\pi$) and τ. From Eq. (2-95)

$$F(0) = \int_{-\infty}^{\infty} f(t)\,dt \tag{2-97}$$

[i.e., the d-c component represents the area under the pulse, and is thus proportional to the average value of $f(t)$, as expected.] Then

$$\tau f(0) = \int_{-\infty}^{\infty} f(t)\,dt = F(0) = \frac{1}{2\,\Delta\omega}\int_{-\infty}^{\infty} F(j\omega)\,d\omega \tag{2-98}$$

from Eqs. (2-94), (2-96), and (2-97). But

$$f(t) = \frac{1}{2\pi}\int_{-\infty}^{\infty} F(j\omega)e^{j\omega t}\,d\omega \tag{2-99}$$

or

$$f(0) = \frac{1}{2\pi}\int_{-\infty}^{\infty} F(j\omega)\,d\omega \tag{2-100}$$

Combining Eqs. (2-98) and (2-100),

$$\frac{\tau}{2\pi} = \frac{1}{2\,\Delta\omega}$$

or

$$\Delta f = \frac{\Delta\omega}{2\pi} = \frac{1}{2\tau} \tag{2-101}$$

An inverse relationship between pulse rise time and bandwidth can also be demonstrated in a similar manner.

2-11. Impulse Response of Linear Networks. The Fourier transform of a rectangular pulse of height V and width τ was shown in Sec. 2-6 to be given by $V\tau[\sin(\omega\tau/2)/(\omega\tau/2)]$; that is, the area of the pulse ($V\tau$) multiplied by a frequency-dependent function. We noted also in Sec. 2-6 that, as τ is decreased (as the pulse is made narrower), the bandwidth defined as K/τ increases. This result for the rectangular pulse is then just a special case of the inverse time-bandwidth relationship discussed in the last section and phrased in the form of Eq. (2-101). Other examples of this inverse relationship are included among the problems for this chapter.

We now consider the rectangular pulse to be one of extremely short duration and very large amplitude. In particular, we let $\tau \to 0$ and $V \to \infty$ such that $V\tau$, the area under the pulse, remains constant. If

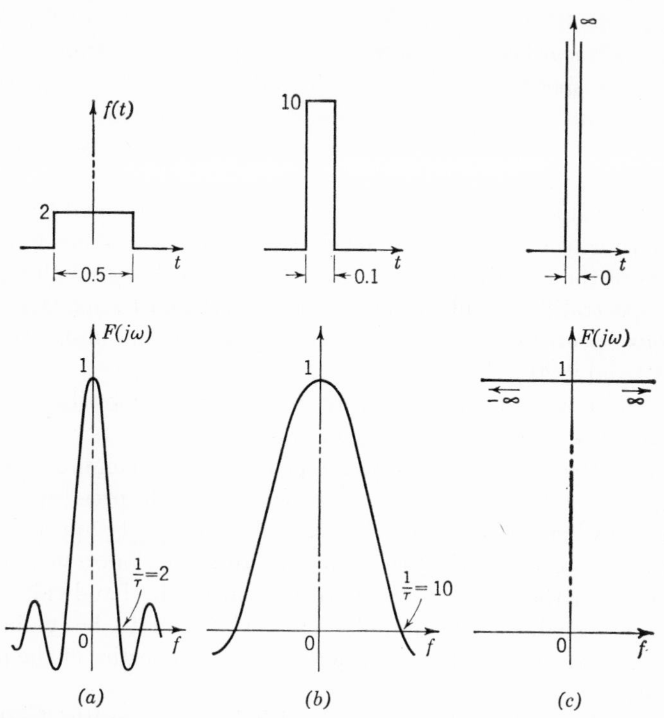

FIG. 2-34. Evolution of a unit impulse and its frequency spectrum. (*a*) $\tau = 0.5$, (*b*) $\tau = 0.1$; (*c*) $\tau = 0$.

$V\tau = 1$ (unit area), we get, by definition, the *unit impulse* in time. The amplitude-frequency spectrum of this pulse becomes constant, or "flat," and equal to 1, at all frequencies. (Since $\Delta f\ \tau$ is a constant, Δf must become very large as τ goes to zero.) The spectrum of three successively narrower and larger pulses is shown in Fig. 2-34. If the area under the pulse is a constant equal to A, the limiting function is an impulse of weight A. The amplitude spectrum equals A at all frequencies.

What is the significance of this impulse function? Why define it? Why use it?

One *practical* reason for using it appears immediately from a consideration of its uniform (flat) spectrum: this time function contains *equal* frequency components at *all* frequencies. If we were to use such a time function (or a good approximation to it) as the input to a linear system, this would be equivalent to *simultaneously* impressing upon the system an array of oscillators covering all possible frequencies, all of equal amplitude and phase. We could determine with this one input the frequency response of the system at *all* frequencies. Any variations in amplitude and phase at the output of the system would be due to the system itself.

We can thus determine the frequency spectrum or frequency transfer function of a *linear* system by applying an impulse at the input and using, for example, a spectrum analyzer at the output. (Note the emphasis on the word *linear*. The superposition of many simultaneous outputs is the crucial concept here and is possible only with linear systems.)

In practice a periodic series of very narrow pulses might be employed so that a repetitive pattern of the frequency spectrum would be obtained. The spectrum of a series of narrow pulses contains discrete frequencies (multiples of the repetition frequency), but with a slow enough repetition rate the spectral lines will be spaced closely enough to approximate the continuous spectrum of a single narrow pulse or impulse. (Compare Figs. 2-19 and 2-20.)

The impulse response of a network represents one possible method of determining the network frequency or transfer function (sweep-generator and variable-frequency oscillators are of course also commonly used for this purpose), and this procedure has come into widespread use. There are some drawbacks, however. We can obviously only approximate an impulse function in practice; the width of an actual pulse used must be much less than the response time (reciprocal of the bandwidth) of the filter to be tested, for the impulse approximation to be valid. This requires some prior knowledge of the frequency properties of the network under test.

For example, if the network bandwidth is of the order of 100 kc, a 1-μsec pulse applied at the input will look very nearly like an ideal impulse so far as the network is concerned. But if the network bandwidth is approximately 1 Mc, a 0.1-μsec pulse would have to be used. In mechanical systems an impulse can be approximated by an impact lasting a short interval of time. If the system response time is of the order of 0.1 sec (bandwidth of 10 cps), the impact would have to be less than 0.01 sec in duration. These numbers are based on the inverse bandwidth-time relationship discussed in the previous section.

So the choice of the right approximation to an impulse depends on some prior knowledge of the response time of the system.

In addition, the large amplitude pulses required may not be practical to use. In amplifier circuits, for example, they could easily drive the tubes or transistors used into nonlinear regions of operation. Although small but narrow pulses could be used as approximations, they contain very little energy and might not give the desired output amplitude.

The impulse response of networks is valuable in determining network frequency response, although with certain practical limitations.

Impulses have many other useful applications, however. They obviously provide us with information as to network time behavior (as is apparent from the close relationship between frequency and time response). We shall see shortly that the response of known networks to various other input functions can be readily determined from the impulse response. The use of the impulse also simplifies much of the mathematics of linear-system analysis, as we shall have occasion to demonstrate shortly. (Parenthetically, we shall see later on that impulse concepts play a leading role in the discussion of power and energy in systems, noise and interference, etc.)

We have discussed qualitatively the usefulness of the impulse concept. How do we formulate many of the useful properties of impulses quantitatively?

Our example of a unit impulse as the limiting case of a narrow rectangular pulse ($V \to \infty$, $\tau \to 0$, $V\tau = 1$) was only one of many that we might

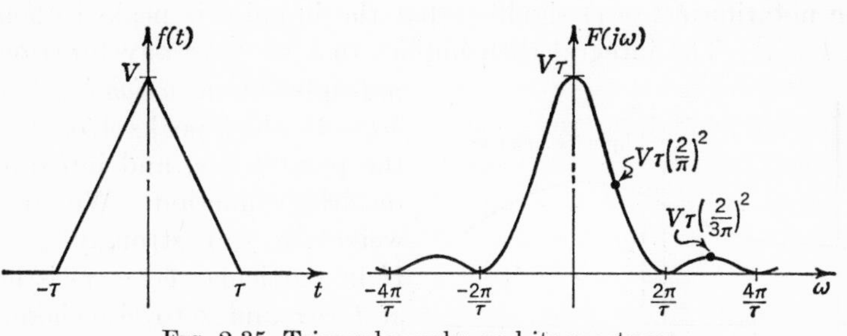

FIG. 2-35. Triangular pulse and its spectrum.

have chosen. Any other pulse shape would have done just as well. For example, a triangle of height V and base width 2τ has as its spectrum $V\tau[\sin(\omega\tau/2)/(\omega\tau/2)]^2$. This is sketched in Fig. 2-35. Again the area of the pulse, $V\tau$, appears multiplied by a frequency function. As $\tau \to 0$ and $V \to \infty$ such that $V\tau = 1$, we again get an infinitesimally narrow pulse of infinite height, while the frequency spectrum approaches a constant value of 1 for all frequencies.

Other examples of unit impulses (i.e., unit area) are obtained from the pulse-type time functions in the following table by considering the limit as $\tau \to 0$, $V\tau = 1$:

$f(t)$	$F(j\omega)$
$\dfrac{Ve^{-\|t\|/\tau}}{2}$	$\dfrac{V\tau}{1 + (\tau\omega)^2}$
$\dfrac{Ve^{-\frac{1}{2}(t/\tau)^2}}{\sqrt{2\pi}}$	$V\tau e^{-\frac{1}{2}(\tau\omega)^2}$
$\dfrac{V \sin (\pi t/\tau)}{\pi t/\tau}$	$V\tau$, $\|\omega\| < \pi/\tau$ 0, $\|\omega\| > \pi/\tau$

Note that in the limit all these pulses tend to cluster about the point $t = 0$. Their amplitude V increases indefinitely, but their area $V\tau$ always remains 1. In the limit they all have a constant, or flat, frequency spectrum $[F(j\omega) = 1]$.

To discuss these impulses quantitatively, we need a mathematical definition of an impulse that will include all the limiting cases mentioned, as well as many other possible ones. There are various acceptable definitions for the unit impulse, or *delta function*, as it is frequently called. One simple definition which satisfies the intuitive approach used above ($V \to \infty$, $\tau \to 0$, $V\tau = 1$) is to define the unit-impulse function $\delta(t)$ by the following integral:

$$f(t) = \int_{-\infty}^{\infty} f(\tau)\, \delta(t - \tau)\, d\tau \tag{2-102}$$

The notation $\delta(t - \tau)$ signifies that the impulse is peaked about the point $t = \tau$. The integral then implies that we take any function $f(\tau)$, multiply by a *weighting function* $\delta(t - \tau)$ which peaks strongly about the point $t = \tau$, and integrate the resulting function. We are thus weighting $f(\tau)$ strongly at $t = \tau$. If in particular $\delta(t - \tau)$ is infinite at $t = \tau$ and zero elsewhere, such that its area is normalized to 1, the integral of Eq. (2-102) will reproduce $f(t)$. $A\delta(t)$, with A a constant, represents an impulse function whose area is equal to A.

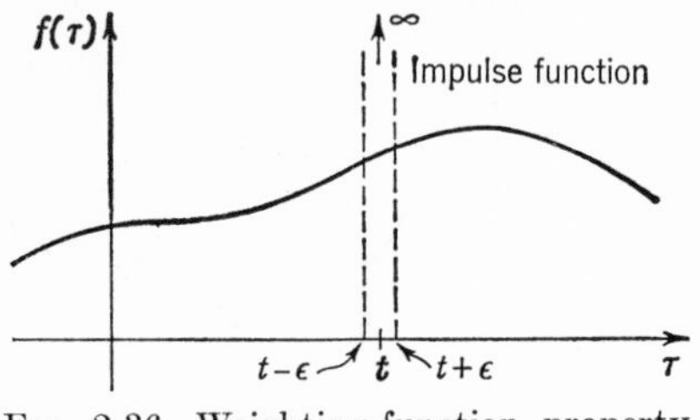

FIG. 2-36. Weighting-function property of impulse functions.

The integral and the weighting-function concept are demonstrated pictorially in Fig. 2-36. We assume there that $\delta(t - \tau)$ peaks sharply at $t = \tau$ and is zero outside an interval $t - \epsilon < \tau < t + \epsilon$. If ϵ is made small enough, $f(\tau)$ is very nearly constant and equal to $f(t)$ over this interval. As ϵ approaches zero, $f(\tau)$ approaches $f(t)$ exactly. Outside the interval the product $f(t)\, \delta(t - \tau)$ is zero. The integral can thus be approximated by

$$f(t) \doteq f(t) \int_{t-\epsilon}^{t+\epsilon} \delta(t - \tau)\, d\tau = f(t) \tag{2-103}$$

with $\delta(t)$ normalized so that the area under the curve is equal to 1 (*unit impulse*).

The integral thus satisfies our previous intuitive concept, namely, that $\delta(t-\tau) = 0$, $t \neq \tau$; $\delta(t-\tau) = \infty$, $t = \tau$; $\int_{-\infty}^{\infty} \delta(t-\tau)\, d\tau = 1$. It serves to generalize the concept of the delta, or impulse, function and enables us to treat it mathematically.

As an example of the use of the integral, consider in particular that the function $f(\tau)$ is the unit-step function $u(\tau)$. We shall show very simply that the integral does reproduce $u(t)$. Thus

$$\begin{aligned} u(t) &= \int_{-\infty}^{\infty} u(\tau)\, \delta(t-\tau)\, d\tau \\ &= \int_{0}^{\infty} \delta(t-\tau)\, d\tau \end{aligned} \tag{2-104}$$

since

$$\begin{aligned} u(\tau) &= 0 \qquad \tau < 0 \\ u(\tau) &= 1 \qquad \tau > 0 \end{aligned}$$

For $0 < t < \infty$, $\int_0^{\infty} \delta(t-\tau)\, d\tau = 1$ and $u(t) = 1$, as expected. For $t < 0$, the integral is zero. [The point $\tau = t$ at which $\delta(t-\tau)$ peaks occurs outside the range of integration.] So we get of course $u(t) = 1$, $t > 0$; $u(t) = 0$, $t < 0$. This is nothing new but again demonstrates the agreement of the defining integral for $\delta(t)$ with our intuitive notions of $\delta(t)$.

In Eq. (2-104) let us now shift our origin of coordinates by defining $x = t - \tau$. The integral then becomes by substitution of variables in both the integrand and the limits of integration

$$u(t) = \int_{-\infty}^{t} \delta(x)\, dx \tag{2-105}$$

The unit-step function is thus the integral of the unit impulse.

This is a fundamental relation between the impulse and step functions and is frequently also used as a definition of the impulse function.

To see that this agrees with the previous discussion of the impulse function, note that, if $\delta(x) = 0$ for $x \neq 0$ and $\delta(x) = \infty$ for $x = 0$, $u(t)$ will be zero for $t < 0$ and equals $\int_{-\infty}^{t} \delta(x)\, dx = 1$ if $t > 0$.

Alternatively, if $u(t) = 0$, $t < 0$; $u(t) = 1$, $t > 0$, $\delta(x)$ must be a function which is zero for $t < 0$. It must be infinite at $t = 0$ to make $u(t)$ jump by one unit in zero time at $t = 0$, and it must again be zero for $t > 0$. (Otherwise the integral could not be constant and equal to 1 for $t > 0$.) *The unit-step function is simply the integral of the δ function.* This property is a very useful one in studying linear systems. In a heuristic sense we might also consider $\delta(t)$ to be $du(t)/dt$. This is a troublesome concept mathematically since the usual definition of a derivative implies continuity, while $u(t)$ is obviously a discontinuous function. For this reason the definition of $\delta(t)$ in terms of its integral form is to be preferred. We shall, however, have occasion to refer to $\delta(t)$ as du/dt and shall find this relation useful later in this section.[1]

Now how do we utilize the impulse function in linear-system analysis? We have shown, by example, that the unit impulse has a flat frequency spectrum of unit amplitude for all frequencies. That this is a necessary condition for *any* impulse function can be easily demonstrated by means of the integral definition for $\delta(t)$. Thus the Fourier transform of the impulse function is

$$F(j\omega) = \int_{-\infty}^{\infty} \delta(t) e^{-j\omega t}\, dt \tag{2-106}$$

But, from the integral definition of $\delta(t)$,

$$\int_{-\infty}^{\infty} \delta(t) e^{-j\omega t}\, dt = e^{-j\omega t}\Big|_{t=0} = 1$$

or

$$F(j\omega) = 1 \tag{2-107}$$

as expected.

For an impulse displaced t_0 sec in time, the Fourier transform is

$$F(j\omega) = \int_{-\infty}^{\infty} \delta(t - t_0) e^{-j\omega t}\, dt = e^{-j\omega t_0} \tag{2-108}$$

This again gives a flat-amplitude frequency spectrum but introduces the familiar phase factor to account for the time delay assumed. An impulse of weight A, or one whose area equals A, written as $A\delta(t)$, would have as its Fourier transform just A. If the function is $A\delta(t - t_0)$, the Fourier transform becomes $Ae^{-j\omega t_0}$.

We could of course have found the Laplace transform of $\delta(t)$ first and then, with $p = j\omega$, have obtained the Fourier transform. This would have given us

$$F(p) = e^{-pt_0} \tag{2-109}$$

as the Laplace transform of $\delta(t - t_0)$ and

$$F(p) = 1 \tag{2-110}$$

as the Laplace transform of $\delta(t)$. The corresponding Laplace transforms of $A\delta(t - t_0)$ and $A\delta(t)$ are, respectively, Ae^{-pt_0} and A.

The fact that the unit step is the integral of the impulse function now

[1] This concept can be treated more rigorously by defining $u(t)$ as the limit of a continuous function with a continuous first derivative. For example, $u(t) \equiv 0$, $t < 0$; $u(t) \equiv \lim_{a\to 0} (1 - e^{-at} - ate^{-at})$, $t > 0$. If we differentiate *before* taking the limit, we get a pulse-type function which approaches $\delta(t)$ in the limit. See E. Weber, "Linear Transient Analysis," vol. 1, p. 193, John Wiley & Sons, Inc., New York, 1954.

follows quite naturally. For we know from Laplace-transform theory that $(1/p)F(p)$ is the Laplace transform of $\int_0^t f(t)\,dt$, with $F(p)$ the Laplace transform of $f(t)$. In particular, since $(1/p)e^{-pt_0}$ is the Laplace transform of $u(t - t_0)$,

$$u(t - t_0) = \int_0^t \delta(t - t_0)\,dt \tag{2-111}$$

using Eq. (2-109).

Now consider a linear network with transfer function $H(p)$. We know that the output $G(p)$ is given by

$$G(p) = H(p)F(p)$$

with $F(p)$ the Laplace transform of the input $f(t)$.

If $f(t) = \delta(t)$, $F(p) = 1$, and

$$G(p) = H(p) \tag{2-112}$$

The unit-impulse response of the system is thus the inverse transform of the network transfer function.

Alternatively, if we determine the impulse response of a linear network, *the Laplace transform of the impulse response gives us the network transfer function.* Thus, with $f(t) = \delta(t)$, the resulting network response $g(t)$ is by definition the unit-impulse response $h(t)$, with $H(p)$ the Laplace transform of $h(t)$.

This agrees with our initial discussion of the impulse function from the frequency point of view. For if $f(t) = \delta(t)$, its Fourier transform is just 1 and the output frequency spectrum must be just the frequency spectrum of the network itself,

$$G(j\omega) = H(j\omega) \tag{2-113}$$

If we measure the output frequency spectrum of the network (more generally, of any linear system) with an impulse applied at the input, we can determine the network transfer function. If we determine the impulse response in time and take its Laplace transform, we can also find the system transfer function. The frequency and time approaches are thus again shown to be related, tied together by the medium of the Fourier and Laplace transforms.

The impulse response of the RC filter of Sec. 2-3 is easily determined as an example. The transfer function of this filter is

$$H(p) = \frac{1/RC}{p + 1/RC}$$

This corresponds to a time function $h(t) = (1/RC)e^{-t/RC}$. $h(t)$ represents the unit-impulse response, or output voltage with a unit-impulse voltage applied to the input of the deenergized circuit. Note that this seems to contradict the usual assertion, based on the conservation of charge, that the voltage across the capacitor cannot change instantaneously. The voltage apparently jumps instantaneously from 0 to $1/RC$ volts. The apparent difficulty of course arises from the use of a nonphysical voltage pulse of infinite amplitude and zero duration. If we assume a voltage pulse of amplitude V volts ($V \to \infty$), a current of magnitude V/R amp begins to flow. In τ sec ($\tau \to 0$), $V\tau/R$ coulombs is deposited on the capacitor plates and the capacitor voltage charges up to $V\tau/RC$ volts. In the limit, as $\tau \to 0$ with $V\tau = 1$, the capacitor must charge from 0 to $1/RC$ volts in 0 time, checking the result obtained from the impulse response.

As a second example, we can calculate the impulse response of the ideal filter of Sec. 2-7. The frequency transfer function of this filter was

$$H(j\omega) = Ae^{-j\omega t_0} \qquad |\omega| \leq \omega_c$$

and $H(j\omega) = 0$ elsewhere. With an impulse input voltage $f(t) = \delta(t)$, $F(j\omega) = 1$ and $G(j\omega) = H(j\omega)$. The impulse response is then found from the inverse Fourier transform,

$$\begin{aligned} h(t) &= \frac{1}{2\pi} \int_{-\infty}^{\infty} H(j\omega) e^{j\omega t}\, d\omega \\ &= \frac{A\omega_c}{\pi} \frac{\sin \omega_c(t - t_0)}{\omega_c(t - t_0)} \end{aligned} \tag{2-114}$$

The impulse response is simply the familiar $(\sin x)/x$ function in time. This is as might be expected, for the Fourier transform and its inverse are symmetric, respectively, in ω and t, as can be seen by a comparison of Eqs. (2-50) and (2-51). A rectangular pulse in time has for its Fourier transform a $(\sin x)/x$ function in ω, while a rectangular pulse in ω has for its inverse transform a $(\sin x)/x$ function in time. This symmetry of course is the reason for the inverse frequency-time relationship demonstrated throughout this chapter.

Convolution Integral. Since the impulse response provides us with the network transfer function or frequency spectrum, it gives us a means of determining the response to any other input time function. This is immediately apparent from either of the two equivalent relations

$$G(p) = H(p)F(p)$$

or

$$G(j\omega) = H(j\omega)F(j\omega)$$

Thus we can experimentally find $h(t)$ or $H(j\omega)$ by applying an impulse to a given system and measuring the resultant time response $h(t)$ or the frequency response $H(j\omega)$. For any other input $f(t)$ we can then predict the response $g(t)$ by finding the time function corresponding to $G(p)$.

Since $g(t)$ is obviously related to $h(t)$ and $f(t)$ by the Laplace- or Fourier-transform relations, there should be a way of relating the three time functions directly.

We shall show that this relationship appears in the form of the so-called *convolution integral* given by

$$g(t) = \int_{-\infty}^{\infty} f(\tau)h(t - \tau)\, d\tau \tag{2-115}$$

Note how similar this integral is to the integral definition for the delta function introduced previously as Eq. (2-102). If the network impulse response happens to be an impulse function itself, or $h(t) = \delta(t - t_0)$ (a distortionless network is an example of a network with this property), Eq. (2-115) gives as the output a delayed version of the input:

$$g(t) = f(t - t_0)$$

Just as in the case of the defining integral for the delta function, Eq. (2-115) may be interpreted as a weighting-function integral. The network response to an arbitrary input $f(t)$ may be considered a weighted sum of different values of $f(t)$. The impulse response $h(t)$ acts as the weighting function in this case.

We shall first derive the convolution integral and then apply it to the solution of some simple problems. The significance of the integral will then be discussed further.

The derivation is demonstrated by first representing an arbitrary time function $f(t)$ by a series of impulses of varying weight. This we do by approximating the integral definition of the impulse function by a sum. Thus

$$\begin{aligned} f(t) &= \int_{-\infty}^{\infty} f(\tau)\delta(t - \tau)\, d\tau \\ &\doteq \sum_{n=-\infty}^{\infty} f(n\,\Delta\tau)\delta(t - n\,\Delta\tau)\,\Delta\tau \end{aligned} \tag{2-116}$$

This corresponds to breaking the time scale up into small intervals $\Delta\tau$ apart, letting the variable τ become $n\,\Delta\tau$, and summing over n instead of τ. This is shown in Fig. 2-37. For $\Delta\tau$ very small, $\delta(t - n\,\Delta\tau)\,\Delta\tau \doteq 1$ with a peak in the vicinity of $n\,\Delta\tau = t$, and the sum reproduces $f(t)$.

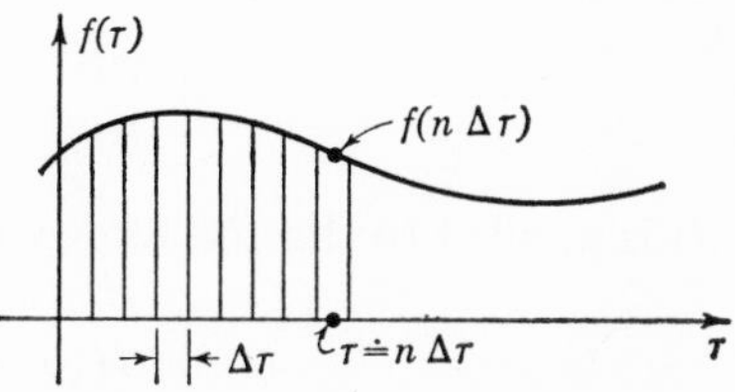

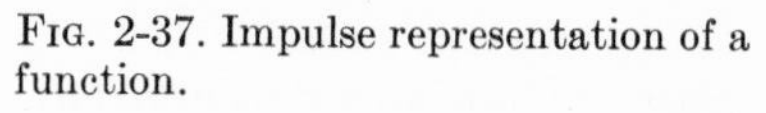

FIG. 2-37. Impulse representation of a function.

Now assume that $f(t)$ is applied to a *linear* system. The response to $f(t)$ may be found by superposing the response to each of the impulses of Eq. (2-116). The response to an impulse $A\,\delta(t - n\,\Delta\tau)$ of weight A is by definition $Ah(t - n\,\Delta\tau)$, so that the output is given by

$$g(t) \doteq \sum_{n=-\infty}^{\infty} f(n\,\Delta\tau)h(t - n\,\Delta\tau)\,\Delta\tau \tag{2-117}$$

In the limit, as $\Delta\tau \to 0$, $n\,\Delta\tau \to \tau$ and the sum becomes the integral

$$g(t) = \int_{-\infty}^{\infty} f(t)h(t - \tau)\,d\tau \tag{2-115}$$

To show that this integral satisfies the transform relations

$$G(p) = F(p)H(p)$$

or $G(j\omega) = F(j\omega)H(j\omega)$, we may take the Fourier (or Laplace) transform of each side of Eq. (2-115). Thus

$$G(j\omega) = \int_{-\infty}^{\infty} e^{-j\omega t}\left[\int_{-\infty}^{\infty} f(\tau)h(t - \tau)\,d\tau\right] dt \tag{2-118}$$

If we now interchange the order of integration (the integrals must be assumed to converge absolutely),

$$G(j\omega) = \int_{-\infty}^{\infty} f(\tau)\left[\int_{-\infty}^{\infty} e^{-j\omega t}h(t - \tau)\,dt\right] d\tau \tag{2-119}$$

But

$$\int_{-\infty}^{\infty} e^{-j\omega t}h(t - \tau)\,d\tau = e^{-j\omega\tau}H(j\omega) \tag{2-120}$$

since a time delay of t sec corresponds to a phase factor $e^{-j\omega t}$ in the Fourier transform. Using Eq. (2-120),

$$\begin{aligned} G(j\omega) &= H(j\omega)\int_{-\infty}^{\infty} f(\tau)e^{-j\omega\tau}\,d\tau \\ &= H(j\omega)F(j\omega) \end{aligned} \tag{2-121}$$

The transfer-function relations are thus seen to be satisfied by the convolution integral.

It is instructive to utilize the convolution integral to solve a simple problem. Assume that $f(t)$ is a simple exponential defined for positive time only.

$$\begin{aligned} f(t) &= e^{-at} \qquad t > 0 \\ f(t) &= 0 \qquad\quad t < 0 \end{aligned} \tag{2-122}$$

$f(t)$ is applied to the RC filter with transfer function

$$H(p) = \frac{1/RC}{p + 1/RC}$$

(assumed initially deenergized). What is the resulting output voltage $g(t)$?

We could use simple differential equations or the Laplace-transform method to find $g(t)$. Either way we find $g(t)$ to be given by

$$g(t) = \frac{e^{-at} - e^{-t/RC}}{1 - aRC} \qquad a \neq \frac{1}{RC} \tag{2-123}$$

(This is the familiar response of an RC network to an exponential input and should be checked by the reader.)

Applying the convolution integral [Eq. (2-115)] to the solution of the same problem, we have

$$f(\tau) = e^{-a\tau} \qquad \tau > 0 \tag{2-124}$$

and

$$h(t - \tau) = \frac{1}{RC} e^{-(t-\tau)/RC} \qquad t > \tau \tag{2-125}$$

[Recall that $h(t) = (1/RC)e^{-t/RC}$ for the RC network.] Then

$$\begin{aligned} g(t) &= \int_{-\infty}^{\infty} f(\tau)h(t - \tau)\, d\tau \\ &= \int_0^t \frac{e^{-a\tau}}{RC} e^{-(1/RC)(t-\tau)}\, d\tau \end{aligned} \tag{2-126}$$

since $f(\tau) = 0$, $\tau < 0$; $h(t - \tau) = 0$, $\tau > t$. Performing the indicated integration, we get

$$\begin{aligned} g(t) &= \frac{e^{-t/RC}}{RC} \left. \frac{e^{\tau(1/RC - a)}}{1/RC - a} \right|_0^t \\ &= \frac{e^{-at} - e^{-t/RC}}{1 - aRC} \end{aligned} \tag{2-127}$$

The general form of the convolution integral [Eq. (2-115)] may be rewritten in somewhat different form for certain special cases. First, we note by a simple change of variables that $g(t)$ is symmetrical in $f(t)$ and $h(t)$. Thus

$$g(t) = \int_{-\infty}^{\infty} f(\tau)h(t - \tau)\, d\tau = \int_{-\infty}^{\infty} h(\tau)f(t - \tau)\, d\tau \tag{2-128}$$

The reader should prove Eq. (2-128) for himself. Note that it is consistent with the transform relation since

$$G(p) = H(p)F(p) = F(p)H(p)$$

Interchanging H and F has no effect on G, and therefore $g(t)$ remains unchanged.

The convolution integral applies to both physically realizable and nonrealizable linear filters. (The ideal low-pass filter is an example of the latter.)

For physically realizable filters, i.e., those which can be synthesized in terms of R, L, C elements and active elements, we can develop an alternate form of the convolution integral by noting that $h(t) = 0$, $t < 0$. This is just a mathematical statement of the fact that no output can appear before the input is applied. [$\delta(t)$, the input, is applied at $t = 0$.] Then $h(t - \tau) = 0$, $t < \tau$, and

$$g(t) = \int_{-\infty}^{t} f(\tau)h(t - \tau)\, d\tau \tag{2-129}$$

Equation (2-129) represents the convolution integral specialized to the case of realizable filters. If now $f(t) = 0$, $t < 0$, or the input is assumed applied at $t = 0$, we get

$$g(t) = \int_{0}^{t} f(\tau)h(t - \tau)\, d\tau \tag{2-130}$$

This is actually the integral we used in finding the response of the simple RC filter to an exponential input. There we stated specifically that $h(t) = e^{-t/RC}/RC$, $t > 0$, and $h(t) = 0$, $t < 0$, and so rewrote the integral directly.

The ideal low-pass filter, on the other hand, was specifically noted to be nonrealizable, and we found in fact the existence of precursor, or anticipatory, transients. Thus, for the filter characteristic given by

$$H(j\omega) = Ae^{-jt_0\omega}$$

$|\omega| \leq \omega_c$, and $H = 0$, $|\omega| > \omega_c$, we had

$$h(t) = \frac{\omega_c A}{\pi} \frac{\sin \omega_c(t - t_0)}{\omega_c(t - t_0)}$$

This impulse response is symmetrical about $t = t_0$, as expected, and has precursor transients. $h(t)$ is in fact defined for all t, $-\infty < t < \infty$. So for the general filter, including idealized networks, the general form of the convolution integral, as given by Eq. (2-115), must be used. If $f(t) = 0$, $t < 0$, however, Eq. (2-115) may be specialized to

$$g(t) = \int_{0}^{\infty} f(\tau)h(t - \tau)\, d\tau \tag{2-131}$$

We have already indicated that the convolution integral contains as a special case the integral definition of the impulse, or delta, function. We can consider as another special case the step response of a linear network. Thus let $f(t) = u(t)$, a unit-step input. Then for the general linear filter (realizable and nonrealizable cases included)

$$g(t) = \int_{0}^{\infty} h(t - \tau)\, d\tau \equiv A(t) \tag{2-132}$$

$A(t)$, the step response, is thus just the integral of the impulse response. A simple change of variables, with $x = t - \tau$, gives us also

$$A(t) = \int_{-\infty}^{t} h(x)\, dx \tag{2-133}$$

In particular, if $h(t) = 0$, $t < 0$ (physically realizable filters),

$$A(t) = \int_0^t h(x)\,dx \tag{2-134}$$

As an example, consider the RC filter again. The impulse response was found to be $h(t) = e^{-t/RC}/RC$, $t \geq 0$. The step response is then

$$\begin{aligned} A(t) &= \int_0^t h(x)\,dx = \frac{1}{RC}\int_0^t e^{-x/RC}\,dx \\ &= 1 - e^{-t/RC} \end{aligned} \tag{2-135}$$

as expected.

The step response of the ideal filter is obtained using Eq. (2-133), since $h(t)$ is not zero for $t < 0$. Thus, with $h(t) = \dfrac{\omega_c A}{\pi}\dfrac{\sin \omega_c(t - t_0)}{\omega_c(t - t_0)}$, the step response of the ideal filter becomes

$$\begin{aligned} A(t) &= \frac{\omega_c A}{\pi}\int_{-\infty}^{t} \frac{\sin \omega_c(x - t_0)}{\omega_c(x - t_0)}\,dx \\ &= \frac{A}{\pi}\int_{-\infty}^{\omega_c(t-t_0)} \frac{\sin y}{y}\,dy \end{aligned} \tag{2-136}$$

with $y = \omega_c(x - t_0)$. We again have the sine integral as a solution. From our previous discussion of the sine integral (Fig. 2-22) we recall that $(1/\pi)\int_{-\infty}^{0} [(\sin x)/x]\,dx = \frac{1}{2}$. The step response thus becomes

$$A(t) = A\left[\frac{1}{2} + \frac{1}{\pi}\,\text{Si}\,\omega_c(t - t_0)\right] \tag{2-137}$$

The impulse and step responses for both the RC filter and the ideal filter are sketched in Fig. 2-38.

The step response of the ideal filter [Eq. (2-137)] may also be obtained from the previous result for the rectangular-pulse response of the same filter [Eq. (2-71) and Fig. 2-24] by letting the pulse width τ become very large. The input pulse then approaches a step, and the response approaches the step response. An alternative method of obtaining Eq. (2-137) is indicated in one of the problems for this chapter.

The convolution integral, in addition to providing us with another method of determining the response of a linear system to a specified input, enables us to draw a visual picture of the system behavior. This we can do by a qualitative discussion of the convolution integral for physically realizable filters,

$$g(t) = \int_0^t f(\tau)h(t - \tau)\,d\tau \qquad f(t) = 0,\ t < 0 \tag{2-138}$$

Here t represents the time at which the filter response $g(t)$ is to be determined and might thus be called the *present*. The variable τ ranges over all values less than t, or values of time in the *past*. The variable $t - \tau$, which appears associated with the impulse response, thus measures time back into the past. (See Fig. 2-39.)

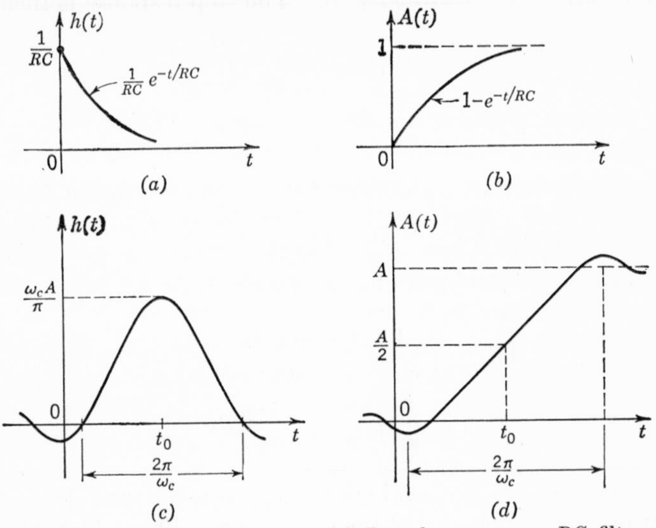

FIG. 2-38. Impulse and step responses. (*a*) Impulse response, RC filter; (*b*) step response, RC filter; (*c*) impulse response, ideal filter; (*d*) step response, ideal filter.

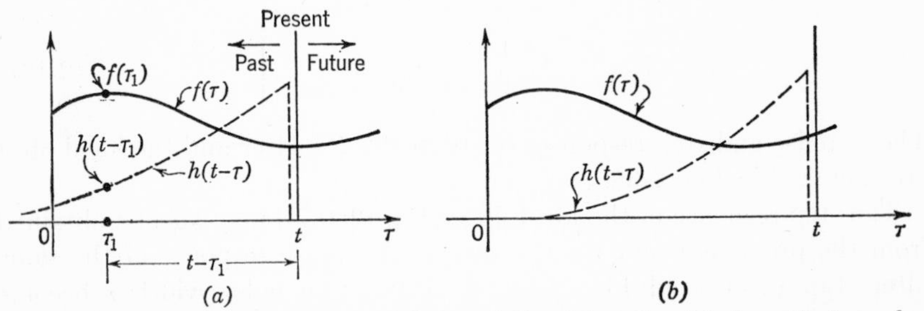

FIG. 2-39. Graphical interpretation of convolution integral. (*a*) A particular value of t; (*b*) t some time later.

For all realizable filters the impulse response $h(t)$ is zero for $t < 0$ and again goes to zero as $t \to \infty$ [for example, $h(t) = (1/RC)e^{-t/RC}$, $t > 0$, for the RC filter]. The function $h(t - \tau)$ which appears in the convolution integral then must be zero for $\tau > t$ and again approaches zero as $t - \tau \to \infty$, or $\tau \to -\infty$. $h(t - \tau)$ thus represents the impulse response turned round, or *folded over*, and extending back into the past. This is shown in Fig. 2-39.

We may thus interpret the filter response $g(t)$ as being the weighted superposition of past values of the input $f(\tau)$. $f(\tau)$, in the past, appears multiplied or weighted by $h(t - \tau)$.

Since $h(t - \tau)$ eventually goes to zero for $t - \tau$ large enough, or τ sufficiently "far back in the past," values of $f(\tau)$ that appeared "far back in the past" have a negligibly small influence on the present output of the network. The filter thus can be looked on as having a "memory" lasting only over the time interval $t - \tau$ for which $h(t - \tau)$ has significant values. This is just the response time of the filter, or the reciprocal of its bandwidth.

As an example, consider the *RC* filter again. The voltage across the capacitor is assumed to be the desired output. The charge on the capacitor at any given time ($\tau = t$, the *present*) is obviously due to all charge applied in the past. However, because of the resistor in series with the capacitor most of the charge applied in the past has been discharged and dissipated in the form of heat. The significant contribution to existing charge may be assumed to have been applied less than $2\pi RC$ sec or about 6 time constants before. ($\Delta\omega = 1/RC, \Delta f = 1/2\pi RC$.) Mathematically this is accounted for by the exponentially decreasing form of the impulse response.

As the present time t varies, the impulse response $h(t - \tau)$ scans the function $f(\tau)$, always producing a weighted sum of past inputs, always weighting most heavily values of $f(\tau)$ closest to the present ($t - \tau \doteq 0$). If the impulse response is quite narrow in width, the output comes close to being an undistorted replica of the input.

The filter weighting effect is analogous to the aperture effect of optical filters. The input $f(\tau)$ is "seen" through a "window," or aperture, whose width is that of the impulse-response function.

This analogy with optical filters is particularly illuminating if $h(t)$ happens to have the form of a rectangular pulse of width Δt. The filter output is then simply the input $f(\tau)$ averaged over the interval Δt. If Δt is small compared with time changes in the input function [if the filter time response is short compared with the rate of change of $f(\tau)$, or if the filter frequency response is wide compared with the input frequency spectrum], there is no aperture distortion and $f(t)$ is reproduced undistorted. This interpretation of course agrees with the previous bandwidth-time discussions of this chapter. Alternatively we can say that, as $\Delta t \to 0$, $h(t - \tau)$ approaches an impulse centered at $t = \tau$ and $f(t)$ is reproduced undistorted.

A simple example will demonstrate the usefulness of this graphical approach to the convolution integral. Assume that both $f(t)$ and $h(t)$ are unit-amplitude rectangular pulses of width Δt sec beginning at $t = 0$ (see Fig. 2-40*a* and *b*). The filter frequency response, or the Fourier transform of $h(t)$, is

$$H(j\omega) = \Delta t\, e^{-j(\omega \Delta t/2)} \frac{\sin (\omega \Delta t/2)}{\omega \Delta t/2}$$

(The impulse response is symmetrical about the point $t = \Delta t/2$, and this gives rise to the phase term.) $F(j\omega)$ is of course identical with $H(j\omega)$.

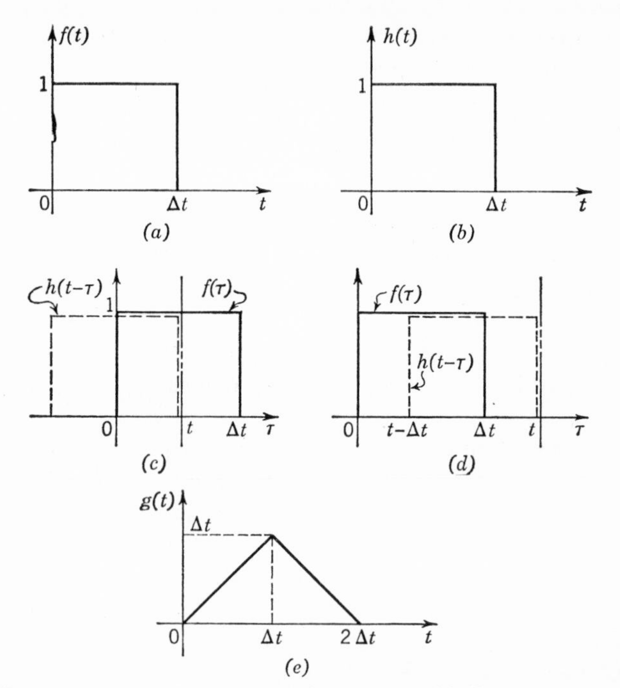

FIG. 2-40. Example of convolution-integral analysis. (a) System input; (b) system impulse response; (c) convolution integral, $t < \Delta t$; (d) convolution integral, $t > \Delta t$; (e) $g(t)$, output response.

We then find the output response $g(t)$ by convolving $f(\tau)$ with $h(t - \tau)$. The τ plane is depicted in Fig. 2-40c and d. Figure 2-40c shows the appropriate functions for $t < \Delta t$, Fig. 2-40d for $t > \Delta t$. In either case we are to multiply $f(\tau)$ by $h(t - \tau)$ and integrate over all values of τ up to t. Since $f(\tau) = 0$, $\tau < 0$, we need integrate only from $\tau = 0$. For $t < \Delta t$ the integral is simply the area under $f(\tau)$ and $h(t - \tau)$ included between 0 and t (see Fig. 2-40c). So

$$g(t) = t \qquad t < \Delta t$$

(Remember that both time functions have unit amplitude.)

For $t > \Delta t$ we can integrate only from $\tau = t - \Delta t$ to $\tau = \Delta t$, since $h(t - \Delta t)$ is zero for $\tau < t - \Delta t$. Again the integral is the area included between the two limits of τ, and

$$g(t) = 2(\Delta t) - t \qquad t > \Delta t$$
$$g(t) = 0 \qquad t > 2\,\Delta t$$

The complete output function is thus a triangular pulse of base width $2\,\Delta t$ and height Δt. $g(t)$ is shown in Fig. 2-40*e*.

We can check this result quite easily from the frequency spectra. Since $F(j\omega)$ and $H(j\omega)$ are identical *in this case*,

$$G(j\omega) = H^2(j\omega) = (\Delta t)^2 e^{-j\omega\,\Delta t}\left[\frac{\sin\,(\omega\,\Delta t/2}{\omega\,\Delta t/2}\right]^2$$

But from our previous study of Fourier integrals and as will be shown shortly by Eq. (2-142), this transform represents a triangular pulse in time, of width $2\,\Delta t$ sec, and whose amplitude is $(\Delta t)^2$. The pulse is symmetrical about the point $t = \Delta t$ from the phase factor. This is of course exactly the pulse of Fig. 2-40*e*.

Although we have discussed the convolution integral in terms of the network impulse response, it actually applies more generally to *any* three functions $a(t)$, $b(t)$, $c(t)$ whose transforms, respectively, are related by

$$A(p) = B(p)C(p) \tag{2-139}$$

Then
$$a(t) = \int_{-\infty}^{\infty} b(\tau)c(t-\tau)\,d\tau = \int_{-\infty}^{\infty} c(\tau)b(t-\tau)\,d\tau \tag{2-140}$$

For example, if we know the response to *any* input (a sine wave, for example), we can find the response to any other input in terms of the convolution integral.

We shall apply the convolution integral to the solutions of some problems in probability later in the book.

The convolution integral provides us with an additional tool in solving linear-system problems, and it enables us to describe the system behavior pictorially. Its application to particular problems is, however, sometimes quite complicated because of the integrals involved. In such cases a direct application of differential equations or transform theory might provide the answer more readily. In the solution of a particular problem *all* available tools should be considered and the simplest and most direct eventually chosen.

2-12. Use of Impulses in Frequency Analysis. We have shown that the impulse response enables us to determine the response of linear networks to any other type of input. This gives us both an analytical tool (the convolution integral) and an experimental method for determining system response.

The impulse function is also particularly helpful in determining the Fourier transform or frequency spectrum of complicated waveshapes.

In particular, if a specified time function can be represented or approximated by a series of straight-line sections, or parabolic arcs, or in general by polynomials in t, its frequency spectrum can be found readily by using impulse functions. For we can successively differentiate the function over any section representable by a polynomial until an impulse or set of impulses remains. The Fourier transform of an impulse at $t = t_0$ is $e^{-j\omega t_0}$. Integrating back again to obtain the original function, we divide $e^{-j\omega t_0}$ by $1/j\omega$ for each integration. Adding up the resultant terms in $j\omega$ by superposition, we obtain the desired spectrum for the original function. Note that this technique obviates the need for tedious and time-consuming integrations. It implies, however, that the time function can be accurately represented either by a polynomial in t or sectionally by polynomials in t.

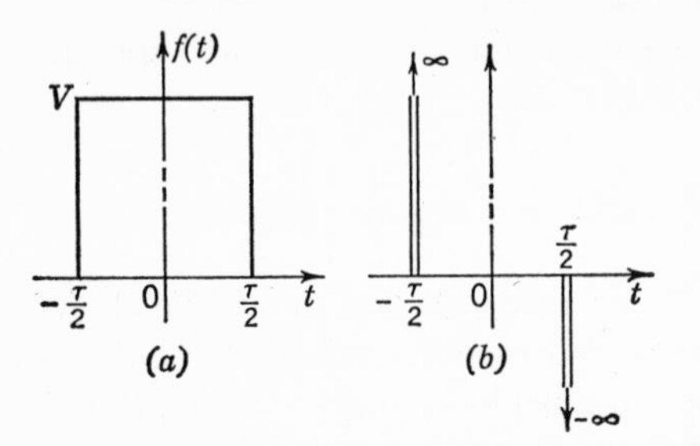

FIG. 2-41. Rectangular pulse and its derivative. (a) $f(t)$; (b) df/dt.

Some examples will demonstrate the method:

1. $f(t)$ a rectangular pulse of width τ and height V (Fig. 2-41a). Differentiating once gives the two impulses of Fig. 2-41b. Each impulse

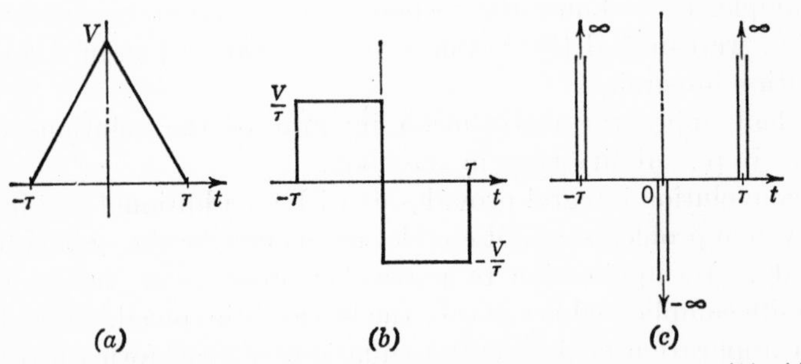

FIG. 2-42. Triangular pulse and successive derivatives. (a) $f(t)$; (b) $f'(t)$; (c) $f''(t)$.

has a weight of V. Then

$$F(j\omega) = \frac{V}{j\omega}(e^{j\omega\tau/2} - e^{-j\omega\tau/2}) = V\tau\,\frac{\sin(\omega\tau/2)}{\omega\tau/2} \qquad (2\text{-}141)$$

as previously.

2. $f(t)$ a triangle of height V and width 2τ (Fig. 2-42a). Here two successive differentiations are needed, and three impulses result. The middle impulse is twice the weight of the other two. Integrating twice to

get $f(t)$ back again, with the appropriate phase factors for the impulses,

$$\begin{aligned} F(j\omega) &= \frac{V}{\tau(j\omega)^2}\,(e^{j\omega\tau} - 2 + e^{-j\omega\tau}) \\ &= \frac{2V}{\tau(j\omega)^2}\,(\cos\omega\tau - 1) = \frac{4V}{\tau\omega^2}\left(\sin^2\omega\,\frac{\tau}{2}\right) \\ &= V\tau\left[\frac{\sin(\omega\tau/2)}{\omega\tau/2}\right]^2 \end{aligned} \qquad (2\text{-}142)$$

again, as obtained previously.

Note that we have to be careful to weight each impulse properly. Here the first derivatives had the magnitudes V/τ and $-V/\tau$, and these were

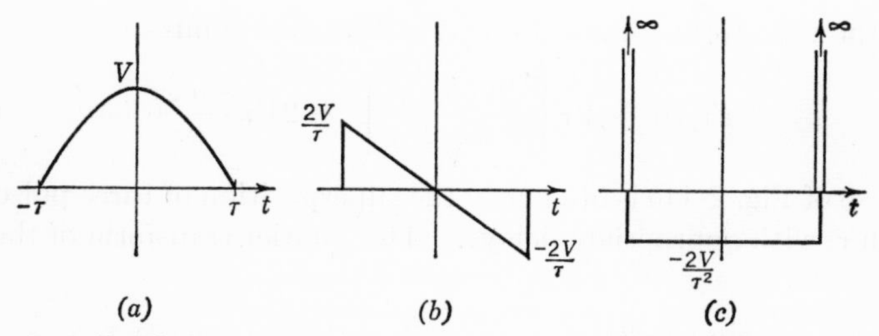

FIG. 2-43. Parabolic pulse and its derivatives. (a) $f(t)$; (b) $f'(t)$; (c) $f''(t)$.

used as the weight of the impulses [that is, $(V/\tau)\,\delta(t-\tau)$, $(-2V/\tau)\,\delta(t)$, $(V/\tau)\,\delta(t+\tau)$].

3. $f(t)$ a parabolic pulse of height V and width 2τ (Fig. 2-43a)

$$\begin{aligned} f(t) &= V\left[1 - \left(\frac{t}{\tau}\right)^2\right] \qquad |t| \le \tau \\ f(t) &= 0 \qquad\qquad\qquad\quad |t| > 0 \end{aligned} \qquad (2\text{-}143)$$

Differentiating once, we get the triangle of Fig. 2-43b. Differentiating a second time, we get two impulses, $(2V/\tau)\,\delta(t+\tau)$, $(2V/\tau)\,\delta(t-\tau)$, and a pulse of amplitude $-2V/\tau^2$, width 2τ. We could differentiate the pulse once more to reduce it to two impulses. Instead we apply superposition at this point, combining the known spectra for the impulses and pulse, and then dividing by $(j\omega)^2$ to obtain $F(j\omega)$. This gives

$$\begin{aligned} F(j\omega) &= \frac{2V}{\tau(j\omega)^2}\,(e^{j\omega\tau} + e^{-j\omega\tau}) - \frac{2V}{\tau^2(j\omega)^2}\,2\tau\,\frac{\sin\omega\tau}{\omega\tau} \\ &= \frac{4V\tau}{(\omega\tau)^2}\left(\frac{\sin\omega\tau}{\omega\tau} - \cos\omega\tau\right) \end{aligned} \qquad (2\text{-}144)$$

The method of superposition is applicable in all our problems and can be used very effectively to find the transforms of various simple shapes made up of impulses, pulses, and triangles. For example, the Fourier

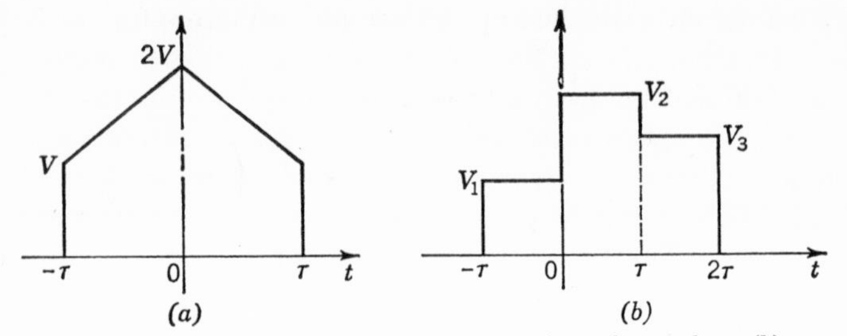

FIG. 2-44. Complex pulse shapes. (a) Another triangular pulse; (b) complex of rectangular pulses.

transform of the raised triangle of Fig. 2-44*a* can be obtained by superposing the transforms of a pulse and a triangle. Thus

$$F(j\omega) = V\tau \left[\frac{\sin(\omega\tau/2)}{\omega\tau/2}\right]^2 + 2V\tau \frac{\sin \omega\tau}{\omega\tau} \tag{2-145}$$

The pulse of Fig. 2-44*b* is obviously the superposition of three pulses, each of width τ, with appropriate delays. The Fourier transform of the group is thus

$$F(j\omega) = \frac{\sin(\omega\tau/2)}{\omega\tau/2}(V_1\tau e^{j\omega\tau/2} + V_2\tau e^{-j\omega\tau/2} + V_3\tau e^{-j(3\omega\tau/2)}) \tag{2-146}$$

Other simple examples are included among the problems for this chapter.

Note that throughout this section, as in the previous sections of this chapter, runs the theme of superposition. This is a basic concept of linear systems and often serves to simplify complex-looking problems. Superposition techniques break down in nonlinear systems, however, as will be noted in the sections on frequency modulation in the next chapter.

The use of impulse, or delta, functions also serves to simplify the mathematics of linear systems, as has been demonstrated in the last two sections. We shall utilize the impulse function in the discussion of various topics throughout this book.

2-13. Television Bandwidth Requirements. Before concluding this chapter on signal transmission through linear networks, we give one further example—the calculation of the bandwidth needed to transmit a typical TV test pattern.[1]

The pattern we choose consists of a series of alternating black and white spots. The pattern is 6 in. high by 8 in. wide, and the spots are 0.0121 in. high and 0.0188 in. wide. (These dimensions have been chosen as a compromise between the ability of the eye to resolve detail and the

[1] S. Deutsch, "Theory and Design of Television Receivers," McGraw-Hill Book Company, Inc., New York, 1951.

frequency bandwidth required.) There are then 6/0.0121 = 495 horizontal lines that must be covered by a scanning beam of electrons. The equivalent of 30 additional lines is allowed to enable the beam to retrace from the final line back to the first again. (Actually interlaced scanning is used in which even-numbered lines are first covered, then odd-numbered lines. This increases the time allotted for scanning the picture. The persistence of the eye is then relied on to give the effect of a more rapid scanning rate.) The total number of lines scanned is thus 525 (the time for the 30 additional lines is blanked out). The standard scanning rate is 30 frames per second, so that each line is scanned in

$$\frac{1}{30 \times 525} = 63.5 \ \mu\text{sec}$$

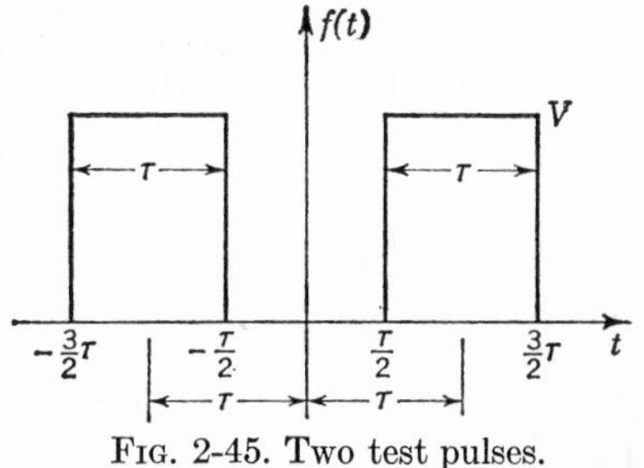

FIG. 2-45. Two test pulses.

This represents the time in which the beam must sweep from left to right through the 8 in. of the pattern and return to the left side again. Allowing 10 μsec for the return, or horizontal, trace interval leaves 53.5 μsec for the actual sweep. In this time 8/0.0188 = 425 alternating black and white spots will be swept through. The electrical output will thus consist of a series of square waves of 53.5/425 = 0.125 μsec width.

Our problem is to determine how much bandwidth is needed to resolve these square-wave pulses of 0.125 μsec duration, separated by the same time interval. We can relate this to the problem of resolving two pulses of width τ, separated by τ sec (τ is 0.125 μsec). These pulses are shown in Fig. 2-45.

The response of the idealized low-pass filter to a single pulse was given by Eq. (2-71). Since the system is assumed linear, superposition may be applied. The two pulses applied to the low-pass filter with bandwidth f_c cps then produce a response at the output given by

$$g(t) = \frac{AV}{\pi}\left\{\text{Si}\left[\omega_c(t - t_0) + \frac{3\tau}{2}\right] - \text{Si}\left[\omega_c(t - t_0) + \frac{\tau}{2}\right] + \text{Si}\left[\omega_c(t - t_0) - \frac{\tau}{2}\right] - \text{Si}\left[\omega_c(t - t_0) - \frac{3\tau}{2}\right]\right\} \quad (2\text{-}147)$$

This equation has been plotted by S. Goldman in his book,[1] and some of these curves are reproduced in Fig. 2-46. (t_0 is assumed zero so that the input and output curves are superimposed for comparison.) These

[1] Goldman, *op. cit.*

results indicate that for resolution of (the ability to separate) the two pulses

$$f_c \geq \frac{1}{2\tau} \tag{2-148}$$

Note that this is a different situation from the one previously stressed in this chapter, in which it was desired to reproduce the pulse faithfully

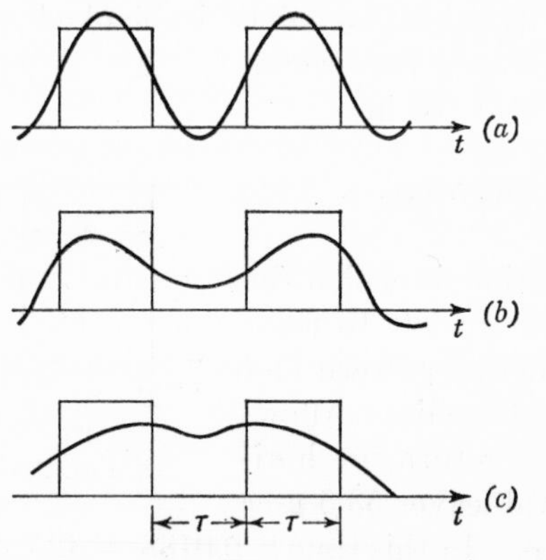

FIG. 2-46. Low-pass filter response to TV test pattern (two pulses). (a) $f_c = 1/\tau$; (b) $f_c = 1/2\tau$; (c) $f_c = 1/3\tau$. *(From S. Goldman, "Frequency Analysis, Modulation, and Noise," McGraw-Hill Book Company, Inc., New York, 1948, by permission.)*

($f_c \gg 1/\tau$). Here the problem is to distinguish between black and white spots or between an on and off signal. The signal detail as such is not important in this application.

If $f_c < 1/2\tau$, the two pulses merge into one and the resolution disappears. If $f_c > 1/2\tau$, the sides of the pulses are sharpened, the rise times decreasing.

For the TV case outlined $\tau = 0.125$ μsec, and

$$f_c \geq 4 \text{ Mc}$$

It will be shown later that in order to transmit these signals at high frequencies bandwidths of $2f_c = 8$ Mc will be required. In practice some bandwidth compression is utilized (vestigial sideband transmission), and 6-Mc bandwidths are prescribed for home TV receivers.

2-14. Summary. Major emphasis has been placed in this chapter on developing, through different examples, the inverse frequency-time relationship of signal transmission.

We demonstrated, first, through the use of the Fourier-series representation for periodic functions and then through the Fourier-integral representation of nonperiodic functions that more rapid time variations in a signal give rise to the higher-frequency components in the signal spectrum.

A general conclusion drawn from an analysis of signal transmission through linear networks was that the system bandwidth had to be approximately the reciprocal of the signal duration in order to produce at the system output a signal of the same general form as the input. For a symmetrical output signal the system phase characteristics had to be linear.

High-fidelity signal reproduction, or reproduction of detail, required bandwidths in excess of the reciprocal of the signal duration. The bandwidths needed were found to be about the reciprocal of the rise time, or the time taken for the signal to change from one level to another.

These conclusions are of importance in the design of practical system circuitry and are also of considerable theoretical importance in the study of information transmission through communication systems.

We recall that in the introductory chapter we discussed in a qualitative way the two system limitations on the amount of information per unit time (system capacity) a system could transmit:

1. Inability of the system to respond instantaneously to signal changes (due to the presence of energy-storage devices).

2. Inability of the system to distinguish infinitesimally small changes in signal level (due to inherent voltage fluctuations or noise).

These two limitations were tied together in a simple expression developed for system capacity,

$$C = \frac{1}{\tau} \log_2 n \qquad \text{bits/sec} \tag{2-149}$$

where τ was the minimum time required for the system to respond to signal changes and n the number of distinguishable signal levels.

In this chapter we have found that this minimum response time is proportional to the reciprocal of the system bandwidth (two alternative ways of referring to the same phenomenon). System capacity thus could be written

$$C = B \log_2 n \qquad \text{bits/sec} \tag{2-150}$$

where B is the system bandwidth in cycles per second.

In the next chapters we shall discuss some common communication systems and their bandwidth requirements. We shall then return to a discussion of the second limitation on the system capacity—inherent noise.

PROBLEMS

2-1. (*a*) Find the Fourier-series representations of each of the pulse trains in Fig. P 2-1. Choose the time origin so that a cosine series is obtained in each case.

(*b*) Plot the first 10 Fourier coefficients vs. frequency for each pulse train. Compare the plot of Fig. P 2-1*a* with each of the other two, paying particular attention to the rate of decrease of the higher-frequency components. Note that Fig. P 2-1*b* represents in form the integral of Fig. P 2-1*a* and has no discontinuities in the function. The pulses of Fig. P 2-1*c* are much narrower than those of Fig. P 2-1*a*.

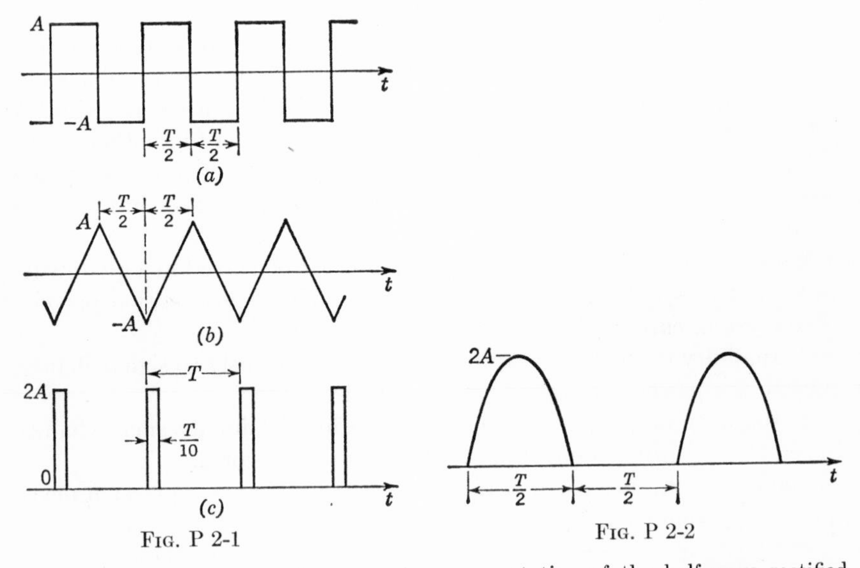

FIG. P 2-1

FIG. P 2-2

2-2. (*a*) Find the cosine Fourier-series representation of the half-wave rectified sine wave of Fig. P 2-2.

(*b*) Compare the successive Fourier coefficients and their rate of decrease with those of Fig. P 2-1*a*.

2-3. Find the complex Fourier series for the two pulse trains of Fig. P 2-3. Plot and compare the two amplitude spectra. What is the significance of the term $e^{-j\omega_n t_0}$ $(\omega_n \equiv 2\pi n/T)$ in the expression for the complex Fourier coefficient for the rectangular pulses?

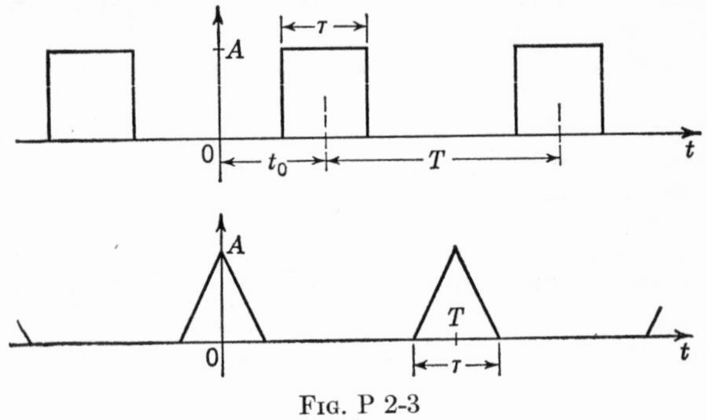

FIG. P 2-3

2-4. Find the complex Fourier series for the periodic function of Fig. P 2-4. (HINT: Use superposition and the result of Prob. 2-3.)

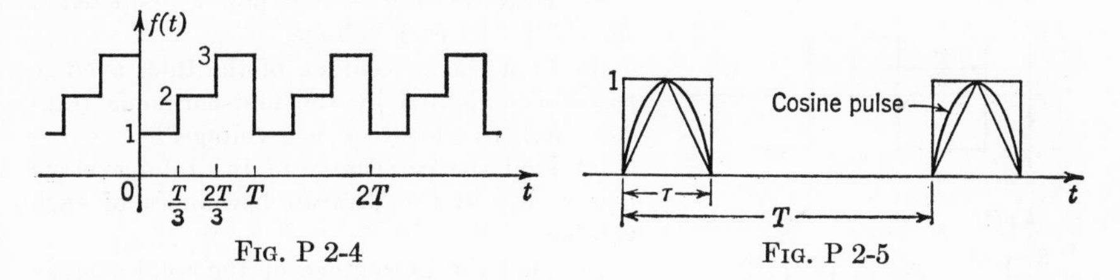

FIG. P 2-4 FIG. P 2-5

2-5. Consider the three cases of a rectangular, a triangular, and a half cosine pulse, all with $\tau/T = 1/10$ (Fig. P 2-5). Plot the amplitude spectra to the first zero crossing in each. What is the per cent of the total power in the first 10 frequency components?

2-6. Find the complex Fourier series for the periodic function of Fig. P 2-6. Find the per cent power in the first six components.

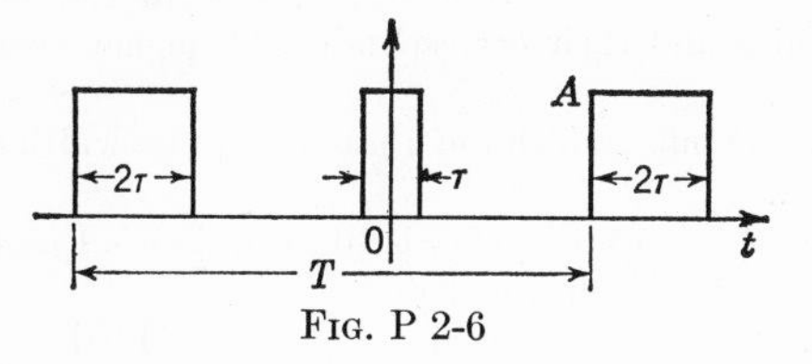

FIG. P 2-6

2-7. Plot the frequency spectra for the pulses of Fig. P 2-7.

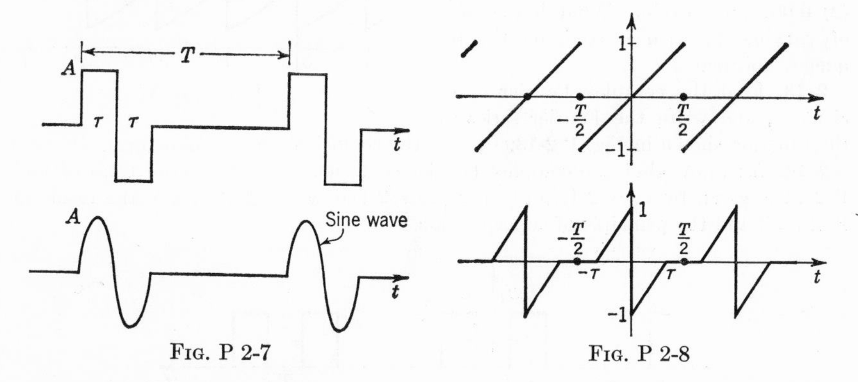

FIG. P 2-7 FIG. P 2-8

2-8. Find the complex Fourier series for the two periodic functions of Fig. P 2-8.

2-9. $f(t) = \sin \omega t$ for $0 \leq t \leq \pi/\omega$. It is undefined for values of t outside this interval.

(*a*) Express $f(t)$ inside the given interval as a sum of cosine terms with fundamental radian frequency ω.

(*b*) Express $f(t)$ in the same interval as a sum of sine terms with fundamental radian frequency ω.

2-10. T is the period of expansion in the Fourier-series representation for the function $f(t)$.

(*a*) Show that if $f(t) = f(t + T/2)$ the Fourier series will contain no odd harmonics.

(*b*) Show that if $f(t) = -f(t + T/2)$ the Fourier series will contain no even harmonics.

2-11. Each of the pulse trains shown in Fig. P 2-11 represents a voltage $v(t)$ appearing across a load resistor of 1 ohm.

(*a*) Find the total average power dissipated in the resistor by each voltage.

(*b*) Find the percentage of the total average power contributed by the first-harmonic (fundamental) frequency of each voltage.

(*c*) Find the percentage of the total average power due to the first 10 harmonics of each voltage.

(*d*) Find the percentage of the total average power due to those harmonics of the voltage within the first zero-crossing interval of the amplitude spectrum.

FIG. P 2-11

2-12. The duty cycle of a train of rectangular pulses is defined to be the ratio of time on to time off, or τ/T in the notation of this book. Sketch the pulse trains and their corresponding frequency spectra for the following cases:

(*a*) 0.1 duty cycle; (1) pulse width τ of 1 μsec; (2) pulse width of 10 μsec. Compare the frequency spectra.

(*b*) Repetition period T is 1 msec; (1) τ is 10 μsec; (2) τ is 1 μsec. What is the effect of varying τ, with T fixed, on the frequency scale? Compare the time and frequency plots.

(*c*) 10-μsec pulses; (1) 0.1 duty cycle; (2) 0.001 duty cycle. What is the effect of varying T, with τ fixed, on the frequency spectrum?

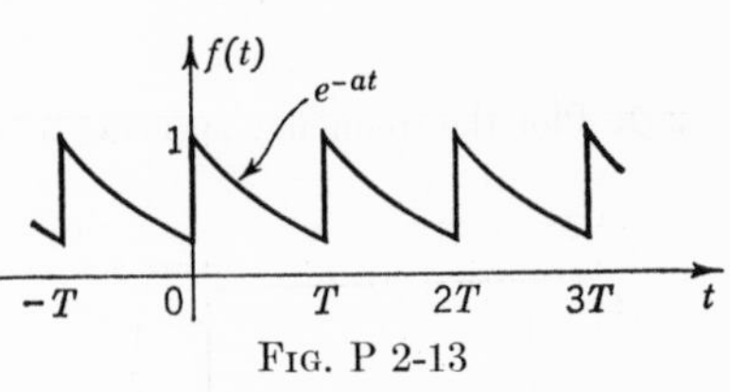

FIG. P 2-13

2-13. Find the complex Fourier coefficient c_n, and write the Fourier series for the function shown in Fig. P 2-13. Leave the coefficients in complex form.

2-14. (*a*) Show that the complex Fourier coefficient c_n of the pulse train of Fig. P 2-14 is given by $c_n = 2A\tau[\sin(\omega_n\tau/2)/(\omega_n\tau/2)]\cos\omega_n\tau$. (HINT: Use the result of Prob. 2-3 and the principle of superposition.)

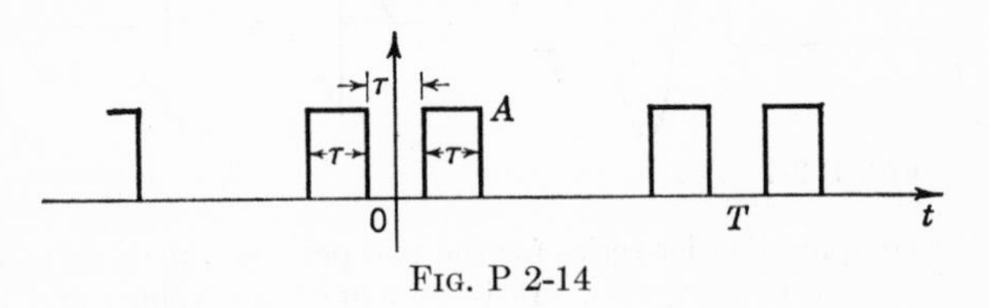

FIG. P 2-14

(*b*) Sketch the spectrum envelope and indicate the location of the spectral lines for $\tau/T = 0.1$.

2-15. The teletype printer uses a code consisting of seven units or time intervals per character (letter). This includes start and stop pulses during the first and last time interval corresponding to each letter. During the remaining five intervals the signal may be either on (a 1) or off (a 0). The average character has the form shown in Fig. P 2-15.

Assuming that the average word in the English language contains five letters and that one character is needed to transmit a space between words, there are on the average six characters per word. The rate of transmission is 25 words per minute.

(*a*) Find the length of one time interval.

(*b*) Find the bandwidth needed to transmit the first five harmonics of the pulse train of Fig. P 2-15. What bandwidth would be needed if the rate of transmission were increased to 100 words per minute? Why are these bandwidths the maximum required to transmit a telegraph signal?

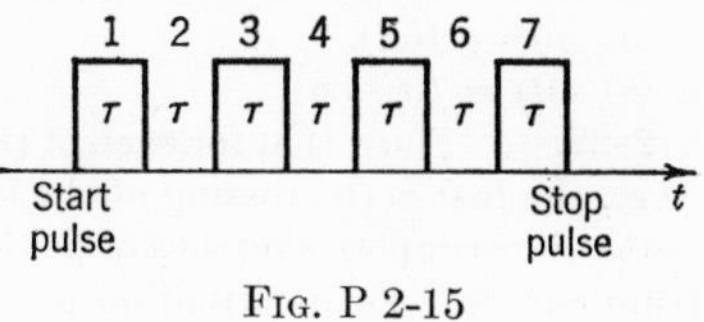

FIG. P 2-15

2-16. A pulse-position modulation (PPM) system produces symmetrical trapezoidal-shaped pulses, 5 μsec wide at the top and 5.5 μsec wide at the base. The average spacing between pulses is 125 μsec.

(*a*) What is the approximate system bandwidth required?

(*b*) If the average pulse spacing were halved, what bandwidth would be required?

(*c*) The pulses are passed through a low-pass filter cutting off at 200 kc. Sketch the waveshape at the input of the filter.

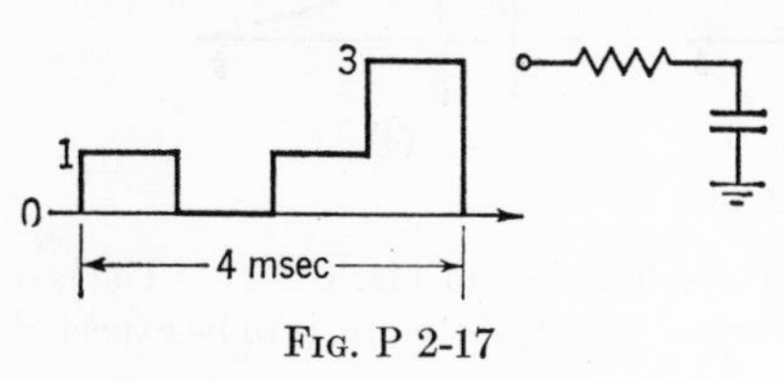

FIG. P 2-17

2-17. (*a*) At what frequency does the amplitude spectrum of the four-pulse group of Fig. P 2-17 first go to zero?

(*b*) The pulse group in (*a*) is put through a single low-pass *RC* section having as its half-power frequency the frequency found in (*a*). Sketch the output waveshape.

2-18. (*a*) What is the bandwidth in which 90 per cent of the power in the trapezoidal pulses of Fig. P 2-18 is contained?

(*b*) What is the effect of passing these pulses through a single *RC* filter with a 3-db (half-power) frequency of 318 kc?

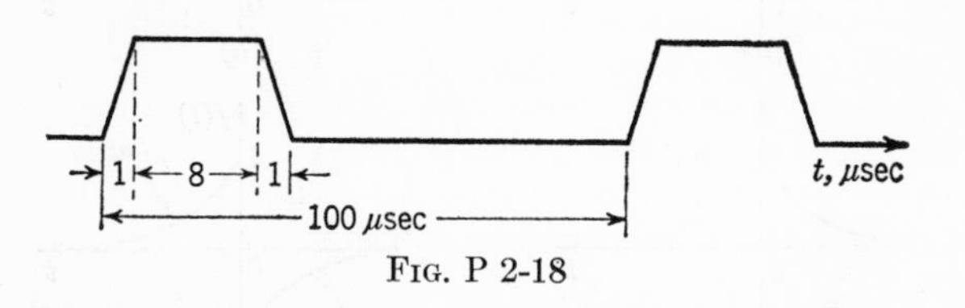

FIG. P 2-18

2-19. Find the exact expression for the repetitive pulse response of the *RC* filter. Show that this contains a term identical with Eqs. (2-22) and (2-27), plus an exponential term involving T/RC.

2-20. Find the Fourier transform of each of the pulses shown in Fig. P 2-20. Compare with the complex Fourier coefficients of the corresponding pulse trains obtained in Prob. 2-5.

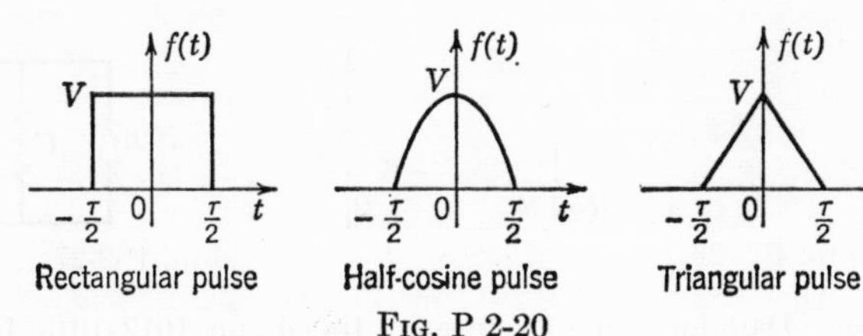

FIG. P 2-20

2-21. The Fourier transform of $f(t)$ is $F(j\omega)$, and the Fourier transform of $g(t)$ is $G(j\omega)$. For each of the following cases, find $G(j\omega)$ in terms of $F(j\omega)$:

(a) $g(t) = f(3t)$.

(b) $g(t) = f(t + a)$.

2-22. (a) Show that for each of the pulses of Prob. 2-20 any "bandwidth" definition (e.g., the first zero crossing of the spectrum) would give $\Delta f = K/\tau$, K a constant.

(b) Superimpose sketches of $|F(j\omega)|$ for each of these pulses, and compare the spectrum curves. Focus attention particularly on the l-f and h-f ends of the spectra.[1]

2-23. Find the Fourier transform of each of the pulses of Fig. P 2-23 in two different ways:

(a) From the Fourier integral directly.

(b) From the Laplace transform of the appropriate time function.

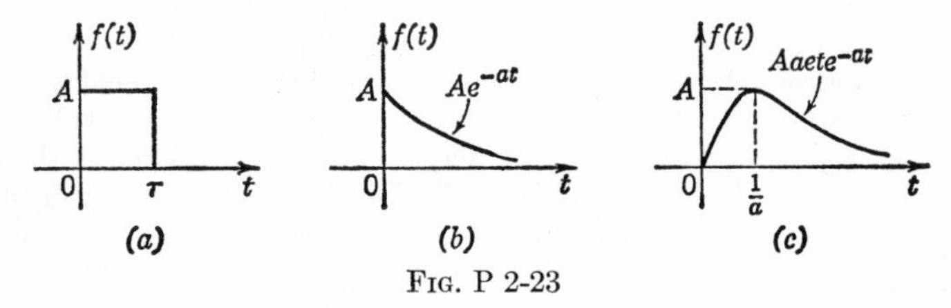

FIG. P 2-23

2-24. Find the Fourier transform of each of the functions of Fig. P 2-24. The last two time functions are even and odd, respectively. What, therefore, is to be expected of their Fourier transforms?

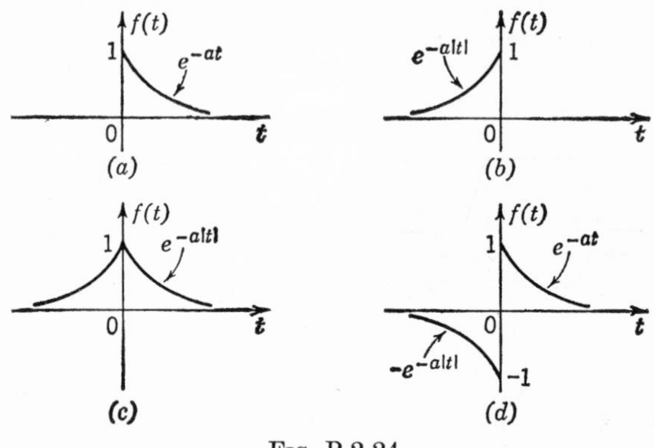

FIG. P 2-24

2-25. Find the Fourier transform of $f(t) = e^{-a|t|} \cos \omega_0 t$.

2-26. Find the frequency spectrum of the output voltage of Fig. P 2-26. Leave the answer in complex form.

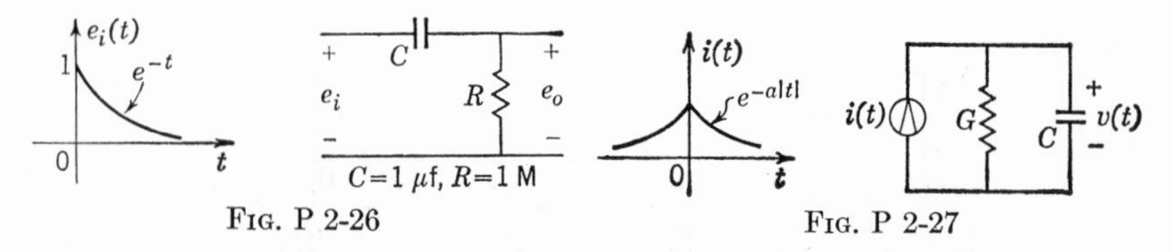

FIG. P 2-26

FIG. P 2-27

[1] See "Reference Data for Radio Engineers," 4th ed., pp. 1012–1015, International Telephone and Telegraph Corporation, New York, 1956.

2-27. For the circuit and the input current shown in Fig. P 2-27 find the capacitor voltage as a function of time. Leave the result in integral form.

2-28. "Integration smoothes out time variations; differentiation accentuates time variations." Verify this statement for the two circuits shown in Fig. P 2-28, by comparing the input and output spectra with an arbitrary input $v_i(t)$.

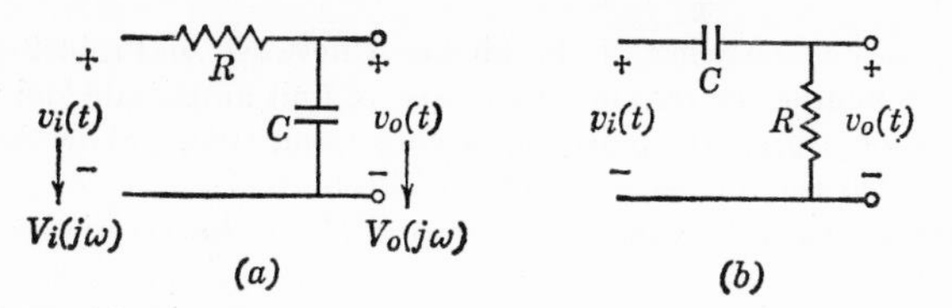

FIG. P 2-28. (a) Integrator ($R \gg 1/j\omega C$); (b) differentiator ($R \ll 1/j\omega C$).

2-29. A voltage of the form $v(t) = Ae^{-a|t|}$ is applied to a series RLC circuit. Find an expression in integral form for the voltage across the capacitor.

2-30. A delay line and integrating circuit, combined as shown in Fig. P 2-30, are one example of a "holding circuit" commonly used in radar work, sampled-data servo systems, and pulse-modulation systems (see Chap. 4).

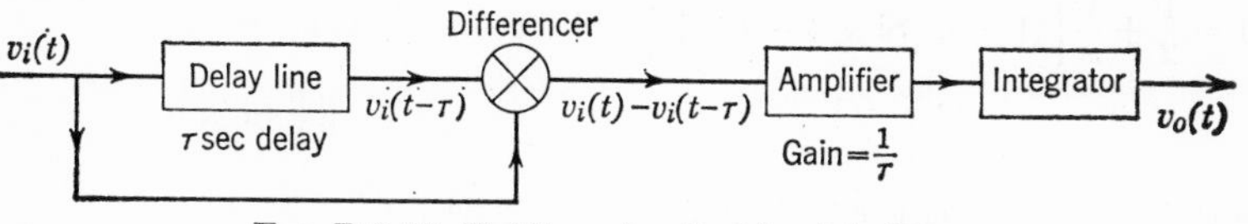

FIG. P 2-30. Holding circuit, $(\sin x)/x$ filter.

(a) Show that the Laplace-transform transfer function is $H(p) = V_o(p)/V_i(p) = (1/\tau p)(1 - e^{-\tau p})$.

(b) Using the results of (a), show that the frequency transfer function is $H(j\omega) = e^{-j\omega\tau/2} \sin(\omega\tau/2)/(\omega\tau/2)$.

(c) If $v_i(t)$ is a rectangular pulse of width τ sec, show that the output is a triangular pulse of width 2τ sec, by (1) actually performing the successive operations indicated in the figure; (2) using the spectrum approach, the results of (b), and the results of Prob. 2-20.

2-31. Two identical low-pass RC sections are connected in tandem. Find the over-all frequency transfer function. Why can this not be obtained by multiplying together the transfer functions of the individual sections?

2-32. A pulse of the form $e^{-at}u(t)$ with $u(t)$ the unit-step function is applied to an idealized network with transfer characteristic $H(j\omega) = Ae^{-jt_0\omega}$, $|\omega| \le \omega_c$; $H(j\omega) = 0$, $|\omega| > \omega_c$.

(a) Show that the output time response is given by

$$g(t) = \frac{A}{\pi} \int_0^{\omega_c} \left[\frac{a \cos \omega(t - t_0)}{a^2 + \omega^2} + \frac{\omega \sin \omega(t - t_0)}{a^2 + \omega^2} \right] d\omega$$

(b) Show that, for $\omega_c \gg a$,

$$g(t) \doteq \frac{A}{\pi} \text{Si}\, \omega_c(t - t_0) + \frac{A}{2} e^{-a|t-t_0|}$$

$$\text{Si}\, x \equiv \int_0^x \frac{\sin x}{x} dx$$

Note that $\int_0^\infty [(\cos mx)/(1 + x^2)]\, dx = (\pi/2)e^{-|m|}$.

2-33. Using the results of Prob. 2-32, show that the *unit-step response* of an idealized network with amplitude A, cutoff frequency ω_c, and phase constant t_0 is given by

$$A(t) = A\left[\frac{1}{2} + \frac{1}{\pi}\,\mathrm{Si}\,\omega_c(t - t_0)\right]$$

Sketch $A(t)/A$.

2-34. The unit-step response of the idealized network of Prob. 2-33 can also be obtained by first finding the response to a pulse of unit amplitude and width τ. As τ is allowed to get very large, the pulse approaches a unit step. Show that the network response approaches the unit-step response of Prob. 2-33.

2-35. A filter has the following amplitude and phase characteristics:

$$\begin{aligned} A(\omega) &= 1 - \alpha + \alpha \cos 2\pi n \frac{\omega}{\omega_c} \qquad & |\omega| \leq \omega_c \\ A(\omega) &= 0 & |\omega| > \omega_c \\ \theta(\omega) &= -t_0\omega \end{aligned}$$

(This represents a filter with ripples in the passband.)

(*a*) Show that the step response has the form

$$A(t) = \frac{1}{2} + \frac{1}{\pi}\left\{(1 - \alpha)\,\mathrm{Si}\,\omega_c(t - t_0) + \frac{\alpha}{2}\,\mathrm{Si}\,[\omega_c(t - t_0) + 2\pi n] + \frac{\alpha}{2}\,\mathrm{Si}\,[\omega_c(t - t_0) - 2\pi n]\right\}$$

(Use the approach of either Prob. 2-33 or Prob. 2-34.)

(*b*) Sketch $A(t)$ if $\alpha = \frac{1}{4}$, $n = 2$. Use the straight-line approximation for Si x indicated in Fig. P 2-35.

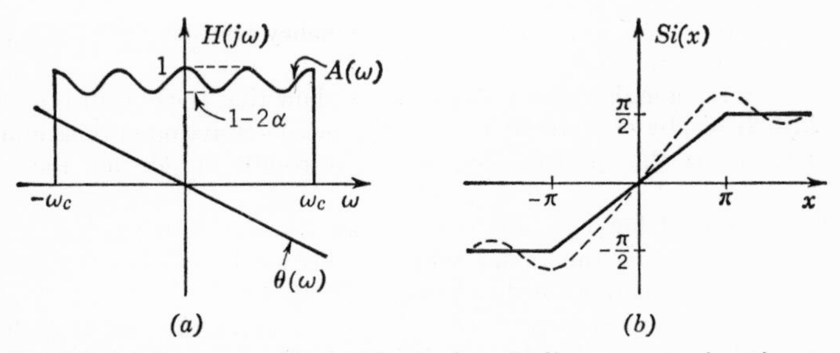

FIG. P 2-35. (*a*) Low-pass filter with ripples; (*b*) linear approximation to Si x.

2-36. In the filter characteristic of Prob. 2-35 let $2n = 1$ and $\alpha = \frac{1}{2}$. Sketch the amplitude characteristic for this case. Find the step response of this filter, and compare with the step response of the idealized filter of Prob. 2-33. This shows the effect of rounding off the sharp corners of the ideal low-pass filter.

2-37. The Butterworth filter is one example of a physically realizable low-pass filter. It has an amplitude transfer characteristic given by

$$A(\omega) = |H(j\omega)| = \frac{1}{\sqrt{1 + (\omega/\omega_c)^{2n}}}$$

The constant n is a positive integer whose value depends on the complexity of the filter. Two examples of such filters, for $n = 3$ and $n = 4$, respectively, are shown in Fig. P 2-37. They are each normalized to a half-power frequency ω_c of 1 radian/sec

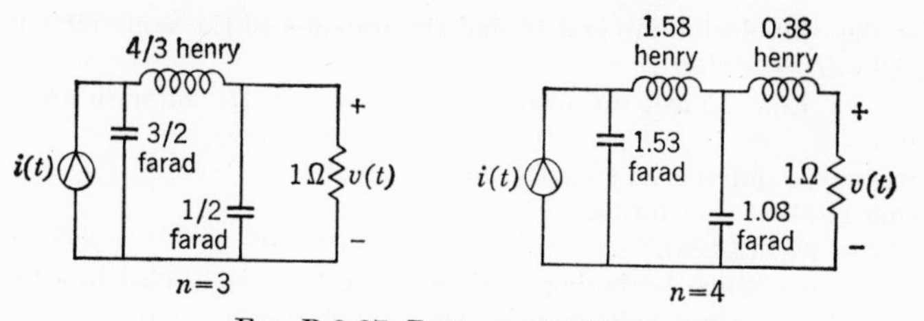

FIG. P 2-37. Butterworth filters.

and with load resistor of 1 ohm. (Note that n represents the number of reactive elements in each filter.)

(*a*) Find the complex frequency transfer function $H(j\omega) = V(j\omega)/I(j\omega)$ for each filter, and show that $|H(j\omega)|$ is given by the Butterworth expression noted above. Sketch this for both cases.

(*b*) Show that the Laplace-transform transfer function $H(p)$ for each of the two filters has poles lying on a unit circle centered about the origin in the p plane and spaced π/n radians apart. The two (complex conjugate) poles closest to the imaginary axis are located $\pi/2n$ radians away from this axis.

(*c*) Find the step response for each of the two filters, and compare with the step response of the ideal low-pass filter (Prob. 2-33).

2-38. Two students were asked the effect of passing the square wave of Fig. P 2-38 through the high-pass RC network shown. John reasoned that since the fundamental frequency of the square wave was four octaves above the 3-db fall-off frequency of the filter its attenuation and that of all the harmonics should be negligible. The output should thus look like the input. Conrad disagreed and to prove his point set up an experiment and obtained the oscilloscope trace for the output shown in the lower part of Fig. P 2-38.

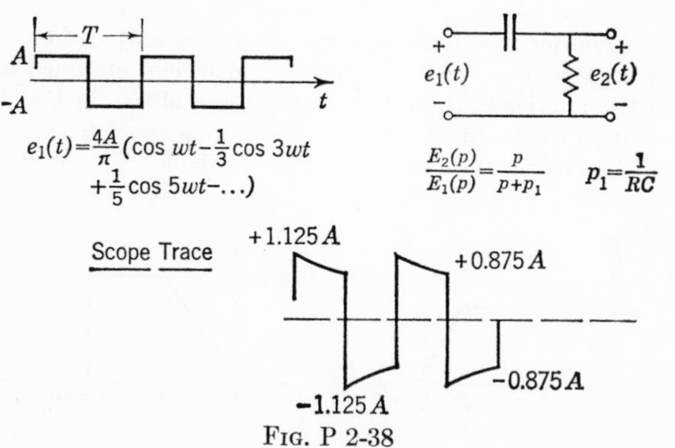

FIG. P 2-38

Explain the fallacy (or fallacies) in John's argument. Describe the characteristics of a network to be connected in tandem with the RC network so that no over-all distortion will result.

2-39. (*a*) Find the impulse response of the Butterworth filters of Prob. 2-37.

(*b*) Use Eq. (2-134) to find the step response.

2-40. (*a*) Find the impulse response of the idealized filter of Prob. 2-35.

(*b*) Use Eq. (2-133) to find the step response.

2-41. (*a*) Find the impulse response of the high-pass RC filter of Fig. P 2-38.

(*b*) Integrate the impulse response to find the step response. (As a check, determine the step response by inspection.)

(c) Use the convolution integral to find the response of the same filter to an input exponential $e_1(t) = e^{-at}u(t)$.

2-42. Check Eq. (2-123), the response of a low-pass RC filter to an exponential input, by:

(a) Solving the differential equation for the circuit.

(b) Using Laplace transforms.

2-43. Prove Eq. (2-128).

2-44. A ramp voltage beginning at time $t = 0$, $tu(t)$, is applied to a low-pass RC section. Find the output voltage, using the convolution integral.

2-45. (a) Repeat Prob. 2-44 if the ramp voltage is suddenly reduced to zero T sec after being applied.

(b) Check the result of (a) by superposing the responses to a ramp voltage $tu(t)$ applied at time $t = 0$ and a negative ramp $-(t - T)u(t - T)$ applied T sec later.

2-46. (a) Use Laplace transforms to prove the relation

$$h(t) = A(0) + \frac{dA}{dt}$$

$h(t)$ and $A(t)$ represent the unit-impulse and unit-step responses, respectively, of a physically realizable linear system.

(b) As an example, find the impulse response of the high-pass RC filter of Prob. 2-41 from the given step response.

(c) Show that the relation stated in (a) agrees with Eq. (2-134).

2-47. Show that a train of unit impulses, periodically spaced T sec apart, may be represented by the Fourier series

$$\frac{1}{T} + \frac{2}{T} \sum_{n=1}^{\infty} \cos \omega_n t \qquad \omega_n = \frac{2\pi n}{T}$$

2-48. Find the Fourier transform of a function $f(t) = \delta(0) - \delta(t - \tau) + \delta(t - 2\tau) - \delta(t - 3\tau)$. Compare $|F(j\omega)|$ with the Fourier coefficient obtained in Prob. 2-14.

2-49. Obtain the Fourier transform of the functions shown in Fig. P 2-49 by successive differentiation to obtain impulses or by breaking the function up into simpler forms for which the Fourier transform is readily available.

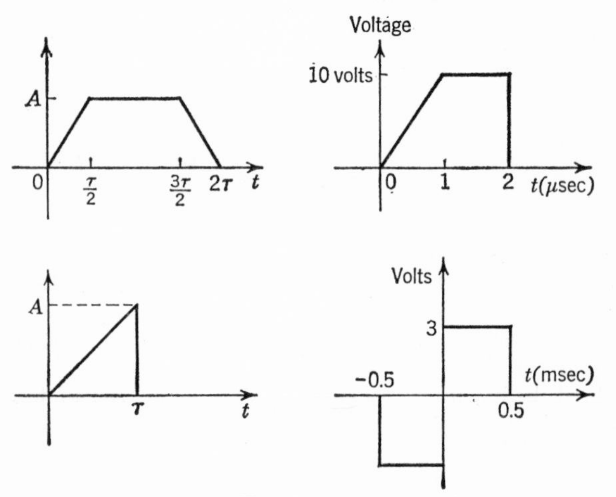

FIG. P 2-49

CHAPTER 3

MODULATION AND MODULATION SYSTEMS

3-1. Introduction. We are basically interested in investigating, in this book, the information-handling capabilities of different communication systems. We have shown in the previous chapter that one important parameter determining the system information capability is the system bandwidth. In Chap. 5 we shall discuss the limitations on system capacity due to noise.

We pause at this point in our discussion to describe some typical communication systems, to compare them on the basis of bandwidth requirements, and to develop further the inverse frequency-time relationship of the previous chapter.

All information-carrying signals must ultimately be transmitted over some medium separating the transmitter and the receiver. The medium may in some cases be the air, in others a set of wires or a hollow conducting tube (a waveguide). Efficiency of transmission—whether measured in terms of bandwidth, power required, complexity of the circuitry, etc.—requires that this information be processed in some manner before being transmitted over an intervening medium.

The step of processing the signal for more efficient transmission is called the *modulation process.*

There are various ways of producing modulated signals, but they break down essentially into two forms:

1. *Continuous-wave (c-w) modulation,* in which the amplitude, phase, or frequency of a specified sine wave (the carrier) is altered in accordance with the information being transmitted.

2. *Pulse modulation,* in which the height, the width, or the position of a set of pulses (the carrier) is again altered in a definite pattern corresponding to the information to be transmitted.

Frequently a complete communication system will utilize combinations of both forms of modulation.

Sine-wave modulation enables signals to be transmitted at frequencies much higher than the signal-frequency components. It is a well-known phenomenon of electromagnetic theory that an efficient radiator of electric energy (the antenna) must be at least the order of magnitude of a wavelength in size. Since the wavelength of a 1-kc tone is 300 km, radio transmission is hardly practicable at audio frequencies. But a 1-Mc carrier wave could be (and is) transmitted efficiently with an antenna 300 ft high.

Continuous-wave modulation also leads to the possibility of frequency multiplexing, or staggering of frequencies over the specified band. This means that many telephone conversations can be transmitted over a single pair of wires (depending of course on the bandwidth allowed for each conversation and the total bandwidth of the system including the wires). In the case of such wideband systems as frequency modulation (FM) or TV many more channels are made available by operating at higher frequencies. [The amplitude-modulation (AM) broadcast band in this country is fixed at 550 to 1,600 kc. This provides for 100 channels, spaced 10 kc apart. This entire band, however, is just a fraction of the band—6 Mc—needed for one TV channel.]

The use of pulse modulation also results in more efficient utilization of transmission facilities. Systems of this type utilize the process of time multiplexing, or staggering of separate information channels in time. Each channel utilizes the full bandwidth available (this provides the limiting factor on pulse widths and rise times). Information in pulse form can further be coded for even more efficient transmission or for digital-computer processing. (Information signals here include temperature, pressure, light intensity, etc., at some point, for example.) In other cases the information *must* be sampled only periodically to avoid disturbing the information source or to allow the use of a low-power source (a delicate temperature-sensing device, for example). Such systems are by their very nature pulse-modulation systems.

The noise and interference characteristics of the different schemes of modulation differ and will in some cases determine the type of modulation to be used.

The discussion of the previous chapter emphasized the close connection between time variations and frequency response. The various communication systems, whether treated from the frequency or the time point of view, must be closely related. We shall attempt to show the connection where possible in this chapter and the one following and shall frequently discuss the process of modulation from both the time and the frequency point of view.

Our procedure here in Chap. 3 will be to discuss first sine-wave modulation, emphasizing specifically amplitude- and angle-modulation systems. An analysis of double-sideband (DSB), or suppressed-carrier, modulation in Chap. 4 will lead us directly into suppressed-carrier pulse-modulation systems (chopper stabilization, for example) and then into pulse amplitude modulation.

3-2. Amplitude Modulation. When we talk of sine-wave modulation we imply that we have available a source of sinusoidal energy with an output voltage or current of the form

$$v(t) = A \cos (\omega_c t + \theta) \tag{3-1}$$

This sinusoidal time function is called a *carrier*. Any one of the three quantities A, ω_c, or θ may be varied in accordance with the information-carrying, or modulating, signal. We restrict ourselves in this section to

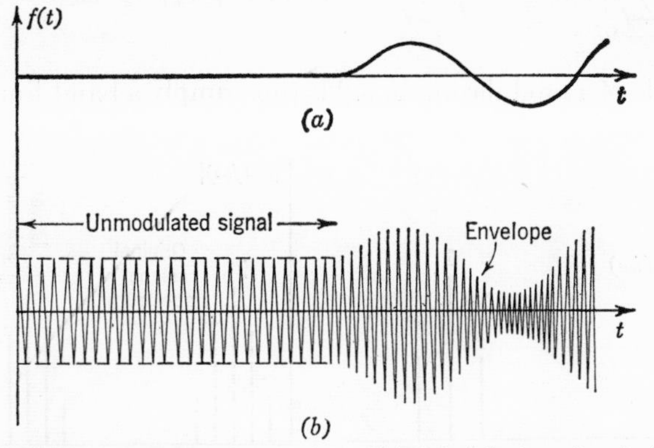

FIG. 3-1. Amplitude modulation of a carrier. (*a*) Modulating signal; (*b*) amplitude-modulated carrier.

AM systems in which A only is assumed to be varied. A basic assumption to be adhered to in all the work to follow will be that the modulating signal varies *slowly* compared with the carrier. This then means that we can talk of an envelope variation, or variation of the locus of the carrier peaks. Figure 3-1 shows a typical modulating signal $f(t)$ and the carrier envelope variation corresponding to it. The amplitude-modulated carrier of Fig. 3-1 can be described in the form

$$f_c(t) = K[1 + mf(t)] \cos \omega_c t \tag{3-2}$$

(We arbitrarily choose our time reference so that θ, the carrier phase angle, is zero.) Obviously $|mf(t)| < 1$ in order to retain an undistorted envelope, in which case the envelope is a replica of the modulating signal. Consider several examples of modulating signals.

1. $f(t) = \cos \omega_m t$ ($\omega_m \ll \omega_c$; otherwise an envelope cannot be described). Then

$$\begin{aligned} f_c(t) &= K(1 + m \cos \omega_m t) \cos \omega_c t \\ &= K \cos \omega_c t + \frac{K}{2} m \cos (\omega_c + \omega_m)t + \frac{K}{2} m \cos (\omega_c - \omega_m)t \end{aligned} \tag{3-3}$$

using the trigonometric sum and difference formulas. Equation (3-3) may of course be represented equally well by the frequency-spectrum plot of Fig. 3-2.

The original frequency component f_m has thus been shifted up in frequency and split into two side frequencies, one on each side of the carrier f_c.

2. General periodic input:

$$f(t) = \frac{1}{T} \sum_{n=-M}^{M} c_n e^{j\omega_n t} = \frac{2}{T} \sum_{n=1}^{M} |c_n| \cos(\omega_n t + \theta_n) \qquad \omega_n = \frac{2\pi n}{T};\ \omega_M \ll \omega_c$$

This example of a modulating signal is thus simply a band-limited periodic

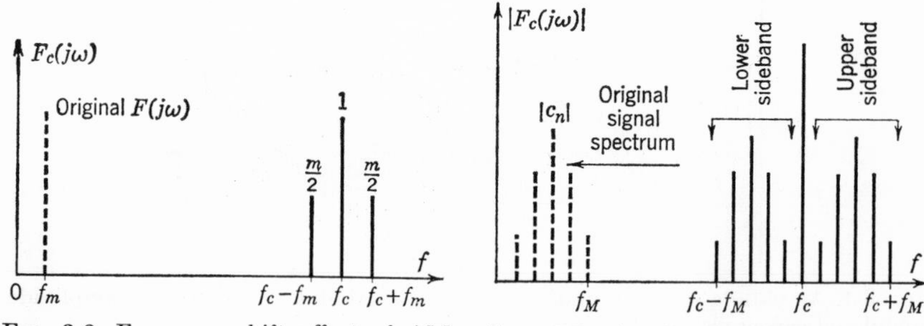

FIG. 3-2. Frequency-shift effect of AM (positive frequencies only are shown here).

FIG. 3-3. Amplitude-modulation spectrum—periodic modulating signal.

signal (with maximum frequency component ω_M) with zero average value (no d-c component). Then

$$f_c(t) = K\left[1 + \frac{2m}{T} \sum_{n=1}^{M} |c_n| \cos(\omega_n t + \theta_n)\right] \cos \omega_c t \tag{3-4}$$

A typical term will have the form

$$\cos(\omega_n t + \theta_n) \cos \omega_c t = \tfrac{1}{2}[\cos(\omega_c t + \omega_n t + \theta_n) + \cos(\omega_c t - \omega_n t - \theta_n)]$$

The amplitude-modulated carrier thus consists of the unmodulated carrier plus cosine terms of sum and difference frequencies,

$$f_c(t) = K \cos \omega_c t + \frac{mK}{T} \sum_{n=1}^{M} |c_n| \{\cos[(\omega_c + \omega_n)t + \theta_n] + \cos[(\omega_c - \omega_n)t - \theta_n]\} \tag{3-5}$$

The amplitude-frequency spectrum for a typical periodic signal appears in Fig. 3-3.

Note again the frequency-shift effect due to AM: the spectrum of the original modulating signal, $f(t)$, appears shifted up in frequency by f_c cps. Again two sets of side frequencies appear—an upper and a lower set. Each set contains a band of frequencies corresponding to the band of frequencies covered by the original signal and is called a *sideband*. Each sideband contains all the spectral lines—both amplitude and phase—of the original signal and so presumably contains all the information carried

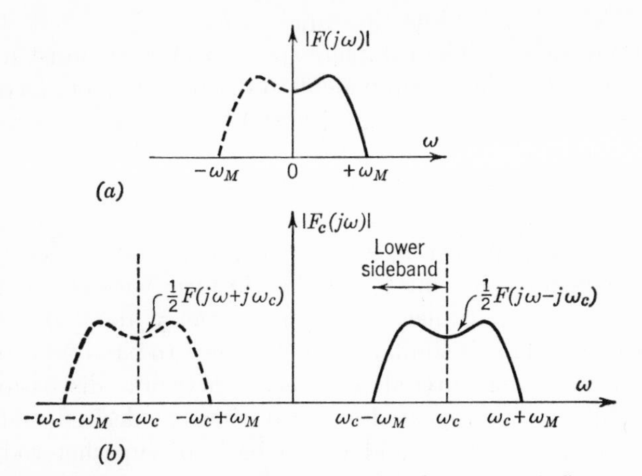

FIG. 3-4. Amplitude spectrum—amplitude-modulated wave. (*a*) Spectrum of modulating signal; (*b*) spectrum of amplitude-modulated wave.

by $f(t)$. Note, however, from Eq. (3-5) that the phase angles of the upper and lower sidebands differ in sign ($+\theta_n$ for the upper, $-\theta_n$ for the lower). This distinction leads to one method of single-sideband (SSB) generation now in use.

3. General nonperiodic input, $f(t)$. Then

$$f_c(t) = K[1 + mf(t)] \cos \omega_c t \tag{3-6}$$

with $f(t)$ band-limited to ω_M ($\omega_M \ll \omega_c$). This is simply a restatement of our original assumption that the modulating signal must vary slowly compared with the carrier. The Fourier transform of $f(t)$ is $F(j\omega)$.

$$F(j\omega) = \int_{-\infty}^{\infty} f(t)e^{-j\omega t}\, dt \tag{3-7}$$

$F(j\omega)$ is zero for all frequencies above ω_M (Fig. 3-4*a*).

The frequency-spectrum representation of $f_c(t)$ in terms of a carrier and sidebands can be demonstrated quite simply by means of Fourier transforms. Consider the second term of Eq. (3-6),

$$f_c'(t) = f(t) \cos \omega_c t = f(t)\tfrac{1}{2}(e^{j\omega_c t} + e^{-j\omega_c t}) \tag{3-8}$$

Taking the Fourier transform of this term,

$$F'_c(j\omega) = \frac{1}{2}\int_{-\infty}^{\infty} f(t)e^{j\omega_c t}e^{-j\omega t}\,dt + \frac{1}{2}\int_{-\infty}^{\infty} f(t)e^{-j\omega_c t}e^{-j\omega t}\,dt$$

$$= \frac{1}{2}F(j\omega - j\omega_c) + \frac{1}{2}F(j\omega + j\omega_c) \qquad (3\text{-}9)$$

by comparison with Eq. (3-7).

$F(j\omega)$ is generally a complex quantity and is defined for negative ω also. $F(j\omega + j\omega_c)$ is thus the same as $F(j\omega - j\omega_c)$, but defined for negative frequencies. The complete spectrum for $f(t)$ must include the first term, $\cos \omega_c t$, which is equivalent to discrete frequency components at ω_c and $-\omega_c$. [$\cos \omega_c t = \frac{1}{2}(e^{j\omega_c t} + e^{-j\omega_c t})$.]

These relations are sketched in Fig. 3-4. They also demonstrate some general conclusions we may draw about AM. Amplitude modulation may be considered a process of translating the frequency range of the modulating signal upward to the range about the carrier frequency. The new frequency spectrum is identical in form with the old. It may be looked upon as a translation from symmetry about $\omega = 0$ to symmetry about ω_c. This is similar to the low-pass to bandpass transformations frequently encountered in electric-network discussions. This frequency shift can be repeated as many times as desired—either up or down the frequency scale—and is the basis of superheterodyne radio operation.

3-3. Modulators. We have discussed, very briefly, the possibility of slowly varying the envelope of the sine-wave carrier in accordance with an information-carrying signal. This process of AM could be viewed as a frequency translation, the original (modulating) signal being shifted up in frequency, its frequency components appearing as sidebands on either side of the carrier.

We now ask ourselves the very pertinent question: How do we physically produce AM of the carrier? To answer this question, note that the mathematical expression for AM appears as a *product* function,

$$f_c(t) = K[1 + mf(t)] \cos \omega_c t \qquad (3\text{-}10)$$

The simplest thing to do then would be to develop a device in which the output occurs as the product of the two input functions.

A simple example might be a galvanometer with separate windings for the magnet and the coil. The force on the coil is then proportional to the product of the currents in each winding,

$$F \propto i_1 i_2 \qquad (3\text{-}11)$$

If

$$i_1 = a[1 + mf(t)] \qquad (3\text{-}12)$$

(i.e., a d-c bias plus the modulating signal) and

$$i_2 = b \cos \omega_c t \tag{3-13}$$

the force on the coil, as a function of time, is of the same form as Eq. (3-10). The coil motion would then appear as an amplitude-modulated signal.

A motor with stator and rotor separately wound would give the same results. A loudspeaker, with the modulating signal and an appropriate d-c bias applied to the voice coil and the carrier to the field winding, is again a similar device. These are all examples of *product* modulators.

These product modulators and other types of modulators commonly used may be classified in one of two categories:

1. Their terminal characteristics are *nonlinear*.
2. The modulation device contains a *switch* independent of the signal which changes the system from one linear condition to another.

In the work to follow we shall have occasion to discuss both types of modulator.

Before proceeding further with the discussion it is best to pause at this point to distinguish between linear, nonlinear, and switching systems. This will avoid unnecessary confusion in the analysis of modulators.

The linear systems we have discussed up to this point are distinguished by two basic properties:

1. The response to a sum of excitations is equal to the sum of the responses to the excitations acting separately.
2. Multiplication of the excitation by a constant multiplies the response by the same constant.

The first condition is of course the familiar statement of superposition that is used continually in the analysis of linear systems. The second condition implies that the static terminal characteristics of any element in the system are linear (at least in the region where used).

Our familiar linear operations are those of multiplication by a constant, addition, subtraction, differentiation, and integration. The combination of these operations gives rise to a linear system governed by constant-coefficient linear differential equations.

Such a linear system can never be used as a modulator for it can generate no new frequencies. As an example, consider the steady-state time response to a single sine wave. A linear device would merely modify the amplitude and phase of the signal (if energy-storage devices are present, implying the operations of differentiation and integration, the amplitude and phase are functions of frequency). *No new frequencies are generated in this process.*

If we now add a switch to a linear system which switches the system in a specified manner from one linear condition to another (a simple example would be a switch turning the system on and off) and which does this independently of the signal, the system is still basically linear: the two basic characteristics of a linear system still apply. Such a system is still governed by linear differential equations, but the coefficients of the equations now vary with time according to the prescribed switching action. The system is now a linear time-varying system. As we shall see shortly, such a system can be used for modulation and will generate new frequencies.

If instead of a switch we now introduce a device whose static terminal characteristics are *nonlinear*, the differential equations governing the system become nonlinear differential equations. Again, as we shall see, modulation or generation of new frequencies becomes possible. Two typical kinds of nonlinear characteristics are shown in Fig. 3-5. Actually all physical devices have some curvature or nonlinearity in their static terminal characteristics, but we usually assume the region of operation to be small enough so that the characteristics are very nearly linear over this region.

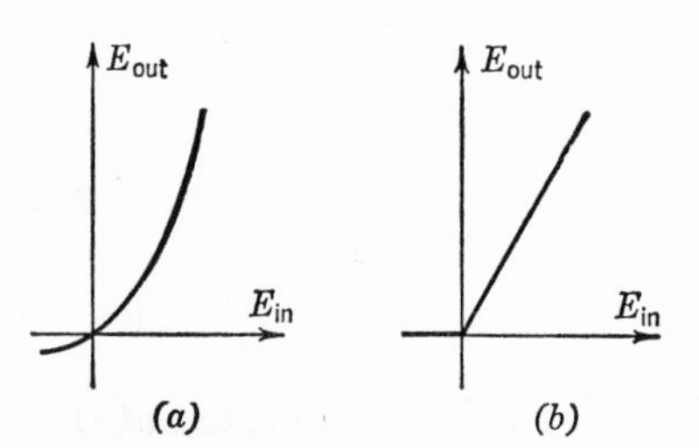

FIG. 3-5. Nonlinear characteristics. (*a*) Nonlinearity due to curvature of characteristics; (*b*) "strong" discontinuity; piecewise-linear characteristic.

Figure 3-5*a* might be the characteristic of a typical square-law diode or of a triode in certain portions of its characteristics (a constant grid-bias curve). Figure 3-5*b* might represent an approximation to a linear rectifier. The two curves differ in the *type* of nonlinearity. The linear rectifier of Fig. 3-5*b* has a strong nonlinearity at one point and is approximated by linear characteristics elsewhere. (The use of the term *linear* rectifier and the piecewise-linear characteristics assumed have sometimes led to the mistaken conclusion that the device is linear.) The characteristics of Fig. 3-5*a* have no one point of strong nonlinearity but are everywhere nonlinear owing to the curvature of the characteristics.

Figure 3-5*b* can also be used as the representation of the characteristics of a switching device and, in fact, serves as a good example of the distinction between linear, nonlinear, and switching characteristics. Thus, if the device is operated in one of the linear portions of the curve only, it behaves as a linear device. Typically the device would be biased to operate in a region far from the discontinuity, and the signals applied would be small enough to keep it in that region. The output is then a linear replica of the input, and if two signals are applied, the output is a superposition of the response to each. If the signal applied to the device is now increased to the point where the discontinuity is crossed and the two linear regions are involved, the output no longer is a simple linear function of the input. If one signal is applied, the output is a distorted version, and if two signals are applied, the output no longer can be found by superposing the two input responses separately. The output is then a nonlinear function of the input: as the input amplitude changes, the output does not change proportionally.

If the input-signal level is now dropped back to its original small value but is somehow switched in a predetermined fashion between the two linear regions of Fig. 3-5*b*, we have a linear switch with the corresponding linear time-varying equations.

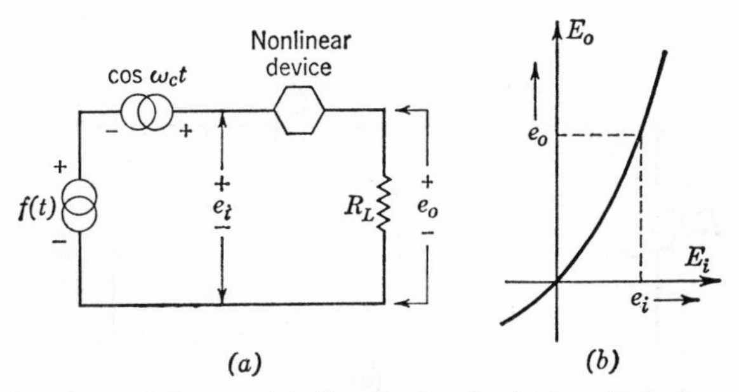

FIG. 3-6. Simple modulator. (*a*) Simple circuit; (*b*) terminal characteristics.

Most modulators in use can thus be classified as having one of the two types of characteristics of Fig. 3-5, if switches are included as represented by Fig. 3-5*b*.

We shall first analyze simple modulators incorporating the nonlinear characteristics of Fig. 3-5. The analysis will then be used later in discussing switches and pulse-modulation systems.

Square-law Modulator. The simplest form of this type of modulator appears in Fig. 3-6. e_o and e_i represent the incremental output and input variations, respectively, away from some fixed operating point (Fig. 3-6*b*). The nonlinear characteristics of this case are assumed continuous so that e_o may be expanded in a power series in e_i,

$$e_o = a_1 e_i + a_2 e_i^2 + a_3 e_i^3 + \text{(higher-order terms)} \tag{3-14}$$

The quadratic term in the power series denotes the presence of curvature in the characteristics and is all-important in the modulation process.

For the circuit in Fig. 3-6*a*

$$e_i = \underbrace{\cos \omega_c t}_{\text{Carrier}} + \underbrace{f(t)}_{\text{Modulating signal}} \tag{3-15}$$

Then, retaining just the first two terms of the power series of Eq. (3-14), we get

$$e_o = a_1 \cos \omega_c t + a_1 f(t) + a_2[\cos^2 \omega_c t + 2f(t) \cos \omega_c t + f^2(t)]$$
$$= \underbrace{a_1 f(t) + a_2 \cos^2 \omega_c t + a_2 f^2(t)}_{\text{Unwanted terms}} + \underbrace{a_1 \cos \omega_c t \left[1 + \frac{2a_2}{a_1} f(t)\right]}_{\text{Amplitude-modulated terms}} \quad (3\text{-}16)$$

The second term thus contains the desired AM signal. (Let $m \equiv 2a_2/a_1$, $K \equiv a_1$.) The first term contains unwanted terms that can be filtered out. [$\cos^2 \omega_c t$ gives $\frac{1}{2}(1 + \cos 2\omega_c t)$ = dc and twice the carrier frequency.

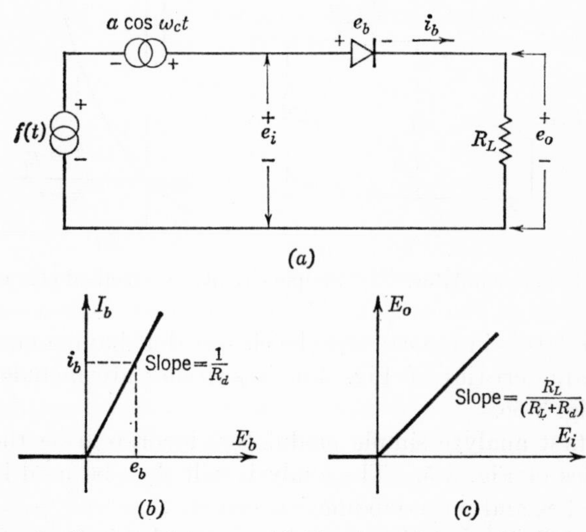

FIG. 3-7. Piecewise-linear modulator. (a) Simple modulator; (b) diode characteristic; (c) circuit characteristic.

$f^2(t)$ contains frequency components from dc to twice the maximum frequency component of $f(t)$, that is, $2f_M$. This is left as an exercise for the reader.] It may be noted in passing that this device could be used as a second-harmonic generator also, if $\cos \omega_c t$ only were introduced and its second harmonic retained.

Piecewise-linear Modulator (*Strong Nonlinearity*). A typical circuit (identical with the circuit of Fig. 3-6*a*) and the piecewise-linear characteristics for such a device (here chosen as a "linear" rectifier) are shown in Fig. 3-7. R_L is the load resistance, R_d the diode forward resistance.

We should like to demonstrate that the piecewise-linear characteristics can also be used for simple AM. The discontinuity assumed in the terminal characteristics prevents the use of the power-series expansion as was done in the previous modulator.

We could of course approximate the characteristics by a polynomial. This would convert them to the continuous form of Fig. 3-6 with the discontinuity more pronounced at the origin. Both types of nonlinearity could thus be treated simultaneously. We prefer, however, to use a different approach which will be applicable to the case of switches also.

We shall assume that the carrier amplitude is much greater than the maximum value of $f(t)$,

$$|f(t)| \ll a$$

If the carrier alone were present, the rectifier would clip the negative halves of the carrier. Under the assumption of a strong carrier the clipping of the carrier plus modulating signal will occur approximately at the same point in the cycle as the carrier alone. Thus, for

$$\begin{aligned} e_i &= a \cos \omega_c t + f(t) && |f(t)| \ll a \\ e_o &\doteq \frac{R_L e_i}{R_L + R_d} = b e_i && a \cos \omega_c t > 0 \\ e_o &\doteq 0 && a \cos \omega_c t < 0 \end{aligned} \tag{3-17}$$

Since the output now varies between two values (be_i and 0) periodically, at the frequency of the carrier, the input may be looked on as having been switched between two regions of the diode operation. By the simple expedient of assuming a weak signal compared with the carrier we have converted the nonlinear device into a linear switching device. Since the transitions from one region of operation to another are now variables of time independent of the signal $f(t)$, we have effectively replaced a nonlinear equation by a linear time-varying one. This approach is the one actually used in solving some types of nonlinear differential equations. It is to be emphasized, however, that this is an approximate technique, valid only for small signals. In discussing switches and periodic sampling in the next chapter, with the system a linear time-varying one rather than a nonlinear one, the switching analysis will be used directly.

Equation (3-17) can be written mathematically as

$$e_o \doteq [a \cos \omega_c t + f(t)]S(t) \tag{3-18}$$

with

$$S(t) = b \qquad -\frac{1}{4}T < t < \frac{1}{4}T,\ T = \frac{1}{f_c}$$

$$S(t) = 0 \qquad t \text{ elsewhere}$$

and repeating at multiples of $T = 1/f_c$ sec. $S(t)$ is thus a periodic square-

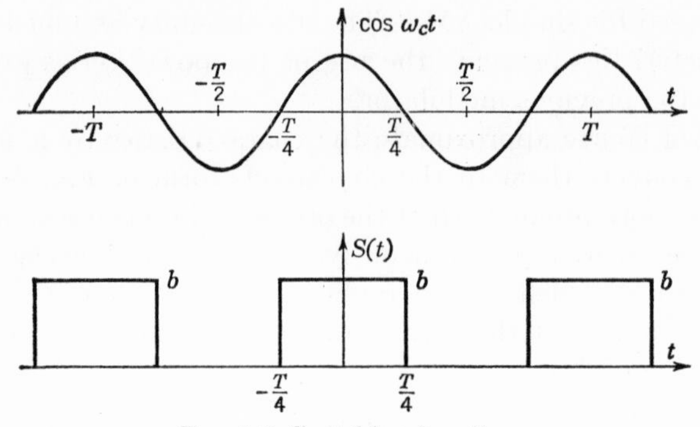

FIG. 3-8. Switching function.

wave switching function as shown in Fig. 3-8. As such it may be expanded in its Fourier representation.

$$S(t) = \frac{1}{T} \sum_{n=-\infty}^{\infty} c_n e^{j\omega_n t} = \frac{c_0}{T} + \frac{2}{T} \sum_{n=1}^{\infty} |c_n| \cos (\omega_n t + \theta_n) \tag{3-19}$$

where $\omega_n = \dfrac{2\pi n}{T} = n\omega_c$

and $c_n = \dfrac{bT}{2} \dfrac{\sin (\omega_n T/4)}{\omega_n T/4} = \dfrac{bT}{2} \dfrac{\sin (n\pi/2)}{n\pi/2}$ (3-20)

Thus
$$S(t) = b \left[\frac{1}{2} + \sum_{n=1}^{\infty} \frac{\sin (n\pi/2)}{n\pi/2} \cos n\omega_c t \right] \tag{3-21}$$

(Note that the even terms in n vanish.) But

$$e_o = [a \cos \omega_c t + f(t)]S(t)$$

By using the Fourier-series expansion for $S(t)$, performing the indicated multiplication, and collecting terms, e_o can be written in the following form:

$$e_o(t) = b \Bigg(\bigg\{ \frac{1}{2} f(t) + \frac{2}{\pi} a \cos^2 \omega_c t + \sum_{n=3}^{\infty} \frac{\sin (n\pi/2)}{n\pi/2} [f(t) + a \cos \omega_c t] \cos n\omega_c t \bigg\} + \frac{a}{2} \cos \omega_c t \left[1 + \frac{4}{\pi a} f(t) \right] \Bigg) \tag{3-22}$$

Again we can filter this output. The terms in the braces give direct current, low frequencies up to ω_M [the maximum frequency component of $f(t)$], and then higher frequencies: $2\omega_c$, $3\omega_c - \omega_M$, $3\omega_c$, $3\omega_c + \omega_M$, etc.

After filtering

$$e_o(t) \doteq K[1 + mf(t)] \cos \omega_c t \tag{3-23}$$

where

$$K = \frac{ab}{2}$$

$$m = \frac{4}{\pi a}$$

The piecewise-linear modulator of Fig. 3-7 thus produces an amplitude-modulated output upon proper filtering.

We have actually demonstrated this modulation property for the device considered as a switch rather than as a nonlinear device, under the

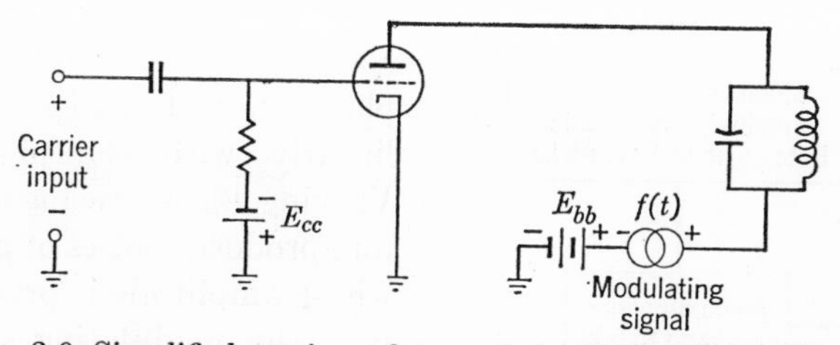

FIG. 3-9. Simplified version: plate-modulated class C amplifier.

assumption of a small signal (relative to the carrier). The truly nonlinear solution leads to harmonics of the signal $f(t)$ and higher-order modulation products of the carrier and its harmonics. These additional terms would be filtered out in an actual modulator, leaving Eq. (3-23) as the solution in the more exact analysis also.

The two nonlinear devices just discussed are representative of many types that are used for low-level (i.e., low-power) modulation purposes. Examples include nonlinear-resistance modulators [a commerically available nonlinear resistor is Thyrite, a General Electric (GE) trade name for a granular aggregate of silicon carbide], semiconductor or vacuum-tube diode modulators, mechanical-contact modulators (also called "choppers," or *vibrators*—basically switching devices of the piecewise-linear type previously discussed), semiconductor modulators such as photocells and Hall-effect modulators using germanium crystals, magnetic modulators, nonlinear-capacitor modulators, vacuum-tube modulators, transistor modulators, etc.

For standard radio-broadcast work these low-level modulators are highly inefficient (their use in balanced modulator circuits for SSB transmission or as parts of servo systems will be deferred until later in this chapter and until the following chapter). Class C amplifier operation provides high efficiency of power generation. Standard broadcast transmitters thus commonly utilize grid- or plate-modulated class C amplifiers. The modulation process here involves the gross nonlinearity due to class C operation (the grid highly negative). The tuned circuit at the plate of the amplifier then provides the necessary filtering to obtain the desired amplitude-modulated wave: a carrier plus sidebands.

A simplified example of a plate-modulated class C amplifier is shown in Fig. 3-9. With E_{cc} highly negative the tube is normally cut off. Conduction thus occurs only at the peak of the carrier input signal. The output is then a series of pulses at the carrier frequency. (The carrier "switches" the tube on, just as in the case of the piecewise-linear rectifier previously analyzed as one basic prototype for many nonlinear circuits.) The magnitude of the plate current varies very nearly linearly with the plate voltage. Varying E_{bb} by means of $f(t)$ therefore produces pulses of plate current whose amplitude is proportional to $f(t)$—the modulating signal. The presence of the desired carrier and sidebands, the amplitude-modulated signal, can of course be demonstrated just as in the case of the piecewise-linear rectifier by expanding the mathematical expression for the modulated pulses in a Fourier series.

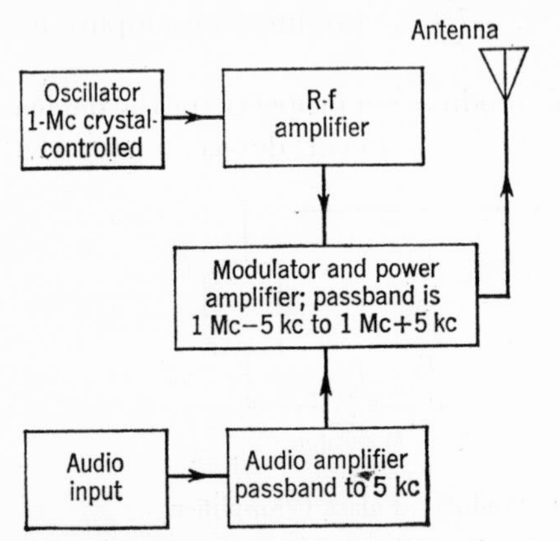

FIG. 3-10. Standard high-level broadcast transmitter.

A block diagram of a typical standard broadcast transmitter is shown in Fig. 3-10. This is a simplified version with only the essential elements shown.

3-4. Single-sideband Transmission[1] **and Balanced Modulators.** We note from the frequency plot of the amplitude-modulated carrier (Fig. 3-4) that the desired information to be transmitted [as originally given by variations of the modulating signal, $f(t)$] is carried in one of the two sidebands. The carrier itself carries no information. Transmission of the entire spectrum thus represents a waste of frequency space since transmitting both sidebands requires double the bandwidth needed for transmitting one sideband. It also represents a waste of power (especially power in the carrier). This has resulted in the widespread use of SSB transmission for transoceanic radiotelephone circuits and wire communications. In this type of transmission the carrier and one sideband are suppressed and the remaining sideband only transmitted.

There is also experimental evidence to the effect that SSB transmission is less susceptible to fading than AM transmission.

The frequency-spectrum conservation feature of SSB transmission

[1] Single-sideband issue, *Proc. IRE*, vol. 44, no. 12, December, 1956.

has led the Federal Communications Commission (FCC) to announce that it will require the use of SSB sideband for radiotelephony in the fixed and mobile radio services at frequencies below 25 Mc. This is specifically intended to conserve spectrum space and allow the use of more channels.

With the apparent advantages of SSB over AM, why is it that SSB is not used for standard radiobroadcasting? The answer is that the circuitry *required at the receiver* is too complex *at present*. The economics of mass-producing relatively cheap home radio receivers forbids SSB use. To demonstrate these statements more quantitatively, we must discuss methods of producing and then detecting SSB signals.

A method commonly used to generate an SSB signal is first to suppress the carrier of the AM signal. The resulting transmission is called *suppressed-carrier*, or *double-sideband*, transmission. One of the two sidebands is then filtered out. The carrier suppression is usually accomplished by means of a *balanced modulator*, as indicated in the block diagrams of Fig. 3-11. (Suppressed-carrier transmission is not limited to radio work alone, but occurs commonly in control systems, as also in other communication systems.)

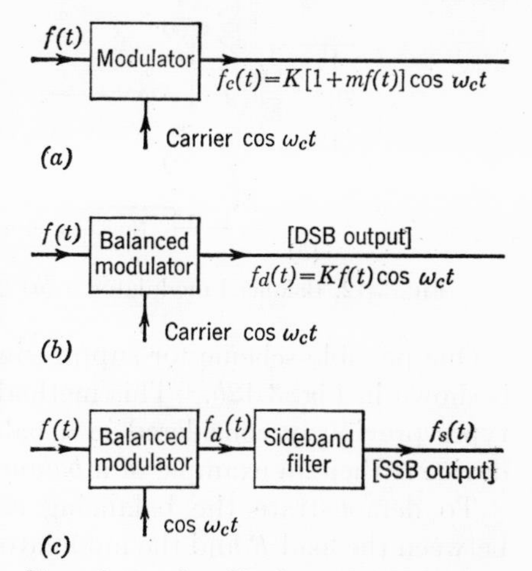

FIG. 3-11. Amplitude-modulation systems. (*a*) Normal AM; (*b*) suppressed carrier, or DSB; (*c*) SSB.

A normal AM output has the form

$$f_c(t) = K[1 + mf(t)] \cos \omega_c t \tag{3-24}$$

The corresponding mathematical expression for a DSB output is

$$f_d(t) = K'f(t) \cos \omega_c t \tag{3-25}$$

The DSB system differs from normal AM simply by suppressing the carrier term. This means that with no modulating signal applied the output should be zero. If we recall the nonlinear devices discussed previously, the carrier term arose because of a quiescent condition or d-c bias somewhere in the modulator. If we can *balance out* this quiescent condition, we have a simple product modulator with the output given by Eq. (3-25). (In the case of the magnetic product modulators mentioned—the galvanometer, motor, loudspeaker—the assumption was that a d-c term appeared in one of the currents. If we balance out this d-c current, we have the desired suppressed-carrier output.)

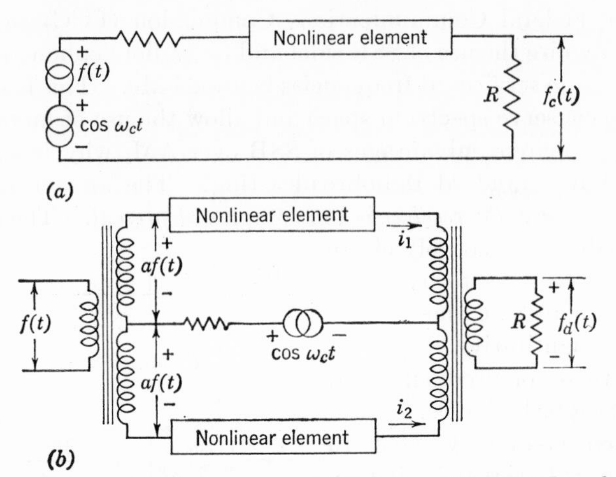

FIG. 3-12. Balanced modulator. (a) Modulator; (b) balanced modulator.

One possible scheme for suppressing or balancing out the carrier term is shown in Fig. 3-12b. This method uses two nonlinear elements of the types previously considered in a balanced arrangement. The resulting device is then an example of a *balanced modulator.*

To demonstrate the balancing effect, assume that the transformer between the load R and the modulator is ideal. The modulator then sees the resistive load. The upper and the lower sections of the balanced modulator are then each identical with Fig. 3-12a, and the previous analysis of such nonlinear circuits holds. In particular, the two currents flowing may be written in the form

$$i_1 = K[1 + mf(t)] \cos \omega_c t \quad (3\text{-}26)$$

and

$$i_2 = K[1 - mf(t)] \cos \omega_c t \quad (3\text{-}27)$$

(the other terms generated in the nonlinear process are assumed filtered out). But the load voltage $f_d(t)$ is proportional to $i_1 - i_2$, or

$$f_d(t) = K'f(t) \cos \omega_c t \quad (3\text{-}28)$$

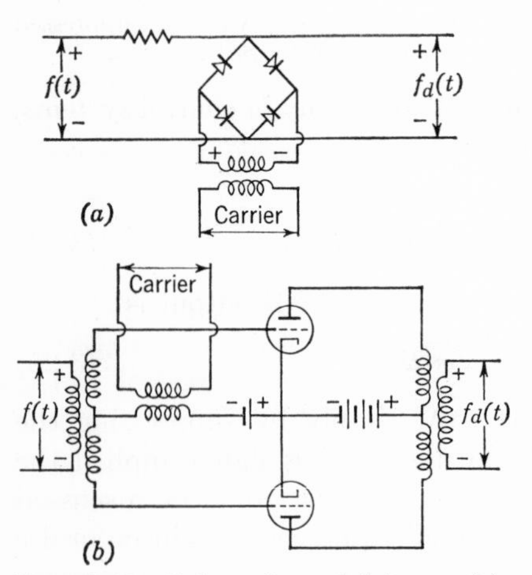

FIG. 3-13. Balanced modulators. (a) Shunt-bridge diode modulator; (b) balanced modulator (vacuum triodes).

Two examples of balanced modulators are shown in Fig. 3-13. The diodes in the bridge modulator may be treated as switches, switching on and off at the carrier rate. With the diodes assumed identical (i.e., balanced) the bridge is balanced when $f(t) = 0$ and there is no output; with the carrier input of the polarity indicated the diodes are essentially short-circuited out, and the output is again zero. When the carrier reverses polarity, however, the diodes open and $f_d(t)$ is equal to $f(t)$. The output is thus alternately $f(t)$ and 0, switching at the carrier-frequency rate. The mechanical-contact balanced modulator to be considered later will be shown to be of the same form as the electronic switching device, and the actual analysis of such a circuit is deferred until that time.

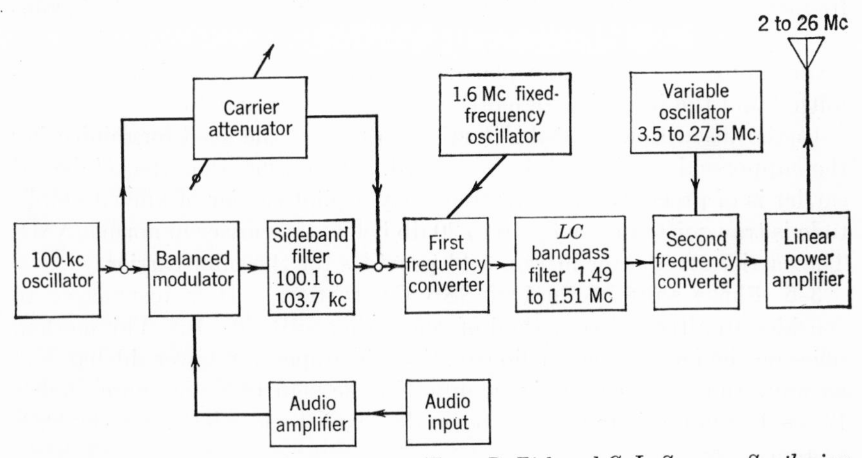

FIG. 3-14. Single-sideband transmitter. (*From B. Fisk and C. L. Spencer, Synthesizer Stabilized Single-sideband Systems, Proc. IRE, vol.* 44, *no.* 12, *p.* 1680, *December,* 1956, *by permission.*)

The balanced modulator is essentially the heart of the SSB transmitters most commonly used at the present time. The balanced modulators are operated at low power levels, with linear amplifiers then following to reach the required transmitted power. This is in contrast to ordinary AM (Fig. 3-10), where the modulation is frequently carried out at high power levels, with class C amplifiers.

In addition to the balanced modulator the SSB system requires a sideband filter with sharp cutoff characteristics at the edges of the passband. (Attenuation at the carrier frequency must be especially high.) Because of the stringent requirements on the filter the modulation is commonly performed at a relatively low fixed frequency at which it is possible to design the required sideband filter.

A typical SSB transmitter incorporating the two features mentioned—low-level balanced modulator and low-frequency (l-f) filtering—is shown in Fig. 3-14. The modulation process in this transmitter is carried out at 100 kc/sec. Two levels of frequency conversion, or mixing, are employed, with the signal successively shifted up in frequency by the frequency of the two injected signals (1.6 Mc/sec and the final variable frequency).

Frequency converters are basically similar to the modulators previously discussed, with a large injected signal of frequency close to that of the incoming signal superimposed on an incoming wave. The combined signal is then put through a nonlinear device, and sum and difference frequencies again obtained. In the transmitter shown in Fig. 3-14 the difference frequencies of the second converter are rejected and sum frequencies transmitted. This serves to raise the frequency of the incoming signal by the frequency of the injected signal. In a receiver the reverse process would take place: the difference frequencies are transmitted and the incoming signal thus lowered in frequency.

In the discussion of SSB detection to follow, the need for reinjecting the suppressed carrier will be discussed. To ensure that the reinjected carrier is of precisely the right frequency a pilot carrier of known amplitude is transmitted (usually 10 to 20 db below the carrier in normal AM). The carrier attenuator in Fig. 3-14 provides for the pilot carrier.

3-5. Phase-shift Method of SSB Generation.[1] It is instructive to consider an alternative method of generating SSB signals. This method relies on the fact, noted previously, that the upper and lower sidebands of an amplitude-modulated signal differ in the sign of their phase angles. Phase discrimination may thus be used to cancel one sideband of the DSB system.

To demonstrate this more concretely, consider the modulating signal $f(t)$ to be a pure cosine wave. A balanced-modulator, or DSB, output would thus be written

$$f_{d1}(t) = \cos \omega_m t \cos \omega_c t = \tfrac{1}{2}[\cos (\omega_c + \omega_m)t + \cos (\omega_c - \omega_m)t] \tag{3-29}$$

$\cos \omega_m t$ is the modulating signal and $\cos \omega_c t$ the carrier. An SSB signal would have the simple form $\cos (\omega_c - \omega_m)t$. This implies that we must add to Eq. (3-29) an expression of the form

$$f_{d2}(t) = \tfrac{1}{2}[\cos (\omega_c - \omega_m)t - \cos (\omega_m + \omega_c)t] = \sin \omega_m t \sin \omega_c t \tag{3-30}$$

Upon adding Eqs. (3-29) and (3-30) the upper sideband cancels, leaving the desired lower sideband,

$$\cos (\omega_c - \omega_m)t$$

But Eq. (3 30) indicates that a product modulator, or a balanced modulator, is again needed, with the modulating signal now $\sin \omega_m t$, multiplied

[1] D. E. Norgaard, The Phase-shift Method of Single-sideband Signal Generation, *Proc. IRE*, vol. 44, no. 12, p. 1718, December, 1956.

by the phase-shifted carrier $\sin \omega_c t$. It is apparent that this method of generating SSB signals actually requires two balanced-modulator circuits, 90° phase-shift networks, and an adding network. The method can be summarized by means of the following step-by-step table:

	System 1	System 2
Modulating signal......	$f_1(t) = \cos \omega_m t$	$f_2(t) = \sin \omega_m t = \cos (\omega_m t - \pi/2)$
Carrier signal	$\cos \omega_c t$	$\sin \omega_c t = \cos (\omega_c t - \pi/2)$
Balanced-modulator output	$\cos \omega_c t \cos \omega_m t = \frac{1}{2}[\cos (\omega_c - \omega_m)t + \cos (\omega_c + \omega_m)t]$	$\sin \omega_c t \sin \omega_m t = \frac{1}{2}[\cos (\omega_c - \omega_m)t - \cos (\omega_c + \omega_m)t]$
Adder output	$\cos (\omega_c - \omega_m)t$	

A block diagram of such a phase-shift SSB system is shown in Fig. 3-15.

One major problem in the design of such a system is the practical realization of the wideband 90° phase-shift network, for *all* the frequency components of the modulating signal $f(t)$ must be shifted by 90°.

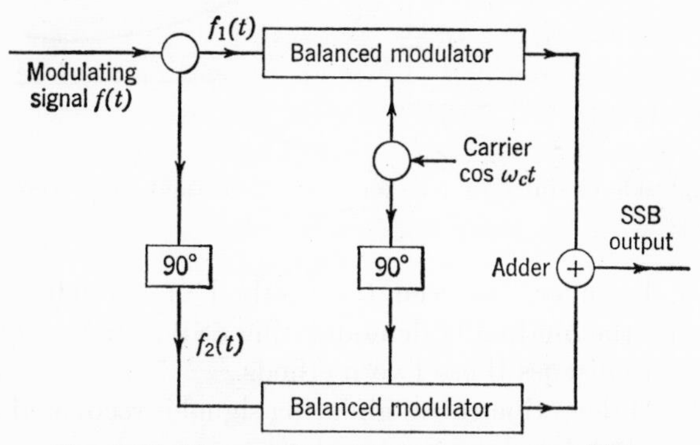

FIG. 3-15. Phase-shift method of generating SSB.

A modified version of the phase-shift method of generating SSB signals consists in inserting a phase shift $\beta(f)$ in the $f_1(t)$ branch of Fig. 3-15 and a phase shift $\beta(f) + 90°$ in the $f_2(t)$ branch. $\beta(f)$ varies in an arbitrary manner with frequency. The details of the analysis are left to the reader as an exercise. The design requirements in this case are for a set of two parallel phase-shift curves 90° apart. This is more easily accomplished than the constant 90° curve required for the method of Fig. 3-15.

3-6. Demodulation, or Detection. The process of separating a modulating signal from a modulated carrier is called demodulation, or detection. Detection is of course necessary in all radio receivers where the information to be received is carried by the modulating signal.

Demodulation is basically the inverse of modulation and requires nonlinear or linear time-varying parameter devices also. Since the nonlinear circuits used are essentially the same, the details of detector operation are left as exercises for the reader. (Again two types of nonlinear detector may be considered: the so-called "square-law" detector with the current-voltage characteristics represented by a power series, and the piecewise-linear detector with a nonlinearity concentrated at one point.) There is

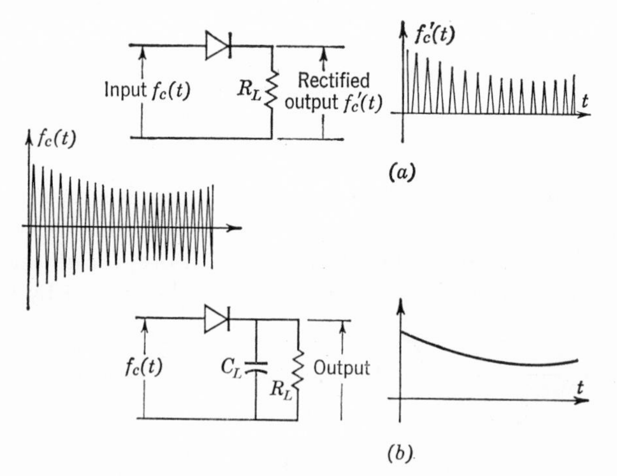

FIG. 3-16. Amplitude-modulation detector. (a) Detection, no filtering; (b) detection with filtering.

a distinction, however, between the method of demodulating normal AM signals and the method of demodulating SSB signals. It is therefore of importance to discuss these two methods.

In normal AM detection the modulating signal is recovered by applying the amplitude-modulated carrier to a half-wave rectifier. The output is then filtered to provide the desired modulating signal. Alternatively, we can talk of the combined rectification and filtering as providing an output which follows the envelope variations of the incoming signal. These envelope variations of course contain the desired information. The simple AM detector circuit, both without and with filtering, is shown in Fig. 3-16.

The analysis of the detector of Fig. 3-16*a* is carried out very simply by again approximating the diode as a piecewise-linear device, with switching occurring at the carrier-frequency rate. Thus with the input given by

$$f_c(t) = K[1 + mf(t)] \cos \omega_c t \tag{3-31}$$

the output may be written

$$f_c'(t) = K[1 + mf(t)] \cos \omega_c t S(t) \tag{3-32}$$

with $S(t)$ a switching function defined as was the switching function for the piecewise-linear modulator analysis. By again expanding $S(t)$ in its Fourier series it can be shown very simply that the output contains a component proportional to $f(t)$ plus higher-frequency terms (sum and difference frequencies of carrier and modulating signal).

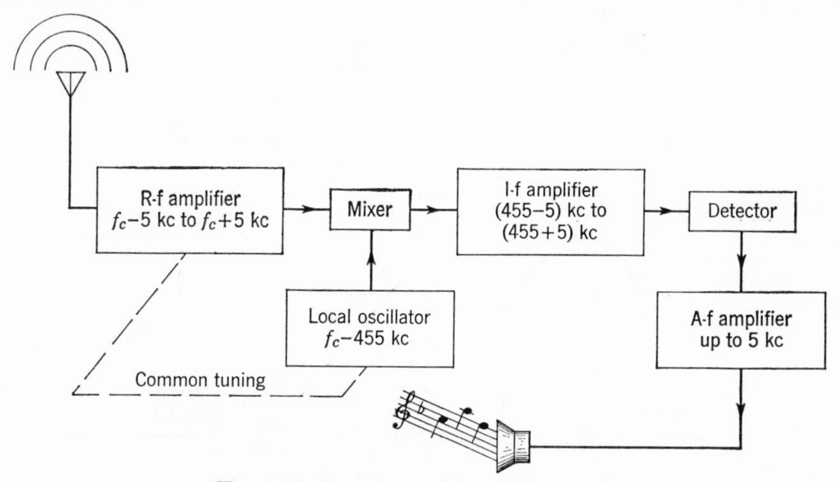

FIG. 3-17. Superheterodyne AM receiver.

The capacitor of Fig. 3-16*b* serves to filter out these higher-frequency terms. Looked at another way, C_L is chosen so as to respond to envelope variations, but the circuit time constant (including the diode forward resistance) does not allow the circuit to follow the high-frequency (h-f) carrier variations. A block diagram of a typical superheterodyne radio receiver, incorporating such a detector, is shown in Fig. 3-17.

The incoming signal passes first through a tuned radio-frequency (r-f) amplifier which can be tuned variably over the radio band 550 to 1,600 kc. This signal is then mixed with a locally generated signal (frequently in a pentagrid-type tube). The sum and difference frequencies generated contain a term centered about 455 kc/sec. (The local oscillator and r-f amplifier are tuned together so that there is always a difference frequency of 455 kc/sec between them.) The mixer acts as a frequency converter, shifting the incoming signal down to the fixed intermediate frequency of 455 kc/sec. Several stages of amplification are ordinarily used, with double-tuned circuits providing the coupling between stages. The intermediate-frequency (i-f) signal is then detected as described above, amplified further in the audio-frequency (a-f) amplifiers and applied to the loudspeaker. The superheterodyning operation refers to the use of a frequency converter and fixed tuned i-f amplifiers before detection.

In the case of SSB detection the carrier must be supplied at the receiver before the modulation can take place. The sum of the signal and the locally generated carrier could be rectified to produce difference frequencies and then filtered to select the components corresponding to the desired modulating signal. It is more common in practice to use the carrier to shift the SSB signal down to the required audio band by using a

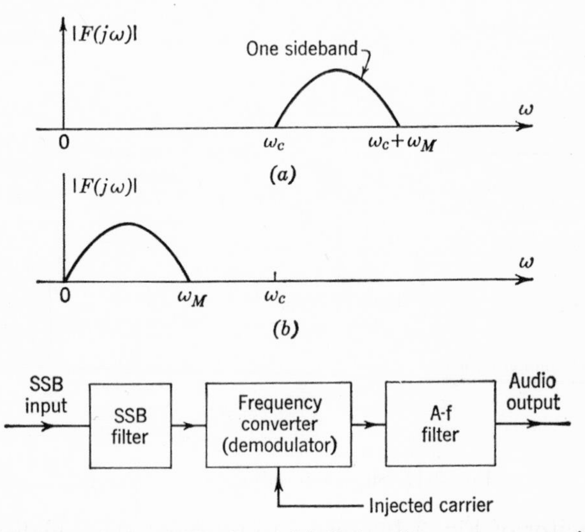

FIG. 3-18. Single-sideband demodulation. (a) Before frequency conversion; (b) after frequency conversion.

frequency converter. Amplitude-modulation detection and SSB detection, as encountered in practice, thus differ in their form: AM uses envelope detection; SSB uses frequency conversion or mixing to shift the signal down to the audio range. [Although the SSB signal contains the desired input signal $f(t)$, the time waveshape of the SSB signal does not in any way "look like" $f(t)$. For this reason the simple envelope detection of normal AM is not possible.] The SSB spectrum before and after mixing is shown in Fig. 3-18. It is left as an exercise for the reader to show that the frequency of the carrier injected at the receiver must be identical to that of the original carrier for distortionless demodulation to take place.

The problem of providing a carrier at the receiver of exactly the right frequency has been the block in the path of widespread use of SSB transmission.

A typical SSB-receiver block diagram is shown in Fig. 3-19.

The carrier filter and sideband filter are used to separate the sideband and the pilot carrier normally transmitted (refer to the previous discussion on SSB generation). Double frequency conversion (the first and the second mixers) is used, just as in the case of the SSB transmitter (Fig. 3-14), to obtain a convenient range of frequency for the filters. The output of the carrier filter is amplified and limited and used for automatic

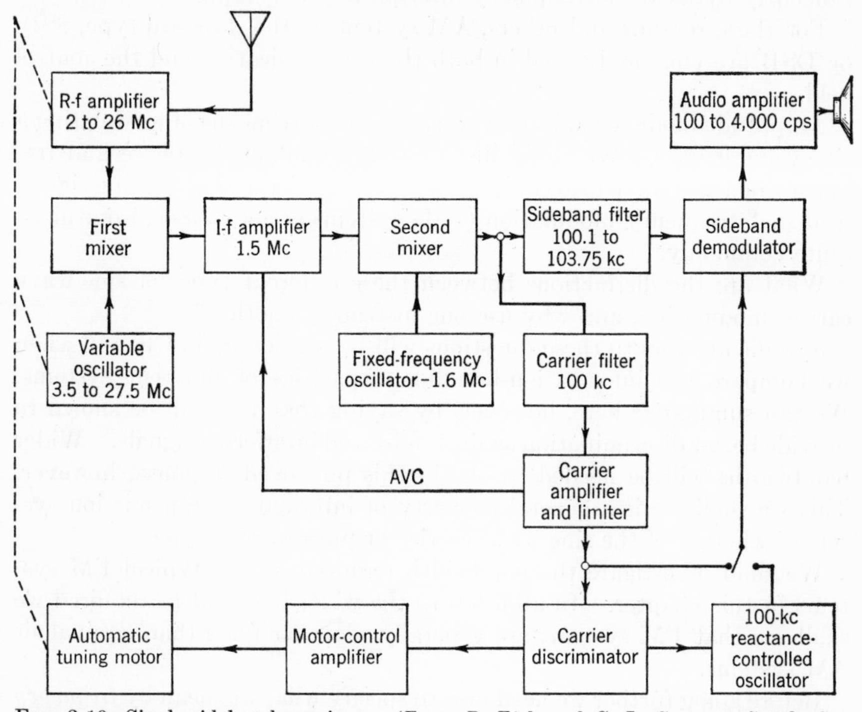

FIG. 3-19. Single-sideband receiver. (*From B. Fisk and C. L. Spencer, Synthesizer Stabilized Single-sideband Systems, Proc. IRE, vol.* 44, *no.* 12, *p.* 1680, *December,* 1956, *by permission.*)

tuning controls, either as a reinsertion carrier directly or to lock the frequency of a local oscillator that furnishes a suitable insertion carrier.

The precision frequency control required of both SSB transmitters and receivers is the basic limitation to their widespread use at the present time. The degree of precision frequency control required in the 2- to 30-Mc frequency range is 1 part in 10^7.

3-7. Frequency Modulation. We have investigated thus far in this chapter the effect of slowly varying the amplitude of a sinusoidal carrier in accordance with some information to be transmitted. The desired information is then found to be concentrated in sidebands about the carrier frequency. By choosing the carrier frequency high enough, information transmission by means of radio (through the air) becomes practicable. Alternatively, with AM the signal-frequency spectrum may be shifted to a frequency range where circuit design becomes more feasible, where circuit components are more readily obtained and more economically built, or where equipment size and weight can be reduced. In addition, many information channels may be transmitted simultaneously by means of frequency-multiplexing techniques.

For these reasons and others, AM systems of the standard type, SSB, or DSB are commonly used in both the communication and the control field.

Amplitude modulation is, however, not the only means of modulating a sine-wave carrier. We could just as well modulate the phase and frequency of a sine wave in accordance with some information-bearing signal. And such frequency-modulation (FM) systems are of course also utilized quite commonly.

What are the distinctions between these different types of sine-wave carrier modulation, and why use one instead of another?

Specific answers to these questions will be considered in Chap. 6 when we compare the information-handling capacities of different systems. We can summarize here, however, by saying that FM will be shown to provide better discrimination against noise and interfering signals. Wider bandwidths will be needed to obtain this improved response, however. This we shall see is a general property of information-transmission systems—whether of the sine-wave-carrier or pulse-carrier type.

We shall investigate the bandwidth requirements of typical FM systems in this chapter. In addition to the wider bandwidths required we shall see that FM systems are generally more complex than equivalent AM systems.

Before going further we need first to specify what we mean by *frequency modulation*. We might start intuitively by saying that we shall consider a sine-wave carrier system in which the frequency of the carrier is caused to vary in accordance with some specified information-carrying signal. Thus we might write the frequency of the carrier as $\omega_c + Kf(t)$, where $f(t)$ represents the signal and K is a constant of the system. This is of course analogous to the AM case. We run into some difficulty, however, when we attempt to express the resultant frequency-modulated carrier mathematically. For we can talk about the frequency of a sine wave only when the frequency is constant and the sine wave persists for all time. Yet here we are attempting to discuss a variable frequency!

The difficulty lies in the fact that, strictly speaking, we can talk only of the sine (or cosine) of an *angle*. If this angle varies linearly with time, we can specifically interpret the frequency as the derivative of the angle.

Thus, if

$$f_c(t) = \cos \theta(t) = \cos (\omega_c t + \theta_0) \tag{3-33}$$

the usual expression for a sine wave of frequency ω_c, we are implicitly assuming $\theta(t)$ to be linear with time, with ω_c its derivative.

When $\theta(t)$ does not vary linearly with time, we can no longer write Eq. (3-33) in the standard form shown, with a specified frequency term. To obviate this difficulty, we shall define an *instantaneous radian frequency* ω_i to be the derivative of the angle as a function of time. Thus, with

$$f_c(t) = \cos \theta(t) \tag{3-34}$$

$$\omega_i \equiv \frac{d\theta}{dt} \tag{3-35}$$

(This then agrees of course with the usual use of the word *frequency* if $\theta = \omega_c t + \theta_0$.)

If $\theta(t)$ in Eq. (3-34) is now made to vary in some manner with a modulating signal $f(t)$, we call the resulting form of modulation *angle modulation*. In particular, if

$$\theta(t) = \omega_c t + \theta_0 + K_1 f(t) \tag{3-36}$$

with K_1 a constant of the system, we say we are dealing with a *phase-modulation* system. Here the *phase* of the carrier wave varies linearly with the modulating signal.

Now let the *instantaneous frequency*, as defined by Eq. (3-35), vary linearly with the modulating signal,

$$\omega_i = \omega_c + K_2 f(t) \tag{3-37}$$

Then

$$\theta(t) = \int \omega_i \, dt = \omega_c t + \theta_0 + K_2 \int f(t) \, dt \tag{3-38}$$

This of course gives rise to an FM system.

Both phase modulation and frequency modulation are seen to be special cases of angle modulation. In the phase-modulation case the phase of the carrier varies with the modulating signal, and in the frequency-modulation case the phase of the carrier varies with the integral of the modulating signal.

There is thus no essential difference between phase and frequency modulation.[1] In fact, if we first integrate our modulating signal $f(t)$ and then allow it to phase-modulate a carrier, this gives rise to a frequency-modulated wave. This is exactly the method used for producing a frequency-modulated carrier in the Armstrong indirect FM system, as we shall see shortly. We shall use the term *frequency modulation* generally to include both phase and frequency modulation.

[1] For further discussion of this point see H. S. Black, "Modulation Theory," chaps. 3 and 12, D. Van Nostrand Company, Inc., Princeton, N.J., 1953.

A frequency-modulated carrier is shown sketched in Fig. 3-20*c*. The modulating signal is assumed to be a repetitive saw tooth of period T ($\omega_m = 2\pi/T \ll \omega_c$). As the modulating wave increases in magnitude, the FM wave oscillates more rapidly. Its amplitude remains unchanged, however.

Frequency modulation is a nonlinear process, and so, as pointed out in previous sections, we would expect to see new frequencies generated

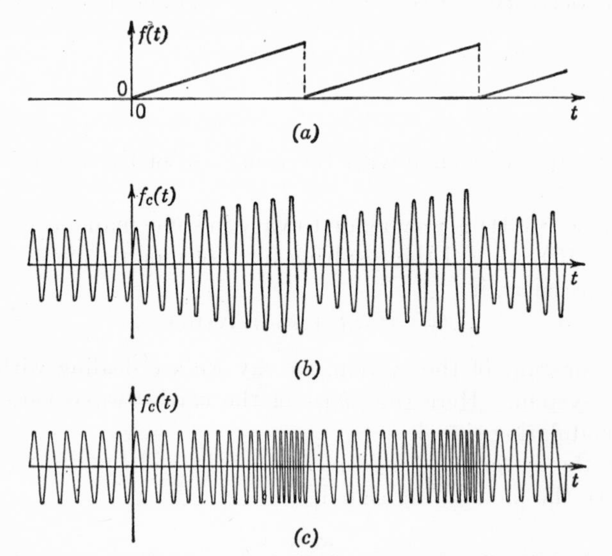

FIG. 3-20. Frequency modulation. (*a*) Modulating wave; (*b*) AM carrier; (*c*) FM carrier.

by the modulation process. Since the FM signal oscillates more rapidly with increasing amplitude of the modulating signal, we would expect the frequency spectrum of the FM wave, or its bandwidth, to widen correspondingly. This will be borne out in the discussion to follow.

The analysis of the process of FM is inherently much more complicated than that for AM, particularly in dealing with a general modulating signal $f(t)$. To simplify our discussion, then, we shall repeat our AM approach by first considering $f(t)$ to be a single sine wave. Although this is again a rather poor "approximation" to our information-carrying signals, which may vary randomly and unpredictably with time, this approach will nonetheless provide useful information as to bandwidths and the interference-rejection properties of FM. (Because of the nonlinearity of the FM process superposition cannot be applied so that even the analysis for two sine waves becomes quite cumbersome.)

As the simplest example of the FM process, then, assume a sinusoidal modulating signal at frequency f_m,

$$f(t) = a \cos \omega_m t \tag{3-39}$$

The instantaneous radian frequency ω_i is

$$\omega_i = \omega_c + \Delta\omega \cos \omega_m t \qquad \Delta\omega \ll \omega_c \tag{3-40}$$

where $\Delta\omega$ is a constant depending on the amplitude a of the modulating signal and on the circuitry converting variations in signal amplitude to corresponding variations in carrier frequency.

The instantaneous radian frequency thus varies about the unmodulated carrier frequency ω_c, at the rate ω_m of the modulating signal and with a maximum deviation of $\Delta\omega$ radians. $\Delta f = \Delta\omega/2\pi$ gives the maximum frequency deviation away from the carrier frequency and is called the *frequency deviation.*

The phase variation $\theta(t)$ for this special case is given by

$$\theta(t) = \int \omega_i \, dt = \omega_c t + \frac{\Delta\omega}{\omega_m} \sin \omega_m t + \theta_0 \tag{3-41}$$

θ_0 may be taken as zero by referring to an appropriate phase reference, so that the frequency-modulated carrier is given by

$$f_c(t) = \cos(\omega_c t + \beta \sin \omega_m t) \tag{3-42}$$

with

$$\beta \equiv \frac{\Delta\omega}{\omega_m} = \frac{\Delta f}{f_m} \tag{3-43}$$

β is called the *modulation index* and is by definition the ratio of the frequency deviation to the modulating frequency. β represents the maximum phase shift of the carrier.

We noted previously that increasing the amplitude of the modulating signal should increase the bandwidth occupied by the FM signal. Increasing the modulating-signal amplitude corresponds to increasing the frequency deviation Δf or the modulation index β. We would thus expect the bandwidth of the FM wave to depend on β. This will be demonstrated in the sections to follow. The average power associated with the frequency-modulated carrier is independent of the modulating signal, however, and is in fact the same as the average power of the unmodulated carrier. This is again in contrast to the AM case, where the average power of the modulated carrier varies with the modulating-signal amplitude.

That this statement is true may be demonstrated by using Eq. (3-42) for a sinusoidal modulating signal. Assuming that $f_c(t)$ represents the instantaneous voltage impressed across a 1-ohm resistor, the average power over a cycle of the modulating frequency is given by

$$\frac{1}{T}\int_0^T f_c^2(t)\,dt = \frac{1}{T}\int_0^T \cos^2(\omega_c t + \beta \sin \omega_m t)\,dt$$

where $T = 1/f_m$. This expression may be rewritten as

$$\frac{1}{T}\int_0^T \frac{1 + \cos(2\omega_c t + 2\beta \sin \omega_m t)}{2}\,dt$$

The second term of the integral goes to zero since it is periodic in T. The first term gives ½ watt. If the amplitude of the carrier had been written as A_c volts, the average power would have been found to be $A_c^2/2$ watts for a 1-ohm resistor.

Although shown only for a sinusoidal modulating signal, the above result is true for any modulating signal whose highest frequency component, f_M cps, is small compared with f_c, the carrier frequency. This is left as an exercise for the reader.

3-8. Narrowband FM. To simplify the analysis of FM, we shall treat it in two parts. We shall first consider the sinusoidally modulated carrier with $\beta \ll \pi/2$, and then with $\beta \geq \pi/2$. Small β corresponds to narrow bandwidths, and FM systems with $\beta \ll \pi/2$ are thus called *narrowband FM systems.* The equations for *narrowband FM* appear in the form of the equations of the product modulator of the previous sections on AM and so give rise to sideband frequencies equally displaced about the carrier, just as in the case of AM.

To demonstrate this point, consider the sinusoidally modulated carrier of Eq. (3-42), and assume $\beta \ll \pi/2$. (This implies that the maximum phase shift of the carrier is much less than $\pi/2$ radians. This is ordinarily taken to mean $\beta < 0.2$ radian, although $\beta < 0.5$ radian is sometimes used as a criterion.) We have

$$\begin{aligned} f_c(t) &= \cos(\omega_c t + \beta \sin \omega_m t) \\ &= \cos \omega_c t \cos(\beta \sin \omega_m t) - \sin \omega_c t \sin(\beta \sin \omega_m t) \end{aligned} \qquad (3\text{-}44)$$

But, for $\beta \ll \pi/2$, $\cos(\beta \sin \omega_m t) \doteq 1$, and $\sin(\beta \sin \omega_m t) \doteq \beta \sin \omega_m t$.

The frequency-modulated wave for small modulation index thus appears in the form

$$f_c(t) \doteq \cos \omega_c t - \beta \sin \omega_m t \sin \omega_c t \qquad \beta \ll \frac{\pi}{2} \qquad (3\text{-}45)$$

Note that this expression for $f_c(t)$, the frequency-modulated carrier, has a form similar to that of the output of a product modulator: it contains the original unmodulated carrier term plus a term given by the product of the modulating signal and carrier. For the sinusoidal modulating signal, $\beta \sin \omega_m t$, this product term provides sideband frequencies displaced $\pm\omega_m$ radians from ω_c. The bandwidth of this narrowband FM signal is thus $2f_m$ cps.

If we had assumed a general modulating signal $f(t)$ instead of the sinusoidal modulating signal used here, we would have obtained similar results. For, as shown by Eqs. (3-37) and (3-38), we then have

$$\omega_i = \omega_c + K_2 f(t)$$
$$\theta(t) = \int \omega_i \, dt = \omega_c t + \theta_0 + K_2 \int f(t) \, dt$$

Suppressing the arbitrary phase angle θ_0, and defining a new time function $g(t)$ to be the integral of $f(t)$, $g(t) \equiv \int f(t) \, dt$, we have as the frequency-modulated carrier

$$f_c(t) = \cos\left[\omega_c t + K_2 g(t)\right] \tag{3-46}$$

If K_2 and the maximum amplitude of $g(t)$ are now chosen small enough so that $|K_2 g(t)| \ll \pi/2$,

$$f_c(t) \doteq \cos \omega_c t - K_2 g(t) \sin \omega_c t \tag{3-47}$$

Our previous discussion of product modulators indicates that the spectrum of this general case of narrowband FM consists of the carrier plus two sidebands, one on each side of the carrier and each having the form of the spectrum of the function $g(t)$. Narrowband FM is thus equivalent, in this sense, to AM. The bandwidth of a narrowband FM signal, in general, is $2f_M$ cps, where f_M is the highest frequency component of either $g(t)$ or its derivative $f(t)$, the original modulating signal. (Remember that the linear process of integration adds no new frequency components. The lower frequency components, however, are accentuated in comparison with the higher frequency components.)

Although AM and narrowband FM have similar frequency spectra and their mathematical representations both appear in the product-modulator form, they are distinctively different methods of modulation. In the AM case we were interested in variations of the carrier envelope, its frequency remaining unchanged; in the FM case we assumed the carrier amplitude constant, its phase (and effectively the instantaneous frequency also) varying with signal. This distinction between the two types of modulation must be retained in the narrowband FM case also (here maximum phase shift of the carrier is assumed less than 0.2 radian).

To emphasize this distinction in the two types of modulation, note that the product modulator or sideband term in either Eq. (3-45) or Eq. (3-47) appears in phase quadrature with the carrier term ($\sin \omega_c t$ as compared with $\cos \omega_c t$). In the AM case we had both carrier and sideband terms in phase,

$$f_c(t) = \cos \omega_c t + mf(t) \cos \omega_c t$$

For the narrowband FM case we have

$$f_c(t) = \cos \omega_c t - K_2 g(t) \sin \omega_c t$$

That the inphase, or phase-quadrature, representation is fundamental in distinguishing between AM and narrowband FM (or, alternatively,

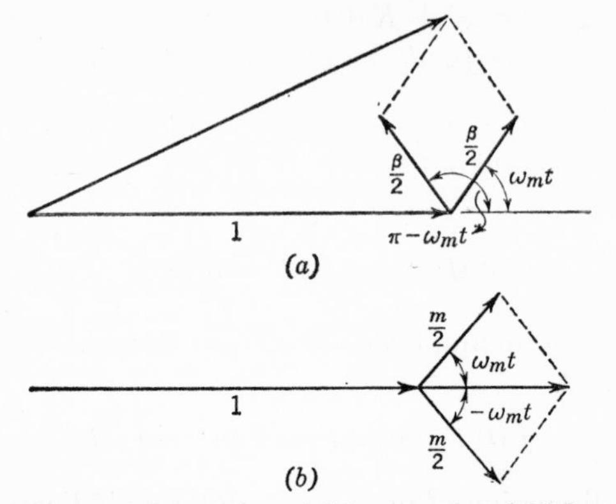

FIG. 3-21. Vector representation of (a) narrowband FM and (b) AM.

small-angle phase modulation) is demonstrated very simply by the use of rotating vectors.[1]

We rewrite Eq. (3-45) in its sideband frequency form,

$$\begin{aligned} f_c(t) &= \cos \omega_c t - \beta \sin \omega_m t \sin \omega_c t \\ &= \cos \omega_c t - \frac{\beta}{2} [\cos (\omega_c - \omega_m)t - \cos (\omega_c + \omega_m)t] \end{aligned} \tag{3-48}$$

This can also be written in the form

$$f_c(t) = \text{Re}\left[e^{j\omega_c t}\left(1 - \frac{\beta}{2} e^{-j\omega_m t} + \frac{\beta}{2} e^{j\omega_m t}\right)\right] \tag{3-49}$$

where Re [ ] represents the real part of the expression in the square brackets.

$e^{j\omega_c t}$ may be represented as a unit vector rotating counterclockwise at the rate of ω_c radians/sec. Superimposed on this rotation are changes in the vector due to the three terms in parentheses. We then take the real part of the resultant vector, or its projection on the real axis. If we suppress the continuous ω_c rotation and concentrate solely on the three terms in parentheses, we may plot these as the three vectors of Fig. 3-21*a*. Note that the resultant vector deviates in phase from the unmodulated vector, while its amplitude is very nearly unchanged. (This is for the case $\beta \ll \pi/2$. Here β is shown larger for the sake of clarity.)

[1] *Ibid.*, pp. 186–187.

We can use the same vector approach for the AM case and get

$$\begin{aligned} f_c(t) &= \cos \omega_c t + m \cos \omega_m t \cos \omega_c t \\ &= \cos \omega_c t + \frac{m}{2} [\cos (\omega_c + \omega_m)t + \cos (\omega_c - \omega_m)t] \\ &= \text{Re} \left[e^{j\omega_c t} \left(1 + \frac{m}{2} e^{j\omega_m t} + \frac{m}{2} e^{-j\omega_m t} \right) \right] \end{aligned} \tag{3-50}$$

The three quantities in parentheses here are likewise shown plotted in Fig. 3-21*b*. Note that the two sideband vectors have been rotated by $\pi/2$ radians as compared with the FM case. The resultant vector here varies in amplitude but remains in phase with the unmodulated carrier term.

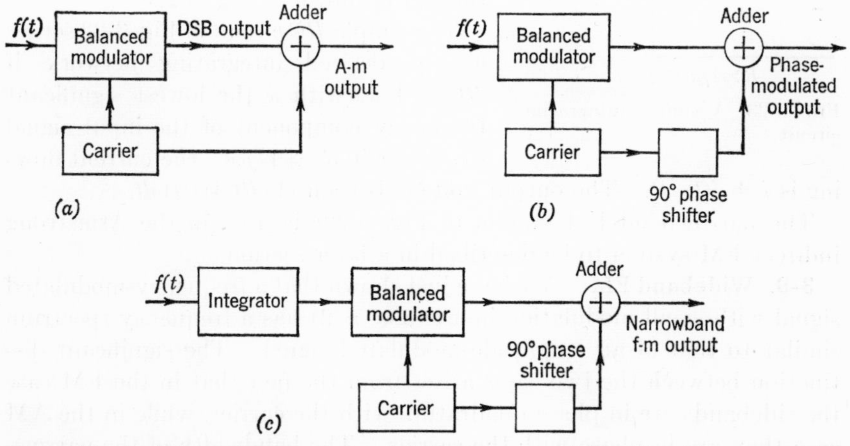

FIG. 3-22. Evolution of a narrowband FM system. (*a*) Possible AM system; (*b*) phase-modulation system (small phase deviations < 0.2 radian); (*c*) narrowband FM system ($\beta < 0.2$ radian).

We can summarize by saying that the resultant of the two sideband vectors in the FM case will always be perpendicular to (or in phase quadrature with) the unmodulated carrier, while the same resultant in the AM case is collinear with the carrier term. The FM case thus gives rise to phase variations with very little amplitude change ($\beta \ll \pi/2$), while the AM case gives amplitude variations with no phase deviation.

The distinction and similarity between AM and narrowband FM (or phase modulation as well) lead us to a commonly used method of generating a frequency-modulated wave with small modulation index ($\beta < 0.2$ radian).

We demonstrated in our discussion of AM systems that the output of a balanced modulator provides just the product or sideband term required by Eq. (3-47). For an *amplitude-modulated* output we would then add to this output the *inphase* carrier term. This is shown in block-diagram form in Fig. 3-22*a*.

To obtain a *phase-modulated* output, according to our previous discussion, we must add a *phase-quadrature* carrier term to the balanced-modulator output. Such a system in block-diagram form is shown in Fig. 3-22*b*. (Remember that this is restricted only to small phase variations, 0.2 radian or less.)

As we demonstrated previously, however, phase modulation and FM differ only by a possible integration of the input modulating signal [Eq. (3-38)]. To obtain a narrowband frequency-modulated output, then, we need only integrate our input signal and then apply it to the phase-modulation system of Fig. 3-22*b*. The resultant narrowband FM system ($\beta < 0.2$ radian) is shown in Fig. 3-22*c*.

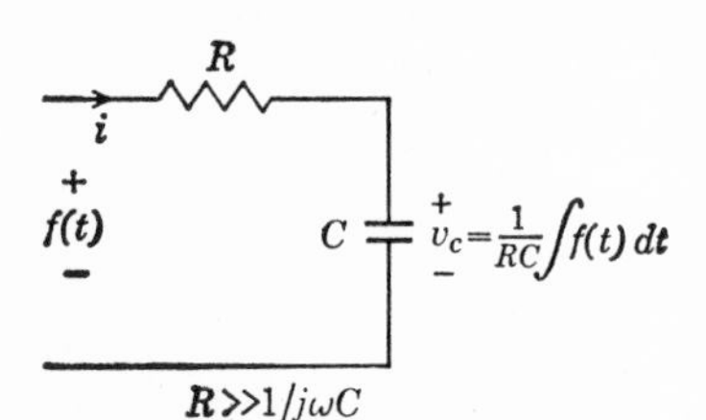

FIG. 3-23. A simple integrating circuit.

The simple RC circuit of Fig. 3-23 serves as the desired integrating network if $RC \gg 1/\omega$, with ω the lowest significant frequency component of the input signal $f(t)$. For if $R \gg 1/j\omega C$, the current flowing is $i \doteq f(t)/R$. The output voltage is then $(1/RC)\int f(t)\,dt$.

The narrowband FM system of Fig. 3-22*c* is used in the Armstrong indirect FM system to be described in a later section.

3-9. Wideband FM. We have just shown that a frequency-modulated signal with small modulation index ($\beta \ll \pi/2$) has a frequency spectrum similar to that of an amplitude-modulated signal. The significant distinction between the two cases arises from the fact that in the FM case the sidebands are in phase quadrature with the carrier, while in the AM case they are in phase with the carrier. The bandwidth of the narrowband FM signal, just like the AM signal, is thus $2f_M$, with f_M the maximum frequency component of the modulating signal.

The noise- and interference-reduction advantages of FM over AM, mentioned previously, become significant, however, only for large modulation index ($\beta > \pi/2$). The bandwidths required to pass this signal become correspondingly large, as pointed out in Sec. 3-7. Most FM systems in use are of this wideband type.

Here the comparison between FM and AM that was valid for small modulation index ($\beta \ll \pi/2$) ends. We shall show that the previous results for narrowband FM can be extended to the wideband case, however.

To demonstrate the increase in signal bandwidth with increasing β, we again resort to the idealization of a sinusoidal modulating signal. The frequency-modulated carrier is again written in the expanded form

$$f_c(t) = \cos \omega_c t \cos (\beta \sin \omega_m t) - \sin \omega_c t \sin (\beta \sin \omega_m t) \qquad (3\text{-}51)$$

For $\beta \ll \pi/2$ we would of course get our previous result of a single carrier and two sideband frequencies. But now let β be somewhat larger at first. We can expand $\cos(\beta \sin \omega_m t)$ in a power series to give us

$$\cos(\beta \sin \omega_m t) \doteq 1 - \frac{\beta^2}{2} \sin^2 \omega_m t \qquad \beta^2 \ll 6 \tag{3-52}$$

If we assume $\beta \ll \sqrt{6}$ and retain just the first two terms in the power series for the cosine, we get the additional term $\sin^2 \omega_m t \cos \omega_c t$ in the

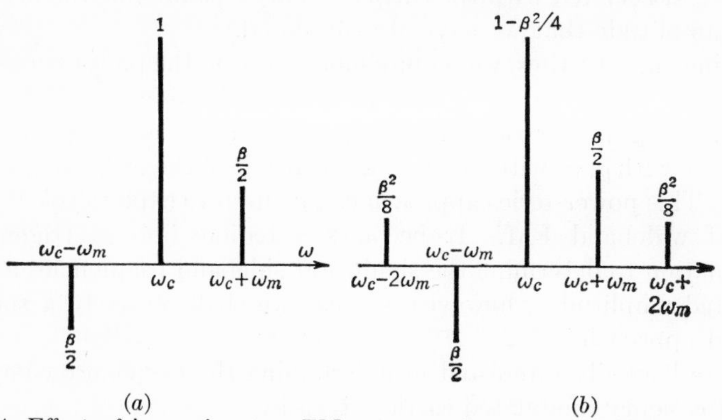

FIG. 3-24. Effect of increasing β on FM spectrum ($\beta^2 \ll 6$). (a) Narrowband case, $\beta \ll \pi/2$; (b) increasing β.

expression for $f_c(t)$. This term gives, upon trigonometric expansion, additional sideband frequencies spaced $\pm 2\omega_m$ radians from the carrier and also contributes a term $-\beta^2/4$ to the carrier. $\sin(\beta \sin \omega_m t)$ can still be represented by $\beta \sin \omega_m t$, the first term in its power-series expansion, for $\beta^2 \ll 6$, so that $f_c(t)$ becomes

$$\begin{aligned} f_c(t) \doteq \left(1 - \frac{\beta^2}{4}\right) \cos \omega_c t - \frac{\beta}{2} [\cos(\omega_m - \omega_c)t - \cos(\omega_m + \omega_c)t] \\ + \frac{\beta^2}{8} [\cos(\omega_c + 2\omega_m)t + \cos(\omega_c - 2\omega_m)t] \qquad \beta^2 \ll 6 \end{aligned} \tag{3-53}$$

Note that the carrier term has now begun to decrease somewhat with increasing β, the first-order sidebands at $\omega_c \pm \omega_m$ increase with β, and a new set of sidebands (the second-order sidebands) appear at $\omega_c \pm 2\omega_m$. The spectrum of this signal is shown in Fig. 3-24b, while the narrowband case is plotted in Fig. 3-24a. This appearance of new sidebands with increasing modulation index is a phenomenon that we have not previously encountered in this book. It is distinctly different from the AM case, where the number of sideband frequencies was dependent solely on the number of modulating frequencies, and not on the amplitude of the modulating signal. Here new sets of significant sidebands appear as the modulation index increases. For a fixed modulating frequency β is proportional to the amplitude of the modulating signal, so that increases in signal amplitude generate new sidebands. This produces a corresponding increase in bandwidth. (The bandwidth has been doubled in this case, going from $2f_m$ to $4f_m$.)

Since the average power in the frequency-modulated wave is independent of the modulating signal (Sec. 3-7), increasing power in the sideband frequencies must be accompanied by a corresponding decrease in the power associated with the carrier. This accounts for the decrease in carrier amplitude that we have already noted.

As β increases further, we require more terms in the power-series expansion for both $\cos(\beta \sin \omega_m t)$ and $\sin(\beta \sin \omega_m t)$. This gives rise to increasingly more significant sideband components, and the bandwidth begins to increase with β, or with increasing amplitude of the original modulating signal. This power-series approach can be used to explore the characteristics of wideband FM. It becomes a tedious job of trigonometric manipulation to determine the significant sideband frequencies and their associated amplitudes, however, so that we shall resort to a somewhat different approach.

We are basically interested in determining the frequency components of the frequency-modulated carrier given by

$$f_c(t) = \cos(\omega_c t + \beta \sin \omega_m t) = \cos \omega_c t \cos(\beta \sin \omega_m t) \\ - \sin(\beta \sin_m t) \sin \omega_c t$$

But we note that both $\cos(\beta \sin \omega_m t)$ and $\sin(\beta \sin \omega_m t)$ are periodic functions of ω_m. As such, each may be expanded in a Fourier series of period $2\pi/\omega_m$. Each series will contain terms in ω_m and all its harmonic frequencies. Each harmonic term multiplied by either $\cos \omega_c t$ or $\sin \omega_c t$ as the case may be will give rise to two sideband frequencies symmetrically situated about ω_c. We thus get a picture of a large set of sideband frequencies in general, all displaced from the carrier ω_c by integral multiples of the modulating signal ω_m. The sidebands corresponding to the $\sin \omega_c t$ term will be quadrature sidebands, while those corresponding to the $\cos \omega_c t$ term will be inphase sidebands. For small values of β, $\cos(\beta \sin \omega_m t)$ and $\sin(\beta \sin \omega_m t)$ vary slowly, and so only a small number of the sidebands about ω_c will be significant in amplitude. As β increases, these two terms vary more rapidly and the amplitudes of the higher-frequency terms become more significant. This picture of course agrees with our previous conclusion that increasing β produces a wider bandwidth signal. It is again in contrast to the AM case, where the carrier and a single set of sidebands only appear.

These remarks are given more significance by considering some plots of cos (β sin $\omega_m t$). These are shown in Fig. 3-25 for various values of β. The four curves drawn demonstrate some interesting points:

1. For $\beta < 0.5$ the curve can be represented approximately by a d-c component plus a small component at twice the fundamental frequency ω_m. But these terms multiplied by cos $\omega_c t$ give just the carrier and the second-order sideband terms that we obtained previously for $\beta \ll \sqrt{6}$.

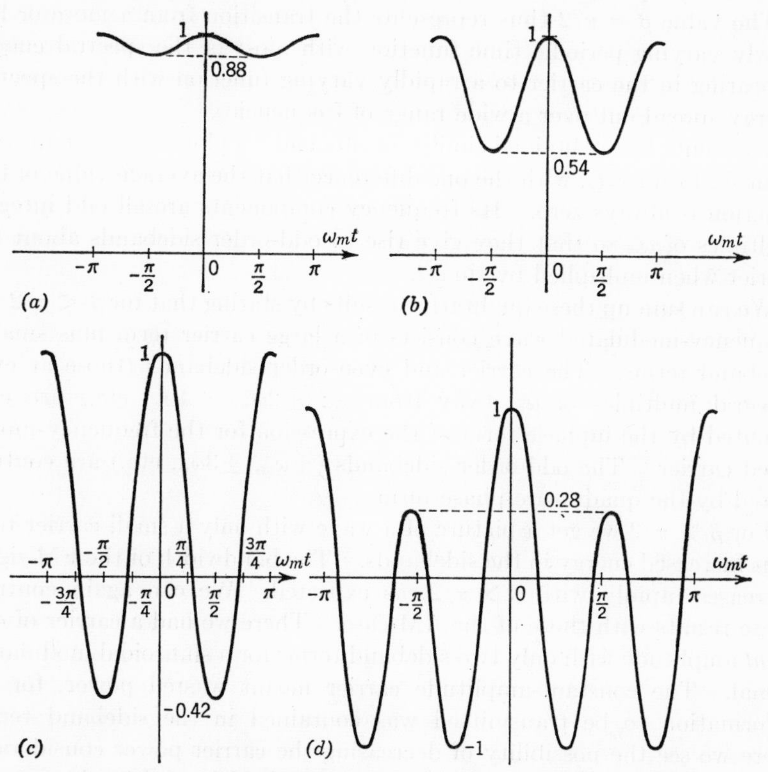

FIG. 3-25. Plots of cos (β sin $\omega_m t$) for various β. (a) $\beta = 0.5$; cos (0.5 sin $\omega_m t$); (b) $\beta = 1$; cos (sin $\omega_m t$); (c) $\beta = 2$; cos (2 sin $\omega_m t$); (d) $\beta = 5$; cos (5 sin $\omega_m t$).

2. For $\beta < \pi/2 = 1.57$ the function remains positive and appears as a d-c component with some ripple superimposed. One would thus expect a Fourier analysis to give a large d-c component plus successively decreasing harmonics. This d-c component, or average value of the function, decreases with β, however. Again, if we multiply this by cos $\omega_c t$, we obtain a picture of a carrier term decreasing with β, while the sidebands increase with β. These sidebands are all displaced from the carrier by even integral values of ω_m ($\pm 2\omega_m$, $\pm 4\omega_m$, etc.).

3. For $\beta > \pi/2 = 1.57$ the function takes on negative values. As β increases, the positive and negative excursions become more rapid and one would expect a greatly increased harmonic content, with much less energy at direct current. Again converting these results to variations about the carrier frequency, we would expect a rapid decrease in the energy content of the carrier for $\beta > \pi/2$ and increased energy in the sideband components.

The value $\beta = \pi/2$ thus represents the transition from a more or less slowly varying periodic time function with most of the spectral energy appearing in the carrier to a rapidly varying function with the spectral energy spread out over a wide range of frequencies.

We would have obtained similar results had we plotted the quadrature term $\sin(\beta \sin \omega_m t)$, with the one difference that the average value of this function is always zero. Its frequency components are all odd integral multiples of ω_m so that they give rise to odd-order sidebands about the carrier when multiplied by $\sin \omega_c t$.

We can sum up these qualitative results by stating that for $\beta < \pi/2$ the frequency-modulated wave consists of a large carrier term plus smaller sideband terms. The carrier and even-order sidebands (those at even integral multiples of ω_m away from ω_c: $\pm 2\omega_m$, $\pm 4\omega_m$, etc.) are contributed by the inphase term of the expression for the frequency-modulated carrier. The odd-order sidebands ($\pm\omega_m$, $\pm 3\omega_m$, etc.) are contributed by the quadrature-phase term.

For $\beta > \pi/2$ we get a picture of a wave with only a small carrier term plus increased energy in the sidebands. The bandwidth of the FM signal increases rapidly with $\beta > \pi/2$, as expected. We can again contrast these results with those of the AM case. There we had a carrier of *constant* amplitude with only two sideband terms for a sinusoidal modulating signal. The constant-amplitude carrier meant wasted power, for the information to be transmitted was contained in the sideband terms. Here we see the possibility of decreasing the carrier power considerably if we take $\beta > \pi/2$. This implies wide bandwidths and is of course, as pointed out previously, the desirable situation in most FM systems used for their good noise- and interference-rejection properties.

By wideband FM we shall thus mean a frequency-modulated signal with $\beta > \pi/2$.

To demonstrate these conclusions more quantitatively, we must actually determine the frequency components and their amplitudes for the frequency-modulated signal of arbitrary β and sinusoidal modulating signal. As was noted previously, this may be done by expanding both $\cos(\beta \sin \omega_m t)$ and $\sin(\beta \sin \omega_m t)$ in their respective Fourier series. Multiplying the cosine term by $\cos \omega_c t$ and the sine term by $\sin \omega_c t$ then gives us our FM signal.

Both series may be found simultaneously by considering the periodic complex exponential

$$v(t) = e^{j\beta \sin \omega_m t} \qquad -\frac{T}{2} < t < \frac{T}{2} \tag{3-54}$$

The real part of this function gives us our cosine function; the imaginary part, the sine function. If we expand this exponential in its Fourier series, we can expect to get a real part consisting of even harmonics of ω_m and an imaginary part consisting of the odd harmonics. [This is deduced from our previous discussion of cos (β sin $\omega_m t$) and the associated Fig. 3-25.] By equating reals and imaginaries we shall then obtain the desired Fourier expansions for cos (β sin $\omega_m t$) and sin (β sin $\omega_m t$), respectively.

The Fourier coefficient of the complex Fourier series for the exponential of Eq. (3-54) is given by

$$c_n = \int_{-T/2}^{T/2} e^{j(\beta \sin \omega_m t - \omega_n t)}\, dt \qquad \omega_m = \frac{2\pi}{T},\ \omega_n = \frac{2\pi n}{T} = n\omega_m \tag{3-55}$$

Normalizing this integral by letting $x = \omega_m t$, we get

$$\frac{c_n}{T} = \frac{1}{2\pi} \int_{-\pi}^{\pi} e^{j(\beta \sin x - nx)}\, dx \tag{3-56}$$

This integral can be evaluated only as an infinite series (as was the case in Chap. 2 for the sine integral Si x). It occurs very commonly in many physical problems, however, and so has been tabulated in many books.[1] It is called the *Bessel function of the first kind* and is denoted by the symbol $J_n(\beta)$. [Note from Eq. (3-56) that c_n is a function of both β and n.]

In particular,

$$J_n(\beta) \equiv \frac{1}{2\pi} \int_{-\pi}^{\pi} e^{j(\beta \sin x - nx)}\, dx \tag{3-57}$$

so that

$$c_n = TJ_n(\beta) \tag{3-58}$$

For $n = 0$ we get $c_0 = TJ_0(\beta)$, the d-c component of the Fourier-series representation of the periodic complex exponential of Eq. (3-54). Increasing values of n give the corresponding Fourier coefficients for the higher-frequency terms of the Fourier series. The spectrum of the complex exponential of Eq. (3-54) (and ultimately that of the frequency-modulated signal) will thus be given by the value of the Bessel function and

[1] See, for example, E. Jahnke and F. Emde, "Tables of Functions," Dover Publications, New York, 1945.

will depend on the parameter β. Thus

$$e^{j\beta \sin \omega_m t} = \frac{1}{T} \sum_{n=-\infty}^{\infty} c_n e^{j\omega_n t}$$

$$= \sum_{n=-\infty}^{\infty} J_n(\beta) e^{j\omega_n t} \qquad \omega_n = n\omega_m \tag{3-59}$$

As an example, let $n = 0$. Then

$$J_0(\beta) \equiv \frac{1}{2\pi} \int_{-\pi}^{\pi} e^{j\beta \sin x}\, dx \tag{3-60}$$

is the d-c component of the Fourier series of Eq. (3-59). But

$$e^{j\beta \sin x} = 1 + j\beta \sin x + \frac{(j\beta \sin x)^2}{2!} + \frac{(j\beta \sin x)^3}{3!} + \cdots \tag{3-61}$$

using the series expansion for the exponential.

The power terms in $\sin x$ may be rewritten as sines and cosines of integral multiples of x, so that Eq. (3-61) can also be written

$$e^{j\beta \sin x} = 1 + j\beta \sin x - \frac{\beta^2}{2} \frac{1 - \cos 2x}{2} + \cdots \tag{3-62}$$

If we now integrate over a complete period of 2π radians [as called for by Eq. (3-60)], the terms in $\sin x$, $\cos 2x$, etc., vanish, leaving us with

$$J_0(\beta) = 1 - \frac{\beta^2}{4} + \cdots \tag{3-63}$$

an infinite series in β. [This is of course one method of evaluating the integral of Eq. (3-57).] But a comparison with Eq. (3-53) shows that this is exactly the coefficient of the carrier term of our FM signal, obtained there by a power-series expansion of $\cos(\beta \sin \omega_m t)$. The advantage of the present approach, using a Fourier-series expansion, is that the Bessel function is already tabulated so that we do not have to repeat the evaluation of Eq. (3-57) for different values of n by means of an infinite series.

From Eq. (3-59), the Fourier-series expansion of the complex exponential, we can obtain our desired Fourier series for $\cos(\beta \sin \omega_m t)$ and $\sin(\beta \sin \omega_m t)$. It can be shown, either from the integral definition of $J_n(\beta)$ [Eq. (3-57)] or from the power-series expansion of $J_n(\beta)$, that

$$\begin{aligned} &J_n(\beta) = J_{-n}(\beta) && n \text{ even} \\ \text{and} \quad &J_n(\beta) = -J_{-n}(\beta) && n \text{ odd} \end{aligned} \tag{3-64}$$

Writing out the Fourier series term by term, and using Eq. (3-64) to combine the positive and negative terms of equal magnitude of n, we get

$$e^{j\beta \sin \omega_m t} = J_0(\beta) + 2[J_2(\beta) \cos 2\omega_m t + J_4(\beta) \cos 4\omega_m t + \cdots] + 2j[J_1(\beta) \sin \omega_m t + J_3(\beta) \sin 3\omega_m t + \cdots] \quad (3\text{-}65)$$

But

$$e^{j\beta \sin \omega_m t} = \cos (\beta \sin \omega_m t) + j \sin (\beta \sin \omega_m t) \quad (3\text{-}66)$$

Equating real and imaginary terms, we get

$$\cos (\beta \sin \omega_m t) = J_0(\beta) + 2J_2(\beta) \cos 2\omega_m t + 2J_4(\beta) \cos 4\omega_m t + \cdots \quad (3\text{-}67)$$

and

$$\sin (\beta \sin \omega_m t) = 2J_1(\beta) \sin \omega_1 t + 2J_3(\beta) \sin 3\omega_m t + \cdots \quad (3\text{-}68)$$

Equations (3-67) and (3-68) are the desired Fourier-series expansions for the cosine and sine terms. As noted previously, the cosine term has only the even harmonics of ω_m in its series, the sine term containing the odd harmonics.

The spectral distribution of the frequency-modulated carrier is now readily obtained. As previously written,

$$f_c(t) = \cos \omega_c t \cos (\beta \sin \omega_m t) - \sin \omega_c t \sin (\beta \sin \omega_m t) \quad (3\text{-}69)$$

Using the Fourier-series expansions for the cosine and sine terms, and then utilizing the trigonometric sum and difference formulas (as in the AM analysis), we get

$$\begin{aligned} f_c(t) = J_0(\beta) \cos \omega_c t &- J_1(\beta)[\cos (\omega_c - \omega_m)t - \cos (\omega_c + \omega_m)t] \\ &+ J_2(\beta)[\cos (\omega_c - 2\omega_m)t + \cos (\omega_c + 2\omega_m)t] \\ &- J_3(\beta)[\cos (\omega_c - 3\omega_m)t - \cos (\omega_c + 3\omega_m)t] \\ &+ \cdots \end{aligned} \quad (3\text{-}70)$$

We thus have a time function consisting of a carrier and an infinite number of sidebands, spaced at frequencies $\pm f_m$, $\pm 2f_m$, etc., away from the carrier. This is in contrast to the AM case, where the carrier and only a single set of sidebands existed. The odd sideband frequencies arise from the quadrature term of Eq. (3-69), the even sideband frequencies from the inphase ($\cos \omega_c t$) term. This of course agrees with our previous qualitative discussion based on Fig. 3-25.

The magnitudes of the carrier and sideband terms depend on β, the modulation index, this dependence being expressed by the appropriate Bessel function. Again this is at variance with the AM case, where the carrier magnitude was fixed and the two sidebands varied only with the modulation factor.

We showed previously, from qualitative considerations of the time variation of the function $f_c(t)$, that for $\beta \ll \pi/2$ we should have primarily a carrier and one or two sideband pairs. For $\beta > \pi/2$ we should have increasingly more significant sideband pairs as β increases. The magnitude of the carrier should also decrease rapidly.

We can now verify these qualitative conclusions by referring to plots or tabulations of the Bessel function.[1] As an example, a graph of the functions $J_0(\beta)$, $J_1(\beta)$, $J_2(\beta)$, $J_8(\beta)$, and $J_{16}(\beta)$ is shown in Fig. 3-26. Note that for $\beta > \pi/2$ the value of $J_0(\beta)$ decreases sharply. $J_0(\beta)$ represents the magnitude of the carrier term, so that this result agrees with that obtained from the curves of Fig. 3-25.

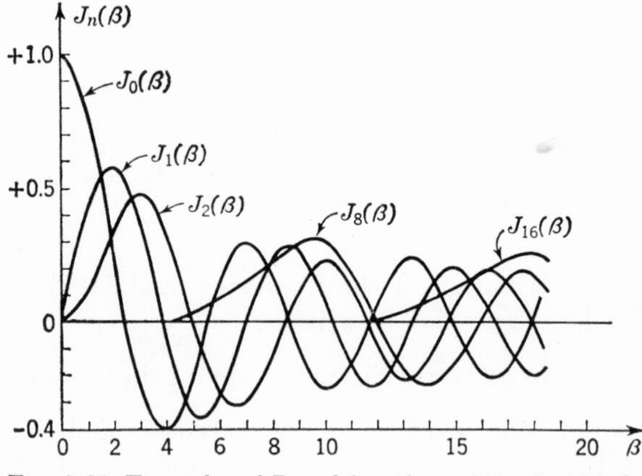

FIG. 3-26. Examples of Bessel functions of the first kind.

For β small ($\beta \ll \pi/2$) the only Bessel functions of significant magnitude are $J_0(\beta)$ and $J_1(\beta)$. The FM wave thus consists essentially of the carrier and the two first-order sideband frequencies. This is of course the narrowband FM case considered previously. As β increases, however, the magnitudes of the higher-order sidebands begin to increase, the carrier magnitude begins to decrease, and the bandwidth required increases. The significant number of sideband terms depends on β, the modulation index. Note that $J_8(\beta)$ is essentially zero up to $\beta = 4$ and then begins to increase to a peak value at $\beta = 9.5$. $J_{16}(\beta)$ begins to increase significantly for $\beta > 12$ and peaks at about $\beta = 18$.

It is apparent from the curves of Fig. 3-26, and can be shown in general, that the higher-order Bessel functions, $J_n(\beta)$ with $n \gg 1$, are essentially zero to the point $\beta \doteq n$. They then increase to a peak, decrease again, and eventually oscillate like damped sinusoids. This means that for $\beta \gg 1$ the number of significant sideband frequencies in the frequency-modulated wave is approximately equal to β. [$J_n(\beta) \doteq 0$, $n > \beta$, so that the corresponding sideband terms are negligible.] Since

[1] See, for example, the various curves and tables in A. Hund, "Frequency Modulation," chap. 1, McGraw-Hill Book Company, Inc., New York, 1942.

the sidebands are all f_m cps apart, and since there are two sets of them, on either side of the carrier, the bandwidth, $2B$, of the FM signal is approximately

$$2B \doteq 2\beta f_m = 2 \frac{\Delta f}{f_m} f_m = 2\,\Delta f \qquad \beta \gg 1 \tag{3-71}$$

This assumes a sinusoidal modulating signal of frequency f_m cps. Δf represents the maximum frequency deviation away from f_c, the unmodulated carrier frequency, and depends on the amplitude of the modulating signal. So for large β the bandwidth is directly proportional to the amplitude of the modulating signal. This is again to be compared with the AM or narrowband FM case where the bandwidth is $2f_m$.

The bandwidth is equal to $2\,\Delta f$ only for very large modulation index. For smaller values of β we can determine the bandwidth by counting the significant number of sidebands. The word *significant* is usually taken to mean those sidebands which have a magnitude at least 1 per cent of the magnitude of the unmodulated carrier. We have been assuming an unmodulated carrier of unit amplitude ($\cos \omega_c t$), so that the significant sidebands will be those for which $J_n(\beta) > 0.01$. The number will vary with β and can be determined readily from tabulated values of the Bessel function.

An example of such a determination is shown by the following table for values of β up to 2:

TABLE OF SIGNIFICANT SIDEBANDS

β	$J_0(\beta)$	$J_1(\beta)$	$J_2(\beta)$	$J_3(\beta)$	$J_4(\beta)$	No. of sidebands	Bandwidth
0.01	1.00	0.005	....	....	....	1	$2f_m$
0.20	0.99	0.100	....	....	....	1	$2f_m$
0.50	0.94	0.24	0.03	....	....	2	$4f_m$
1.00	0.77	0.44	0.11	0.02	....	3	$6f_m$
2.00	0.22	0.58	0.35	0.13	0.03	4	$8f_m$

Using such a table, we can plot bandwidth vs. the modulation index β. Such a curve has been drawn in Fig. 3-27. The ordinate is given in units of bandwidth/Δf, and the curve is seen to approach a value of 2 for large β.

We are now in a position to make some calculations of the required bandwidth for typical sinusoidal signals. Since the bandwidth ultimately varies with Δf, the frequency deviation, or the *amplitude* of the modulating signal, some limit must be put on this amplitude to avoid excessive bandwidth. The FCC has fixed the maximum value of Δf at 75 kc for commercial FM broadcasting stations. What does this imply in the way of required bandwidth? If we take the modulating frequency f_m to be 15 kc (typically the maximum audio frequency in FM transmission), $\beta = 5$, or the required bandwidth is 240 kc, from Fig. 3-27. (Alternatively, for $\beta = 5$, there are eight significant sideband frequencies, or $2 \times 8 \times 15 = 240$ kc is the bandwidth required.) For $f_m < 15$ kc (the lower audio frequencies) β increases above 5, and the bandwidth eventually approaches $2\,\Delta f = 150$ kc. So it is the *highest* modulating frequency that determines the required bandwidth. (These are the extreme cases, since $\Delta f = 75$ kc corresponds to the maximum possible amplitude of the modulating signal.)

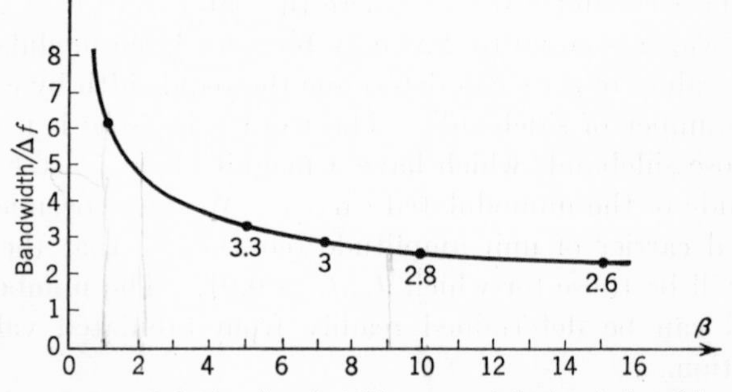

FIG. 3-27. Frequency-modulation bandwidth vs. modulation index (sinusoidal modulating signal).

Frequency modulation is used for transmission of the sound channel in commercial TV, and the maximum frequency deviation there (corresponding to the maximum amplitude of the modulating signal) has been fixed at 25 kc by the FCC. For a 15-kc audio signal this gives $\beta = 1.7$, or a bandwidth of 110 kc. The lower audio frequencies require bandwidths well within this limit, for with f_m decreasing and $\beta > 15$, the bandwidth required approaches $2\,\Delta f = 50$ kc.

The relatively large bandwidths required for commercial FM, as compared with AM sound transmission, are the price one has to pay to obtain significant improvement in noise and interference rejection. This question will be discussed in detail in Chap. 6.

The amplitude spectra of a frequency-modulated signal are shown plotted in Fig. 3-28 for $\beta = 0.2$, 1, 5, 10. The sinusoidal modulating signal is assumed to be of constant modulation frequency f_m, so that β is proportional to the signal amplitude. The amplitude of the spectral line at frequency $f_c \pm nf_m$ is given by $J_n(\beta)$. If the amplitude of the modulating signal is fixed (for example, $\Delta f = 75$ kc for all signals) and different audio frequencies are considered, β increases as f_m decreases and we get spectrum plots similar to those of Fig. 3-28. For these plots Δf is fixed, however, so that we get a picture of more and more spectral lines

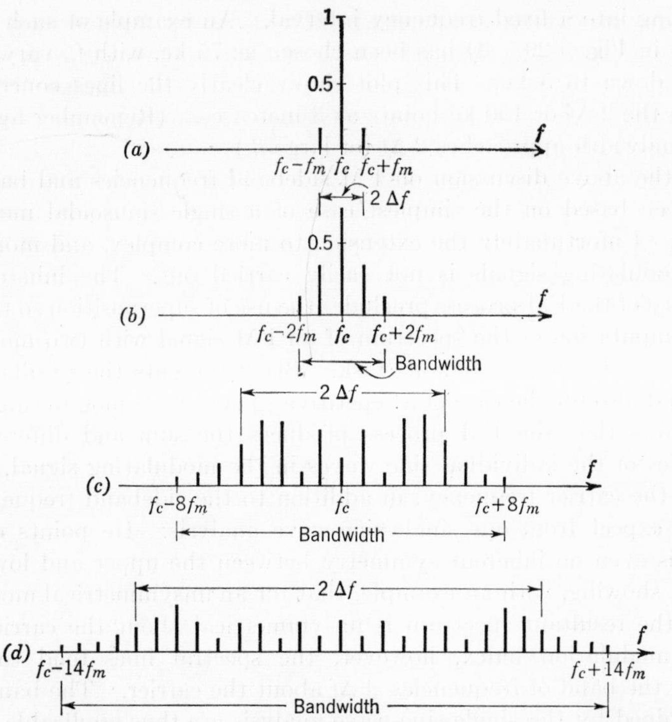

FIG. 3-28. Amplitude-frequency spectrum, FM signal (sinusoidal modulating signal, f_m fixed, amplitude varying). (*a*) $\beta = 0.2$; (*b*) $\beta = 1$; (*c*) $\beta = 5$; (*d*) $\beta = 10$.

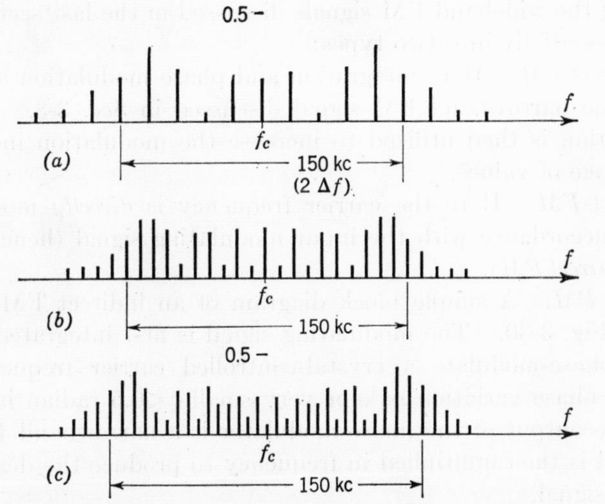

FIG. 3-29. Amplitude-frequency spectrum, FM signal (amplitude of Δf fixed, f_m decreasing). (*a*) f_m = 15 kc (β = 5); (*b*) f_m = 7.5 kc (β = 10); (*c*) f_m = 5 kc (β = 15).

crowding into a fixed frequency interval. An example of such a plot is shown in Fig. 3-29. Δf has been chosen as 75 kc, with f_m varying from 15 kc down to 5 kc. This plot shows clearly the lines concentrating within the 2 Δf or 150-kc points as β increases. (Remember again that the bandwidth approaches 2 Δf for large β.)

All the above discussion on FM sideband frequencies and bandwidth has been based on the simplest case of a single sinusoidal modulating signal. Unfortunately the extension to more complex, and more realistic, modulating signals is not easily carried out. The inherent nonlinearity of the FM process precludes the use of superposition so that even the computation of the spectrum of an FM signal with two modulating sine waves becomes a tedious task. Black presents the results for this case and also for the case of a repetitive square-wave modulating signal.[1] He shows that the FM process produces the sum and difference frequencies of the individual sine waves in the modulating signal, arrayed about the carrier frequency, in addition to the sideband frequencies we would expect from our single-sine-wave analysis. He points out that there is even no inherent symmetry between the upper and lower sidebands, showing, with an example, that for an unsymmetrical modulating wave the resultant spectrum is unsymmetrical about the carrier. For large modulation index, however, the spectral lines tend to cluster within the band of frequencies $\pm\Delta f$ about the carrier. The bandwidths determined by the single-sine-wave analysis are thus applicable to more complex modulating signals and so provide useful engineering information.

3-10. Generation of Frequency-modulated Signals. The methods of generating the wideband FM signals discussed in the last section can be grouped essentially into two types:

1. *Indirect FM.* Here integration and phase modulation are used to produce the narrowband FM signal discussed in Sec. 3-8. Frequency multiplication is then utilized to increase the modulation index to the desired range of values.

2. *Direct FM.* Here the carrier frequency is *directly* modulated or varied in accordance with the input modulating signal (hence the classification *direct FM*).

Indirect FM. A simple block diagram of an indirect FM system is shown in Fig. 3-30. The modulating signal is first integrated and then used to phase-modulate a crystal-controlled carrier frequency. The maximum phase variation is kept very small (<0.5 radian in practice) so that the output of the phase modulator is a narrowband FM signal. This signal is then multiplied in frequency to produce the desired wideband FM signal.

[1] Black, *op. cit.*, pp. 195–202.

At the output of the phase modulator the FM signal has the form

$$f_{c_1}(t) = \cos\,[\omega_{c_1}t + \theta_1(t)] \qquad \theta_1(t) = k\int f(t)\,dt \tag{3-72}$$

For a sine-wave modulating signal this would be

$$f_{c_1}(t) = \cos\,(\omega_{c_1}t + \beta_1 \sin \omega_m t) \qquad \beta_1 = \frac{\Delta f}{f_m} \tag{3-73}$$

The signal frequency is multiplied n times by the frequency multiplier so that at its output the signal appears in the form

$$f_c(t) = \cos n\,[\omega_{c_1}t + \theta_1(t)] \tag{3-74}$$

For the sine-wave modulating signal, then,

$$\begin{aligned} f_c(t) &= \cos\,(n\omega_{c_1}t + n\beta_1 \sin \omega_m t) \\ &= \cos\,(\omega_c t + \beta \sin \omega_m t) \qquad \beta = n\beta_1,\ \omega_c = n\omega_{c_1} \end{aligned} \tag{3-75}$$

By picking n appropriately β may be set at any desired value.

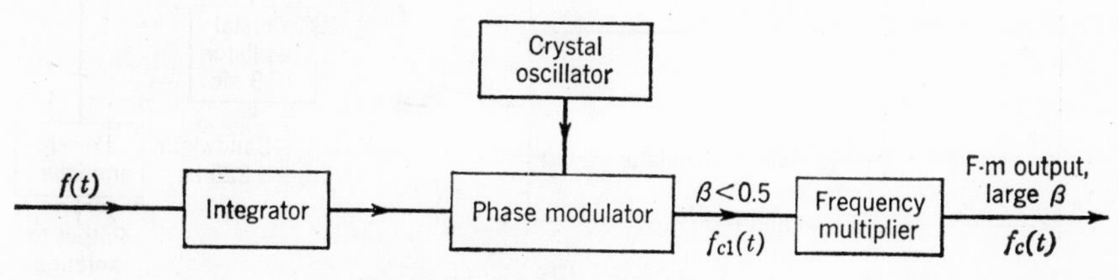

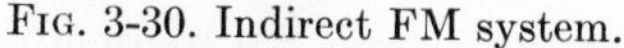
FIG. 3-30. Indirect FM system.

As an example, assume that the audio signal contains frequencies of 50 cps to 15 kc. The maximum frequency deviation Δf is 75 kc. β then ranges from 1,500 ($f_m = 50$ cps) down to 5 ($f_m = 15$ kc).

We indicated, in Sec. 3-8, that $\beta_1 < 0.2$ radian corresponds to a narrowband FM signal. In practice $\beta_1 < 0.5$ radian is used. The resultant signal has some AM associated with it (5 per cent residual AM distortion for $\beta = 0.5$), but amplitude limiting in the frequency multipliers is utilized to eliminate most of this undesired AM.

Since a *maximum* modulation index of 0.5 radian is called for at the phase-modulator output, this must be associated with the *lowest-frequency* modulating signal. For example, if $\beta_1 = 0.5$ radian for a 50-cps signal, $\beta_1 = 0.5/300$ radian for a 15 kc signal. ($\beta_1 = \Delta f/f_m$; $\Delta f = 75$ kc.) The narrowband FM signal must then be multiplied in frequency 3,000 times to produce the desired modulation index at the output:

$$n = \frac{\beta}{\beta_1} = \frac{1{,}500}{0.5} = 3{,}000$$

Alternatively, the maximum frequency deviation Δf_1 will be 75 kc/3,000 = 25 cps at the input to the multiplier and 75 kc at the output.

Note then that, although the required *bandwidth* of an FM signal depends on the *highest* modulating frequency (as shown in the previous section), the choice of *modulation index* and required frequency multiplication depend on the *lowest* modulating frequency. For this reason 50 cps is usually chosen as the lowest audio frequency to be passed in an indirect FM system. Still lower modulating frequencies would require

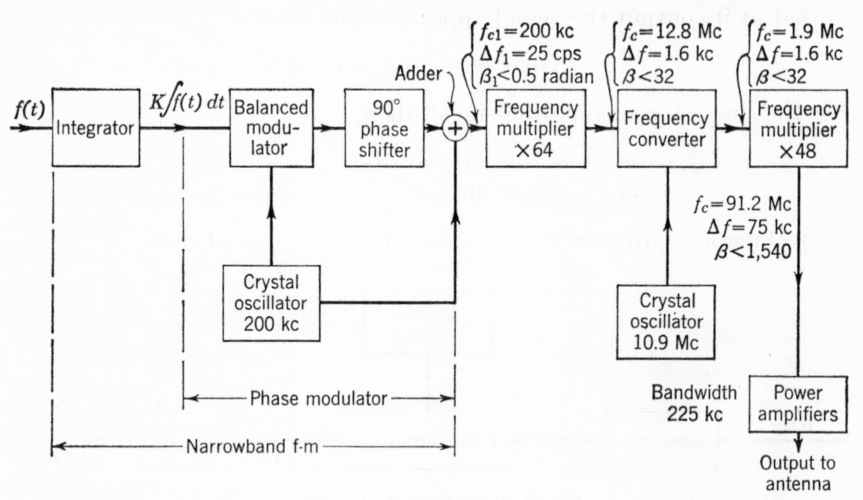

FIG. 3-31. An Armstrong-type indirect FM transmitter (simplified diagram).

excessively large frequency multiplication and attendant complications in the circuitry of the system.

A straight frequency multiplication of 3,000 would produce inordinately high carrier frequencies at the output of the multipliers. (For example, if f_c = 200 kc, f_c = 600 Mc.) In practice, then, a combination of both frequency multiplication and frequency conversion is used to produce a wideband FM signal at the desired carrier frequency. The frequency converters employed are essentially those discussed previously in connection with AM demodulators. They produce at their output the difference frequencies between the input signal and an injected sinusoidal signal. This serves to shift the FM spectrum downward to a specified carrier frequency but keeps the multiplied modulation index intact.

The points discussed above are all incorporated in the Armstrong indirect FM transmitter. E. H. Armstrong was one of the first engineers to recognize the possible merits of FM broadcasting and pioneered in many of the important developments in the field. As A. Hund points out in his book, "Frequency Modulation,"[1] it was Armstrong's demon-

[1] *Op. cit.*, p. 231.

stration of the merits of FM in a paper presented at an IRE meeting in 1935 that stirred up interest in the field and eventually resulted in the recognition of the capabilities of FM transmission.

A block diagram of an Armstrong-type transmitter is shown in Fig. 3-31. (A detailed diagram of the original Armstrong transmitter and a thorough discussion of its component parts may be found in Hund's book and in the literature cited there.) The transmitter shown operates at an unmodulated carrier frequency of 91.2 Mc with a maximum frequency deviation of 75 kc. The transmitter is crystal-controlled, starting

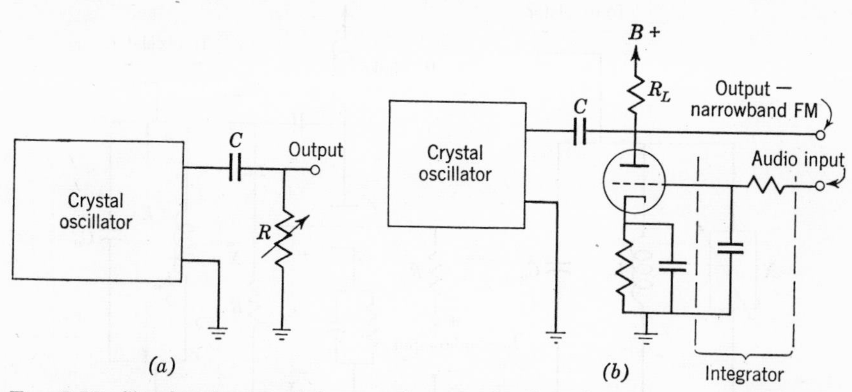

FIG. 3-32. Simple phase modulator and narrowband FM system. (*a*) Method of obtaining phase modulation; (*b*) more detailed circuit.

at the controlled carrier frequency of 200 kc. There is a total frequency multiplication of $64 \times 48 = 3{,}072$ so that the maximum modulation index at the multiplier input can be fixed at 0.5 radian. An injected frequency of 10.9 Mc is used to shift the carrier frequency down from 12.8 to 1.9 Mc between multiplier sections.

The combination integrator–phase-modulator system used before frequency multiplication is just the narrowband FM system using a balanced modulator that was described in Sec. 3-8 and outlined in block-diagram form in Fig. 3-22*c*.

The use of a balanced modulator and quadrature carrier to produce a phase-modulated carrier is one of several methods that may be used in a phase-modulation or narrowband FM system. The simplest method conceptually is to vary the carrier phase directly in accordance with the modulating-signal input. A simple method of doing this is shown in Fig. 3-32. The output of a crystal oscillator is applied to an RC voltage divider in Fig. 3-32*a*. If R is varied at the desired audio rate, the output voltage will vary in both phase and amplitude. The amplitude variations can be reduced by making $R \gg 1/\omega C$, or by using a constant-impedance phase shifter. Figure 3-32*b* indicates one method of varying

R at the desired audio rate. If $R_L \gg r_p$ for the tube, the output impedance of the circuit is effectively r_p. This varies with grid voltage, so that changes in the input signal (at a rate slow compared with the carrier frequency) reflect themselves in a phase-modulated output. An RC integrating circuit is also shown in Fig. 3-32*b* so that the output is actually a narrowband FM signal.

Direct FM. As apparent from the terminology used, direct FM systems are those in which the modulating signal directly varies the carrier

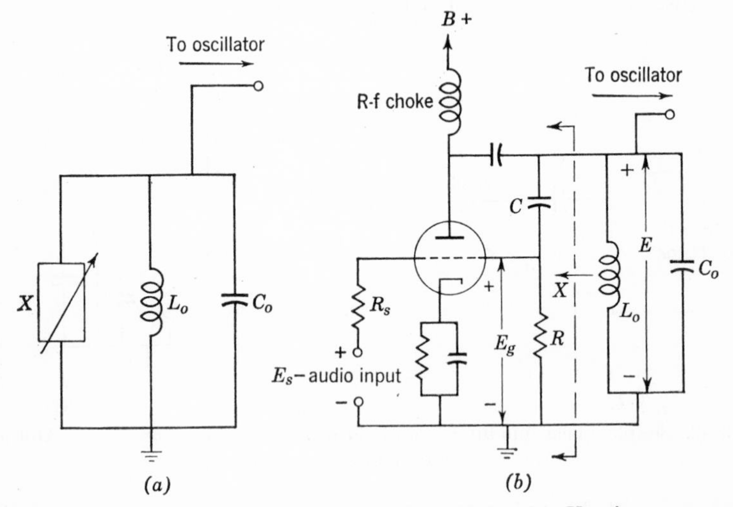

FIG. 3-33. Reactance-tube modulator for direct FM. (*a*) Varying resonant frequency by variable reactance; (*b*) reactance-tube modulator used to produce variable reactance.

frequency. These direct FM systems normally require a much smaller amount of frequency multiplication than the indirect systems. Because the carrier frequency must be directly varied, however, crystal-controlled oscillators cannot be used and electronic or mechanical frequency-stabilization techniques using feedback must be employed.

At the heart of the direct FM transmitter is the device employed to vary the carrier frequency. The carrier frequency is normally generated by an oscillator whose frequency-determining circuit is a high-Q resonant circuit. Variations in the inductance or capacitance of this resonant circuit will then change the resonant frequency or the oscillator frequency. The *reactance-tube modulator* is commonly used to produce these variations in the tuned-circuit reactance in accordance with the modulating-signal input. Figure 3-33*a* shows the oscillator tuned circuit with a variable reactance connected in parallel. Figure 3-33*b* is one example of a reactance-tube modulator that simulates the variation of a reactance.

The operation of this circuit is readily explained. Assume first that zero audio signal is applied. With $1/\omega C \gg R$, and also $R \ll R_s$, the current through R leads E, the voltage across the tuned circuit, by 90°. Then E_g also leads E by 90°. But E_g is the grid voltage of the tube and causes an additional current $g_m E_g$ to flow which also leads E by 90°.

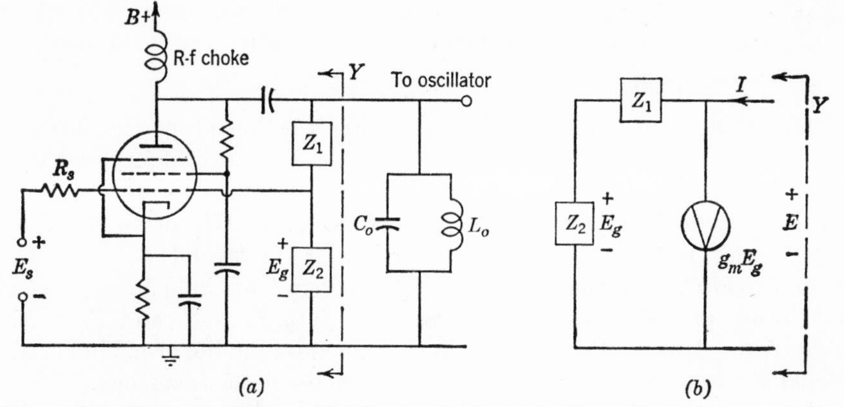

FIG. 3-34. Reactance-tube modulator analysis. (*a*) Generalized reactance-tube modulator; (*b*) simplified equivalent circuit ($g_p = 0$, $R_s \gg Z_2$).

This current thus appears to be drawn by an additional capacitive susceptance given by $g_m E_g/E \doteq g_m R/(1/j\omega C) = j\omega(g_m RC)$. The total effective capacitance of the tuned circuit under zero signal conditions is thus

$$C_0 + C + g_m RC \doteq C_0 + g_m RC \qquad g_m R \gg 1$$

Slow variation of the audio input voltage E_s (slow compared with the oscillator frequency) now serves to shift the grid bias at the audio rate. g_m, the tube transconductance, varies with grid bias, causing a corresponding variation $g_m RC$ in the effective capacitance introduced across the tuned circuit.

The reactance-tube modulator of Fig. 3-33*b* is one of four possible variations that may be used. Two of these introduce an equivalent capacitance varying with g_m, the other two an equivalent inductance. The more general form of the reactance-tube modulator, incorporating all four cases and using a pentode for the tube, is shown in Fig. 3-34*a*. Figure 3-34*b* is the same circuit redrawn for small variations about the zero-signal case, so that the linear incremental model (equivalent circuit) of the tube may be used. The plate conductance g_p has been neglected, and we assume $R_s \gg Z_2$.

From the circuit of Fig. 3-34b we note that the admittance Y is given by

$$Y = \frac{I}{E} = \frac{1}{Z_1 + Z_2} + \frac{g_m E_g}{E} \qquad g_p \doteq 0,\ R_s \gg Z_2 \tag{3-76}$$

But

$$E_g = \frac{Z_2}{Z_1 + Z_2} E \tag{3-77}$$

so that

$$Y = \frac{1}{Z_1 + Z_2}(1 + g_m Z_2) \doteq \frac{g_m Z_2}{Z_1} \tag{3-78}$$

if $Z_1 \gg Z_2$ and $g_m Z_2 \gg 1$.

The admittance seen across the tuned circuit is thus proportional to g_m under the assumptions made. If either Z_2 or Z_1 is a reactance and the other impedance a resistance, we have as Y a susceptance proportional to g_m. For example, if $Z_1 = 1/j\omega C$, $Z_2 = R$, $Y = j\omega g_m CR$, or an effective capacitance is seen, as shown before. If $Z_1 = R$ and $Z_2 = 1/j\omega C$, $Y = g_m/j\omega RC$, and the modulator "looks like" an inductance. The two other possibilities are of course $Z_1 = j\omega L$, $Z_2 = R$, and $Z_1 = R$, $Z_2 = j\omega L$. It is worth noting again that the input audio, or modulating, signal serves only to vary g_m and in turn the oscillator frequency.

An example of a typical reactance-tube modulator calculation is instructive. Assume that the carrier frequency f_c is 5 Mc and that the frequency deviation Δf is 10 kc. The reactance-tube circuit of Fig. 3-33 is to be used. What values of capacitances C and C_0 and resistance R shall be used? What is the required variation Δg_m in transconductance to provide the desired frequency deviation? What grid-voltage variation will in turn produce the transconductance variation?

For the reactance-tube circuit of Fig. 3-33, $Z_1 = 1/j\omega C$ and $Z_2 = R$. With $R \ll 1/\omega C$ and $g_m \gg 1$ the reactance-tube circuit acts as an effective capacitance $C' = g_m RC$, appearing in parallel with the oscillator tuned-circuit parameters C_0 and L_0.

The resonant frequency of the over-all tuned circuit, including capacitance C', is given by

$$\omega^2 = \frac{1}{L_0(C_0 + C')} = \frac{1}{L_0 C_0 (1 + C'/C_0)} \tag{3-79}$$

Now assume that the effective capacitance C' is small compared with capacitance C_0. With this assumption the resonant frequency can be approximated by

$$\omega = \omega_0 \sqrt{\frac{1}{1 + C'/C_0}} \doteq \omega_0 \left(1 - \frac{C'}{2C_0}\right) \qquad \omega_0{}^2 \equiv \frac{1}{L_0 C_0},\ C' \ll C_0 \tag{3-80}$$

The equation for resonant frequency as a function of the transconductance g_m is thus

$$\omega \doteq \omega_0 \left(1 - \frac{g_m RC}{2C_0}\right) \qquad g_m RC \ll C_0 \tag{3-81}$$

The resonant frequency varies linearly with g_m provided that the effective capacitance $g_m RC$ is small compared with capacitance C_0.

Now let $g_m = g_{m0} + \Delta g_m$, with g_{m0} the transconductance with zero signal (the grid voltage is then just the grid bias) and Δg_m the variation in g_m due to a change in grid voltage. The transconductance–grid-bias

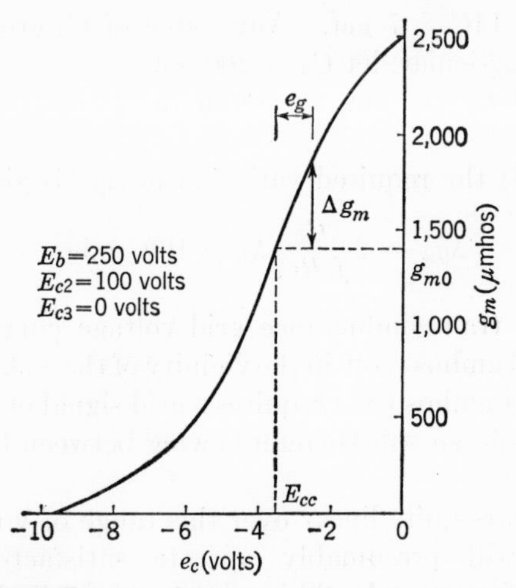

FIG. 3-35. Transconductance–grid-voltage curve 6SJ7.

curve for the 6SJ7 is drawn as an example in Fig. 3-35. With a grid bias E_{cc} of -3.5 volts, g_{m0} is 1,400 μmhos. Δg_m represents variations in g_m about this point. The total grid voltage is given by $e_c = E_{cc} + e_g$, with e_g the signal component of the voltage applied to the grid.

With zero signal applied, $g_m = g_{m0}$ and the resonant frequency is just ω_c, the unmodulated carrier frequency. Thus

$$\omega_c \doteq \omega_0 \left(1 - \frac{g_{m0} RC}{2C_0}\right) \qquad \omega_0 = \frac{1}{\sqrt{L_0 C_0}} \tag{3-82}$$

With a signal applied

$$\omega = \omega_c - \frac{\omega_0 RC}{2C_0} \Delta g_m = \omega_c - \Delta\omega \tag{3-83}$$

from Eq. (3-81). The frequency deviation Δf in cycles per second is thus given by

$$\Delta f = \frac{f_0 RC}{2C_0} \Delta g_m \tag{3-84}$$

The required variation in g_m, Δg_m can be found from Eq. (3-84).

For the problem under consideration $f_c = 5$ Mc, and $\Delta f = 10$ kc. Assume that a 6SJ7 tube is to be used for the reactance-tube modulator with the grid bias chosen at -3.5 volts. (This gives a reasonably linear variation of g_m with e_c, as is apparent from Fig. 3-35.) Then $g_{m0} = 1{,}400$ μmhos. To satisfy the condition $g_m R \gg 1$, let $R = 10{,}000$ ohms. Since we must also have $1/\omega C \gg R$ at the 5-Mc carrier frequency, let $C = 0.5$ $\mu\mu$f. C_0 is now chosen to satisfy the condition

$$C_0 \gg C' = g_m RC$$

In this case $C' = 14C = 7$ $\mu\mu$f. Any value of C_0 greater than 100 $\mu\mu$f will suffice. In particular, let $C_0 = 200$ $\mu\mu$f.

The inductance L_0 can now be found from either Eq. (3-79) or Eq. (3-82).

From Eq. (3-84) the required variation in Δg_m is given by

$$\Delta g_m = 2 \frac{C_0}{f_0 RC} \Delta f = 160 \ \mu\text{mhos}$$

The slope of the transconductance–grid-voltage curve for the 6SJ7 is approximately 400 μmhos/volt in the vicinity of the -3.5-volt 1,400-μmho point. $\Delta g_m = 160$ μmhos thus requires a grid signal of approximately 0.4 volt. The grid voltage will therefore swing between limits of -3.1 and -3.9 volts.

The curve appears quite linear over this range of voltages, and so the reactance tube will presumably operate satisfactorily. To ensure linearity of operation, Δg_m should be chosen as small as possible. A different set of parameters (larger R and C for example) might perhaps be chosen to decrease the required variation in g_m, and hence grid voltage.

Some additional reactance-tube calculations are included among the problems for this chapter. They include the use of a different tube, the 6CH8, and a reactance-tube circuit with R and C interchanged to provide an effective inductance.

The reactance-tube modulator is not the only means employed to frequency-modulate a carrier in a direct manner. The Miller-effect capacitance of a tube (proportional to the tube gain and hence to g_m) can be used to change the effective capacitance of the oscillator tuned circuit. The capacitance cannot be varied over as wide a range as is possible with the reactance-tube modulator, however, so that the frequency deviations obtainable are not as great.

Another modulator used is the diode modulator. Here the effective resistance of a diode is varied at the modulating-signal rate. The diode is connected in series with a capacitor, and with proper choice of the components the effective capacitance of the series combination may be made to vary in the desired manner. This method produces less noise and distortion than does the reactance-tube modulator, and the frequency deviation can be made more nearly proportional to the modulating signal. But it is again not capable of as large a frequency deviation as the reactance-tube modulator.

A block diagram of a typical direct FM transmitter is shown in Fig. 3-36. This transmitter incorporates the reactance-tube modulator, uses a frequency multiplication of 18, and employs a feedback comparison

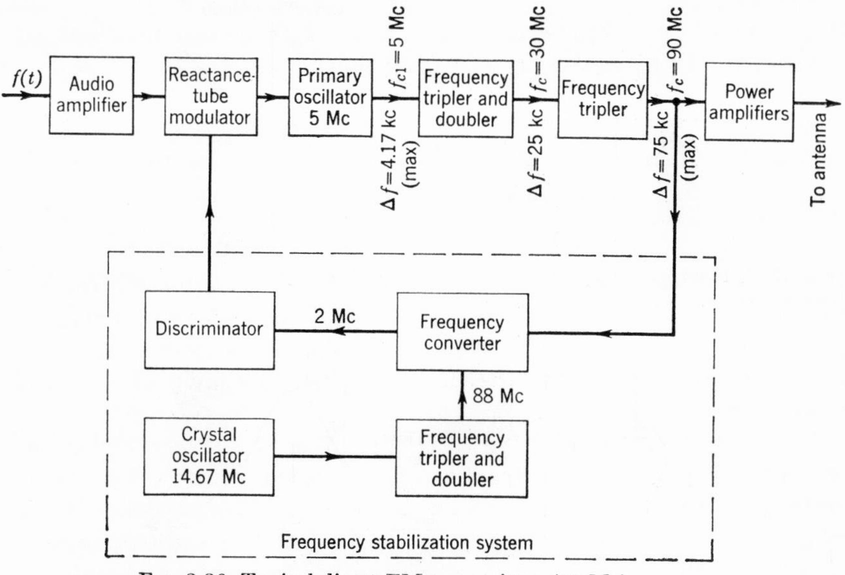

FIG. 3-36. Typical direct FM transmitter (90 Mc).

method to stabilize the unmodulated oscillator frequency. (The discriminator used to effect the comparison converts frequency variations to amplitude variations and will be discussed in the next section.) A preemphasis circuit is usually also incorporated in the transmitter. This circuit, in conjunction with a deemphasis circuit in the receiver, serves to help reduce receiver noise. Discussion of these circuits is deferred until Chap. 6.

3-11. Frequency Demodulation. Frequency demodulation, the process of converting a frequency-modulated signal back to the original modulating signal, can be carried out in a variety of ways. Ultimately, however, the process used must provide an output voltage (or current) whose *amplitude* is *linearly* proportional to the *frequency* of the input FM signal. The term *frequency discriminator* is commonly used to characterize a device providing this frequency-amplitude conversion. An ideal characteristic for such a device is depicted in Fig. 3-37*b*.

The simple single-tuned circuit is an approximation to such a frequency discriminator. If the circuit is detuned so that the unmodulated carrier frequency lies on the positively sloping part of the amplitude-frequency characteristic and the frequency variations occur within a small region about the unmodulated carrier, the amplitude of the output wave will follow the instantaneous frequency of the input. The tuned circuit and its characteristic are shown in Fig. 3-38. The region over which the

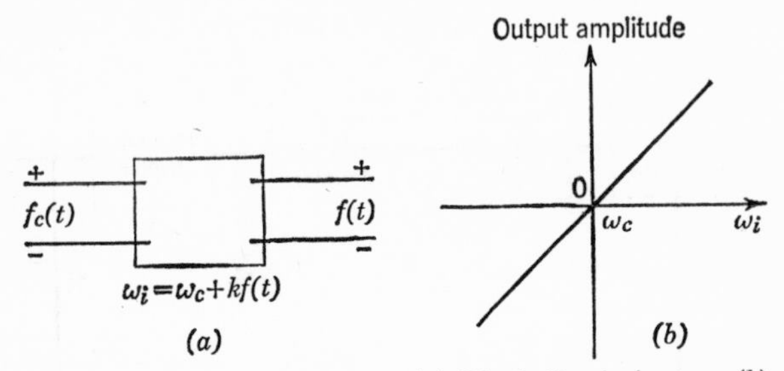

FIG. 3-37. Ideal frequency discriminator. (a) Ideal discriminator; (b) discriminator characteristic.

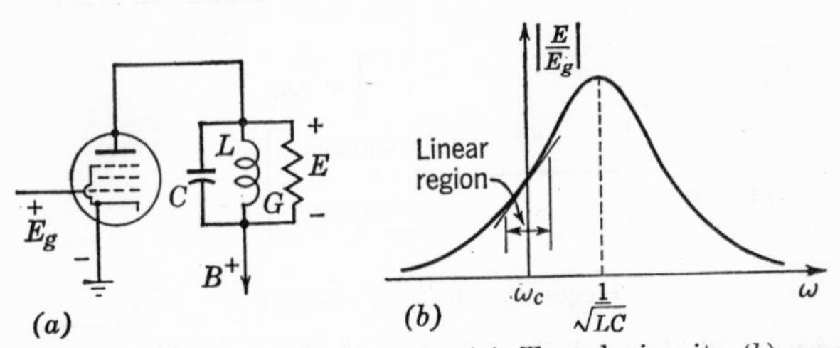

FIG. 3-38. Tuned circuit as discriminator. (a) Tuned circuit; (b) amplitude characteristic.

characteristics are very nearly linear must be wide enough to cover the maximum frequency deviation (± 75 kc for commercial FM).

The single-tuned circuit is not very practical as a frequency demodulator, however, for variations in the output voltage are superimposed on the large nonzero signal present with an unmodulated carrier. This signal must be balanced out to attain the desired characteristics of Fig. 3-37*b*. The balancing procedure can be accomplished, just as was done with the balanced modulator, by connecting two tuned circuits in a balanced or "back-to-back" arrangement.

More commonly, however, the discriminator takes the balanced form of Fig. 3-39 and utilizes a double-tuned circuit with transformer coupling. In the idealized form of Fig. 3-39*a* the diode-capacitor combination serve as peak detectors. The output of the upper capacitor is thus the peak value of $E_1 + E_2$. The corresponding voltage across the lower capacitor is the peak value of $E_1 - E_2$. In the actual circuit of Fig. 3-39*b* the balanced diodes and their associated *RC* filter circuits serve as envelope detectors, just like the envelope detectors considered in the section on AM envelope detection. The output signal thus represents an l-f (audio) signal whose amplitude is proportional to the instantaneous frequency of the input FM signal.

Coil *L* in Fig. 3-39*b* is an open circuit at the carrier frequency (it provides a d-c return path for the diodes), while capacitor C_c is a coupling

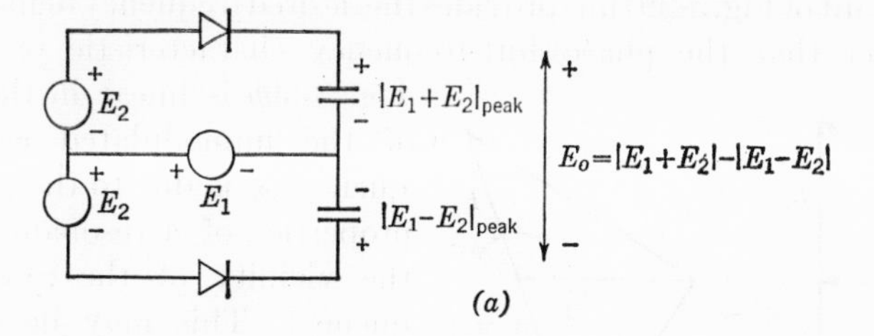

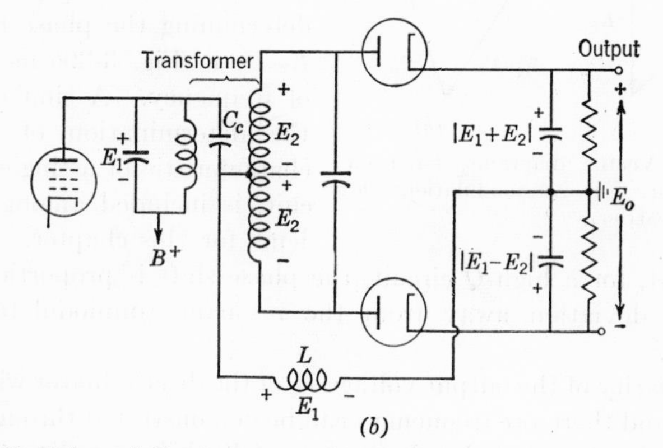

FIG. 3-39. Balanced discriminator. (*a*) Idealized form; (*b*) actual circuit.

capacitor and has zero impedance at the carrier frequency. The secondary of the transformer is center-tapped as shown.

With both primary and secondary tuned to the unmodulated carrier frequency the secondary voltage E_2 will lead the primary voltage E_1 by 90°. This is shown in Fig. 3-40*a*.

The r-f voltage across the upper diode and its associated circuit is $E_1 + E_2$, from Fig. 3-39*b*, while the r-f voltage across the lower diode and circuit is $E_1 - E_2$ (*L* is an open circuit at radio frequency). With the diodes assumed short circuits the envelopes of each of these voltages appear across the diode *RC* combinations. The output audio voltage is thus

$$E_o = |E_1 + E_2| - |E_1 - E_2| \tag{3-85}$$

just as in the idealized case of Fig. 3-39*a*.

From Fig. 3-40*a*, $|E_1 + E_2|$ and $|E_1 - E_2|$ are equal for the unmodulated carrier, and the output is zero. As the carrier frequency changes, however, the phase of E_2 shifts with respect to E_1, $|E_1 + E_2|$ and $|E_1 - E_2|$ become unbalanced, as shown in Fig. 3-40*b*, and an output voltage appears. For small frequency deviations the phase shift of E_2 will be proportional to the frequency deviation. The output voltage E_o will be very nearly proportional to the frequency deviation if its variation is not too great.

The circuit of Fig. 3-39 thus provides the desired frequency demodulation.

The fact that the phase-shift-frequency characteristic of E_2/E_1 in Fig. 3-39*b* is linear in the vicinity of the unmodulated carrier frequency ω_c is due to the phase-shift properties of a resonant circuit in the vicinity of the resonant frequency. This may be shown by determining the phase response of E_2/E_1 in Fig. 3-39*b* as a function of frequency. A similar problem, the determination of the phase characteristic of a single-tuned circuit, is included among the problems for this chapter. It is there shown that, for a high-Q circuit, the phase shift is proportional to the frequency deviation away from the resonant (unmodulated carrier) frequency.

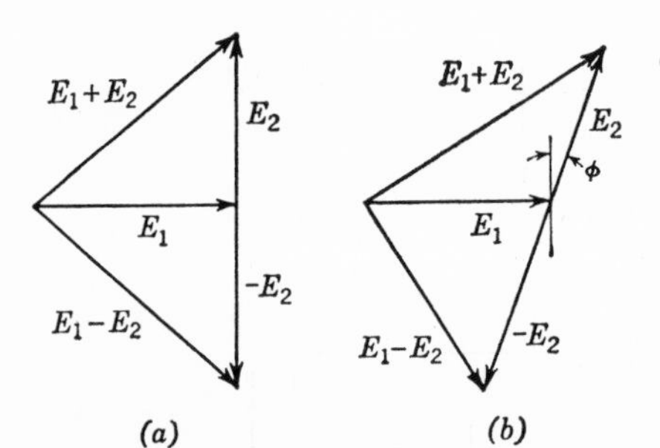

FIG. 3-40. Vector diagrams, balanced discriminator. (*a*) No modulation; (*b*) modulated carrier.

The linearity of the output voltage E_o of the discriminator with changes in phase (and therefore frequency) can be demonstrated through a simple analysis. Assume that the phase angle of E_2 shifts ϕ radians away from balance (Fig. 3-40*b*). The vector ratio E_2/E_1 may then be written

$$\frac{E_2}{E_1} = Ke^{j(\pi/2-\phi)} \tag{3-86}$$

where K is the ratio of the magnitudes of the two voltages. The output voltage E_0 of the discriminator becomes

$$\begin{aligned} E_0 &= |E_1 + E_2| - |E_1 - E_2| \\ &= |E_1(1 + Ke^{j(\pi/2-\phi)})| - |E_1(1 - Ke^{j(\pi/2-)\phi)}| \\ &= |E_1| \left\{ \sqrt{\left[1 + K\cos\left(\frac{\pi}{2} - \phi\right)\right]^2 + \left[K\sin\left(\frac{\pi}{2} - \phi\right)\right]^2} \right. \\ &\qquad \left. - \sqrt{\left[1 - K\cos\left(\frac{\pi}{2} - \phi\right)\right]^2 + \left[K\sin\left(\frac{\pi}{2} - \phi\right)\right]^2} \right\} \end{aligned} \tag{3-87}$$

After some simple trigonometric manipulations Eq. (3-87) reduces to the following form,

$$E_0 = |E_1| \sqrt{1 + K^2} \left(\sqrt{1 + a \sin \phi} - \sqrt{1 - a \sin \phi}\right) \qquad (3\text{-}88)$$

where $a \equiv 2K/(1 + K^2)$.

Now assume $\phi \ll \pi/2$. Then $\sin \phi \doteq \phi$. The parameter a ranges from 0 ($K = 0$ or K very large) to a maximum value of 1 ($K = 1$).

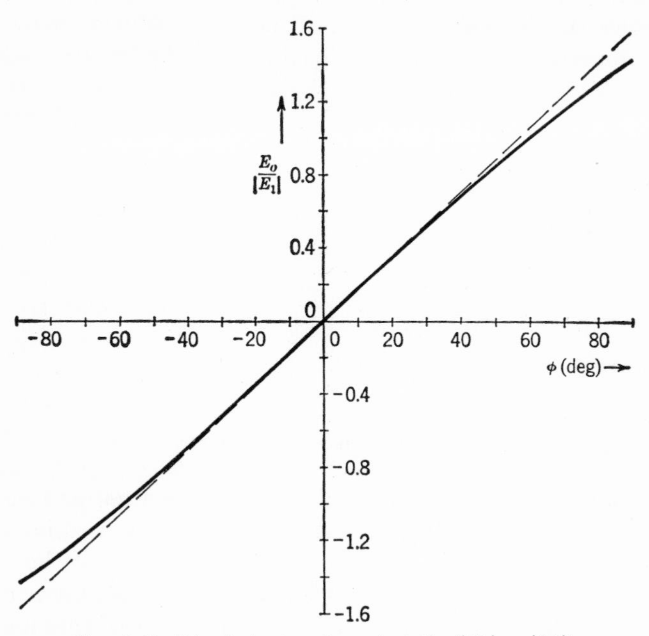

FIG. 3-41. Discriminator characteristic ($|E_1| = |E_2|$).

Then, for $\sin \phi \ll 1$, $a \sin \phi \ll 1$, and $\sqrt{1 + a \sin \phi} \doteq 1 + a\phi/2$. Equation (3-88) then reduces for this case to the very simple form

$$E_0 \doteq |E_1| \frac{2K}{\sqrt{1 + K^2}} \phi \qquad \phi \ll \frac{\pi}{2} \qquad (3\text{-}89)$$

The output voltage is thus proportional to ϕ for small angular deviations as previously stated. The actual limit on ϕ for linear operation of the discriminator may be determined by plotting Eq. (3-88). The worst possible case occurs for $K = 1$ (E_1 and E_2 of Figs. 3-39 and 3-40 equal). The discriminator characteristic of Fig. 3-41 has been plotted for this case. Note that, for $\phi < 10°$, the discriminator output voltage is very nearly linear with ϕ.

Implicit in the discriminator analysis has been the assumption of complete balance. The same voltage, E_2, must be assumed applied to each diode, and the diodes must in turn be identical.

In addition, the discriminator circuits of Fig. 3-39 are sensitive to amplitude changes. The actual output voltage varies not only with the phase shift ϕ_1 but also with the amplitudes E_1 and E_2 of the applied voltages. This is apparent from Fig. 3-40 and from Eqs. (3-88) and (3-89). Although the transmitted FM signal is usually maintained at constant amplitude, the received signal commonly varies in amplitude because of fading, noise and interference, etc. These amplitude variations must first be suppressed before the FM signal is applied to the discriminator.

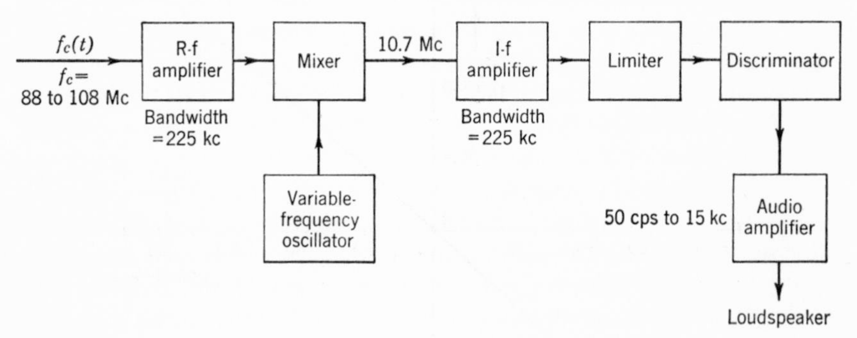

FIG. 3-42. Typical FM receiver.

The amplitude variations are usually removed in a *limiter* stage before the discriminator. (Two limiter stages are frequently used in practice.) This limiter clips the positive and negative amplitudes of the signal so that the signal becomes a sequence of square waves of uniform amplitude but of varying frequency. (The crossings of the zero axis are unchanged in the clipping process, and these crossings contain the desired information as to frequency variation.) A tuned circuit in the limiter removes the higher frequency components of the square waves generated, so that the signal going to the discriminator is a frequency-modulated sine wave of constant amplitude. The limiter may take any one of a number of forms. One possibility frequently used is a pentode with low screen voltage and very small grid bias so that large positive signals saturate the tube and large negative signals cut it off.

A block diagram of a typical FM receiver, covering the broadcast range of 88 to 108 Mc, is shown in Fig. 3-42. Note that except for the limiter and discriminator circuits the form of the receiver is similar to that of a conventional AM receiver. All h-f circuits prior to the discriminator must be designed for the FM bandwidth of 225 kc, however, while the audio amplifier which amplifies the recovered modulating signal need cover only the 50-cps to 15-kc range. The i-f amplifiers are tuned to a center frequency of 10.7 Mc. The audio amplifier normally includes a deemphasis circuit. This circuit, in conjunction with a preemphasis circuit in the transmitter, provides additional discrimination against noise and interference. It is discussed in detail in Chap. 6.

3-12. Summary. This chapter and Chap. 4 to follow represent basically applications of the spectrum and bandwidth concepts of Chap. 2 to various types of practical communication systems.

We have stressed the nonlinear or linear time-varying modulation process inherent in all these systems, paying particular attention in this chapter to those systems with sine-wave carriers. In the next chapter we shall extend the concept of modulation to pulse carrier systems. By again focusing attention on the modulation process we shall obtain a unity of development of these two types of communication systems.

The process of modulation was shown to produce a shift of the signal spectrum to the range of frequencies about the carrier. In the case of AM and narrowband FM the signal spectrum was found to be preserved, although displaced in frequency. The r-f bandwidth of these systems is thus either twice the signal bandwidth, or just the signal bandwidth in the case of SSB transmission. The spectrum of a wideband frequency-modulated carrier takes on a much more complex form, however, and depends on the maximum amplitude of the modulating signal as well as its particular form. For large modulation index the FM bandwidth approaches twice the maximum frequency deviation.

Both AM and narrowband FM systems were found to require some type of product modulator for the modulation process. We shall encounter this *balanced modulator* again in the next chapter. In particular we shall first discuss a mechanical form of this modulator which will lead us into the concepts of periodic switching, sampling, and pulse-modulation systems.

PROBLEMS

3-1. Assume that in the amplifier of Fig. P 3-1 the load voltage e_L can be represented by the equation

$$e_L = A_1 e_g + A_2 e_g^2$$

for small variations of the incremental grid voltage e_g.

(*a*) $e_g = \cos \omega_m t$. Find all the frequencies present in the output. How could this device be used as a second-harmonic generator?

(*b*) $|A_1| = 10$, $|A_2/A_1| = 0.05$. Determine the ratio of second-harmonic amplitude to fundamental amplitude. (This is frequently called the *second-harmonic distortion.*)

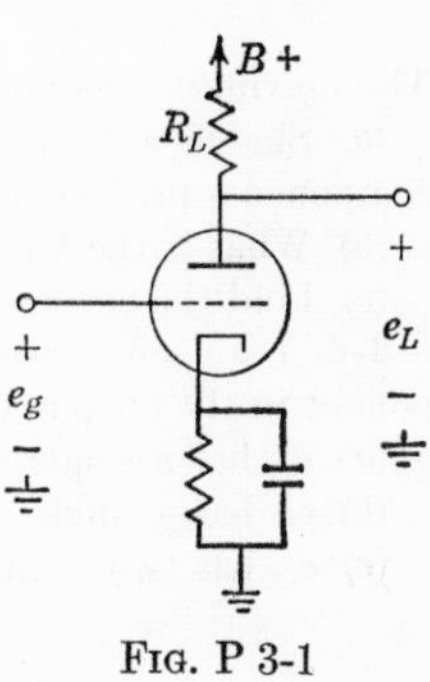

FIG. P 3-1

3-2. (*a*) Let $e_g = 0.1 \cos 500t$ in the amplifier of Prob. 3-1. Determine the frequency terms present in the output and the amplitude of each. Repeat for $e_g = 0.2 \cos 3{,}000t$.

(b) $e_g = 0.1 \cos 500t + 0.2 \cos 3{,}000t$. Determine the different frequency terms present in the output and the amplitude of each. What new frequency terms appear that were not present in the two cases of (a)? These are known as the *intermodulation* frequencies and are due to the nonlinear mixing of the two frequency terms.

3-3. A voltage $e_g = 0.1 \cos 2{,}500t + 0.2 \cos 3{,}000t$ is applied at the input to the amplifier of Prob. 3-1. The output voltage e_L is in turn applied to an ideal rectangular filter passing all frequencies between 50 cps and $4{,}000/2\pi$ cps with unity gain, rejecting all others. Calculate the power at the output of the filter in the frequency terms generated by the amplifier nonlinearity. Determine the ratio of power in these terms to the power in the 2,500 and 3,000 radians/sec terms at the filter output.

3-4. The dependence of the plate current of a triode on the grid and plate voltage, e_c and e_b, respectively, is given by $i_b = f(e_c + e_b/\mu)$, μ a constant. This functional relation may be expanded in a Taylor's series about the quiescent operating point to give as the incremental current

$$i_p = g_m\left(e_g + \frac{e_p}{\mu}\right) + \frac{1}{2!}g_m'\left(e_g + \frac{e_p}{\mu}\right)^2 + \frac{1}{3!}g_m''\left(e_g + \frac{e_g}{\mu}\right)^3 + \cdots$$

e_g and e_p are the incremental grid and plate voltages, respectively, $g_m = \partial i_b/\partial e_c$, $g_m' = \partial g_m/\partial e_c$, etc., all evaluated at the point in question.

Show that, for a *resistive plate load* R_L, a first approximation to the incremental plate current, obtained from the first term in the series, is given by

$$i_{p1} = \frac{\mu e_g}{R_L + r_p} \qquad r_p \equiv \frac{\mu}{g_m}$$

Show similarly that the first two terms in the series give as a second approximation to the current

$$i_{p2} = i_{p1} + \tfrac{1}{2} g_m' \frac{e_g^2}{(1 + R_L/r_p)^3}$$

3-5. A band-limited signal $f(t)$ may be expressed in terms of the finite Fourier series

$$f(t) = \frac{c_0}{T} + \frac{2}{T}\sum_{n=1}^{M} |c_n| \cos(\omega_n t + \theta_n) \qquad \omega_n = \frac{2\pi n}{T}$$

The maximum frequency component of $f(t)$ is $f_M = M/T$.

(a) Sketch a typical amplitude spectrum for $f(t)$. Then indicate the frequency components present in $f^2(t)$.

(b) What is the *highest* frequency component of $f^2(t)$?

(c) Find the spectrum of $f(t) \cos \omega_c t$ ($\omega_c \gg \omega_M$), and compare with that of $f(t)$.

3-6. For each network shown in Fig. P 3-6, calculate the *maximum* frequency component in the output voltage.

(a) e_{in} has a single component of frequency f cps.

(b) e_{in} has a single component of frequency $2f$ cps.

(c) e_{in} has two frequency components, f and $2f$.

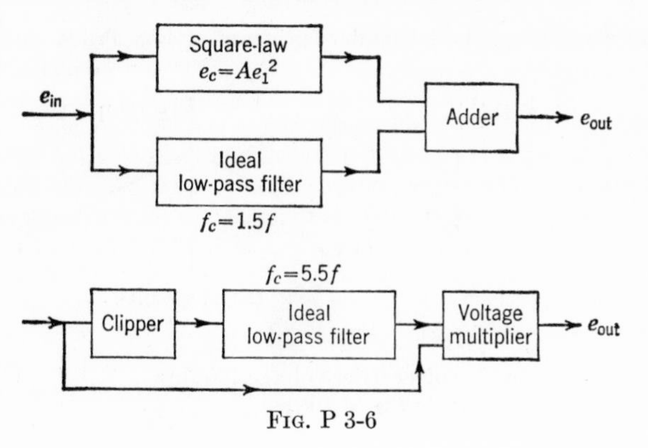

FIG. P 3-6

3-7. Spectrum of coherent radar pulses. These pulses may be generated by turning a sine-wave generator of frequency f_c on and off periodically at the same phase points. For the example shown in Fig. P 3-7

$$f_c(t) = V \cos \omega_c t \qquad \frac{-\tau}{2} < t < \frac{\tau}{2}$$

$$f_c(t) = 0 \qquad \text{elsewhere in a period}$$

(*a*) Find the spectrum of $f_c(t)$ by expanding the pulsed carrier in a Fourier series (Use the exponential form of $\cos \omega_c t$.)

(*b*) Write $f_c(t) = V \cos \omega_c t \; S(t)$, with $S(t)$ a rectangular pulse train. Expand $S(t)$ in a Fourier series. Find the spectrum of $f_c(t)$, and compare with the result of (*a*).

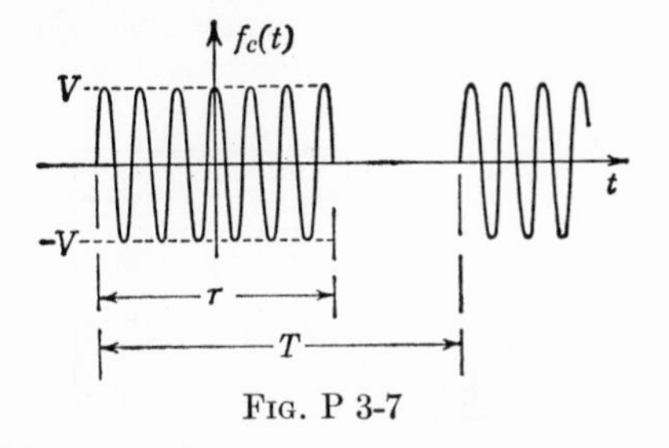

FIG. P 3-7

3-8. A periodic function $f(t)$ is band-limited to 10 kc and has a uniform or flat amplitude spectrum from 1 to 10 kc. It is given by

$$f(t) = \sum_{n=1}^{10} \cos n\omega t \qquad \omega = 2\pi \times 1{,}000$$

Show that the function $f^2(t)$ has an amplitude spectrum decreasing linearly from 1 to 20 kc. The envelope of the spectrum of $f^2(t)$ is thus triangular in shape.

3-9. A function $f(t)$ has as its Fourier transform

$$|F(j\omega)| = K \qquad |\omega| < \omega_M \qquad\qquad |F(j\omega)| = 0 \qquad |\omega| > \omega_M$$

If $f(t)$ is the input voltage to a square-law device with the characteristics $e_o = Ae_i^2$, show that the output has the triangular spectrum of Fig. P 3-9. (Compare with Prob. 3-8.)

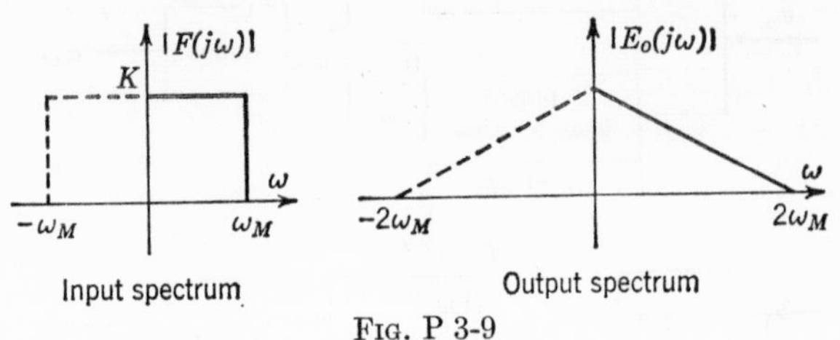

FIG. P 3-9

3-10. An AM signal consists of a carrier voltage 100 sin ($2\pi \times 10^6t$) plus the voltage (20 sin $6{,}280t$ + 50 sin $12{,}560t$) sin ($2\pi \times 10^6t$).

(*a*) Draw the amplitude vs. frequency plot of the modulated signal.

(*b*) How much peak power will this signal deliver to a 100-ohm load?

(*c*) What is the average power (over a modulation cycle) delivered to a 100-ohm load?

(*d*) Sketch the envelope over a modulation cycle. (Indicate numerical values at key points.)

3-11. Assume that the carrier in Prob. 3-10 is suppressed after modulation. Repeat Prob. 3-10 under this condition.

3-12. Frequency converter. In the superheterodyning process commonly used in communication systems a modulated wave is shifted in frequency by mixing with a locally generated oscillator signal. With filtering used to eliminate extraneous frequency terms the modulated wave appears centered about the difference frequency between the original carrier and the local signal. The nonlinear or product modulation necessary in this mixing process is frequently accomplished with the pentagrid tube shown in Fig. P 3-12.

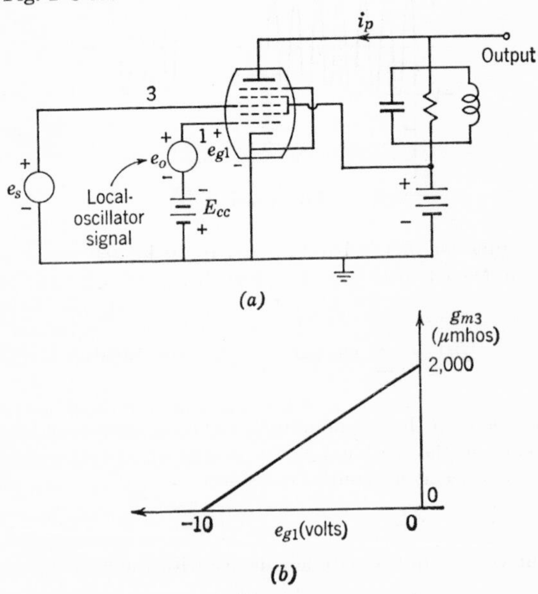

FIG. P 3-12. Frequency converter.

With a large plate resistance, $i_p \doteq g_{m3}e_s$, with g_{m3} the transconductance defined as $g_{m3} \equiv \partial i_b/\partial e_{c3}$. Assume that g_{m3} varies with e_{g1} as shown in Fig. P 3-12. (Compare with the curve of g_{m1} versus e_{g1} for the 6SJ7, as given by Fig. 3-35.)

(*a*) $e_s = [1 + f(t)] \cos \omega_c t$; $e_o = 5 \cos \omega_o t$; $E_{cc} = -5$ volts. Show that i_p has a component given by $g_c[1 + f(t)] \cos (\omega_c - \omega_o)t$. The output voltage will be of this form if the tuned circuit is tuned to a frequency $(\omega_c - \omega_o)$.

(*b*) Find g_c, the *conversion transconductance*, and compare with the maximum value of g_{m3}.

3-13. Problem 3-12 is to be repeated with the local oscillator signal e_o now connected to the control grid through the *RC* network shown in Fig. P 3-13. With a large

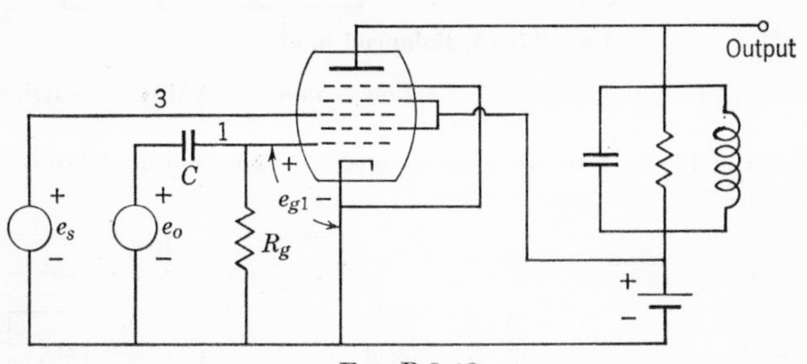

FIG. P 3-13

positive oscillator signal the control grid is clamped to zero potential with respect to the cathode. The transconductance g_{m3} is then constant and equal to 2,000 μmhos. (See Fig. P 3-12.)

Assume that the oscillator voltage is so large that clamping takes place over the entire positive portion of its cycle. Assume that over the entire negative portion of the cycle the tube is cut off.

(*a*) Show that the plate current again has a component given by

$$g_c[1 + f(t)] \cos (\omega_c - \omega_o)t$$

(*b*) Compare g_c in this case with the value of g_c found in the previous problem.

3-14. Frequency conversion. An amplitude-modulated carrier,

$$f_c(t) = A[1 + mf(t)] \cos \omega_c t$$

is to be raised or lowered in frequency to a new carrier frequency $\omega_c' = \omega_c \pm \Delta\omega$. The resultant time function will appear in the form $f_c'(t) = A'[1 + mf(t)] \cos \omega_c' t$.

(*a*) Show that a product modulator producing an output $f_c(t) \cos \Delta\omega t$ will accomplish this frequency conversion. Draw a simple block diagram for this frequency converter. Specify the filtering required in the two cases of frequency raised by $\Delta\omega$ and lowered by $\Delta\omega$ radians/sec.

(*b*) Show that a nonlinear device with terminal characteristics $e_o = a_1e_i + a_2e_i^2$ will perform this frequency conversion if $f_c(t) + \cos \Delta\omega t$ is applied at the input. Sketch a typical amplitude spectrum of the output signal, and specify the filtering necessary to produce the frequency conversion.

3-15. Balanced modulator. Consider the balanced circuit of Fig. P 3-15. Assume $i_{p1} = a_1e_{g1} + a_2e_{g1}^2$, $i_{p2} = a_1e_{g2} + a_2e_{g2}^2$. (The tubes are assumed identical.)

(*a*) $e_1 = f(t)$, $e_2 = \cos \omega_c t$. Show that e_o appears in the form of a suppressed-carrier wave if the output of the balanced circuit is tuned to the frequency ω_c.

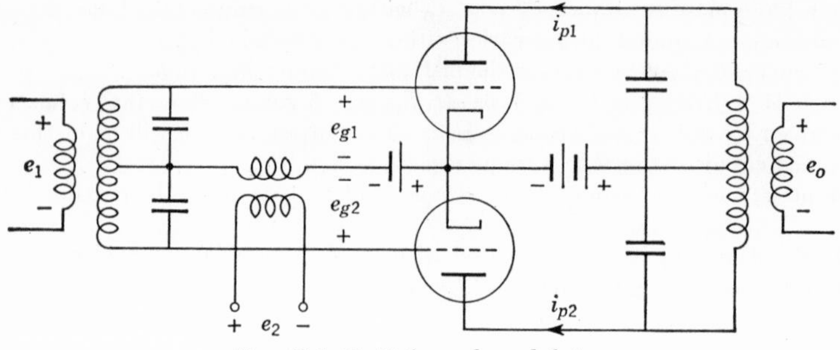

FIG. P 3-15. Balanced modulator.

(b) $e_1 = \cos \omega_c t$, $e_2 = f(t)$. Show that e_o now is a normal AM wave (carrier included) if the output is tuned to ω_c radians/sec.

3-16. Shown in Fig. P 3-16 are some examples of balanced modulators used in a-c servomechanisms.[1]

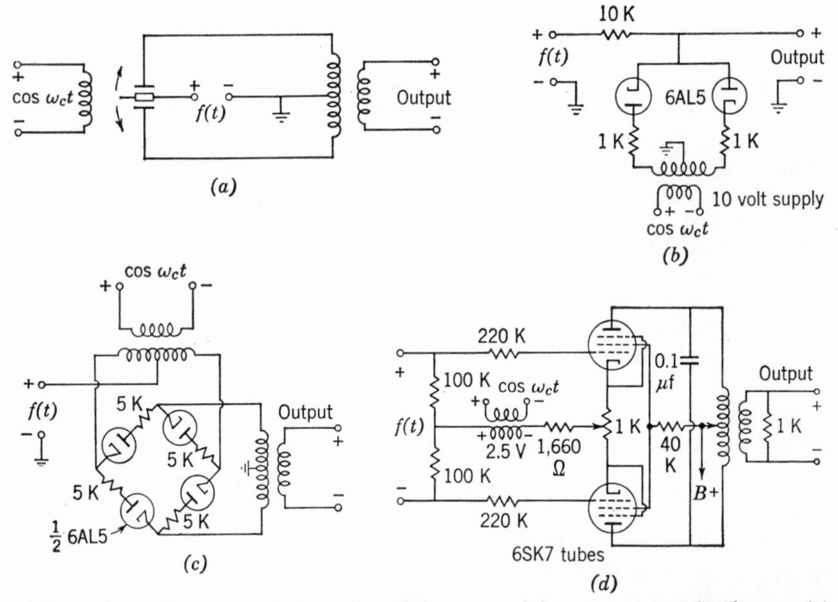

FIG. P 3-16. Examples of balanced modulators used in a-c servomechanisms. (a) Mechanical vibrator; (b) diode modulator; (c) ring modulator; (d) pentode modulator. (*By permission of W. R. Ahrendt, "Servomechanism Practice," chap.* 5, *McGraw-Hill Book Company, Inc., New York,* 1954.)

(a) Show that in all cases the output signal is of the suppressed-carrier type, i.e., zero output for zero input signal $f(t)$.

(b) In some cases the output is given by $f(t) \cos \omega_c t$, in some by $f(t)S(t)$. The voltage $\cos \omega_c t$ is usually a 60- or 400-cps supply voltage. $S(t)$ is a square-wave switching function at the supply-voltage frequency.

[1] See W. R. Ahrendt, "Servomechanism Practice," chap. 5, McGraw-Hill Book Company, Inc. New York, 1954.

Specify which of the circuits might most simply be analyzed as switching devices, which as nonlinear devices, and which might be treated either way.

3-17. (*a*) The switching function $S(t)$ of Prob. 3-16 is a square wave which is on half a cycle, off the other half. Sketch the amplitude spectrum of $f(t)S(t)$, and indicate how the term $f(t) \cos \omega_c t$ could be obtained from this output.

(*b*) $f_c = 400$ cps. Find the maximum possible frequency component f_M of $f(t)$ for the case of (*a*).

(*c*) $S(t)$ is a square wave which is alternately positive and negative. Repeat (*a*) and (*b*).

3-18. A simple example of a transistor modulator is shown in Fig. P 3-18. The voltage e_m represents the modulating signal and is a negative voltage as shown. The

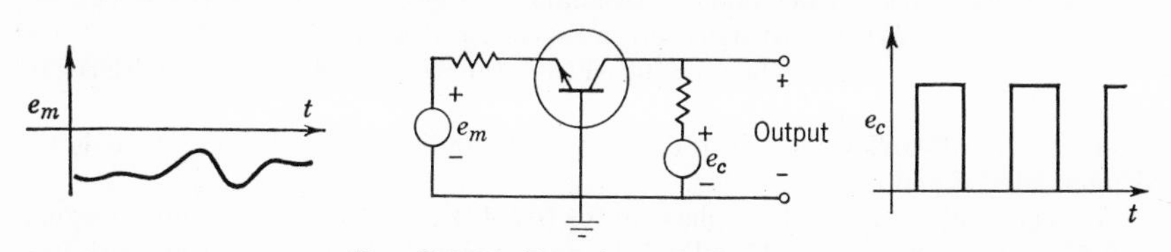

FIG. P 3-18. Transistor modulator.

collector voltage e_c is the periodic square wave shown. Discuss the operation of the modulator, using a piecewise-linear approximation for a typical set of transistor characteristics.

3-19. A general nonlinear device has output-input characteristics given by $e_o = a_1 e_i + a_2 e_i^2 + \cdots$ (this could represent a diode, transistor, vacuum triode, etc.).

(*a*) Show that all combinations of sum and difference frequencies appear in the output if e_i is a sum of cosine waves.

(*b*) Show that this device can be used as a modulator if $e_i = f(t) + \cos \omega_c t$.

(*c*) The input is a normal AM wave given by $e_i = K[1 + mf(t)] \cos \omega_c t$. Show that this nonlinear device will demodulate the wave, i.e., reproduce $f(t)$.

(*d*) Show that this device can act as a frequency converter if

$$e_i = K[1 + mf(t)] \cos \omega_c t + \cos \Delta\omega t$$

In particular, show that with proper filtering the AM wave spectrum can be shifted up or down by $\Delta\omega$ radians/sec.

3-20. A function appears in the form

$$f_c(t) = \cos \omega_c t - K \sin \omega_m t \sin \omega_c t$$

Using block diagrams, show how to generate this, given $\cos \omega_c t$ and $\sin \omega_m t$ as inputs.

3-21. Amplitude-modulation detector. An amplitude-modulated voltage

$$f_c(t) = K[1 + mf(t)] \cos \omega_c t$$

is applied to the diode-resistor combination of Fig. P 3-21. The diode has the piece-

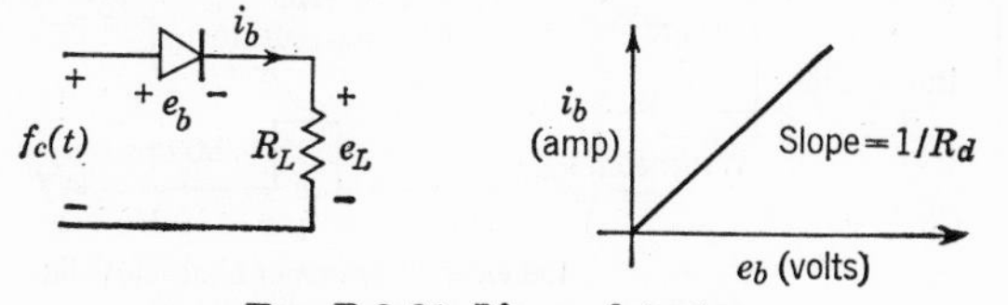

FIG. P 3-21. Linear detector.

wise-linear characteristics shown. (It is then called a *linear detector.*) Show that for $|mf(t)| < 1$ the l-f components of the load voltage e_L provide a perfect replica of $f(t)$.

8-22. Repeat Prob. 3-21 for the case where the diode-resistor combination of Fig. P 3-21 has the square-law characteristic $e_L = a_1e_i + a_2e_i^2$. Show that e_L contains a component proportional to $f(t)$.

3-23. (*a*) A DSB (suppressed-carrier) signal of the form $f(t) \cos \omega_c t$ is to be demodulated. Show that multiplying this signal by $\cos \omega_c t$ in a product modulator reproduces $f(t)$.

(*b*) "The DSB demodulator is phase-sensitive." Demonstrate the validity of this statement by multiplying $f(t) \cos \omega_c t$ by $\cos (\omega_c t + \theta)$ and letting θ vary from 0 to π radians.

3-24. Single-sideband detection. An audio tone $\cos \omega_m t$ and a carrier $\cos \omega_c t$ are combined to produce an SSB signal given by $\cos (\omega_c - \omega_m)t$.

(*a*) Show that $\cos \omega_m t$ can be reproduced from the SSB signal by mixing with $\cos \omega_c t$ as a local carrier.

(*b*) The local carrier drifts in frequency by $\Delta\omega$ radians to $\omega_c + \Delta\omega$. What is the demodulated signal now?

(*c*) The local carrier shifts in phase to $\cos (\omega_c t + \theta)$. Find the audio output signal.

3-25. (*a*) Refer to Fig. 3-15. Find the output signal if a phase-shift network providing $\beta(f)$ deg is inserted in the $f_1(t)$ branch and a network giving $\beta(f) + 90°$ is inserted in the $f_2(t)$ branch. The input signal $f(t)$ may be assumed a sine wave.

(*b*) How may $f(t)$ be reproduced at the receiver?

3-26. The 90° phase shift in the $f_2(t)$ branch of Fig. 3-15 is replaced by θ deg of phase shift, while the carrier phase shift of 90° is replaced by $180 - \theta$ deg. Find the output signal. Is it in the form of an SSB signal? How does it compare with the case of $\theta = 90°$?

3-27. (*a*) An amplitude-modulated voltage given by

$$v_c(t) = V(1 + m \cos \omega_m t) \cos \omega_c t \qquad \text{volts}$$

is applied across a resistor R. Calculate the percentage average power in the carrier and in each of the two sideband frequencies. Calculate the *peak* power.

(*b*) The voltage $v_c(t)$ is now a suppressed-carrier voltage $v_c(t) = V \cos \omega_m t \cos \omega_c t$ applied across R ohms. What is the fraction of the total average power in each of the sideband frequencies?

3-28. An SSB radio transmitter radiates 1 kw of average power summed over the entire sideband. What total average power would the transmitter have to radiate if it were operating as a DSB (suppressed-carrier) system and the same distance coverage were required?

3-29. An AM transmitter is tested by using the dummy load and linear narrowband receiver of Fig. P 3-29. The r-f amplifier portion of the receiver is swept successively and continuously over the range 100 kc to 10 Mc. Its frequency characteristic at any frequency f_c in this range is shown in the figure.

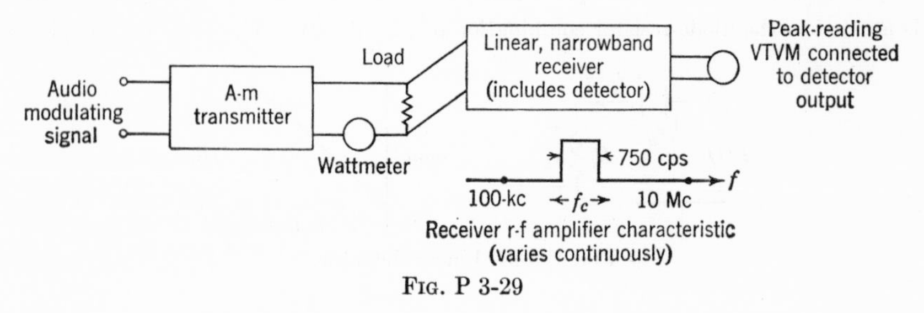

FIG. P 3-29

With no audio input the wattmeter reads 100 watts average power. The peak-reading vacuum-tube voltmeter (VTVM) and r-f amplifier tuning characteristic indicate an output of 10 volts peak at 1 Mc.

(*a*) With an audio input signal of 10 volts peak at 1 kc the wattmeter reads 150 watts. At what frequencies are there receiver outputs? What are the various amplitudes, as read on the VTVM?

(*b*) The 1-kc modulating signal is replaced by the composite signal 2 cos 12, 560t + 3 cos 18, 840t. What is the new wattmeter reading? At what frequencies will there be receiver outputs? What are the various amplitudes?

(*c*) The transmitter modulator is modified so that the carrier is suppressed but the other characteristics are unchanged. An audio signal of 10 volts peak at 1 kc is applied. What is the wattmeter reading? What are the receiver output frequencies and amplitudes? Sketch the pattern that would be seen on an oscilloscope connected across the load. (The left-to-right sweep period is 2,000 μsec; the return takes negligible time.)

3-30. The radio receiver of Fig. P 3-30 has the r-f amplifier and i-f amplifier characteristics shown. The mixer characteristic is given by $e_3 = e_2(a_0 + a_1 e_{01})$, with

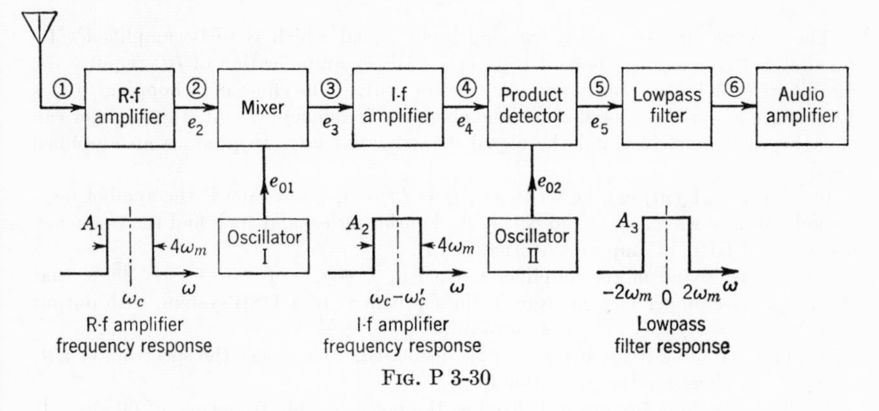

Fig. P 3-30

a_0 and a_1 constants, and $e_{01} = A \sin \omega_c' t$. The product-detector output is $e_5 = e_4 e_{02}$, with $e_{02} = B \cos (\omega_c - \omega_c')t$.

Find the signals at points 4 and 6 for each of the following signals at point 1:

(*a*) Normal AM; $(1 + \sin \omega_m t) \sin \omega_c t$.

(*b*) Double sideband, suppressed carrier; $\sin \omega_m t \sin \omega_c t$.

(*c*) Single sideband; $\cos (\omega_c - \omega_m)t$.

3-31. The product detector and oscillator II in Fig. P 3-30 are replaced by an envelope detector with the characteristic $e_5 = b e_4^2$. The r-f amplifier can be continuously tuned over the range $f_c = \omega_c/2\pi = 535$ to 1,605 kc. The tuning capacitor of oscillator I is ganged to the tuning capacitor of the r-f amplifier so that $f_c' = \omega_c'/2\pi = f_c + 455$ kc at all times. The circuit is then that of a superheterodyne radio receiver. The passband of the amplifiers is ±5 kc about the center frequency.

(*a*) Determine all frequencies present at points 3 and 4 if the signal at 1 is a 1-Mc unmodulated carrier.

(*b*) A 1-kc audio signal amplitude-modulates the 1-Mc carrier. Determine the frequencies present at points 2 and 4.

(*c*) The r-f amplifier is tuned to 650 kc. To your amazement, however, a radio station at 1,560 kc (WQXR in the New York City area) is heard quite clearly. Can you explain this phenomenon?

(*d*) The input at point 1 is the DSB signal of Prob. 3-30, with $f_c = 1$ Mc and $f_m = \omega_m/2\pi = 1$ kc. Find the frequencies present at points 5 and 6. Compare with the product-detector output of Prob. 3-30.

3-32. Chopper technique for amplifying slowly varying signals. The coil-switch combination of Fig. P 3-32 is called a *chopper* and is used as a mechanical modulator here. (Compare with the vibrator of Fig. P 3-16.) The bipolar switch vibrates between contacts 1 and 2 f_c times per second.

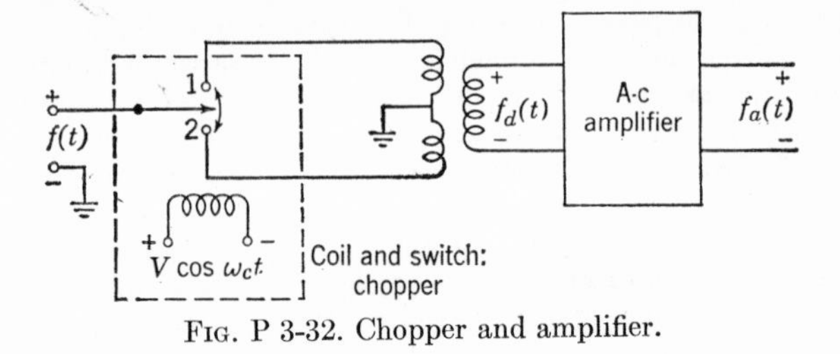

FIG. P 3-32. Chopper and amplifier.

The voltage $f(t)$ is a slowly varying input signal which is to be amplified. Its maximum frequency component is f_M cps. Direct amplification of $f(t)$ requires d-c amplifiers with high stability and low rates of drift. The effect of "chopping" $f(t)$ is to produce a signal centered about the chopping frequency f_c. An a-c amplifier can then be used as shown and the signal demodulated later to produce an amplified version of $f(t)$.

(*a*) Show that $f_d(t)$ can be written $f_d(t) = f(t)S(t)$, where $S(t)$ is the symbol for a periodic square wave. Expand $S(t)$ in its Fourier series, and then find the frequency spectrum of $f_d(t)$. Compare with that of $f(t)$.

(*b*) The passband of the amplifier is fixed at $f_c - f_m < f < f_c + f_M$. Show that the amplifier-chopper combination is the equivalent of a DSB system, with output voltage $f_a(t) = Kf(t) \cos \omega_c t$, K a constant.

(*c*) The switching frequency f_c is to be decreased. How does the spectrum of $f_d(t)$ change? Is there a minimum value for f_c?

(*d*) The switching frequency is fixed at the power-supply frequency of 60 cps. Is there a maximum value of f_M? Repeat for a power-supply frequency of 400 cps.

3-33. (*a*) A 1-kc sine wave frequency-modulates a 10-Mc carrier. The amplitude of this audio signal is such as to produce a maximum frequency deviation of 2 kc. Find the bandwidth required to pass the frequency-modulated signal.

(*b*) Repeat (*a*), if the modulating signal is a 2-kc sine wave.

(*c*) The 2-kc sine wave of (*b*) is doubled in amplitude, so that $\Delta f = 4$ kc. Find the required bandwidth.

3-34. (*a*) A 100-Mc sine-wave carrier is to be frequency-modulated by a 10-kc sine wave. An engineer designing the system reasons that he can minimize bandwidth by decreasing the audio amplitude. He arranges for a maximum frequency deviation Δf of only ± 10 cps away from the 100-Mc carrier frequency and assumes that he requires only 20 cps bandwidth. Find the fallacy in his reasoning, and specify the actual bandwidth required.

(*b*) Would he have been right to assume a bandwidth of 2 Mc if the audio amplitude had been chosen to produce a Δf of 1 Mc?

Explain the difference between the results of (*a*) and (*b*).

3-35. An FM receiver similar to that of Fig. 3-42 is tuned to a carrier frequency of 100 Mc.

(*a*) A 10-kc audio-signal frequency-modulates a 100-Mc carrier, producing a β of 0.1. Find the bandwidths required of the r-f and i-f amplifiers and of the audio amplifier.

(*b*) Repeat (*a*) if $\beta = 5$.

(*c*) Two signals at 100 Mc are tuned in alternately. The carriers are of equal intensity. One is modulated with a 10-kc signal and has $\beta = 5$; the other is modulated with a 2-kc signal and has $\beta = 25$. Which requires the larger bandwidth? Explain. Compare the audio-amplifier outputs in the two cases.

(*d*) Two other signals are tuned in alternately. The carriers are again of equal intensity. One has a frequency deviation of 10 kc with $\beta = 5$, the other a deviation of 2 kc with $\beta = 25$. Which requires the larger bandwidth? Which gives the larger audio output?

3-36. A general frequency-modulated voltage has the form $f_c(t) = A_c \cos [\omega_c t + K\int f(t)\,dt]$. Show that the average power dissipated in a 1-ohm resistor is $A_c^2/2$ averaged over a modulating cycle.

3-37. (*a*) A modulating signal $f(t) = 0.1 \sin 2\pi \times 10^3 t$ is used to modulate a 1-Mc carrier in both an AM and an FM system. The 0.1-volt amplitude produces a 100-cps frequency deviation in the FM case. Compare the receiver r-f-amplifier and audio-amplifier bandwidths required in the two systems.

(*b*) Repeat (*a*) if $f(t) = 20 \sin 2\pi \times 10^3 t$.

3-38. A sine wave is switched periodically from 10 to 11 Mc at a 5-kc rate. Sketch the resultant waveshape. What is the form of the modulating signal if this frequency-shifted wave is considered an FM signal? What is the required transmission bandwidth if the modulating signal is approximated by a sine wave of the same amplitude and modulation index β?

3-39. Consider the reactance-tube circuit of Fig. P 3-39.

(*a*) What is the oscillator frequency if $g_m = 4{,}000$ μmhos?

(*b*) What is the modulation index β if g_m varies from 3,000 to 5,000 μmhos at a 1-kc rate?

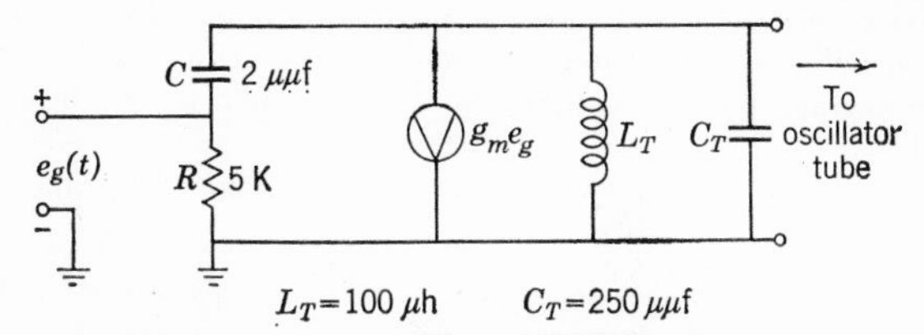

FIG. P 3-39. Reactance-tube circuit.

3-40. A 6SJ7 tube is to be used in a reactance-tube modulator circuit similar to that of Fig. P 3-39. The operating conditions are $E_{b0} = 250$ volts, $E_{c2} = 100$ volts, $E_{c3} = 0$ volts.

The oscillator frequency is 5 Mc. The maximum frequency deviation of Δf is to be 4.17 kc. The *RC* combination of Fig. P 3-39 is to be used to produce an effective capacitance.

(*a*) Pick the control-grid bias to provide a linear variation of g_m with grid voltage.

(*b*) Choose R, C, C_T to satisfy the reactance-tube equations. Find the inductance L_T. (The symbols used are those of Fig. P 3-39.)

(*c*) The applied grid voltage is $e_g = E_g \cos \omega_m t$. What value of E_g is required to produce the desired frequency deviation of 4.17 kc?

3-41. Repeat Prob. 3-40, using a 6CH8-type tube. (See a tube handbook such as the RCA Tube Handbook for the transconductance–control-grid characteristics.)

3-42. Consider a reactance-tube circuit as in Fig. P 3-39, but with R and C interchanged. Calculate the effective inductance introduced. Develop the reactance-tube equations for this case. Repeat Prob. 3-40.

3-43. A reactance-tube circuit such as the one referred to in Prob. 3-42, which provides an inductance varying with grid voltage, has the parameters $R = 100$ kilohms, $C = 50$ $\mu\mu$f, and $L_T = 100$ μhenrys. The tuning capacitor C_T is chosen to make the entire circuit resonant at 1 Mc with $g_m = 5$ millimhos.

(*a*) The grid voltage is varied at a 100-cps rate. Find the variation in g_m necessary to make $\beta = 100$.

(*b*) What transmission bandwidth would the FM system require for the example of (*a*)?

(*c*) The grid now varies at a 20-kc rate. The variation of g_m is the same as in (*a*). What is the bandwidth required?

3-44. A reactance-tube circuit similar to that of Fig. P 3-39 provides an effective capacitance $C' = [-2e_g(t) + 6]10^{-12}$ farad appearing in parallel with C_T and L_T. For this case $C_T = 14$ $\mu\mu$f, $L_T = 50$ μhenrys, and $e_g(t) = 0.5 \sin 2\pi 500t$.

(*a*) What is the carrier frequency?

(*b*) What is the frequency deviation Δf?

(*c*) Determine β, the modulation index. Show a rough sketch of the frequency spectrum of the FM wave indicating the approximate bandwidth.

(*d*) Repeat (*c*) if the frequency deviation is reduced to one-hundredth of its value in (*b*), with the modulating frequency unchanged.

3-45. Consider a sine-wave modulated FM signal with a modulation index $\beta = 1$. Then the instantaneous frequency is $f = f_c + \Delta f \cos \omega_m t$, with f_c the unmodulated carrier frequency and $\Delta f/f_m = 1$.

Plot both the signal-envelope amplitude and f as a function of $\omega_m t$ for the cases where:

(*a*) Only the carrier and the first sideband pair are considered, the other sidebands neglected.

(*b*) The carrier plus the first two sideband pairs are considered.

(*c*) The carrier plus the first three sideband pairs are considered.

What is the average power, evaluated as a per cent of the total, supplied by the third sideband pair?

3-46. The linearity of phase response with frequency shift for a single-tuned circuit is to be investigated (Fig. P 3-46).

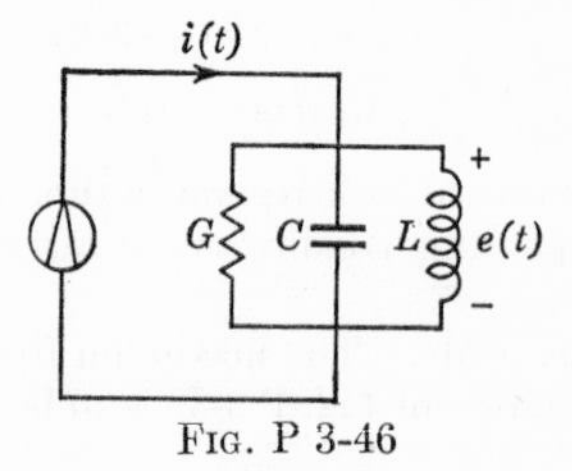

FIG. P 3-46

(*a*) Determine the pole-zero plot of the transfer function $E(p)/I(p)$.

(*b*) Let $Q \equiv \omega_c C/G$, $\omega_c^2 = 1/LC$. Show that, for $Q \gg 1$, the poles are located approximately at $-\omega_c/2Q \pm j\omega_c$.

(*c*) The input driving current is initially a sinusoid of frequency ω_c radians/sec. Show that, if the frequency shifts to $\omega_c + \Delta\omega$ ($\Delta\omega \ll \omega_c$), the output voltage shifts in phase by $\phi = \tan^{-1}[\Delta\omega/(\omega_c/2Q)] \doteq \Delta\omega/(\omega_c/2Q)$ for small ϕ.

(*d*) The carrier frequency is $f_c = 10$ Mc; ϕ is to be 10° maximum. Find the Q necessary if $\Delta f = 75$ kc.

CHAPTER 4

PERIODIC SAMPLING AND PULSE MODULATION

4-1. Transition from Sine-wave to Pulse Modulation. In Chap. 3 we placed primary emphasis on sine-wave modulation systems. Specifically, we discussed normal amplitude-modulation (AM), single-sideband (SSB), and frequency-modulation (FM) generation and detection. In the analysis included in the discussion we treated the application of nonlinear and linear time-varying devices to modulation and demodulation. In most of this chapter we shall concern ourselves primarily with different examples of pulse-modulation systems. Such systems find application both in the controls field and in communications.

Although sine-wave modulation and pulse-modulation systems appear vastly different from one another, particularly when communication and control applications are considered, we shall show that there is an essential unity between the different systems. Rather than treat separate systems one by one, each in its profusion of specific circuits and specialized concepts, we shall attempt to reveal some of the common and fundamental principles underlying the different systems.

Basic to all this will be the concept of periodic switching. The simple analysis of the piecewise-linear rectifier as a sine-wave modulator in Sec. 3-3 was based primarily upon the introduction of a periodic switching function $S(t)$ which we were able to expand in a Fourier series. This showed the existence of the desired amplitude-modulated sine-wave carrier terms. An extension of this analysis to other types of switching devices, particularly mechanical switches, will enable us to develop some of the important concepts in the study of pulse-modulation systems.

We can demonstrate these statements very simply by recalling that for our AM systems we required some type of product modulator. Thus we were looking for a device whose output contained a term of the form

$$f(t) \cos \omega_c t$$

This form by itself represents a suppressed-carrier, or double-sideband (DSB), output. A nonlinear device or switching device of some sort is necessary to generate this product term. The addition of the carrier to this term gives normal AM. Single-sideband can be produced by filtering, after generation of this term.

If the nonlinear device is basically piecewise-linear (i.e., if the nonlinearity is primarily concentrated at one point), it may be represented for small-level operation as a switching device. For such devices and for actual switches the output of the circuit containing the switch can be written

$$f(t)S(t)$$

with $S(t)$ the periodic switching function made up of $\cos \omega_c t$ and its harmonics. Proper filtering then eliminates all the harmonics, and we have the desired term $f(t) \cos \omega_c t$. This can then be used to generate any one of the three types of sine-wave AM schemes—normal AM, SSB, or DSB.

If, however, rather than filter the switched output we further enhance its harmonic content by letting $S(t)$ become a periodic series of narrow equal-amplitude pulses (simple methods of doing this will be demonstrated shortly), we obtain the simplest form of a pulse-amplitude-modulation (PAM) system.

4-2. Suppressed-carrier (DSB) Modulation Using Mechanical Choppers. The product term $f(t) \cos \omega_c t$ represents of course the DSB output. Although DSB systems have not been used widely in communication work (the major emphasis having been placed on AM and SSB), they occur commonly in the controls or servomechanisms field. There the term *suppressed-carrier system* is more commonly used than DSB system.

In many servomechanisms applications, for example, a slowly varying signal must ultimately be used to drive a two-phase a-c servomotor. A balanced modulator is then used to convert the signal to a suppressed-carrier signal and, after amplification, may be fed directly into the motor. In other applications the signal may appear as a suppressed-carrier signal (for example, the output of an a-c tachometer) and demodulators may be used to obtain the desired information-carrying signal.

Suppressed-carrier detection or demodulation depends significantly on the phase of an injected carrier, and so the demodulators used are called *phase-sensitive detectors.* (The term *synchronous detection* is also used since the injected carrier must be exactly in phase with the carrier originally used for modulation.)

To demonstrate this, consider a suppressed-carrier signal $f(t) \cos \omega_c t$ multiplied, by means of a nonlinear device, by the carrier $\cos \omega_c t$. The demodulated output is

$$f_o(t) = f(t) \cos^2 \omega_c t = \tfrac{1}{2} f(t)(1 + \cos 2\omega_c t) \tag{4-1}$$

The desired output $f(t)$ is thus obtained by filtering out the high-frequency (h-f) terms located about $2\omega_c$. Now let the demodulating carrier be $\cos (\omega_c t + \theta)$ (i.e., a phase difference of θ deg between original and inserted carrier). The output then becomes

$$f_o'(t) = f(t)[\cos \omega_c t \cos (\omega_c t + \theta)] = \tfrac{1}{2} f(t)[\cos (2\omega_c t + \theta) + \cos \theta] \tag{4-2}$$

or, after filtering,

$$f_o'(t) = \tfrac{1}{2}f(t) \cos \theta \tag{4-3}$$

The *maximum* output is thus obtained for $\theta = 0$. Note the possibility of *zero output* if $\theta = \pi/2$. The suppressed-carrier detector is thus phase-sensitive, and synchronous detection must be used to ensure maximum output.

The balanced modulators discussed in the previous chapter were the devices basic to the generation of suppressed-carrier signals and are used in control systems for that purpose. It is of interest to consider one further type of modulator—the mechanical vibrator, or chopper. The concept of synchronous detection will emerge almost naturally upon analyzing this device. The analysis of this device will then be extended quite simply to the concept of pulse modulation.

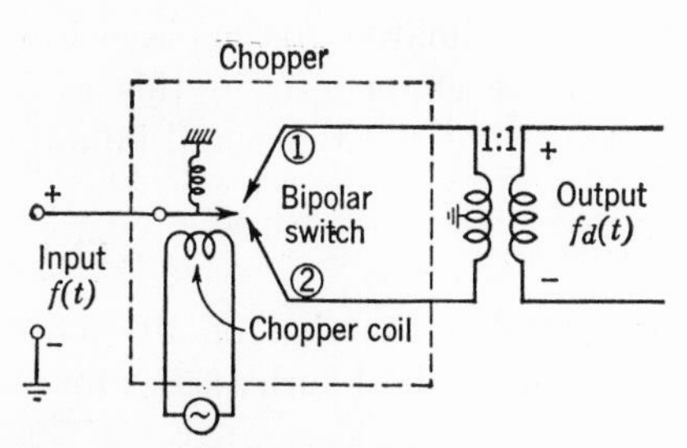

FIG. 4-1. Mechanical balanced modulator, using bipolar chopper.

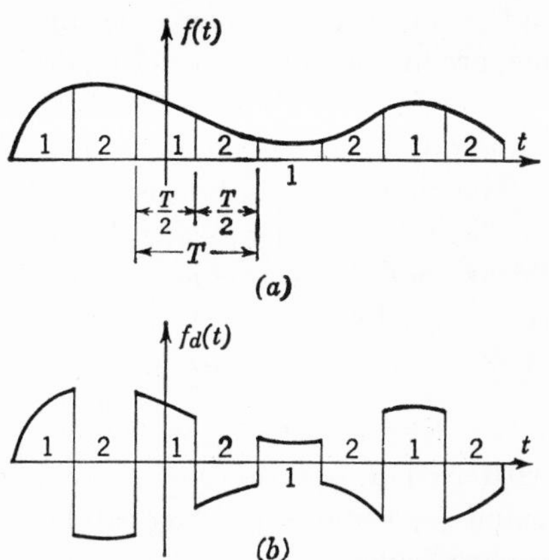

FIG. 4-2. Bipolar chopper output. (*a*) Input signal; (*b*) chopper output signal.

One type of mechanical chopper used in a balanced-modulator circuit is shown in Fig. 4-1. (The switching action could of course be accomplished electronically, by using diodes, for example. The result would be one form of the balanced modulator considered previously.) The chopper used consists of a bipolar switch and associated coil. As the switch vibrates between contacts 1 and 2, the input voltage $f(t)$ is successively applied first to the upper side of the output transformer, then to the lower side. The resultant output then resembles a modulated square wave: negative output with the switch in position 2, and the amplitude of the output equal to the input $f(t)$ at any instant. A complete period, T sec, corresponds to the time the switch remains on contact 1 plus the time on contact 2. If the voltage applied to the chopper coil is of frequency f_c cps, $f_c = 1/T$.

A comparison between the input and output voltages is shown in Fig. 4-2.

[The assumption made that the chopper is on either of the two contacts all the time does not quite hold in practice. Many choppers are of the single-pole double-throw (SPDT), break-before-make contact type. There is then an *off time* occurring twice in each cycle, during which time neither contact is closed. The *dwell time*, or *on time*, is ordinarily much greater than the off time and also occurs twice each cycle—one for each contact. In addition there is an effective phase lag between the contacts and the driving signal at the coil. This lag is due to a lagging coil current and the mechanical inertia of the system and may range typically between 30 and 100 electrical degrees. A series RC circuit is frequently connected in the coil circuit to overcome this lag. These factors, off time and phase lag, are important in the actual design of chopper circuits, but they do not substantially affect our analysis of chopper action. We shall thus neglect these quantities and assume ideal choppers.]

The chopper operation is a true switching action and can be described mathematically just as was the switching approximation to the piecewise-linear modulator previously considered. The chopper is in this case represented as a perfect switch with zero forward resistance and infinite back resistance. Thus

$$f_d(t) = f(t)S(t) \tag{4-4}$$

with $S(t)$ a square-wave switching or sampling function of alternate values, $+1$ and -1. $S(t)$ can be represented by the Fourier series for a square wave,

$$S(t) = 2 \sum_{n=1}^{\infty} \frac{\sin (\pi n/2)}{\pi n/2} \cos n\omega_c t \tag{4-5}$$

The expression for the output signal is thus

$$f_d(t) = 2f(t) \left[\sum_{n=1}^{\infty} \frac{\sin (n\pi/2)}{n\pi/2} \cos n\omega_c t \right] \tag{4-6}$$

Note that only odd harmonics of the vibrator frequency f_c appear in the output. Each term $f(t) \cos n\omega_c t$ gives rise to the sum and difference frequencies centered about $n\omega_c$ in the amplitude-spectrum plot. This is shown in Fig. 4-3.

The shape of the output spectrum thus is identical to the input spectrum shifted up to f_c, $3f_c$, $5f_c$, etc. The amplitude at each center frequency, however, is multiplied by $[\sin n\pi/2)/(n\pi/2)] = 2/\pi$, $-2/3\pi$, $2/5\pi$, etc. If this output is now passed through an amplifier (or filter) of passband $f_c - f_m$ to $f_c + f_m$, the resulting filtered signal is exactly of the suppressed-carrier DSB type.

It may be pointed out here that the chopper-amplifier combination is sometimes used to avoid difficulties with d-c amplifiers. Slowly varying signals cannot be amplified by the commonly used a-c amplifier with its attendant blocking capacitors and bypass capacitors. Direct-current amplifiers have been designed for amplification of such signals, but problems arise of stabilization of these amplifiers against drift (a slowly varying quantity itself). A chopper serves to shift the slowly varying signal up in frequency so that a-c amplifiers can then be used. More

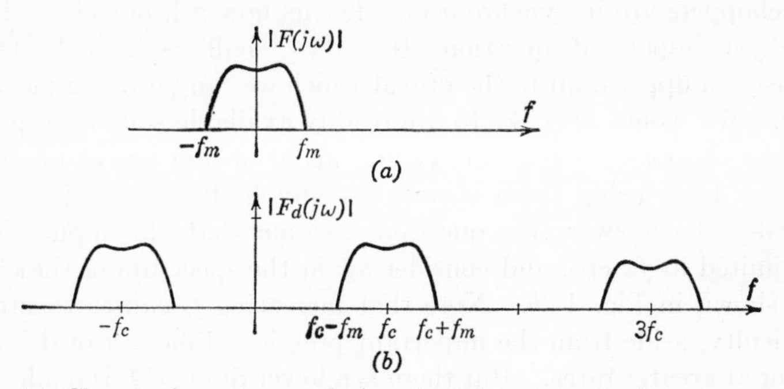

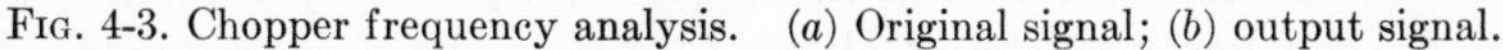

FIG. 4-3. Chopper frequency analysis. (*a*) Original signal; (*b*) output signal.

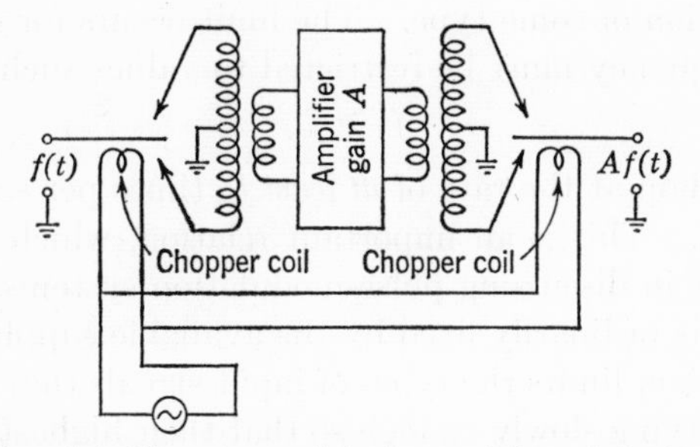

FIG. 4-4. Chopper modulation and demodulation.

commonly, however, d-c amplifiers *are* used, and choppers are then employed to stabilize the amplifiers. (Chopper stabilization of d-c amplifiers is used in many modern analogue computers.)

As mentioned previously, demodulation or detection of a suppressed-carrier signal is frequently necessary in a servo system. Alternatively, if a chopper amplifier were used, we would eventually want to demodulate the chopped signal after amplification. The demodulation of the chopped signal of Fig. 4-2*b* is obvious by inspection. It is done simply by reversing the polarity of the negative parts of the signal shown. But this implies using another chopper synchronized to the original one, as shown in Fig. 4-4. If the modulation and demodulation can be accomplished in close proximity, the two switches can be mounted together and one coil used. Otherwise the two coils must be used and driven from the same supply, or the two supplies must be synchronized.

Synchronous detection is thus necessary, as indicated in the introductory statements on suppressed-carrier transmission. We showed this previously by multiplying through by $\cos \omega_c t$. Here the final amplified signal output can be written

$$Af(t)S^2(t) = Af(t)$$

if the choppers are in synchronism. Let us now ask ourselves the very simple yet important question: How fast shall we chop? There is obviously an upper limit to the rate at which we can vibrate a mechanical switch. We would also like to use readily available sources of power to drive the chopper. These are usually at 60 or 400 cps in many servo systems. Does using these sources set any limit on the signals to be chopped? To answer this question, assume that the input signal is band-limited at f_m cps, and consider again the spectrum of the chopped signal shown in Fig. 4-3*b*. Note that increasing f_c causes theoretically no difficulty, aside from the important practical difficulty of driving the vibrator at greater rates. But there *is* a lower limit: if f_c is made smaller than f_m, the lower sideband about f_c crosses the zero-frequency axis, implying distortion of some type. The limit occurs for $f_c - f_m = 0$, and the chopper frequency must be restricted to values such that

$$f_c \geq f_m \tag{4-7}$$

We must thus chop at the rate of *at least* f_m times per second in order to avoid distortion. This is an important relation, which we shall extend and modify later in discussing pulse-modulation systems.

In practice f_c is ordinarily fixed by the available supply voltage—60 or 400 cps. This then limits the types of input signals that can be chopped: they must be varying slowly enough so that their highest-frequency component f_m is less than the supply frequency of either 60 or 400 cps.

4-3. Single-ended Chopper Modulator. We have just discussed a mechanical balanced-modulator circuit using a mechanical vibrator, or chopper, as a switching element. By an obvious extension we can treat a single-ended mechanical modulator (also used in chopper-amplifier circuits). This will lead us directly into the theory of sampling, sampled-data systems, and also pulse-modulation systems.

A single-ended modulator is shown in Fig. 4-5. This mechanical switch, vibrating f_c times per second, is the mechanical analogue of the piecewise-linear switching device treated in Sec. 3-3 as a small-signal approximation to the nonlinear modulator. (The "switching" in that case was done by the carrier in series with the modulating input.)

As in the previous cases treated, the input to the amplifier, $f_s(t)$, may be written as a product of $f(t)$ and the switching function $S(t)$,

$$f_s(t) = f(t)S(t) \tag{4-8}$$

$S(t)$ is the periodic square wave of Fig. 4-6. Its Fourier-series representation is simply

$$S(t) = \tfrac{1}{2}\left[1 + 2\sum_{n=1}^{\infty} \frac{\sin (n\pi/2)}{n\pi/2} \cos n\omega_c t\right] \tag{4-9}$$

with $f_c = 1/T$, the vibrator frequency. Note that except for the d-c term this is the same expression obtained for the double-ended switch

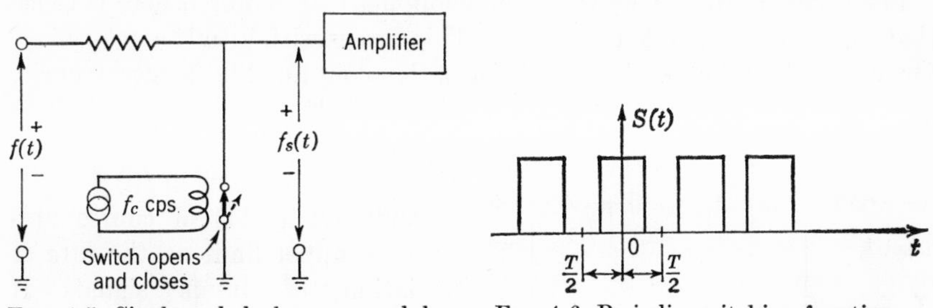

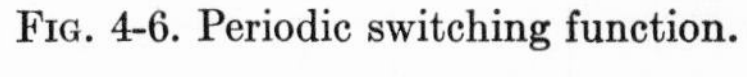

FIG. 4-5. Single-ended chopper modulator.

FIG. 4-6. Periodic switching function.

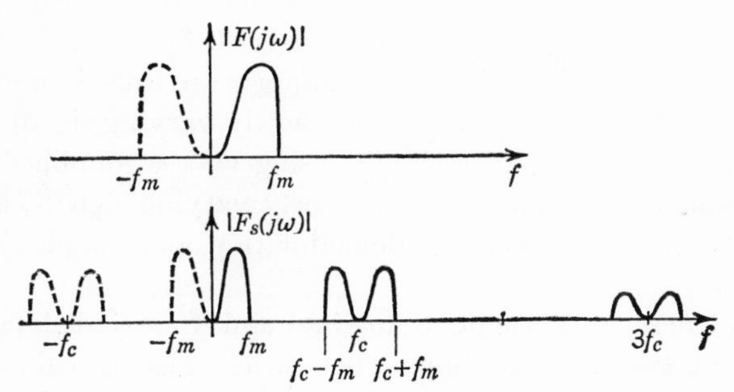

FIG. 4-7. Amplitude spectrum of single-ended chopper.

modulator. (The square wave in that case was symmetrical about the 0 axis. Here the symmetry is about the d-c value, ½). By using Eqs. (4-8) and (4-9), the input to the amplifier may be written

$$f_s(t) = \tfrac{1}{2}f(t)\left[1 + 2\sum_{n=1}^{\infty} \frac{\sin (n\pi/2)}{n\pi/2} \cos n\omega_c t\right] \tag{4-10}$$

$f_s(t)$ thus consists of the original input $f(t)$ plus sideband terms located about the odd harmonics of the switching frequency. The information carried by $f(t)$ is therefore retained in any one of the sidebands and may be recovered by demodulation and filtering. The amplitude spectra for a typical band-limited input function are shown in Fig. 4-7.

Again, as in the double-ended chopper case, we may ask ourselves the very pertinent question: Is there any limit on the rate of chopping?

Alternatively, with f_c fixed at 60 or 400 cps, is there any limit on the types of signal that can be chopped? The answer is again yes, as seen from an inspection of Fig. 4-7. For as f_c is decreased, there is an obvious lower limit: $f_c - f_m = f_m$. If f_c were to decrease further, the first lower sideband (about f_c) and the frequency components about $f = 0$ would overlap and distortion would result. The limit on f_c is thus

$$f_c \geq 2f_m \tag{4-11}$$

For a given input bandwidth the chopping rate required here is twice that for the double-ended chopper. This agrees with intuitive reasoning, for we are chopping out half the information contained in $f(t)$ every cycle. We must thus chop at least twice as fast to retain the necessary information as to variations in $f(t)$.

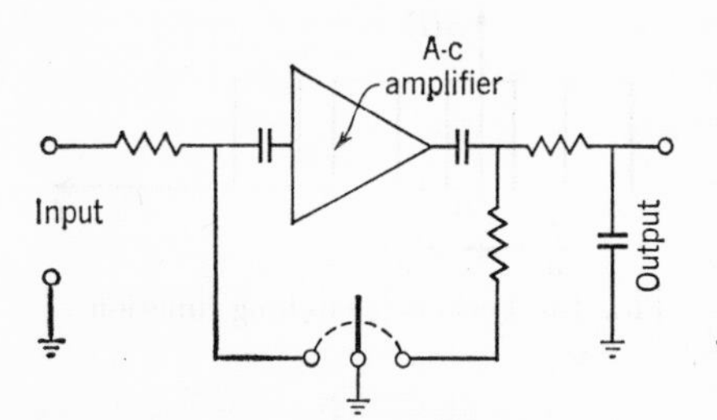

FIG. 4-8. Chopper amplifier including modulator and demodulator.

Equation (4-11) of course also puts an upper limit on the rate of variation of input signals. If $f_c = 60$ cps, the highest-frequency component in $f(t)$ that can be handled is 30 cps. These mechanical choppers are thus limited ordinarily to slowly varying signals.

A typical chopper-amplifier circuit, using an a-c amplifier to replace the d-c amplifier for amplification of slowly varying signals, is shown in Fig. 4-8. Both modulation and demodulation and simple filtering are included.

4-4. Extension to Periodic Sampling and Sampled-data Systems. Although we introduced the chopper for use as a mechanical modulator— shifting up the center frequency of the input spectrum so that a-c amplification could be used— the concept of chopping, or *sampling*, a signal has many far-reaching implications.

In many information-transmission devices a continuous time signal is either not available or not possible to use. For example, a radar system provides target information only once every complete scan. A temperature-sensing transducer used to measure temperatures in the rotating member of a turbine might provide temperature information only once every rotation. Alternatively the power output of a temperature or pressure transducer might be so low or the measured system-transducer combination so sensitive that the information would be measured only periodically instead of continuously. This would minimize the disturbing influence of the measuring equipment on the transducer and system measured.

In all these cases *periodic samples* of a signal are present. Is it possible, just as in the case of the chopped signal, to reconstruct a continuous information-carrying wave from these samples? We might again feel intuitively that this is possible if the information being sampled varies only slightly between sampling intervals. That this "feeling" is correct will be demonstrated shortly.

Information-transmission systems that are designed to handle periodically sampled signals are called sampled-data systems. Although the information is available only periodically in many applications, there are others in which the periodic sampling is purposely built in. For sampling of a signal means immediately that there are times in which no information is being transmitted through a system. It is thus possible to transmit other information from other sources in the vacant intervals. The transmission of samples of information from several signal channels simultaneously through one communication system with different channel samples staggered in time is called *time multiplexing*. (This compares with the *frequency-multiplexing* process, in which different information channels are used to modulate sine-wave carriers of different frequencies. These different carriers may then be combined in one wideband channel accommodating the entire range of frequencies involved.) Figure 4-9 shows a time diagram of a time-multiplexed signal system having four information carriers.

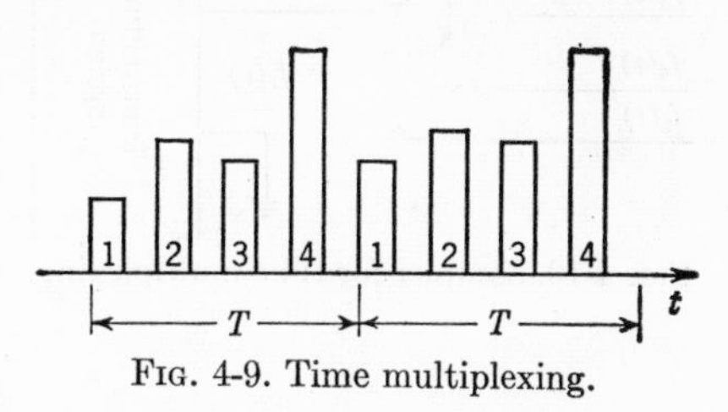

FIG. 4-9. Time multiplexing.

Time multiplexing has been widely used in the radio, teletype, and telephone fields and for telemetering purposes. There are other reasons for using time-multiplexed sampled-data systems. The samples are ordinarily available in the form of pulses and may be readily adapted for digital-computer processing. This procedure has become particularly important in the past few years. The samples may be coded into pulses of uniform height and reshaped when necessary. This minimizes the effect of noise and interference in many cases. Unfortunately the fast-rising pulses used in many pulse-communication systems require much wider bandwidths (several megacycles) than the corresponding frequency-multiplexed sine-wave-carrier systems. These pulses are frequently used, however, to modulate a sine-wave carrier for radio transmission. If the radio transmission is at high enough frequencies (many pulse communication systems operate at microwave frequencies), the bandwidth is not so important a factor.

The simplest type of sampled-data system, with time multiplexing incorporated, consists of a multichannel input connected through a multiposition switch to the transmission system. Such a sampler is shown in Fig. 4-10. A mechanical switch is shown in the diagram, but electrical switching could be used equally well. The device is thus obviously an extension of the chopper, with a multiposition rotating switch used instead of the vibrator.

Assume that the switch remains on each position τ sec and rotates at the rate of $f_c = 1/T$ times per second. A typical input function $f_1(t)$, the sampling times, and the sampled output corresponding to one channel

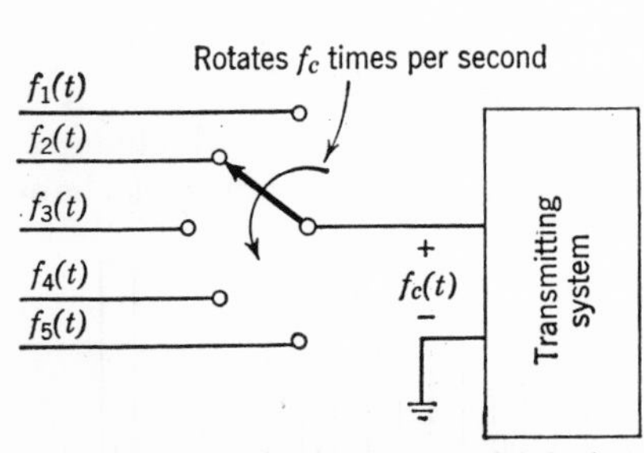

FIG. 4-10. Sampler for time multiplexing.

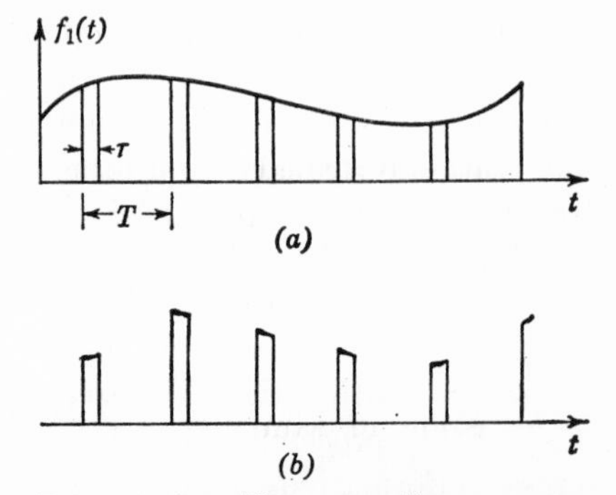

FIG. 4-11. The sampling process. (τ = sampling time; $T = 1/f_c$: sampling interval.) (a) Input $f_1(t)$; (b) sampled output $f_s(t)$ (one channel only).

are shown in Fig. 4-11. The time-multiplexed sampled output, corresponding to the superposition of all the channels, resembles the pulses of Fig. 4-9. T is called the *Nyquist*,[1] or sampling, interval.

As previously, the sampled output of one channel, $f_{s1}(t)$, may be written

$$f_{s1}(t) = f_1(t)S(t) \tag{4-12}$$

with $S(t)$ a periodic series of pulses of unity amplitude, width τ, period $T = 1/f_c$. Thus

$$\begin{aligned} S(t) &= \frac{\tau}{T} \sum_{n=-\infty}^{\infty} \frac{\sin (n\pi\tau/T)}{n\pi\tau/T} e^{jn\omega_c t} \\ &= d\left(1 + 2 \sum_{n=1}^{\infty} \frac{\sin n\pi d}{n\pi d} \cos \frac{2\pi n t}{T}\right) \end{aligned} \tag{4-13}$$

with $d \equiv \tau/T$, the duty cycle.

Although Eqs. (4-12) and (4-13) are for the sampled signal, they could have just as well been obtained by amplitude-modulating a train of periodic pulses. In this case we would say that the pulse train represents

[1] After H. Nyquist of Bell Laboratories.

a pulse carrier. Such a system would be called a *PAM system.* A sampled-data system (the term ordinarily used in the controls field) and a PAM system (the term used in communication work) are thus basically the same. They represent the extension of sine-wave modulation schemes to pulse modulation. We shall have more to say about actual PAM systems later, but it is thus apparent that our discussion of the simple sampler of Fig. 4-10 is directly applicable to PAM systems.

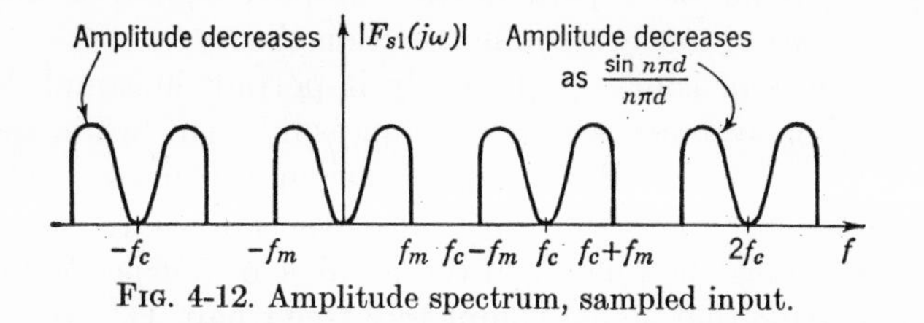

FIG. 4-12. Amplitude spectrum, sampled input.

The amplitude spectrum of the sampled output is readily obtained from Eqs. (4-12) and Eq. (4-13) and takes the form shown in Fig. 4-12 (for a typical band-limited input).

4-5. Sampling Theorem. Again we can ask the same question we asked in the case of the choppers: Are there any limits to the rate at which we sample? From Fig. 4-12 we get the same limit as in the single-ended chopper case,

$$f_c \geq 2f_m \tag{4-14}$$

(There is theoretically no upper limit on f_c, although practical limits might be encountered. However, increasing f_c implies sampling the signal more often. There is then less time available between samples, and fewer channels can be multiplexed. As $f_c \to \infty$, we of course approach the continuous input again: no sampling.)

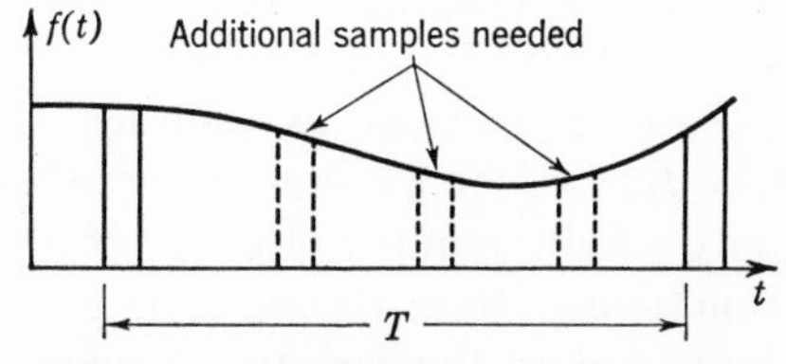

FIG. 4-13. Sampling frequency too low.

The lower limit on the sampling frequency indicated by Eq. (4-14) is highly significant. We might again feel intuitively that there must be a minimum value of f_c in order not to lose information or to be able eventually to reconstruct the continuous input signal. For we note that if we sample at too low a rate the signal may change radically between sampling times. We thus lose information and eventually produce a distorted output. A sampling rate too low for the signal involved is shown in Fig. 4-13. In order not to lose the signal dips and rises, additional sampling pulses must be added as shown.

There is obviously a relation between the rate at which a signal varies and the number of pulses needed to reproduce it exactly. The rate at which a signal varies is of course related to its maximum frequency component, or bandwidth, f_m. Equation (4-14) tells us that at least $2f_m$ uniformly spaced samples are needed every second in order eventually to reproduce the signal without distortion.

This statement, arising quite naturally out of a consideration of the frequency spectrum of a periodically sampled signal, is the famous *sampling theorem*[1] of modern communication theory.

The theorem is of course particularly important in sampled-data and pulse-modulation systems, where sampling is inherent in the operation of the system. But it has deep significance in the modern concepts of information theory. For any measure of the information content of a specified signal must be related to the number of *independent* quantities needed to describe that signal completely (see Chap. 1). If the number is written in the form of binary units, the information content is measured in bits.

Although our statement of the sampling theorem, arising from Eq. (4-14), relates to the periodic sampling of a band-limited signal, the theorem can be generalized to *any* group of independent samples. Thus the more general theorem states that *any $2f_m$ independent samples per second will completely characterize a band-limited signal. Alternatively any $2f_mT'$ unique (independent) pieces of information are needed to completely specify a signal over an interval T' sec long.*

These statements should come as no surprise to us, for we use similar results constantly in applying the Taylor's-series expansion of calculus: a function, obeying certain conditions, may be expressed and completely specified at any point in terms of the value of the function and its successive derivatives at another point. All polynomials, for example $y = t, t^2, t^3$, etc., possess a finite number of nonzero derivatives, and so only a finite number of pieces of information are needed to describe these functions. Here the number of independent pieces of information are measured in the vicinity of one point and are not periodically spaced samples.

The proof of the more general form of sampling theorem, that *any* $2f_mT'$ pieces of information are needed to characterize a signal over a T'-sec interval, follows readily from an application of the Fourier series. Thus assume that we are interested in a band-limited function $f(t)$ over an interval T' sec long. We may then expand $f(t)$ in a Fourier series with T' as the base period. But with $f(t)$ band-limited to f_m cps we get only a finite number of terms in the Fourier series,

[1] H. S. Black, "Modulation Theory," chap. 4, D. Van Nostrand Company, Inc., Princeton, N.J., 1953.

$$f(t) = \frac{c_0}{T'} + \frac{2}{T'} \sum_{n=1}^{f_mT'} |c_n| \cos (\omega_n t + \theta_n) \qquad \omega_n = \frac{2\pi n}{T'} \tag{4-15}$$

or

$$f(t) = \frac{c_0}{T'} + \frac{2}{T'} \sum_{n=1}^{f_mT'} (a_n \cos \omega_n t + b_n \sin \omega_n t) \tag{4-16}$$

with $|c_n| = \sqrt{a_n^2 + b_n^2}$, $\theta_n = -\tan^{-1}(b_n/a_n)$. [Since f_m is the maximum frequency component of $f(t)$, ω_n has a maximum value

$$\omega_m = 2\pi f_m = \frac{2\pi m}{T'}$$

The maximum value of n is thus f_mT'.]

The c_0 term is the d-c term. It merely serves to shift the level of $f(t)$ and does not provide any new information. (Information implies signals *changing* with time, as pointed out in Chap. 1.) There are thus $2f_mT'$ independent Fourier coefficients (the sum of the c_n's and θ_n's or a_n's and b_n's), and any $2f_mT'$ independent samples of $f(t)$ are needed to specify $f(t)$ over the T'-sec interval.

One point must be mentioned, however. Strictly speaking a band-limited signal is physically impossible to attain. For all physical signals begin at some time and are zero before that time, or they are nonzero over a finite interval. The Fourier series or Fourier integrals for such physically attainable signals contain components at *all* frequencies (although with greatly diminished amplitudes over certain frequency ranges). A band-limited signal exists, on the other hand, for all time: a physical impossibility. (Recall our discussion of the ideal band-limited filter in Chap. 2. There the effect of band limiting manifested itself with the appearance of precursors, or time responses before the signal was applied to the filter. The idealized output signal thus "existed" for all time.) This is as to be expected, for complete band limiting calls for physically unrealizable filters with the phase and amplitude independently chosen.

The signals used in practice can be made to approach the band-limited case by proper filtering, however, and the errors involved in neglecting higher-frequency terms can be made negligible. We thus ignore these second-order effects.

It is of interest to note at this point the connection between the sampling theorem just discussed and the equation for channel capacity developed in Chap. 1 and rephrased at the end of Chap. 2,

$$C = B \log_2 n \qquad \text{bits/sec} \tag{4-17}$$

where B is the channel bandwidth in cycles per second. In T' sec the channel will allow the transmission of

$$BT' \log_2 n \qquad \text{bits}$$

This expression for system capacity includes possible effects of noise ($\log_2 n$), but, aside from noise considerations, it says simply that the information that can be transmitted over a band-limited system is proportional to the product of bandwidth times the time for transmission. The concept embodied in this last sentence was first developed by R. V. L. Hartley of Bell Laboratories in 1928 and is called *Hartley's law.*[1] Modern communication theory has extended Hartley's law to include the effects of noise, giving rise to Eq. (4-17), the expression for system capacity.

Hartley's law and the sampling theorem (as developed by Nyquist in 1928) are in essence the same. For a band-limited signal may be viewed as having been "processed," or emitted, by a band-limited system. The information carried by this signal must thus be proportional to BT', or to f_mT' by Hartley's law. This of course is the same result as that obtained from the sampling theorem. (The factor of 2 that appears to distinguish the expression for channel capacity and the results of the sampling theorem can be accounted for by using $\tau = 1/2B$ instead of $1/B$ in the development of the channel-capacity expression of Chap. 2.)

4-6. Demodulation of Sampled Signals. If $2f_mT'$ (or $2BT'$) samples completely specify a signal, it should be possible to recover the signal from the samples. This is the demodulation process required for sampled-data or pulse-modulation systems. How do we accomplish it?

Note that the sampled output was expressed by Eqs. (4-12) and (4-13) in the form

$$f_s(t) = df(t)\left(1 + 2\sum_{n=1}^{\infty} \frac{\sin n\pi d}{n\pi d} \cos \frac{2\pi nt}{T}\right) \tag{4-18}$$

The simplest way to demodulate this output signal would be to pass the sampled signal through a low-pass filter of bandwidth f_m cps. This is shown in Fig. 4-14.

If we sample at exactly the Nyquist rate ($f_c = 2f_m$), the filter required must have infinite cutoff characteristics, as shown in Fig. 4-14*a*. This requires an ideal filter, an impossibility in practice. A practical low-pass filter with sharp cutoff characteristics could of course be used, with resulting complexity in filtering and some residual distortion (part of the lower sideband about f_c would be transmitted). This situation can of course be relieved somewhat by sampling at a higher rate, as shown in Fig. 4-14*b*. A guard band is thus made available, and filter requirements are less severe: the filter must cut off between f_m and $f_c - f_m$,

[1] *Ibid.*

its attenuation at $f_c - f_m$ being some prescribed quantity measured with respect to the passband.

As an example, voice transmission is commonly limited to 3.3 kc in commercial pulse-modulation systems. The Nyquist sampling rate would be 6.6 kc. A sampling rate of 8 kc is most frequently used, however, so that the filter guard band is 1.4 kc (from 3.3 to 8.0 − 3.3 = 4.7 kc).

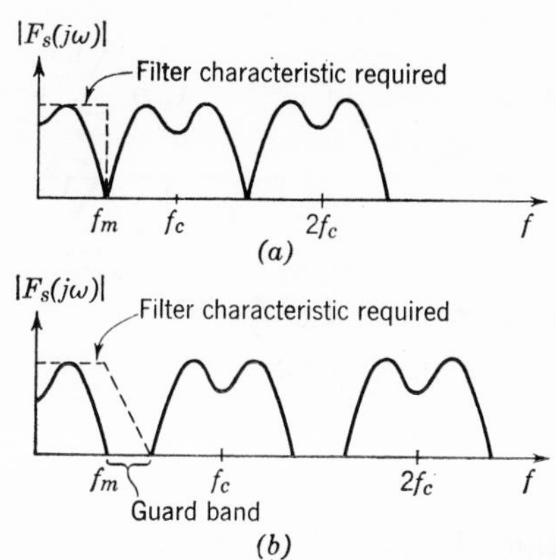

FIG. 4-14. Sampled-data demodulation using low-pass filter. (a) $f_c = 2f_m$; (b) $f_c > 2f_m$.

It is instructive to consider a simple proof for the low-pass filter demodulation of periodic samples.[1] This will fill out in a more quantitative way our rather qualitative discussion based on Eq. (4-18) and Fig. 4-14. It also helps to clarify further the actual mechanism of filtering.

Thus assume that a signal $f(t)$ band-limited to B (or f_m) cps has been sampled at intervals of $1/2B$ sec. We shall first show that $f(t)$ may be reconstructed from these samples (a necessary result from the sampling theorem) and shall then demonstrate that an ideal low-pass filter is called for in the reconstruction or demodulation process.

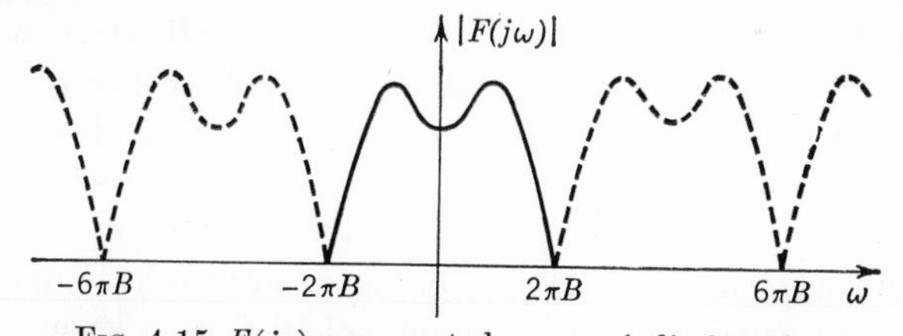

FIG. 4-15. $F(j\omega)$ represented as a periodic function.

To show that the given samples suffice to reproduce $f(t)$, take the Fourier transform $F(j\omega)$ of $f(t)$,

$$F(j\omega) = \int_{-\infty}^{\infty} f(t)e^{-j\omega t}\,dt \tag{4-19}$$

Then

$$F(j\omega) = 0 \qquad |\omega| > 2\pi B \tag{4-20}$$

by virtue of the band-limited assumption on $f(t)$.

$F(j\omega)$ can be arbitrarily made periodic with a period of $4\pi B$, as shown in Fig. 4-15. It can then be expanded in a Fourier series of period $4\pi B$

[1] B. M. Oliver, J. R. Pierce, and C. E. Shannon, Philosophy of PCM, *Proc. IRE*, vol. 36, no. 11, p. 1324, November, 1948.

to be used within the interval $|\omega| \leq 2\pi B$. Thus

$$\begin{aligned} F(j\omega) &= \frac{1}{4\pi B} \sum_{-\infty}^{\infty} c_n e^{j(2\pi n/4\pi B)\omega} \\ &= \frac{1}{4\pi B} \sum_{n=-\infty}^{\infty} c_n e^{jn\omega/2B} \qquad |\omega| < 2\pi B \\ F(j\omega) &= 0 \qquad |\omega| > 2\pi B \end{aligned} \tag{4-21}$$

with c_n defined by

$$c_n = \int_{-2\pi B}^{2\pi B} F(j\omega) e^{-jn\omega/2B} \, d\omega \tag{4-22}$$

But, since $F(j\omega)$ is the Fourier transform of $f(t)$, $f(t)$ can be written

$$f(t) = \frac{1}{2\pi} \int_{-\infty}^{\infty} F(j\omega) e^{j\omega t} \, d\omega = \frac{1}{2\pi} \int_{-2\pi B}^{2\pi B} F(j\omega) e^{j\omega t} \, d\omega \tag{4-23}$$

In particular, at time $t = -n/2B$

$$f\left(-\frac{n}{2B}\right) = \frac{1}{2\pi} \int_{-2\pi B}^{2\pi B} F(j\omega) e^{-jn\omega/2B} \, d\omega = \frac{c_n}{2\pi} \tag{4-24}$$

from Eq. (4-22).

This means that, if we are given $f(t)$ at the various sampling intervals (for example, $t = -3/2B$, $-2/2B$, $-1/2B$, 0, $1/2B$, etc.), we can find the corresponding Fourier coefficient c_n. But, knowing c_n, we can in turn find $F(j\omega)$ from the Fourier series of Eq. (4-21). Knowing $F(j\omega)$, we find $f(t)$ for *all* possible times by Eq. (4-23). A knowledge of $f(t)$ at sampling intervals $1/2B$ sec apart thus suffices to determine $f(t)$ at all times. This completes the first part of our proof: we have demonstrated that $f(t)$ may be reproduced completely, solely from a knowledge of $f(t)$ at the periodic sampling intervals. How do we now actually reconstruct $f(t)$ from these samples?

If we substitute the Fourier-series expansion for $F(j\omega)$ [Eq. (4-21)] into Eq. (4-23), the Fourier-integral representation of $f(t)$, we get

$$\begin{aligned} f(t) &= \frac{1}{2\pi} \int_{-2\pi B}^{2\pi B} F(j\omega) e^{j\omega t} \, d\omega \\ &= \frac{1}{2\pi} \int_{-2\pi B}^{2\pi B} \frac{1}{4\pi B} \left(\sum_n c_n e^{jn\omega/2B} \right) e^{j\omega t} \, d\omega \end{aligned} \tag{4-25}$$

If the order of integration and summation are now interchanged (the integral is finite and no difficulties can arise because of improper integrals; the c_n coefficients also approach zero for n large enough), the resulting integral may be readily evaluated. We get

$$f(t) = \sum_n \frac{c_n}{2\pi} \frac{1}{4\pi B} \int_{-2\pi B}^{2\pi B} e^{j\omega(t+n/2B)}\, d\omega$$

$$= \sum_n \frac{c_n}{2\pi} \frac{\sin 2\pi B(t + n/2B)}{2\pi B(t + n/2B)} \tag{4-26}$$

But $c_n/2\pi = f(-n/2B)$, from Eq. (4-24). Therefore

$$f(t) = \sum_{n=-\infty}^{\infty} f\left(-\frac{n}{2B}\right) \frac{\sin 2\pi B(t + n/2B)}{2\pi B(t + n/2B)}$$

$$= \sum_{n=-\infty}^{\infty} f\left(\frac{n}{2B}\right) \frac{\sin 2\pi B(t - n/2B)}{2\pi B(t - n/2B)} \tag{4-27}$$

since all positive and negative values of n are included in the summation. Mathematically, then, Eq. (4-27) indicates that we are to take each sample, multiply it by a $(\sin x)/x$ weighting factor centered at the sample's time of occurrence, and sum the resultant terms. This is exactly what is done, however, when we pass the samples through an ideal low-pass filter cutting off at B cps.

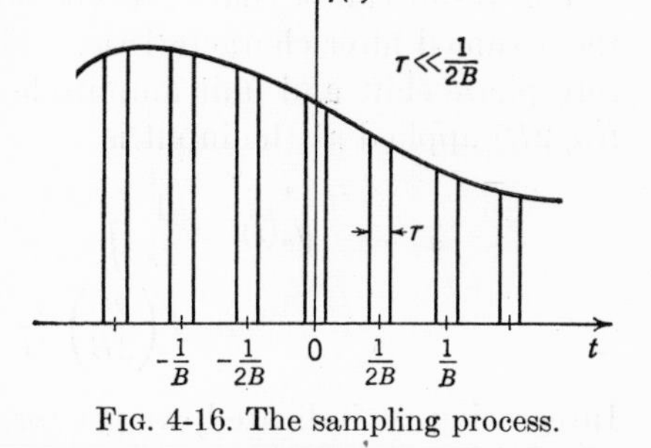

FIG. 4-16. The sampling process.

We can demonstrate this very simply in the following manner: Assume $f(t)$ again limited to B cps. We sample $f(t)$ for a length of time τ (the sampling time) periodically at intervals of $1/2B$ sec. If $\tau \ll 1/2B$, $f(t)$ may be assumed very nearly constant over the sampling time (Fig. 4-16).

The individual sample $f(n/2B)$ has a Fourier transform (or frequency spectrum) given by

$$F_n(j\omega) = \int_{-\infty}^{\infty} f\left(\frac{n}{2B}\right) e^{-j\omega t}\, dt \doteq \tau f\left(\frac{n}{2B}\right) e^{-jn\omega/2B} \tag{4-28}$$

since $f(t)$ is assumed constant over the τ-sec interval and zero elsewhere.

But note that this is just the Fourier transform of an impulse (delta function) of amplitude $\tau f(n/2B)$ and located at $t = n/2B$ in time. [It should be recalled from Eq. (2-108) that the Fourier transform of $K\delta(t - n/2B) = Ke^{-jn\omega/2B}$.]

The amplitude factor $\tau f(n/2B)$ represents the area under the curve of the individual sample. By assuming the sample duration τ to be very small we have effectively approximated the sample by an impulse of the same area.

Assume that this impulse is now passed through an ideal low-pass filter of bandwidth B cps with zero phase shift and unity amplitude assumed for simplicity. (The idealized linear phase shift just serves to delay the occurrence of the output signal, as pointed out in Chap. 2.) The response of this idealized filter to an impulse $K\delta(t - t_0)$ was shown in Eq. (2-114) to be given by

$$2KB \frac{\sin 2\pi B(t - t_0)}{2\pi B(t - t_0)}$$

[In Eq. (2-114) ω_c is the radian bandwidth and is just $2\pi B$ in the present notation.] The output response $g_n(t)$ of the ideal low-pass filter to the individual sample $f(n/2B)$ must thus be given by

$$g_n(t) = 2\tau f\left(\frac{n}{2B}\right) B \frac{\sin 2\pi B(t - n/2B)}{2\pi B(t - n/2B)} \tag{4-29}$$

This result can of course also be obtained directly from Eq. (4-28) and the assumed filter characteristic. Thus, for an ideal low-pass filter with zero phase shift and unit amplitude, the output response to the sample $f(n/2B)$ applied at the input is

$$\begin{aligned} g_n(t) &= \frac{1}{2\pi} \int_{-2\pi B}^{2\pi B} F_n(j\omega) e^{j\omega t}\, d\omega \\ &= f\left(\frac{n}{2B}\right) \frac{\tau}{2\pi} \int_{-2\pi B}^{2\pi B} e^{j\omega(t-n/2B)}\, d\omega \end{aligned} \tag{4-30}$$

Integrating, as indicated, we get for $g_n(t)$

$$g_n(t) = 2B\tau f\left(\frac{n}{2B}\right) \frac{\sin 2\pi B(t - n/2B)}{2\pi B(t - n/2B)}$$

as in Eq. (4-29). $g_n(t)$ is plotted in Fig. 4-17. Note that $g_n(t)$ has its maximum value at $t = n/2B$ (the filter was assumed to have zero phase shift), and precursors again appear because of the idealized filter characteristics assumed. The output is a maximum at the given sampling point, $t = n/2B$, and zero at all the other sampling points. At the sampling point $g_n(n/2B) = 2B\tau f(n/2B)$, or g_n is just the input $f(n/2B)$ to within a constant. The next sample, occurring $1/2B$ sec later, or at $t = (n + 1)/2B$, likewise produces an output given by Eq. (4-29), but delayed $1/2B$ sec, and proportional to $f[(n + 1)/2B]$.

The peak of each $(\sin x)/x$ term occurs at a sampling point where all other outputs are zero (Fig. 4-17), and the output at each of the sampling points is exactly proportional to the magnitude of the input sample at that point.

Since we have been assuming a linear ideal filter, the complete output is just the superposition of the individual sample outputs, or

$$
\begin{aligned}
g(t) &= \sum_{n=-\infty}^{\infty} g_n(t) \\
&= 2B\tau \sum_{n=-\infty}^{\infty} f\left(\frac{n}{2B}\right) \frac{\sin 2\pi B(t - n/2B)}{2\pi B(t - n/2B)} \\
&= 2B\tau f(t)
\end{aligned}
\tag{4-31}
$$

by comparison with Eq. (4-27). The output of the low-pass filter, $g(t)$, is thus identically proportional to the original signal $f(t)$ at *all* instants of time, not only at the sampling points. [Had we included a linear-phase-

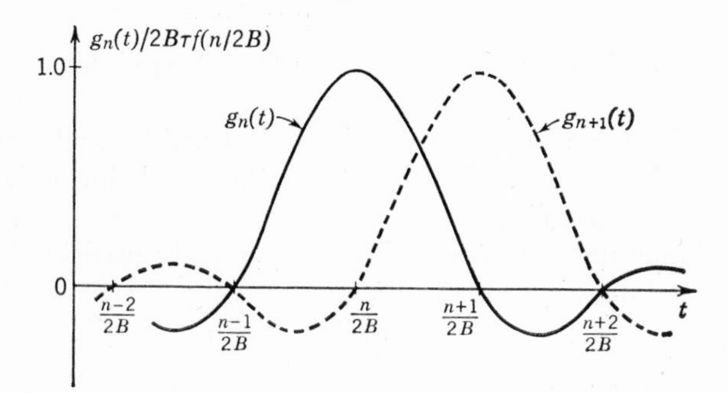

FIG. 4-17. Filter response to sampled inputs.

shift characteristic, we would of course have obtained a constant time delay for the output function. The output $g(t)$ would thus be a delayed replica of $f(t)$.]

The original input $f(t)$ may thus be reproduced from the samples by passing them through an ideal low-pass filter of bandwidth B cps. The $2B\tau$ proportionality factor represents the ratio of the filter and sampling pulse bandwidths. Since we assumed $\tau \ll 1/2B$, and since the effective pulse "bandwidth" is proportional to $1/\tau$ (Chap. 2), the pulse spectral width is much greater than that of the filter. [We in fact assumed the pulse spectrum to be constant over the filter bandwidth, as shown by Eq. (4-28).] Most of the energy of the input sample thus lies outside the filter spectrum, as shown in Fig. 4-14. If the pulse width is so narrow that its spectrum is almost constant (again the justification for representing it by an impulse of the same area), the output amplitude is reduced by the ratio of bandwidths, or just $2B\tau$.

These considerations of filter operation from a frequency point of view of course agree with the time approach. For, as shown by Eq. (4-18), an ideal low-pass filter of unity amplitude and bandwidth B cps would produce $g(t) = df(t)$ at the output. But the pulse duty cycle d is simply τ/T, or $2B\tau$, with $T = 1/2B$ (alternatively $2f_m\tau$), agreeing with the result of Eq. (4-31).

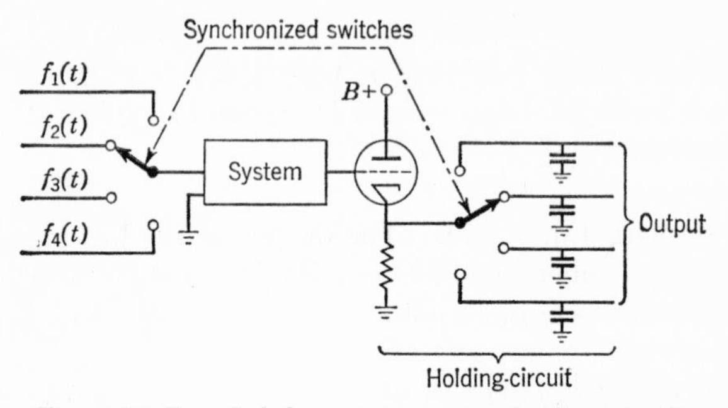

FIG. 4-18. Sampled-data system using holding circuit.

The ideal filter is of course a mathematical artifice and can only be approximated in practice. Actual filter outputs will thus only approximate the actual input $f(t)$.

A very simple demodulator and filter commonly used in time-multiplexed sampled-data systems consists essentially of a channel-selecting switch and a capacitor fed from a low-impedance source. Such a filter is one example of a so-called *holding circuit*. (The boxcar generator of radar fame has similar properties.)

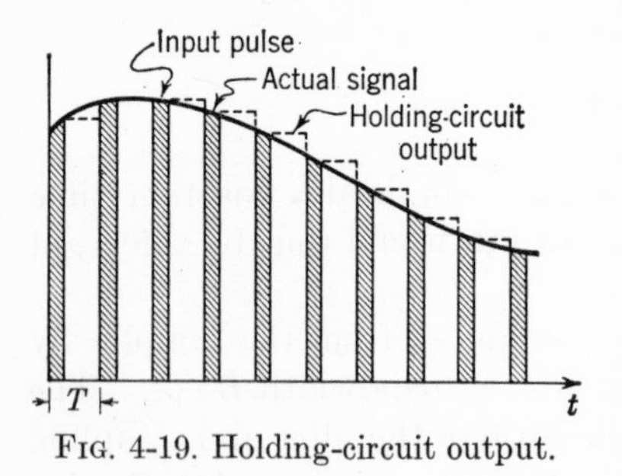

FIG. 4-19. Holding-circuit output.

A simple diagram of a sampled-data system using such a holding circuit for demodulation is shown in Fig. 4-18. The cathode follower provides a low-impedance source here. As the demodulator switch reaches a particular channel position, the capacitor rapidly charges up (at the rate determined by the capacitance and the internal impedance of the cathode follower) to the voltage at the cathode follower. If the switch is properly synchronized, this voltage is just the amplitude of the pulse corresponding to that channel. As the switch leaves the particular position, the capacitor "holds" the charge until the next sampling interval. The holding circuit thus serves to "stretch" the narrow input pulses into rectangular waves of width T—the Nyquist interval.

The holding-circuit operation is shown graphically in Fig. 4-19. It is apparent that the holding-circuit output is a step approximation to the actual signal. Further filtering is frequently used to produce a smoothed and improved version of the desired signal. It is also apparent that increasing the sampling rate tends to improve the holding-circuit approximation to the signal.

That this circuit, described above from the point of view of time response, is actually a crude low-pass filter, of the type deemed necessary for demodulation in Fig. 4-14, may easily be demonstrated. To find the frequency response of this circuit, we first find the Laplace transform and then set $p = j\omega$. This is done very simply by noting that if the applied voltage is a pulse of unity amplitude the capacitor charges up to unity amplitude and holds the charge until the switch again closes, T sec later. If the applied voltage is zero at that time, the capacitor quickly discharges through the low-impedance source.

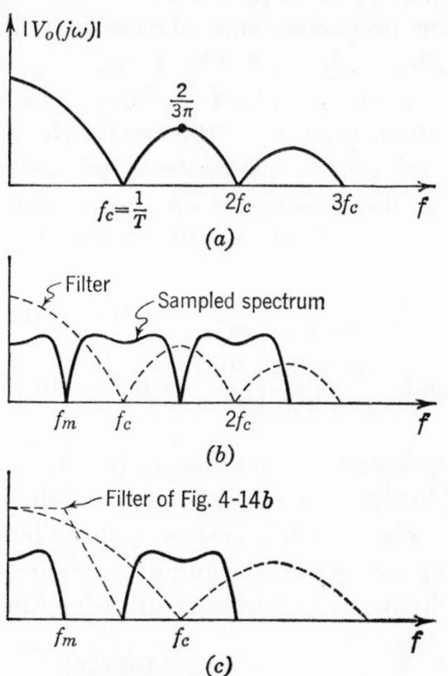

FIG. 4-20. Holding circuit as low-pass filter. (a) $(\sin x)/x$ filter; (b) demodulation with $(\sin x)/x$ filter; $f_c = 2f_m$; (c) $f_c > 2f_m$.

The capacitor voltage may thus be represented as the superposition of two unit steps, one positive step and one negative step delayed in time by T sec. This provides a delay factor e^{-pT} in the Laplace transform, or

$$V_o(p) = \frac{1 - e^{-pT}}{p} \tag{4-32}$$[1]

With $p = j\omega$,

$$V_o(j\omega) = Te^{-\frac{1}{2}j\omega T} \frac{\sin \frac{1}{2}\omega T}{\frac{1}{2}\omega T}$$
$$= Te^{-j\pi f/f_c} \frac{\sin (\pi f/f_c)}{\pi f/f_c} \tag{4-33}$$

with $f_c = 1/T$ the sampling frequency. The holding circuit thus behaves as a $(\sin x)/x$ filter. The frequency response (amplitude only) of such a filter is shown in Fig. 4-20a. (Compare with the filtering in Fig. 4-14.)

[1] If the input voltage is a unit pulse of width τ, $\tau \ll T$, its Laplace transform is approximately τ. The transfer function of the filter is then $V_o(p)/\tau$, with $V_o(p)$ given by Eq. (4-32). The transfer function or frequency response is thus proportional to $V_o(p)$.

It is apparent from Fig. 4-20*b* that the holding circuit, by itself, serves as a rather poor low-pass filter if the minimum Nyquist sampling rate is used. It gives zero output at f_c, instead of cutting off sharply at $f_c/2$. In fact it is down to $2/\pi$, or 0.636 of the peak value at $f = f_c/2$. The filtering properties may of course be improved by increasing the sampling rate, as shown in Fig. 4-20*c*.

As an example of the improvement possible by increasing the sampling rate, assume $f_m = 100$ cps for the particular signal and $f_c = 400$ cps (the minimum Nyquist rate is 200 cps). Ideally we would want a filter having unity response up to and including f_m and tapering off to zero at $f = f_c - f_m$ (the guard band). With these numbers the filter is down to

$$\frac{\sin(\pi 100/400)}{\pi 100/400} = 0.9\ (-1\text{ db}) \qquad \text{at } f = f_m = 100\text{ cps}$$

and

$$\frac{\sin(\pi 300/400)}{\pi 300/400} = 0.3\ (-10\text{ db}) \qquad \text{at } f = f_c - f_m = 300\text{ cps}$$

This may be satisfactory in some applications, but ordinarily additional filtering is inserted to improve the holding-circuit response.

The switch is necessary in understanding the operation of the holding circuit, so that the circuit is essentially a linear time-varying one. Linear circuits with the same transfer function may also be developed. These

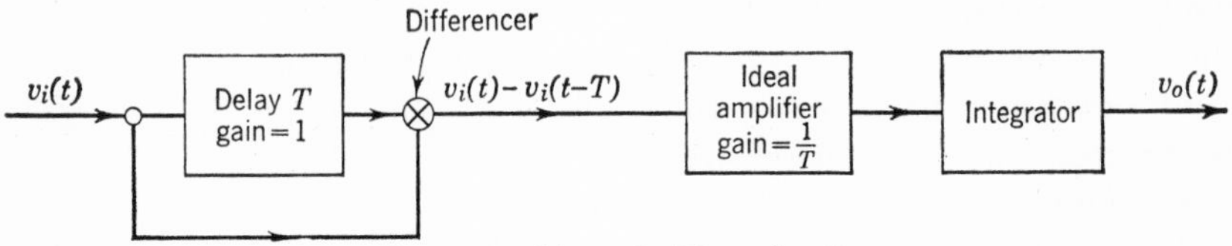

FIG. 4-21. Linear holding circuit.

do not require the use of switches for their operation. One example of such a linear circuit is shown in Fig. 4-21. The derivation of the transfer function is left as an exercise to the reader. (It is included as one of the problems for Chap. 2.)

4-7. Introduction to Pulse Modulation. We pointed out previously that the sampled-data system is in essence a PAM system in which the amplitudes of a periodic sequence of pulses are modulated or varied in accordance with the input signal.

Pulse-amplitude modulation is one example of several types of pulse-modulation systems commonly used in practice. In these systems a periodic sequence of pulses constitutes the carrier. Depending upon the type of system, the input signal may modulate or vary the pulse amplitude (producing PAM), the pulse width, or duration [producing pulse-width modulation (PWM) or pulse-duration modulation (PDM)—both terms have been used], and the pulse position [producing pulse-position modulation (PPM)]. The carrier, a typical input signal, and the three types of modulation output are shown in Fig. 4-22. Note that in the PAM output the amplitude increases or decreases in accordance with the input signal (signal positive or negative). In the PDM output the normal pulse width increases or decreases depending on the signal amplitude (positive or negative). In the PPM case the width and the amplitude of the pulses are unaltered, but the pulse occurrence is delayed or advanced in accordance with the input signal.

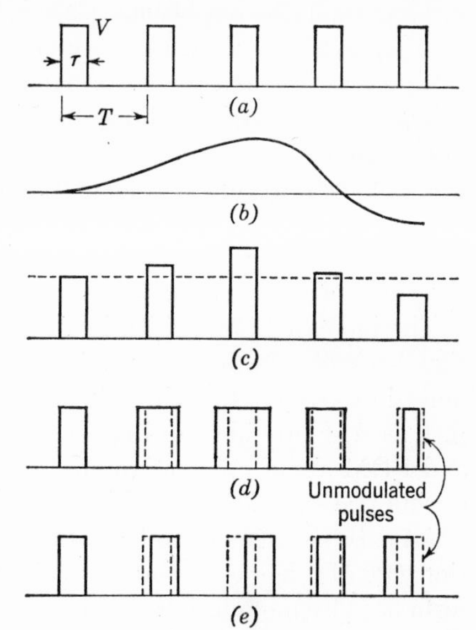

FIG. 4-22. Pulse-modulation systems. (a) Carrier; (b) signal input; (c) PAM output; (d) PDM output; (e) PPM output.

These are the basic types of pulse-modulation systems. Variations of these schemes are of course possible and have been used—double-polarity PAM, PDM with the position of the pulse leading edge fixed and the trailing edge varied, pulse modulation with the period T modulated in accordance with the signal, etc.

These methods of course contrast with the sine-wave modulation or continuous-wave (c-w) systems previously considered, in which the continuous *sine-wave* carrier is modulated by the input signal (AM, FM, phase modulation).

Pulse modulation and sine-wave modulation may at first glance seem unrelated, but, as we have stressed throughout this chapter, there is a certain unity between the different systems. In particular we pointed out during our discussion of the bipolar mechanical modulator (chopper) that the modulator could be used for generating a DSB modulated sine-wave signal by filtering the chopped output. But by extending the chopper technique to the sampling process we obtain PAM signals. As previously shown in Fig. 4-12, the spectrum of these sampled signals resembles a DSB spectrum, but with the sidebands now appearing about all harmonics of the carrier instead of the carrier by itself. By proper filtering the PAM can thus be converted to a DSB signal.

Pulse-amplitude modulation and amplitude modulation are not basically different because the modulation process is essentially the same in both cases: the input signal and the carrier are combined in a nonlinear or linear time-varying device. In one case the carrier is a single sine wave, in the other the sine wave and all its harmonics (the Fourier-series representation of the periodic pulses).

In practice a complete communication system may utilize both pulse-modulation and sine-wave (c-w) modulation techniques. Specific systems will be considered later, but in general the output of the pulse-modulation system will ordinarily be used to amplitude- or frequency-modulate in turn a sine-wave carrier for radio transmission.

Time multiplexing becomes possible with the use of pulse-modulation techniques and is in some cases more economical and simpler to implement equipmentwise than the corresponding frequency multiplexing of signals using a c-w carrier. Pulse-position-modulation and pulse-duration-modulation systems require much greater bandwidths, however, than do the c-w systems, for they depend on the accurate location of the pulse edges. (As will be shown later, this is not so critical in the case of PAM, and systems have been designed which require no more bandwidth than the corresponding SSB AM.[1])

The increased bandwidth in PPM will be shown in Chap. 6 to lead to signal-to-noise improvement, just as wideband FM provides signal-to-noise improvement. There is no signal-to-noise improvement in PAM, just as AM provides no improvement. The modulated pulses of PPM and PDM are of uniform amplitude and so may be reshaped periodically during transmission to avoid excessive distortion.

An extremely important form of pulse modulation, pulse-code modulation (PCM), has come into prominence in the past few years. In this form of pulse modulation the input signal is quantized or broken down into discrete amplitude levels, and pulses are generated corresponding to the different levels. These pulses may then be coded for optimum transmission. PCM with proper coding has been shown to approach the theoretically "best possible" communication system more closely than any other modulation system presently in use. This will be discussed in detail in Chap. 6.

In the next few pages we shall discuss in some detail a particularly simple PAM system that has been in commercial operation for some years and shall briefly touch on some aspects of a commercial PPM system. In our discussion of these systems we shall have occasion to draw on our previous knowledge of the inverse frequency-time relationship and the effect of filtering on signal transmission.

We shall defer actual quantitative comparisons of the different systems —both pulse and c-w—until Chap. 6, after we have dealt with the phenomenon of noise in the next chapter.

4-8. Pulse-amplitude Modulation. As has been pointed out several times already, PAM is basically the same as the sampled-data systems previously discussed. Although we talk of the periodic sequence of

[1] W. P. Boothroyd and C. M. Creamer, Jr., A Time-division Multiplexing System, *Trans. AIEE*, pt. 1, vol. 68, p. 92, 1949.

pulses being amplitude-modulated by an information-carrying signal, the effect is the same as if a sampling switch had been used to select periodic pulsed samples of the input signal. Pulse-amplitude-modulation systems may be designed in which pulse generators are actually used to generate the pulse carrier. In many systems, however, no actual pulses are generated and modulated, the same effect being obtained by the sampling process. Because of the high sampling rate required for radio or telephone transmission (8 kc is normally used), electronic switches are used.

The demodulation process is the same as for the sampled-data systems described, the modulated pulses being passed through a low-pass filter of width f_m (the bandwidth of the original input signal). Holding circuits with additional filtering where necessary are commonly used in the time-multiplexed PAM systems.

A basic problem in demodulation is again the synchronization required between the modulator-sampler and the demodulator-filter. Various methods of accomplishing this have been devised.[1] A typical electronic synchronization method will be described shortly. To establish firmly the essential elements of a PAM system, we have chosen to describe briefly a practical system now in use. This is a relatively simple eight-channel PAM system developed by Western Union and described in the literature.[2] This system incorporates in its design many of the concepts we have developed thus far in this book and so will enable us to consolidate our knowledge and review some fundamental ideas.

The system was designed to transmit eight 3.3-kc voice or 160 duplex teleprinter circuits over a 100-kc information band. (Note that a minimum bandwidth of 26.4 kc would be required for SSB transmission with standard frequency-multiplexing techniques. In practice, a 32-kc bandwidth might be used.) Time-multiplexed PAM was chosen because of its simplicity and relatively low cost. The amplitude-modulated pulses are used in turn to modulate an FM transmitter for short-range transmission. An 8-kc sampling rate is used (the minimum Nyquist rate would be 2×3.3, or 6.6, kc). An electronic distributor is used to sample periodically and time-multiplex the eight voice channels at the transmitter.

A simplified block diagram of the system is shown in Fig. 4-23. All sampling and timing operations are synchronized by the master 64-kc crystal-controlled oscillator shown in the transmitter diagram. The square-wave generators and the box labeled "Distributor" form the electronic sampler, or switch. The output of the transmitter distributor (point 2) thus consists of eight time-multiplexed signals, sampled at an 8-kc rate.

[1] Black, *op. cit.*, chap. 15.

[2] E. M. Marterson and C. B. Young, A Short-haul Radio Communication Link Channelized by Time Division, *Elec. Eng.*, vol. 70, p. 1094, December, 1951.

To ensure that the maximum frequency component of the input channels is 3.3 kc the inputs are passed through a 3.3-kc low-pass filter before being applied to the distributor. The transmitter and receiver distributors represent the heart of the system and will be described in some detail.[1] The sending (transmitter) distributor consists of a series of

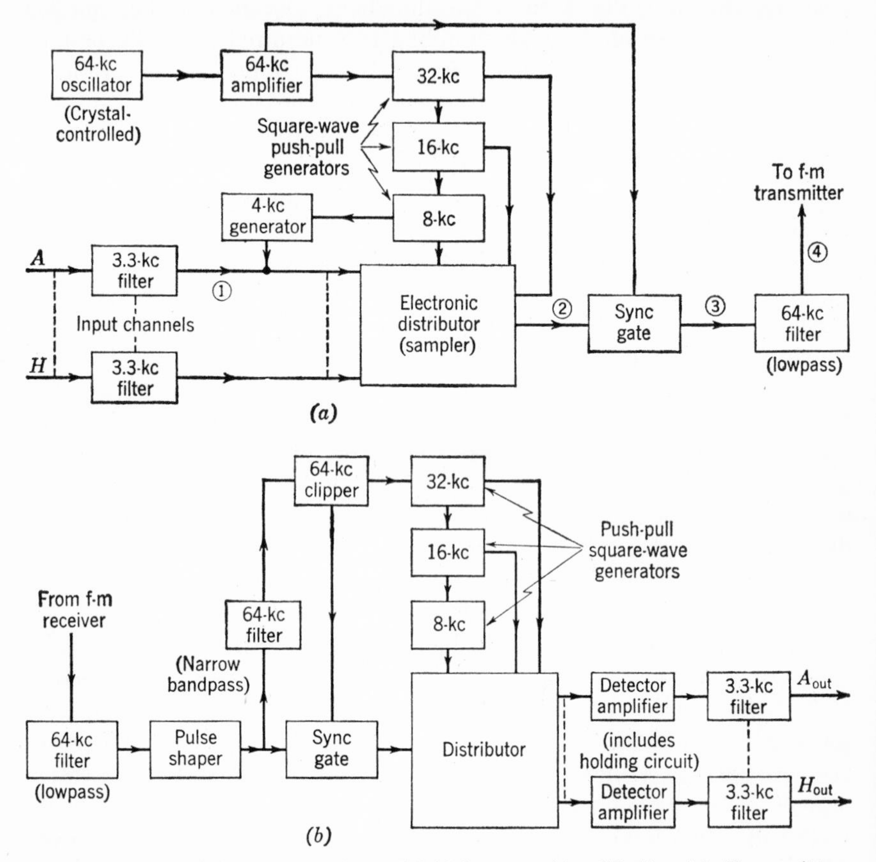

FIG. 4-23. Western Union eight-channel PAM system (simplified). (*a*) Transmitter; (*b*) receiver. (*From E. M. Marterson and C. B. Young, A Short-haul Radio Communication Link Channelized by Time Division, Elec. Eng., vol.* 70, *p.* 1094, *December,* 1951, *by permission.*)

switching tubes connected to each of the eight input channels. The object here is to switch consecutively from one channel to the next, the cycle to be repeated at the Nyquist sampling interval of 1/8kc, or 125 μsec. While one channel is operative, its input voltage being fed

[1] These are examples of *and*, or *coincidence*, circuits. See, e.g., Jacob Millman and Herbert Taub, "Pulse and Digital Circuits," sec. 13-3, McGraw-Hill Book Company, Inc., New York, 1956.

directly through the distributor, the other seven channels are rendered inoperative by the switching tubes. The successive switching is accomplished by utilizing the push-pull outputs of the three square-wave generators at 8, 16, and 32 kc. The distributor connections for two channels (A and E) and the associated square-wave generator connections are shown in Fig. 4-24. The symbols ϕ_1 and ϕ_2 represent the two

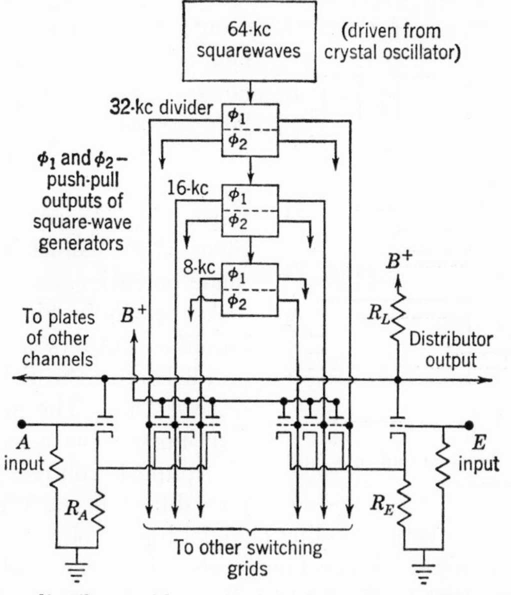

FIG. 4-24. Sending distributor (channels A and E only). (*From E. M. Marterson and C. B. Young, A Short-haul Radio Communication Link Channelized by Time Division, Elec. Eng., vol.* 70, *p.* 1094, *December,* 1951, *by permission.*)

push-pull outputs of each of the square-wave generators. (The generators are actually dividers, successively dividing down by 2 from 64 to 8 kc.)

The divider outputs over a 125-μsec interval are shown in Fig. 4-25. The letters indicate the channels to which they are connected. Each channel has associated with it three switching tubes, each connected to the ϕ_1 or ϕ_2 output of one of the three square-wave generators (Fig. 4-24). A particular switching tube will conduct when the square-wave output associated with it goes positive. The three switching tubes per channel are connected in parallel to the cathode of an amplifier tube associated with that channel. The amplifier tube of that channel (A, for example) is cut off when at least one switching tube conducts (e.g., the current through the resistor R_A with one tube conducting is enough to cut the A tube off). The amplifier tube will conduct only when all three switching tubes are simultaneously cut off. This corresponds to three simultaneously negative outputs of the particular phases of the three square-wave generators associated with the channel.

As an example, the three ϕ_1 outputs are connected to the A channel. From the square-wave output diagram of Fig. 4-25, then, the A-channel amplifier tube conducts once at the beginning of each cycle for a period of 15.6 μsec (125/8). In the second 15.6-μsec interval the ϕ_2 output of the 32-kc divider and the ϕ_1 outputs of the 16- and 8-kc dividers are simultaneously negative. If these three outputs are connected to the B channel the B amplifier tube will conduct during the second interval. The two outputs of each of the three dividers provide 2^3, or 8, different and successive conduction combinations. By the proper connections, then, each channel is consecutively made operative.

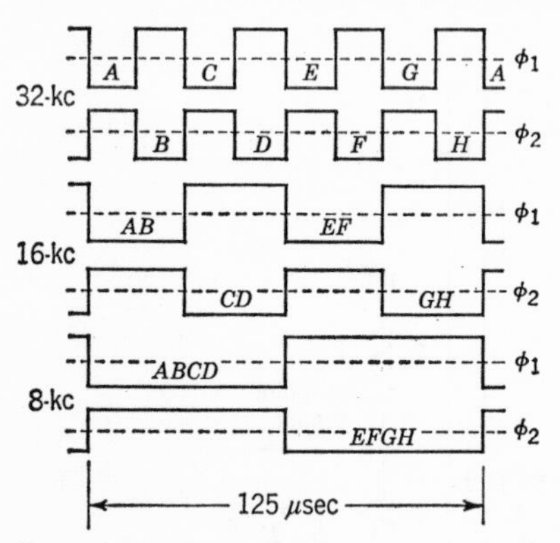

FIG. 4-25. Square-wave outputs and channel connections.

As shown in Fig. 4-24, all eight amplifier outputs are connected in parallel across the distributor output resistor R_L. The output voltage thus appears as a successive series of sampled voltages, each of 15.6 μsec duration, each voltage sample proportional to the corresponding channel input voltage.

To those familiar with the binary counting system the connections represent channels A to H coded to the equivalent binary numbers from 0 to 7. Thus, with ϕ_1 denoted by 0 and ϕ_2 by 1, the following table of connections can be written:

	Generator		
	8 kc	16 kc	32 kc
A 0	0 (ϕ_1)	0 (ϕ_1)	0 (ϕ_1)
B 1	0 (ϕ_1)	0 (ϕ_1)	1 (ϕ_2)
C 2	0	1	0
D 3	0	1	1
E 4	1	0	0
F 5	1	0	1
G 6	1	1	0
H 7	1	1	1

These connections, in binary form, correspond to the connections indicated in Fig. 4-25.

This particular distributor was designed on the binary principle. Other distributors could be devised, using ring counters, switching tubes, delay lines, etc.

The receiving distributor is of similar form and is shown in Fig. 4-26. It utilizes diode switches instead of switching tubes.

It is of interest now to trace the signals through the entire system, compare their shapes, and discuss the functioning of the different blocks in the block diagram of Fig. 4-23.

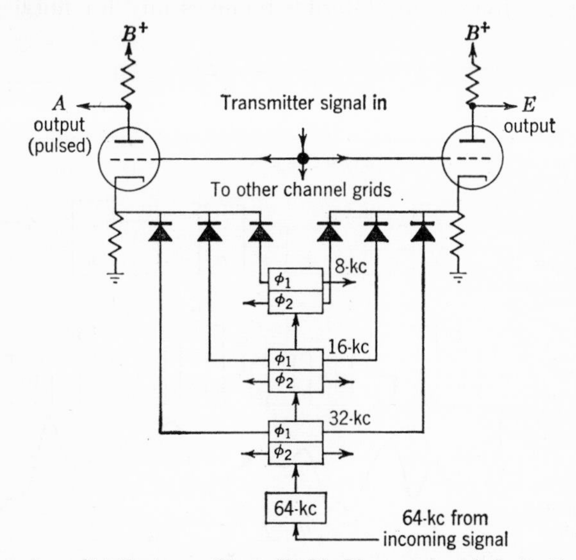

FIG. 4-26. Receiver distributor. (*From E. M. Marterson and C. B. Young, A Short-haul Radio Communication Link Channelized by Time Division, Elec. Eng., vol.* 70, *p.* 1094, *December,* 1951, *by permission.*)

The output of the 3.3-kc band-limiting filter in each input channel (point 1 in Fig. 4-23) is some time-varying waveform as shown in Fig. 4-27. The time-multiplexed output of the distributor (point 2 in Fig. 4-23) is then a series of 15.6-μsec samples as shown in part 2 of Fig. 4-27. Bandwidth limiting in the rest of the system would broaden these pulses and produce channel pulse overlap. This corresponds to cross talk, or interference, between channels at the receiver. To prevent excessive cross talk, a narrow gate, following the distributor and driven at a 64-kc rate, operates to let through just a small portion toward the end of each pulse. The output of this gate (point 3 in Fig. 4-23) is shown in part 3 of Fig. 4-27. Some 64-kc energy is also added at this point to drive the receiver distributor. Transmission of these narrow pulses would require a relatively wideband system. To conserve bandwidth in this system, the gated pulses are passed through a low-pass filter of nominal 64-kc bandwidth (the filter actually tapers off slowly to 100 kc). This gives broadened pulses of roughly sinusoidal shape (see Chap. 2), which are then sent on to the FM transmitter. Note that the broadened pulses again overlap and might again produce cross talk. The overlap is less than in the case of the original 15.6-μsec pulses, however, and further pulse gating at the receiver eliminates this.

After transmission over a microwave relay link the signals are processed in an FM receiver and the audio pulse outputs then passed on to another 64-kc low-pass filter. This filtering removes any h-f noise introduced

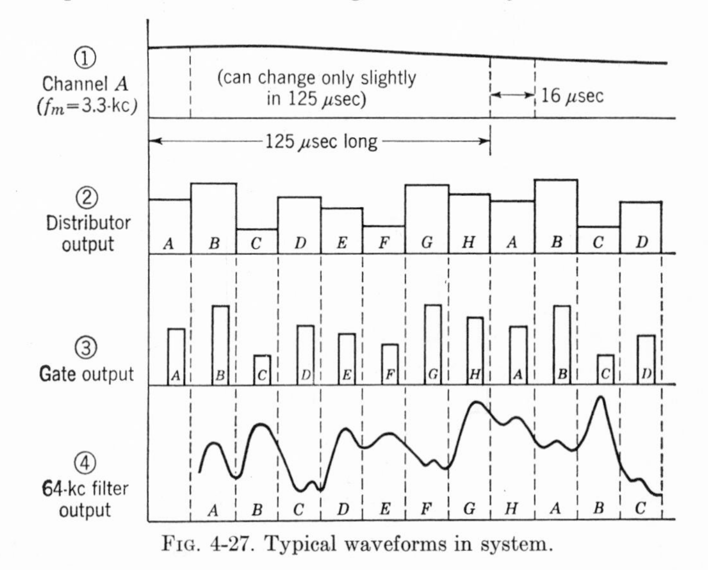

FIG. 4-27. Typical waveforms in system.

during transmission but also serves to broaden the pulses further and introduces considerable pulse overlap. For this reason the pulses are then "reconditioned" in the pulse shaper (a phase-shifter and differentiating circuit) and are sent on to the receiver synchronizing gate. Here a small portion at the center of each pulse (the point of maximum amplitude) is selected and pulse overlapping eliminated. The pulses then move on to the receiving distributor. After distribution to each channel the pulses are "stretched" in the holding circuit, amplified, and further filtered before appearing as an audio output. (It is to be noted that in all the pulse-shaping operations, at both the transmitter and the receiver, the amplitudes at each step are still proportional to the original audio input.)

Synchronization of the receiver distributor to the sending distributor in this system is ensured by transmitting the 64-kc tone previously referred to. This signal is filtered out after the receiver pulse shaper by a narrow-band 64-kc bandpass filter (see Fig. 4-23) and then used, after clipping, to drive the various square-wave generators. The clipped 64-kc output also controls the receiver synchronizing gate.

Synchronization still does not ensure proper registration of channels, for there is nothing to distinguish one channel from any of the others. To align the corresponding transmitter and receiver audio channels with one another, a 4-kc tone (obtained from the 8-kc generator in the transmitter) is sent along on the *A* channel. This drives a scanning circuit (not shown in the system diagram) which lines up the incoming *A* pulse with the receiver channel *A*. Once the transmitter and receiver are aligned with respect to channel *A*, the fixed sampling sequence assures the alignment of the other channels.

The Western Union PAM system was chosen for detailed discussion because of its comparative simplicity. Many of the features incorporated in this system are commonly utilized in more complex systems (with greater numbers of time-multiplexed channels, for example), and the reader should have no trouble in understanding the operation of other commercial PAM systems.

One interesting feature of this system, as pointed out above, is the fact that PAM pulses are purposely broadened to decrease the required transmission bandwidth. A correcting circuit in the receiver is then utilized to minimize pulse overlap or cross talk.

A much more elaborate corrector circuit was described in 1949 by Boothroyd and Creamer (in the article previously referred to) as part of a PAM system developed by the Philco Corporation. This corrector circuit enables very wide PAM pulses to be used and leads to the requirement of 120-kc bandwidth for a 30-channel voice input system. This is the same bandwidth as would be required for an SSB system with the 30 channels frequency-multiplexed. The over-all Philco system is very similar to the Western Union system but uses delay lines for transmitter time-multiplexing and receiver distribution. It also incorporates a holding circuit and low-pass filters in each receiver output channel.

4-9. Pulse-position Modulation. The basic elements of PPM can best be described by considering the pulse time diagrams for a commercial system developed by the Federal Telephone Laboratories.[1]

This system accommodates 23 voice channels, each of frequency range 100 to 3,400 cps. The Nyquist sampling rate used is again 8 kc (greater than $2f_m = 6.8$ kc), and the Nyquist sampling interval is thus again 1/8kc, or 125 μsec. Marker pulses are sent out at the beginning of each new time interval for synchronization purposes so that the equivalent of 24 channels (23 information plus 1 marker channel) must be time-multiplexed in the 125 μsec. This leaves about 5 μsec per channel to be

[1] D. D. Grieg and A. M. Levine, Pulse Time Modulated Multiplex Radio Relay System Terminal Equipment, *Elec. Commun.*, vol. 23, p. 159, 1946.

utilized for varying pulse position (plus and minus about the mean position) in accordance with the voice input. The timing diagram for several such channels is shown in Fig. 4-28. The marker pulses (M) in this system are two identical pulses, spaced by the pulse width. (In other systems single marker pulses of larger amplitude or greater width

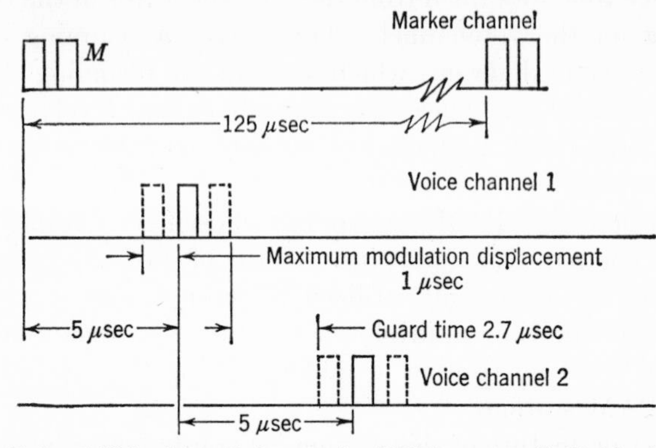

FIG. 4-28. Federal Telephone Laboratories PPM system (individual channels).

than the channel pulses have been used.) The pulses actually used are trapezoidal in shape, with a base width of 0.8 μsec and rise and decay time of 0.15 μsec. The maximum pulse time shift (corresponding to maximum signal input) is ± 1 μsec away from normal (zero input) signal.

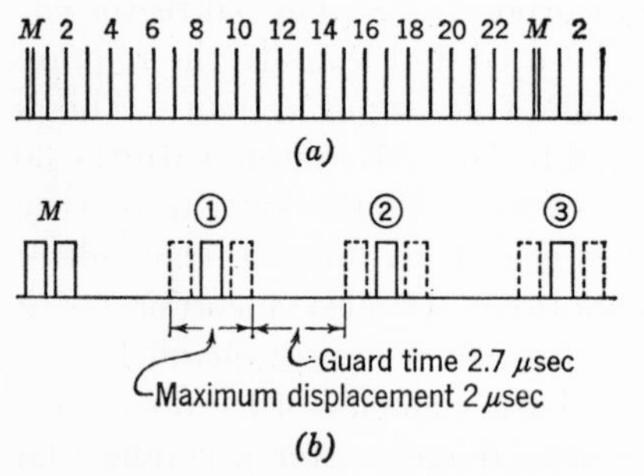

FIG. 4-29. The 23 channels multiplexed. (a) Multiplexed pulse train; (b) details of multiplexing.

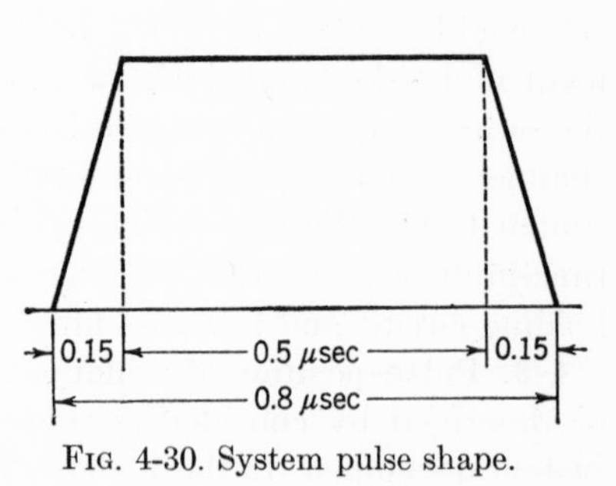

FIG. 4-30. System pulse shape.

The total space required by each channel is 2.3 μsec (2 μsec plus an allowance for the pulse rise and decay time at either end of the maximum displacement points). A guard time of 2.7 μsec is thus made available between the channels. These numbers are all indicated in Fig. 4-28 and repeated in Fig. 4-29, which shows the multiplexed pulse train and the details of multiplexing. The trapezoidal pulse used is shown in Fig. 4-30.

From our time-frequency discussions of Chap. 2 the system bandwidth is inversely proportional to the rise time. Using $\Delta f = 1/(2 \times \text{rise time})$, $\Delta f = 3.3$ Mc. The bandwidth actually used in this system is 2.8 Mc. Note then that the requirement of 23 channels to be multiplexed in 125 μsec, with appropriate provision allowed for maximum pulse displacement and guard time, has led to the use of rather narrow pulses, with very small rise times and correspondingly wide bandwidth. This is of course different from the situation in PAM, where the pulse shape

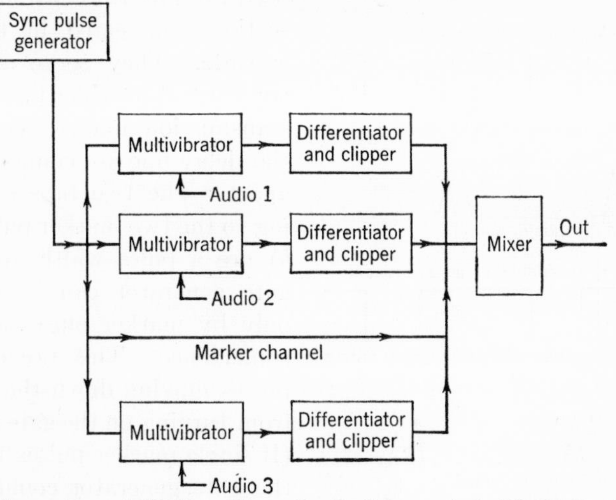

FIG. 4-31. Generation of PPM. (*From D. D. Grieg and A. M. Levine, Pulse Time Modulated Multiplex Radio Relay System Terminal Equipment, Elec. Commun., vol.* 23, *p.* 159, *fig.* 4, 1946, *by permission.*)

was not of extreme importance and lower bandwidths could be used. The sharp pulses obtained with this bandwidth, however, and the uniform amplitudes and shapes used serve to minimize possible difficulties with noise. The noise-improvement possibilities of wideband PPM will be discussed specifically in Chap. 6.

Just as in the case of PAM, there are many possible ways of generating and detecting time-multiplexed PPM signals. One particularly simple method of generating PPM is outlined in the article by Grieg and Levine already referred to. The method is indicated in block-diagram form in Fig. 4-31. The multivibrators shown are all of different time constant and provide successively increasing output pulse widths. They are all turned on periodically at the same time, however, by the synchronizing pulse generator. The multivibrator pulse widths are then grid-modulated by the respective audio channel inputs. The multivibrator pulses, of varying widths, are then differentiated and clipped and combined in the mixer. The synchronizer output is fed directly to the mixer and serves as a marker at the beginning of each cycle. (These marker pulses can be made of greater amplitude or width to distinguish them from the channel pulses.) The successive pulse outputs and the final multiplexed output are shown in Fig. 4-32.

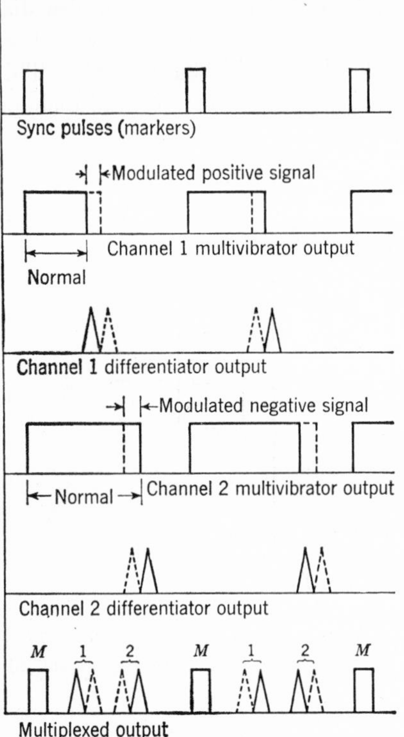

FIG. 4-32. Pulse-position-modulation generator pulse diagrams. (*From D. D. Grieg and A. M. Levine, Pulse Time Modulated Multiplex Radio Relay System Terminal Equipment, Elec. Commun., vol.* 23, *p.* 159, 1946, *by permission.*)

A method of demodulating multiplexed PPM pulses using a tapped delay line is shown in Fig. 4-33. (The delay lines most frequently used are lumped-constant *LC* filter sections connected in tandem or cascade. They serve as lumped-constant approximations to actual transmission lines.) The taps on the delay line are connected 5 μsec apart. The two taps corresponding to the two marker pulses (*a* and *b*) are a pulse width apart. The gate generator can be turned on only by marker pulses *a* and *b* in coincidence. This prevents other pulses moving down the delay line from turning on the gate generator. (If single marker pulses were used, the gate generator could be made to respond to pulses of the marker height or duration only.) The gate-generator pulses last the duration of the maximum plus or minus displacement of the PPM pulses in any one channel (2.3 μsec for the Federal Telephone Laboratories system) and serve to open all channel outputs connected to the respective taps.

During the gate time a pulse arriving at any particular channel turns on a linear sweep in that channel. The sweep is turned off at the end of the gate interval. At the time the sweep is turned off its voltage level is sampled and stored in a capacitor. Pulses advanced in time thus produce greater voltages; those delayed in time provide smaller voltages. Because of the linearity of the sweep the voltage sampled is proportional to the pulse position and, after possible inversion and further filtering, reproduces the original audio signal.

4-10. Summary. We have stressed in this chapter the basic unity between all types of modulation systems. By focusing attention on the use of a balanced chopper as a balanced modulator we were able to show the connection between sine-wave and pulse modulation. The chopper frequency serves as the carrier frequency in both cases. To obtain a suppressed-carrier, or DSB, signal, we filter the chopped output. To obtain a modulated series of pulses, we enhance the harmonic content of the chopped signal by periodically sampling the signal for a short interval of time.

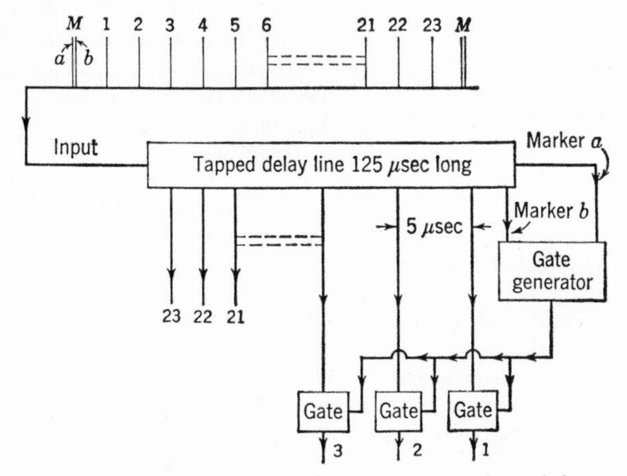

FIG. 4-33. Pulse-position-modulation system demodulator.

The process of sampling a signal was shown to allow the possibility of time-multiplexing a group of information channels on one common transmission channel. Modern pulse-modulation systems, using PAM and PPM techniques among others, commonly utilize time-multiplexing techniques.

To be able eventually to reconstruct or demodulate the original signal from its sampled form, at least $2f_m$ independent samples per second must be made available. f_m represents the highest-frequency component of the signal to be sampled. This statement or variations thereof are frequently referred to as the *sampling theorem.*

Pulse-modulation systems require synchronization of receiver and transmitter in order to redistribute and demodulate the time-multiplexed signal samples. Holding circuits are commonly used to provide some of the filtering needed to reconstruct the original transmitted signals.

In both this chapter and the previous one on sine-wave modulation great stress was placed on the bandwidth requirements of various modulation systems. The prescribed bandwidth of a given system places a limitation on the rate at which it will pass information. This was pointed out in Chaps. 1 and 2. In the next chapter we consider the second basic limitation on system-information capacity, noise in systems. In Chap. 6 we shall return to a discussion of modulation systems and compare them on the basis of both bandwidth and noise limitations.

PROBLEMS

4-1. A 1-cps sinusoidal input and a 60-cps sinusoidal carrier are combined in a product modulator to give $\sin 2\pi t \sin 2\pi \times 60t$.

Sketch this function, and show why simple envelope detection will not reproduce $\sin 2\pi t$.

4-2. The 1-cps input of Prob. 4-1 is applied to a 60-cps bipolar chopper.

(*a*) Sketch the output wave, and compare with the sketch of Prob. 4-1.

(*b*) The chopped signal is now demodulated by another 60-cps chopper. Sketch the resultant output signal for the three cases of (1) the two choppers in synchronism; (2) the two choppers out of phase by ⅛ cycle; (3) the two choppers out of phase by ¼ cycle. Which of these cases will reproduce $\sin 2\pi t$ if filters are available?

4-3. A signal $f(t)$ is first modulated by being passed through a bipolar chopper. After amplification by a constant A the chopped signal is demodulated by another chopper, which lags the first chopper by a fraction αT of the chopper period.

The resultant demodulated signal may be written analytically as $Af(t)S)t - \alpha T)$, with $S(t)$, the switching function, given by Eq. (4-5). This signal is filtered to reproduce $f(t)$.

Compare the outputs of the filter for different values of α. Show that the results are in agreement with those of Prob. 4-2*b* and with Eq. (4-3).

4-4. A transformer is arranged to allow the secondary winding to be rotated mechanically with respect to the primary. Show that, with the primary input a 60-cps sine wave and the secondary rotated at a constant rate of 1 rps, the output voltage is of the suppressed-carrier type.

4-5. Shown in Fig. P 4-5 are two examples of phase-sensitive diode demodulators used in servomechanism practice. The input in each case is either $f(t)S(t)$ or $f(t) \cos \omega_c t$. The power-supply frequency f_c cps is in each case the same as the frequency of the square wave $S(t)$. Explain the operation of these demodulators.

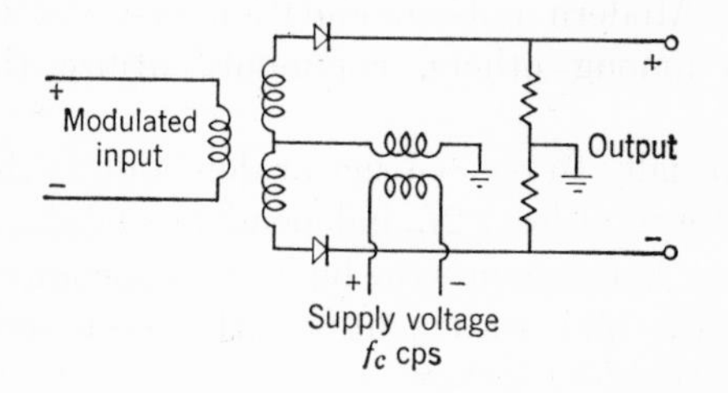

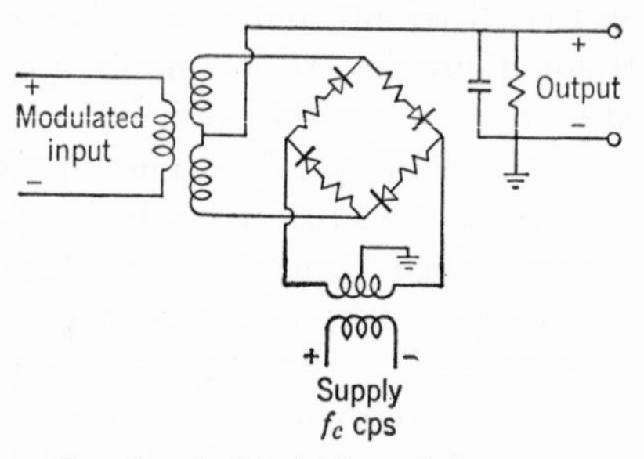

FIG. P 4-5. Diode demodulators.

Which is of the single-ended, which of the double-ended type? Compare with the mechanical demodulator of Fig. 4-4 and with the modulators of Fig. 4-5 and Fig. P 3-16. Why are these devices phase-sensitive?

4-6. Draw a single-ended chopper demodulator similar to the modulator shown in Fig. 4-5. Use an analysis similar to that of Prob. 4-3 to determine the phase sensitivity of a circuit combining the single-ended chopper modulator and demodulator.

4-7. Show that the chopper modulator of Fig. 4-5 can be used for suppressed-carrier DSB modulation.

4-8. A sinusoidal input at 1 cps, $\sin 2\pi t$, is to be sampled periodically.

(*a*) Find the maximum allowable interval between samples.

(*b*) Samples are taken at intervals of $\frac{1}{3}$ sec. Perform the sampling operation graphically, and show to your satisfaction that no other sine wave (or any other time function) of bandwidth less than 1.5 cps can be represented by these samples.

(*c*) The samples are spaced $\frac{2}{3}$ sec apart. Show graphically that these may represent another sine wave of frequency less than 1.5 cps.

4-9. A function $f_1(t)$ is band-limited to 2,000 cps, another function $f_2(t)$ to 4,000 cps. Determine the maximum sampling interval if these two signals are to be time-multiplexed.

4-10. Two signals, $f_1(t) = 10 \sin 2\pi 1{,}000t$ and $f_2(t) = 5 \sin 2\pi 2{,}000t$, are sampled at a rate of 10,000 samples per second and are then time-multiplexed.

(*a*) Sketch the resulting multiplexed function.

(*b*) After transmission the two sampled signals are separated out and fed to holding circuits. Sketch the holding-circuit output in the $f_1(t)$ channel.

4-11. Explain the $e^{-j\omega T/2}$ factor appearing in Eq. (4-33) for the output of the holding circuit. (Compare with Prob. 2-3.) Does this agree with the sketch of a typical output shown in Fig. 4-19?

4-12. Twenty-four signal channels plus one synchronization (marker) channel, each band-limited to 3,300 cps, are sampled and time-multiplexed at an 8-kc rate.

(*a*) Calculate the minimum bandwidth needed if the multiplexed signal, used in a PAM system, amplitude-modulates an h-f sine-wave carrier.

(*b*) Calculate the bandwidth needed to *frequency-multiplex* the same 24 signal channels, using normal AM techniques. What bandwidth would be needed if SSB AM were used in both the modulation and frequency-multiplexing processes?

4-13. Five signal channels are sampled and time-multiplexed. The multiplexed signal is then passed through a low-pass filter. Three of the channels handle signals covering the frequency range 300 to 3,300 cps. The other two carry signals covering the range 50 cps to 10 kc. Included is a synchronization signal.

(*a*) What is the minimum sampling rate?

(*b*) For this sampling rate what is the minimum bandwidth of the low-pass filter?

(*c*) What would the minimum bandwidth be if these channels were frequency-multiplexed, using normal AM techniques?

4-14. A number of 10-kc channels are to be transmitted. Calculate the theoretical minimum bandwidth per channel in using each of the following schemes. In each case state the minimum number of channels necessary if this bandwidth is to be achieved

(*a*) Single-sideband AM.

(*b*) Frequency modulation, $\beta = 1$.

(*c*) Pulse-amplitude modulation. Use 10-μsec-wide sampling pulses. The resulting time-multiplexed pulse train is to be passed through a low-pass RC filter section with time constant $RC = 2$ μsec. The output of the filter is transmitted directly over a wideband line.

4-15. A four-channel time-multiplexed PAM system is to be designed for voice signal transmission. The system is to accept voice signals in the range 300 to 3,300 cps.

Outline a possible block diagram for such a system. Include both the modulator section at the transmitter and demodulator at the receiver. Indicate, in the block diagram, a possible method of sampling and then multiplexing the four channels. Show a possible method of separating the different signals back into their respective channels. (The methods used may incorporate multivibrators, switching circuits, delay lines, counters, gate circuits, etc.)

Include any filters that may be needed in the system. Indicate the bandwidths required for transmission at various points in the system, and show sketches of pulse shapes at different points.

4-16. Indicate, in block-diagram form, a method of generating and multiplexing PPM pulses other than the one shown in the text. Show a possible method of demodulating the multiplexed PPM signals.

4-17. Repeat Prob. 4-15 for a PPM system. Compare the transmission bandwidths required in the two cases if the multiplexed signals are to modulate an SSB transmitter.

4-18. Channel 1 of a two-channel PAM system handles 0- to 5-kc signals; the second channel handles 0- to 10-kc signals. The two channels are sampled by a pulse generator that puts out square waves at the lowest frequency that is theoretically adequate. The sampled signals are then added and passed through a low-pass filter before transmission. After demodulation at the receiver the pulses in each of the two channels are passed through appropriate holding circuits.

(*a*) What is the frequency of the square-wave generator? What is the minimum cutoff frequency of the low-pass filter that will preserve the amplitude of the output pulses?

(*b*) The signal in channel 1 is $2 \sin 2\pi \times 2{,}500t$, and that in channel 2 is $\sin 2\pi \times 5{,}000t$. Sketch these signals, and below them draw the waveshapes at the input to the low-pass filter, at the filter output, and at the output of the holding circuit in channel 2.

4-19. A PAM system has been designed to accommodate 10 voice channels with frequency range 300 to 3,300 cps. The channels are sampled at an 8-kc rate.

(*a*) Calculate the frequency response (in decibels) of a holding circuit in one of the channels at $f = 0, f_m, f_c - f_m$ cps.

(*b*) Design a constant-K and m-derived matching section filter to follow the holding circuit so that the combination of filters, including the holding circuit, meets the following specifications:

f	*Attenuation, db*
0	0
f_m	≤ 3
$\geq f_c - f_m$	≥ 25

Assume that the relative frequency response of the holding circuit in decibels and the attenuation due to each filter section are additive.

CHAPTER 5

NOISE

Chapter 1 of this book stressed the fact, in a somewhat qualitative way, that there were two fundamental limitations to the transmission of information through a communication system:

1. Nonzero response time of the system (inversely related to the bandwidth)
2. Presence of noise in the system

Much of the material of the preceding chapters has been devoted to a discussion of the inverse time-frequency relationship of linear systems and to the time-frequency properties of some typical systems.

We now turn to the second system limitation—*noise in the system.* By exploring the basic meaning of the concept of noise, by discussing the origin of noise in the communication systems, and by developing methods for treating quantitatively the occurrence of noise we shall be able to establish some measure for the limitation on system capacity by noise. This will then enable us to develop quantitative measures of comparison between different communication systems now in use.

By the term *noise* we normally mean any spurious or undesired disturbances that tend to obscure or mask the signal to be transmitted. We can distinguish between various kinds of noise—the so-called "man-made" kind, the erratic disturbances normally beyond our control and occurring irregularly, and the type due to "spontaneous fluctuations."

The man-made type of disturbance may be due to electromagnetic pickup of another interfering signal; it may be from radiation from nearby electrical sources (electrical appliances, ignition radiation, etc.); it may be pickup through a power supply; it could be spurious voltages generated in the balanced modulator; it may be mechanical vibrations converted to electrical disturbances (microphonics), etc. There are literally hundreds of examples of such spurious disturbances that could be listed. They all have the property, however, that their effects can be eliminated or at least minimized by relocating the communication system, by proper shielding, by filtering circuits, by improving the mechanical and electrical design, etc.

Erratic disturbances aside from the man-made type may be due to electrical storms in the atmosphere, to sudden and unexpected voltage surges, etc.

Although both these types of noise are of great importance in system design, we shall concentrate on the third type—that due to spontaneous fluctuations of voltage, current, or their analogues in linear systems. (The erratic disturbances mentioned can be considered spontaneous in origin, too, but are not continuously present and so are listed separately.) These spontaneous fluctuations represent a basic limitation on the transmission of information.

Why "spontaneous fluctuations"? What does the term mean, and how do such fluctuations arise?

Spontaneous fluctuations occur generally throughout our physical world and are due to the noncontinuous, or granular, character of physical quantitites. For example, although we talk of a specific atmospheric pressure on such and such a day, we are actually discussing the effect of countless air molecules striking a wall of a particular container. These molecules are in continuous turbulent motion, moving randomly in all directions, striking and rebounding from one to another. The force on the wall is the resultant force of all the molecules and so will fluctuate or vary in time as fewer or more molecules strike the wall from time to time. Since the numbers of molecules involved are ordinarily tremendously large for normal-sized surfaces, the *average* force in time will remain constant so long as the molecular energy remains constant. The *instantaneous* force, as a function of time, however, will vary randomly about this average value. Increasing the temperature increases the molecular energy, and the average pressure goes up, as do the fluctuations about the average.

In electrical work we encounter similar fluctuations about average values owing to the granular character of matter. Conductors contain a large number of so-called "free" electrons and ions strongly bound by molecular forces. The ions vibrate randomly about their normal (average) positions, however, this vibration being a function of temperature. Collisions between the free electrons and the vibrating ions continuously take place. There is a continuous transfer of energy between electrons and ions. Thus, even with no signal source applied, there are always electrons in motion, giving rise to a randomly fluctuating current flow. Over a long period of time the net current will be zero, but again there are random fluctuations about this zero average. This type of spontaneous fluctuation in electrical circuits is called *thermal noise* because of its dependence on temperature. Although the fluctuations are normally quite small, the fluctuating currents being of the order of millimicroamperes and the voltages measured in microvolts, they may be amplified millions of times in modern amplifier circuits and tend to limit the detectability of desired signals. Alternatively the signals to be amplified may themselves be of the order of microvolts and so may be "lost in the noise" if special precautions are not taken.

Although many types of spontaneous fluctuations in electrical circuits have been studied—each due to a somewhat different mechanism—we shall restrict ourselves, in our quantitative discussions of noise circuits, to the most commonly occurring types: *thermal noise,* just mentioned, and the so-called *shot noise.* Shot noise is most commonly described as noise due to the random emission of electrons from a heated surface

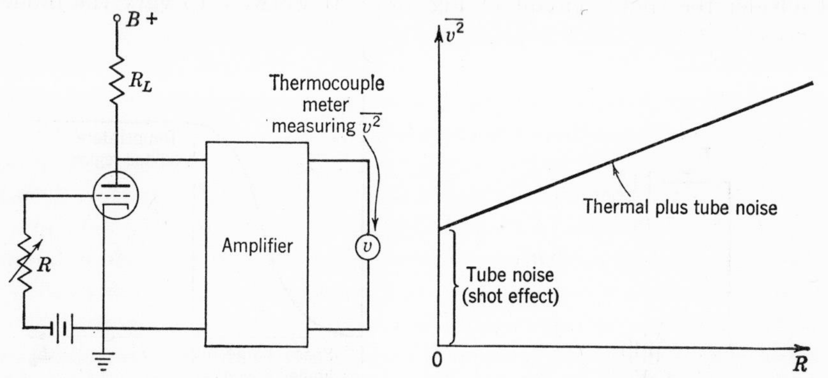

FIG. 5-1. Noise-measurement experiment.

FIG. 5-2. Mean-square fluctuation voltage as function of R.

(as in the vacuum tube, for example), and we shall follow this procedure. Shot-noise phenomena and thermal noise are both encountered in semiconductors.[1] In electrical circuitry we shall find thermal noise associated with resistors in the circuit and shot noise with both vacuum tubes and transistors. We shall commonly talk about mean-squared fluctuations about some average voltage or current. It will then turn out that the effects of shot noise and thermal noise are additive.

As a very simple experiment to perform, demonstrating both shot and thermal noise, consider the circuit in Fig. 5-1.[2] There is no signal applied anywhere in the circuit; yet a thermocouple meter—responding to the mean-square value of voltage ($\overline{v^2}$)—would give a definite indication. Varying the input resistance R, all other quantities constant, would provide the curve of Fig. 5-2. (A d-c meter would read zero.) $\overline{v^2}$ would be found to vary linearly with R; yet for $R = 0$ a nonzero reading would be obtained. This value of $\overline{v^2}$ with $R = 0$ is the shot noise generated in the tube; other values are due to shot noise plus the thermal noise of R. (As

[1] A. Van der Ziel, "Noise," Prentice-Hall, Inc., Englewood Cliffs, N.J., 1954.

[2] L. B. Arguimbau, "Vacuum-tube Circuits and Transistors," 2d ed., John Wiley & Sons, Inc., New York.

will be shown later, the thermal noise generated in R_L and any noise generated in the amplifier will be negligible compared with the two noises mentioned. This is due to the amplifying effect of the tube shown.)

In the following sections we shall treat the shot-noise effect first. We shall then discuss thermal noise and later combine the two in vacuum-tube circuits such as that of Fig. 5-1, as well as in transistor circuits.

5-1. Shot Effect in Temperature-limited Diodes (Low Frequency). The simplest form of shot effect occurs in the temperature-limited diode. Consider the simple circuit of Fig. 5-3. If we were to vary the diode

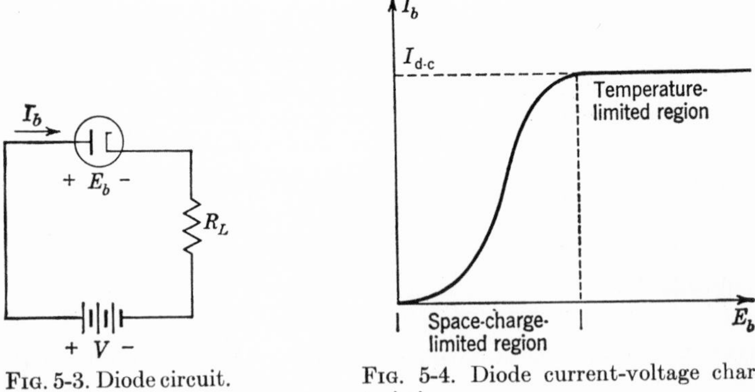

FIG. 5-3. Diode circuit.

FIG. 5-4. Diode current-voltage characteristic.

plate-cathode voltage E_b with the filament temperature fixed, we would obtain the usual diode characteristic of Fig. 5-4.

Heat supplied by the filament causes electrons to be boiled off, or emitted from, the cathode. If the plate voltage is high enough, all the electrons emitted are swept across to the plate and the plate current saturates at the value of I_{dc}, given by the average number of electrons emitted per second. This depends of course on the temperature at the cathode. For smaller values of E_b not all the electrons receive enough energy to reach the anode. They remain in the vicinity of the cathode and constitute a space-charge cloud, or "virtual cathode," which serves to limit the number of electrons reaching the plate. In this space-charge-limited region[1]

$$I_b \doteq CE_b^{3/2} \tag{5-1}$$

[1] We neglect, in all this section, second-order effects due to initial velocities, high-field emission, retarding fields, etc. The derivation of the three-halves-power law of Eq. (5-1) can be found in many electronics books. See, e.g., T. S. Gray, "Applied Electronics," chap. 3, John Wiley & Sons, Inc., New York, 1954; W. B. Davenport, Jr., and W. L. Root, "Introduction to Random Signals and Noise," chap. 9, McGraw-Hill Book Company, Inc., New York, 1958.

The current flow is always due to the emission of electrons from the cathode. Although we talk of a specified current I_b or I_{dc}, the emission of electrons is actually "erratic," or random in form—more electrons are emitted one instant, fewer the next, with the *average* number per unit time the same over a long period of time.

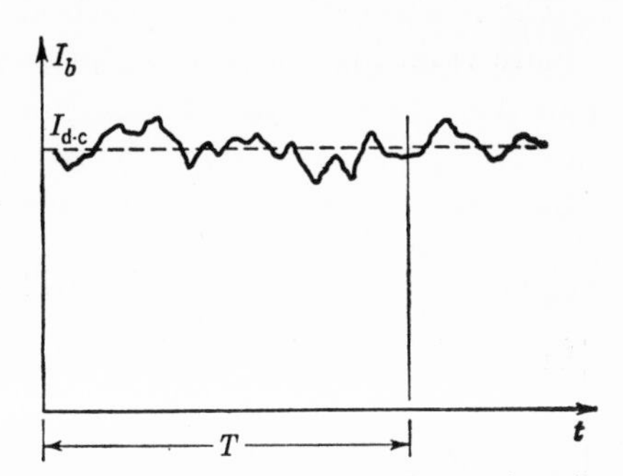

FIG. 5-5. Random current fluctuations in diode.

In the temperature-limited case this average number and the resulting average current I_{dc} are functions of the cathode temperature.

A very sensitive and fast-responding current meter placed in the diode circuit would trace out a current-time curve like that of Fig. 5-5 as a function of time. Because of the random emission of the electrons the current fluctuates randomly about its average value I_{dc}.

We are interested in some quantitative measure of these variations. Obviously, since there is no regular pattern, we cannot write a mathematical equation of current vs. time. We shall ultimately have to use statistical concepts to describe the nature of the fluctuating phenomena completely. At this point, however, it will suffice to talk about *average* effects. For example, these current fluctuations will give rise to an average power dissipation in the load resistor of Fig. 5-3. Can we determine this dissipation quantitatively? Note that it does us no good to consider the average of the variations about I_{dc} (the current fluctuates equally often in either direction about I_{dc}). But we can talk of the average of the square of the variations about I_{dc}, with the average taken over a long period of time. This average will be a positive quantity (the negative terms are squared). If the diode is operating normally, with voltage and temperature fixed, with the cathode surface unchanged, etc., an average of this sort over one time interval should give the same result as the average over another time interval (remember that we deal with tremendous numbers of electrons even in millisecond intervals). One measurement of the average should thus give a reproducible result.

How do we find such an average?

1. We can of course find such an average experimentally by amplifying the current fluctuations and then using a long-persistence oscilloscope to get a picture such as that of Fig. 5-5. We would then perform a graphical average. Alternatively (and more simply) we could measure the amplified mean-square fluctuations directly with a meter of root-mean-square (rms) type (a thermocouple, for example).

2. We can attempt to solve the problem mathematically by reasoning from the principles of the physics of electron emission. This gives a much more general result that can be checked experimentally.

The mathematical approach begins by noting that the desired mean-square variations about I_{dc}, $\overline{i_b^2}$, can be written

$$\overline{i_b^2} \equiv \overline{(I_b - I_{dc})^2} = \frac{1}{T} \int_0^T (I_b - I_{dc})^2 \, dt \tag{5-2}$$

(The small letters on averaging will always imply variations about some constant quantity.)

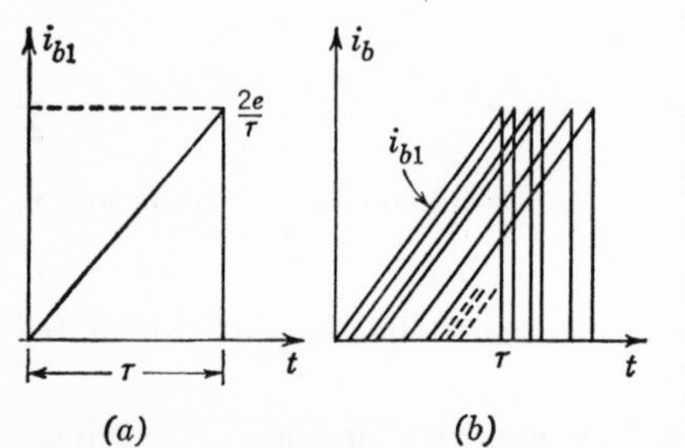

FIG. 5-6. Variations in plate current due to random occurrence of current pulses. (a) Plate-current pulse due to one electron (τ = transit time); (b) overlapping current pulses and their random occurrence.

The total *instantaneous* current I_b represents the superposition of the number of electrons leaving the cathode and hitting the plate over a given time interval, while I_{dc} is the average over a much larger interval. Each electron leaving the cathode thus contributes to the total current. We shall make the *basic assumption*, for temperature-limited conditions, that each electron contributes independently to the current. That this assumption is valid can be checked only by comparing the calculated results with experiment.

On this assumption we can calculate the power dissipated in the resistor by the current due to one electron leaving the cathode (if one can stretch the imagination that far!) and sum over all the electrons in a given time interval to get the total average power dissipated. Part of this power will be the d-c power $I_{dc}^2 R_L$. The remainder will be just our desired $\overline{i_b^2} R_L$.

Consider, then, one electron leaving the cathode. As the electron moves from the cathode to the plate, it induces a current i_{b1} in the plate circuit. One possible representation for i_{b1} is the current pulse of Fig. 5-6*a*. τ is the transit time, or time taken for the electron to move from the cathode to the anode.

As we shall see very shortly, the actual shape of the current pulse is unimportant. Important are two factors:

1. The pulse lasts τ sec.

2. The area under the curve is e, the charge of a single electron, for e coulombs is ultimately deposited on the plate. (Another form for the pulse might have been a rectangular pulse of amplitude e/τ amp and lasting τ sec.)

If any initial velocity the electron might have is neglected, the transit time is simply given by[1]

$$\tau = \sqrt{\frac{2m}{eE_b}}\, d_s \tag{5-3}$$

where E_b is the plate-cathode voltage, d_s the plate-cathode spacing (in meters), and m the mass of the electron (in kilograms). For example, taking d_s as 1 mm, E_b as 10 volts, e/m as 1.96×10^{11} coulombs/kg,

$$\tau \doteq 10^{-9} \text{ sec}$$

But

$$I_{dc} = \frac{re}{T} \tag{5-4}$$

if r electrons leave the cathode in T sec on the average. For $I_{dc} = 1$ ma, $r/T = 6 \times 10^{15}$ electrons per second, or in $\tau = 10^{-9}$ sec there are 6×10^6 electrons leaving the cathode.

There is thus a tremendous overlap of current pulses. In this simple example 6×10^6 current pulses would be initiated in the time taken for one to be completed. The tremendous numbers involved give us the right to use averaging and statistical concepts where needed. The overlap of current pulses is shown in Fig. 5-6*b*. The total plate current is the sum of these randomly occurring pulses and thus varies randomly about I_{dc} (Fig. 5-5).

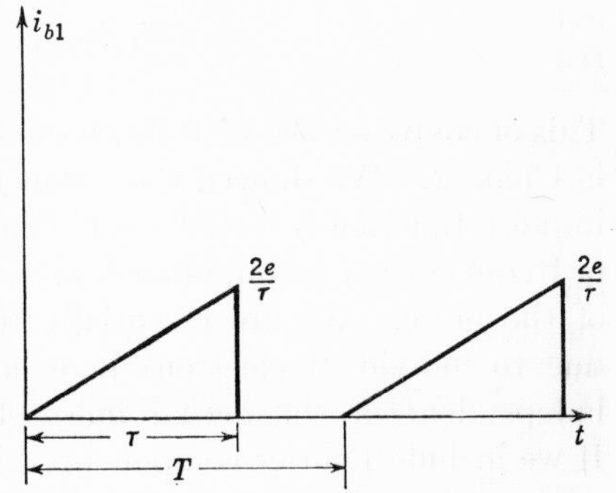

FIG. 5-7. Calculation of pulse Fourier series.

Our procedure will be simply to choose an interval $T \gg \tau$ and calculate the mean-squared current deviation about the average value due to one pulse. We shall then add the mean-square deviations due to r pulses in T sec to obtain $\overline{i_b^2}$. (Since the pulses are assumed independent, their power contributions must add.)

To find the mean-squared current deviation due to one pulse, we consider the pulse repeated over T-sec intervals and expand in a Fourier series (Fig. 5-7). Thus

$$i_{b1}(t) = \frac{1}{T}\left[c_0 + 2\sum_{n=1}^{\infty} |c_n| \cos\left(\frac{2\pi nt}{T} + \theta_n\right)\right] \tag{5-5}$$

[1] This assumes a uniform electric field. The equation can be derived by equating the kinetic energy of the electron at the plate to the decrease in potential energy in moving across the tube. The average speed of the electron, from which τ can be found, is just one-half the final speed for a uniform field.

For example, if the pulse is triangular,

$$|c_n| = e\left[\frac{\sin(n\pi d/2)}{n\pi d/2}\right]^2 \qquad d = \frac{\tau}{T},\ n = 0, 1, 2, 3, \ldots$$

and if the pulse is rectangular,

$$|c_n| = e\left|\frac{\sin n\pi d}{n\pi d}\right|, \text{ etc.}$$

But no matter what the shape of the pulse, the "bandwidth" of the pulse spectrum is approximately $1/\tau$ (see Chap. 2). For our previous example this would be 10^9 cps. (Other choices of numbers might have given 10^8 cps.) For $f \ll 1/\tau$, then, the spectrum amplitude $|c_n|$ is very nearly constant and equal to e,

$$|c_n| = e \qquad f \ll \frac{1}{\tau} \tag{5-6}$$

This of course agrees with the discussion of the impulse, or delta, function in Chap. 2. We showed there that many types of pulses approached an impulse function for very small time duration. The Fourier transform, or frequency spectrum, of such pulses is just a constant equal to the area of the pulse. We are essentially representing the individual currents, due to individual electrons here, as impulses. The spectrum is thus independent of the actual pulse shape up to very high frequencies. If we include Fourier components within a frequency range $\Delta f \ll 1/\tau$,

$$i_{b1,\Delta f} = \frac{e}{T}\left[1 + 2\sum^{\Delta f} \cos\left(\frac{2\pi nt}{T} + \theta_n\right)\right] \tag{5-7}$$

We shall normally discuss *low-frequency* (l-f) shot-noise phenomena in this book so that we need consider only $\Delta f \ll 1/\tau$. The higher-frequency noise phenomena involving transit-time effects lead to increased complications and are treated in the book by Van der Ziel, "Noise." It is important to remember that the results we shall obtain are not valid at the frequencies of 50 Mc and higher.

On this assumption—that we restrict ourselves to frequencies far below the reciprocal of the transit time—the mean-squared deviation about direct current due to one current pulse is simply the sum of all the mean-squared cosine terms of Eq. (5-7). The number of terms to be included in the Δf interval is $\Delta f/(1/T)$ (Fig. 5-8). Thus

$$\overline{i_{b1}^2} \equiv \overline{[i_{b1} - (\text{direct current})]^2}$$

$$= \left(\frac{2e}{T}\right)^2 \frac{1}{2}\frac{\Delta f}{1/T} = 2\frac{e}{T}e\,\Delta f \tag{5-8}$$

where the term ½ comes from averaging the square of the cosine term in Eq. (5-7). Adding the mean-squared deviations due to r electrons in T sec,

$$\overline{i_b{}^2} \equiv \overline{(I_b - I_{dc})^2} = 2r\frac{e}{T}e\,\Delta f \tag{5-9}$$

But
$$I_{dc} = \frac{re}{T}$$

Therefore
$$\overline{i_b{}^2} = 2eI_{dc}\,\Delta f \tag{5-10}$$ [1]

Equation (5-10) is the so-called *shot-effect formula* for the diode mean-squared current fluctuations under *temperature-limited conditions.* Normal diode operation under space-charge-limited conditions and the extension to triodes and pentodes will be considered shortly. Note again that this is an l-f equation only, valid for frequencies where transit-time effects are negligible. The mean-squared noise current is thus proportional to the plate current and to the frequency bandwidth. The rms noise current is proportional to the *square root* of current and bandwidth. *Widening the bandwidth in circuit applications increases the amount of noise power available.* This concept will be explored further later.

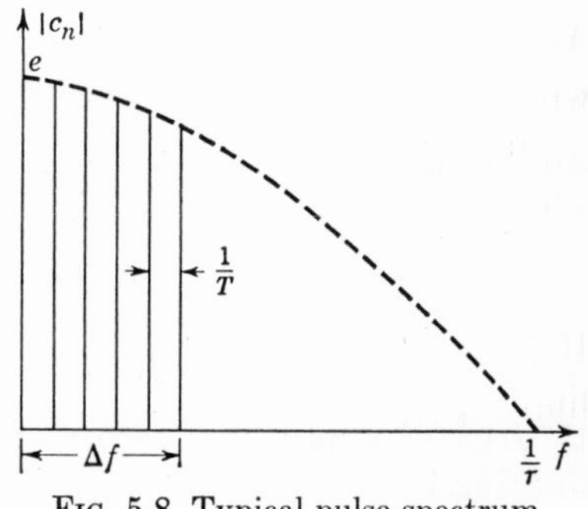

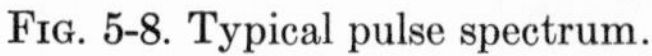

FIG. 5-8. Typical pulse spectrum.

As an example of numbers involved, take I_{dc} as 1 ma, Δf as 5 kc. Then

$$\overline{i_b{}^2} = 2(1.6 \times 10^{-19}) \times 10^{-3} \times (5 \times 10^3) = 1.6 \times 10^{-18}$$

The rms current generated is thus 1.26×10^{-9} amp rms. If this current flows through a 5-kilohm resistor, the rms noise voltage due to this current (we are neglecting at this point additional noise generated in the resistor) is 6.3 μv rms.

If the bandwidth is now quadrupled to 20 kc, the rms noise voltage doubles to 12.6 μv rms. Equation (5-10) has been checked experimentally many times and has even been used for precise measurements of the electron charge e.†

Now what happens if a temperature-limited diode is connected to

[1] More rigorous developments of this equation, and extensions to higher frequencies, may be found in S. O. Rice, Mathematical Analysis of Random Noise, *Bell System Tech. J.*, vol. 23, pp. 282–332, July, 1944; Davenport and Root, *op. cit.*, chap. 7; Van der Ziel, *op. cit.*

† E. B. Moullin, "Spontaneous Fluctuations of Voltage," Oxford University Press, New York, 1938.

some circuit (a filter or an amplifier, for example) with transfer function $H(j\omega)$? This is shown in Fig. 5-9. (The blocking capacitor is included only to indicate that the d-c current is not transmitted.) We are interested in the rms noise voltage $(\overline{e_2^2})^{1/2}$ at the output of the circuit. (We assume that the network itself contributes no noise. Additional noise due to networks will be considered later.)

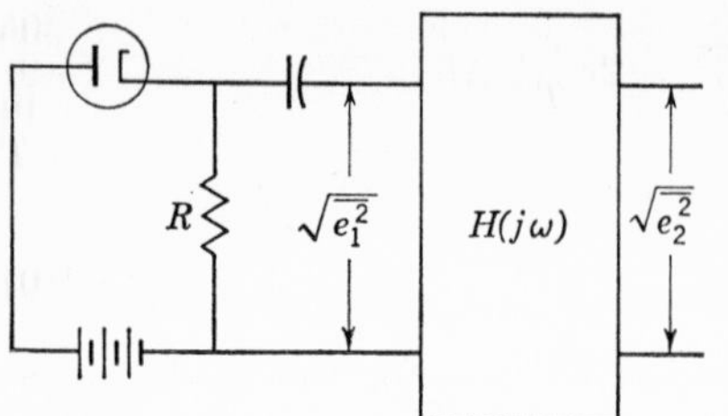

FIG. 5-9. Noise output of a network.

If we consider a frequency interval Δf_1, centered about $\omega = \omega_1$ and small enough so that $H(j\omega_1)$ is essentially constant over this interval,

$$\overline{e_{2,\Delta f_1}^2} = |H(j\omega)|^2 \overline{e_{1,\Delta f_1}^2} \tag{5-11}$$

Adding the contributions to $\overline{e_2^2}$ at each narrowband Δf_1, Δf_2, Δf_3, etc., within a larger bandwidth Δf,

$$\begin{aligned} e_2^2 &= 2eI_{dc}R_2^2[|H(j\omega_1)|^2 \Delta f_1 + |H(j\omega_2)|^2 \Delta f_2 + \cdots] \\ &= 2eI_{dc}R^2 \int_0^{\Delta f} |H(j\omega)|^2 \, df \end{aligned} \tag{5-12}$$

If $|H(j\omega)|^2$ approaches zero at frequencies less than Δf, the frequency limiting is due to the network and we write

$$\overline{e_2^2} = 2eI_{dc}R^2 \int_0^\infty |H(j\omega)|^2 \, df \tag{5-13}$$

As an example, assume that the network under consideration may be represented by a single RC combination [the high-frequency (h-f) cutoff of a one-stage amplifier, for example]. Then

$$H(j\omega) = \frac{A_m}{1 + j(\omega/\omega_H)} \tag{5-14}$$

where A_m is the mid-band transfer constant (amplification factor in an amplifier) and ω_H the 3-db cutoff frequency. Then

$$\overline{e_2^2} = 2eI_{dc}R^2A_m^2 \int_0^\infty \frac{df}{1 + (\omega/\omega_H)^2} \tag{5-15}$$

Defining $x = \omega/\omega_H$ in the integration, with $\omega_H = 2\pi f_H$,

$$\overline{e_2^2} = 2eI_{dc}R^2A_m^2 f_H \int_0^\infty \frac{dx}{1 + x^2} = 2eI_{dc}R^2A_m^2 f_H \frac{\pi}{2} \tag{5-16}$$

Comparing Eq. (5-16) with Eq. (5-10), we note that the effect of the network frequency response has been to limit noise contributions to those within an effective bandwidth $(\pi/2)f_H$; we could have obtained the same result by assuming for the network a rectangular frequency spectrum (the "ideal filter" of Chap. 2) of amplitude A_m and width $(\pi/2)f_H$. The bandwidth of such a rectangular equivalent spectrum is called the *noise equivalent bandwidth* B and may be defined very simply as

$$A_m{}^2B = \int_0^\infty |H(j\omega)|^2\, df \tag{5-17}$$

where A_m is the maximum absolute value of $H(j\omega)$. With this concept of noise equivalent bandwidth, Eq. (5-12) becomes

$$\overline{e_2{}^2} = 2eI_{dc}R^2A_m{}^2B \tag{5-18}$$

Whenever we talk of noise power over a specified bandwidth, this noise equivalent bandwidth will be meant. Thus, if the noise output of the temperature-limited diode carrying 1 ma steady current were impressed across a 5-kilohm resistor and the resulting voltage amplified 10^5 times through an amplifier of 20 kc bandwidth, the output mean-squared voltage would be

$$\overline{e_2{}^2} = 2(1.6 \times 10^{-19}) \times 10^{-3} \times (5 \times 10^3)^2 \times (10^5)^2 \times (20 \times 10^3) = 1.6 \text{ volts}^2$$

The rms output voltage as read on a thermocouple meter would thus be 1.26 volts rms.

5-2. Space-charge-limited Diodes. A quantitative analysis of noise in space-charge-limited diodes is rather cumbersome to attempt. Suffice it to say, however, that it has been found both experimentally and theoretically that the random emission of electrons is smoothed out by the presence of space charge near the cathode. The random fluctuations are decreased, and the noise output drops. This effect may be stated mathematically by writing

$$\overline{i_b{}^2} = 2eI_b\Gamma^2\,\Delta f \tag{5-19}$$

where I_b is the average plate current at the point of operation in the diode space-charge region and Γ^2 is a space-charge reduction factor varying commonly between 0.01 and 1.

The smoothing effect of the space charge may be seen qualitatively by noting that if excess electrons leave the cathode in one interval they will tend to depress the potential minimum below its average value. This prevents all these excess electrons from reaching the anode, and the fluctuations tend to be smoothed out. Without going through the details of the calculation of Γ^2† we can visualize that Γ^2 will depend on the

† See J. L. Lawson and G. E. Uhlenbeck, "Threshold Signals," McGraw-Hill Book Company, Inc., New York, 1950; Davenport and Root, *op. cit.*

velocity of the emitted electrons and the potential distribution within the tube. Both these in turn depend on the cathode heating temperature T_c and the applied voltage E_b (alternatively the plate current I_b). Since Γ^2 is a dimensionless quantity, it must be related to E_b and T_c in dimensionless form. This may be done by noting that eE_b and kT_c, e the electronic charge and k Boltzmann's constant ($k = 1.38 \times 10^{-23}$ joule/°K), both have the dimensions of energy (joules). (Boltzmann's constant appears frequently in the kinetic theory of heat. The temperature of a gas, for instance, is a measure of the kinetic energy of motion of the molecules. It is used to convert temperature to kinetic energy.) Then

$$\Gamma^2 = f\left(\frac{eE_b}{kT_c}\right) \tag{5-20}$$ [1]

The actual functional dependence is rather complicated, but it turns out theoretically that Γ^2 decreases with increasing eE_b/kT_c until saturation (temperature limiting) occurs, the space charge disappears, and Γ^2 rapidly increases to 1.

In the space-charge-limited region, and for $eE_b/kT_c \gg 1$,

$$\Gamma^2 = \frac{6(1 - \pi/4)}{\frac{2}{3}(eE_b/kT_c)} = \frac{2k(0.644T_c)}{\frac{2}{3}eE_b} \tag{5-21}$$

(the reason for keeping the $\frac{2}{3}$ factor separate will become apparent shortly). This equation for Γ^2 may be substituted into Eq. (5-19) for use in actual calculations. Note that $\overline{i_b^2}$ now depends on the ratio I_b/E_b. Current and voltage are related approximately in the space-charge region by Child's law,

$$I_b = CE_b^{3/2} \tag{5-22}$$

By using this equation a simpler expression for rms noise current may be obtained, involving only the diode dynamic plate conductance. Thus the dynamic plate conductance g_d is defined as

$$g_d = \frac{\partial I_b}{\partial E_b} = \frac{3}{2}CE_b^{1/2} = \frac{3}{2}\frac{I_b}{E_b} \tag{5-23}$$

from Eq. (5-22). Substituting Eqs. (5-23) and (5-21) into Eq. (5-19),

$$\overline{i_b^2} = 2eI_b\Gamma^2\,\Delta f = \frac{2eI_b}{\frac{2}{3}eE_b} \times 2k \times 0.644T_c\,\Delta f$$

$$\overline{i_b^2} = 4kg_d(0.644T_c)\,\Delta f \tag{5-24}$$

Equation (5-24) is commonly used for the calculation of the rms noise current in space-charge-limited diodes. T_c, the cathode temperature in

[1] Actually $e(E_b - E_{\min})$, with $E_{\min}$ the potential at the virtual cathode, should be written. We are assuming $E_b \gg E_m$.

degrees Kelvin, is ordinarily taken as 1000°K for oxide-coated cathodes. Using this value for T_c and putting in the known value for k,

$$\overline{i_b^2} = 3.55 \times 10^{-20} g_d \, \Delta f \qquad \text{amp}^2 \tag{5-25}$$

Equations (5-19) and (5-24) have both been found to agree with experimental results, even for low plate currents [where Eq. (5-21) for Γ^2 breaks down].

As an example, if $\Delta f = 5$ kc and $g_d = 0.005$ (a plate resistance of 200 ohms), the rms noise current is 0.94×10^{-9} amp rms. If $\Delta f = 20$ kc (quadrupling the bandwidth), this number doubles to give 1.9×10^{-9} amp rms. The form of Eq. (5-24) is interesting because it is similar to the form of the equation obtained for thermal noise in resistors, as will

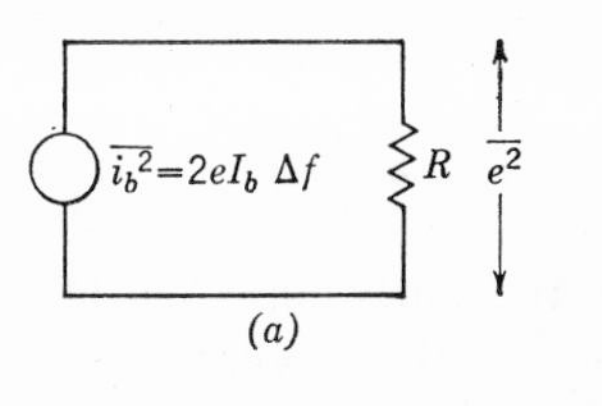

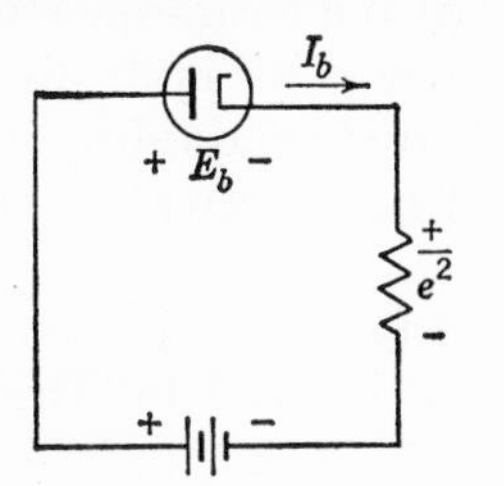

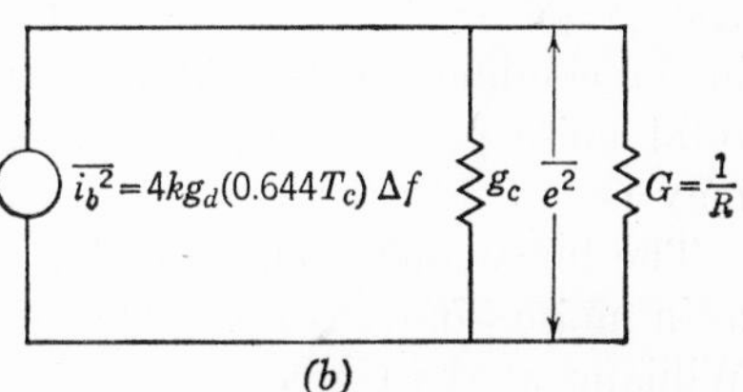

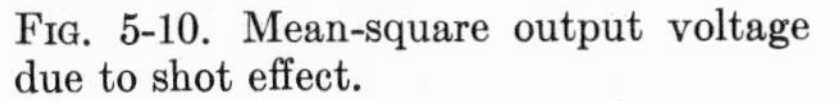

FIG. 5-10. Mean-square output voltage due to shot effect.

FIG. 5-11. Linear incremental models for determining diode shot noise. (a) Temperature-limited case; (b) space-charge-limited case.

be shown shortly. (This would be expected dimensionally, since both space-charge shot noise and thermal noise depend on temperature and the conversion to energy always gives kT.)

Now consider a space-charge-limited diode connected in the circuit of Fig. 5-10. The rms noise voltage across R, $\sqrt{\overline{e^2}}$, was easily obtained in the temperature-limited diode by multiplying rms noise current by R, the diode being essentially a constant-current source in the temperature-limited case. Here diode current varies with plate voltage. Since the noise fluctuations are extremely small, the diode may be represented by its linear incremental model (equivalent circuit), consisting of the noise current source and the plate conductance, for the determination of circuit voltages and currents. The resulting circuit corresponding to Fig. 5-10 is shown in Fig. 5-11. The mean-square output voltage $\overline{e^2}$ is given by

$$\overline{e^2} = \frac{\overline{i_b^2}}{(g_d + G)^2} = \frac{4kg_d \times 0.644T_c \, \Delta f}{(g_d + G)^2} \tag{5-26}$$

It is important to stress the point that the noise fluctuations of voltages and currents are to be treated circuitwise just like any voltage or current sources. We always talk of rms or mean-squared values, however, these being the only quantities which have any significance (average values are zero). If the noise voltage of Eq. (5-26) is now impressed on some network (again assumed noise-free), the resulting output noise voltage, in mean-squared form, may be written

$$\overline{e_2^2} = \frac{4kg_d \times 0.644T_c}{(g_d + G)^2} A_m{}^2 B \tag{5-27}$$

where B is the noise equivalent bandwidth of the network and A_m its maximum transfer amplitude. This is of course the same procedure as was followed for the temperature-limited case. Since the actual magnitude of the diode noise current depends on the bandwidth chosen, noise values are frequently normalized to one cycle of bandwidth. $\overline{i_b^2}/\Delta f$ is thus the mean-squared noise current per cycle, $\overline{e^2}/\Delta f$ the mean-squared noise voltage per cycle, and $\overline{e^2}G/\Delta f$ the mean noise power per cycle dissipated in the conductance G. Multiplying by the desired bandwidth gives the total noise power dissipated or mean-squared noise current as the case may be.

The linear incremental model representation for the diode considered as a noise source was verified experimentally in 1936 by Dr. F. C. Williams at the University of Oxford.[1]

5-3. Shot Noise in Negative-grid Triodes. The negative-grid triode in the space-charge-limited region also exhibits random fluctuations in its plate current. The mathematical analysis of this triode effect follows directly from the diode analysis of the previous section. For the cathode-grid region may be considered an equivalent diode to which the diode analysis applies. The grid-to-cathode potential (analogous to E_b in the diode case) is, however, dependent not only on grid potential but on plate potential also. Additional effects also arise due to the actual grid structure used. Figure 5-12 represents a typical potential-distribution curve taken between the grid wires. E_a is an average potential at points between the grid wires. This potential thus plays the same role as did

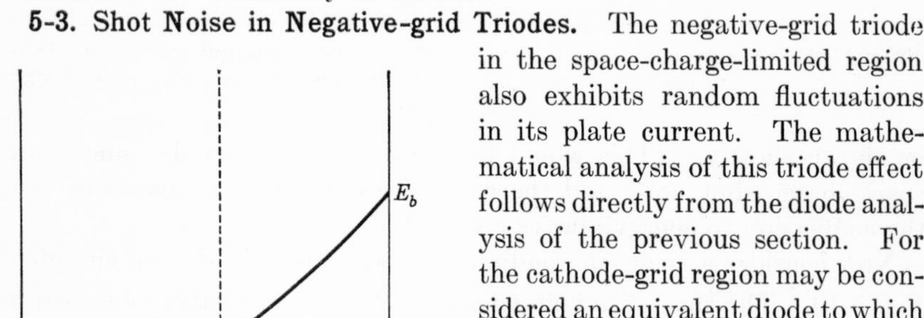

FIG. 5-12. Triode potential distribution (between grid wires).

[1] Moullin, *op. cit.*

the plate potential in the space-charge-limited diode and can be shown[1] to be in the form

$$E_a = \sigma \left(E_c + \frac{E_b}{\mu} \right) \tag{5-28}$$

where E_b is the plate-cathode voltage, E_c the grid-cathode voltage, μ the triode amplification factor, and σ a constant which varies from triode to triode, normally having values between 0.5 and 1. E_a is the effective grid potential, depending on applied grid voltage E_c and plate voltage E_b, which is related to the plate current I_b by the three-halves-power law,

$$I_b = CE_a^{3/2} \tag{5-29}$$

As in the diode case the mean-squared plate fluctuation current may be written as

$$\overline{i_b^2} = 2eI_b\Gamma^2 \,\Delta f \tag{5-30}$$

with Γ^2 a space-charge reduction factor. Here Γ^2 is a function of E_a and the cathode temperature T_c (degrees Kelvin):

$$\Gamma^2 = f\left(\frac{eE_a}{kT_c}\right) \tag{5-31}$$

For $eE_a/kT_c \gg 1$, Γ^2 again approaches the limiting value,

$$\Gamma^2 = \frac{6(1 - \pi/4)}{2eE_a/3kT_c} \tag{5-32}$$

This expression for Γ^2 may be inserted into Eq. (5-30) for calculation purposes, but again, as in the diode case, a simpler and more useful expression may be derived from the three-halves-power law of Eq. (5-29). Thus, by differentiation,

$$\begin{aligned} dI_b &= \frac{3}{2} (CE_a^{1/2})\, dE_a = \frac{3}{2}\frac{I_b}{E_a}\, dE_a \\ &= \frac{3}{2}\frac{I_b}{E_a}\sigma\left(dE_c + \frac{dE_b}{\mu}\right) \end{aligned} \tag{5-33}$$

from Eqs. (5-29) and (5-28). For small variations of grid and plate voltage, however, dI_b may also be written

$$dI_b = g_m\, dE_c + g_p\, dE_b \tag{5-33a}$$

where g_m is the triode transconductance and g_p the plate conductance. Comparing Eqs. (5-33) and (5-33a),

$$\frac{g_m}{\sigma} = \frac{3}{2}\frac{I_b}{E_a} \tag{5-34}$$

[1] See, e.g., Davenport and Root, *op. cit.*, p. 139.

The diode plate conductance is thus replaced by the triode transconductance for calculation of mean-squared plate-current fluctuations in the space-charge-limited region.

Upon substituting Eqs. (5-32) and (5-34) in Eq. (5-30), the triode mean-squared plate fluctuation current becomes

$$\overline{i_b^2} = 4k \times 0.644T_c \frac{g_m}{\sigma} \Delta f \tag{5-35}$$

For example, with $\Delta f = 20$ kc, $g_m = 2{,}000$ μmhos, $\sigma = 0.8$, and $T_c = 1000°$K, the rms plate noise current is 1.33×10^{-9} amp. As with the diode the bandwidth used (20 kc here) is an effective noise bandwidth determined by the over-all system in which the tube is connected. The mean-squared current increases linearly with bandwidth up to frequencies comparable to the reciprocal of the electron transit time (rms current output varies as $\sqrt{\Delta f}$).

Since the triode transconductance is normally of the same order of magnitude as the diode plate conductance (1,000 to 10,000 μmhos), the rms noise currents for both types of tubes are of the same order of magnitude (10^{-9}). The triode rms noise *voltage* appearing at the *plate*, however, will be *larger* by a factor of μ because of the amplification properties of the triode. This follows from the linear model (equivalent circuit) of the triode plate circuit (with negative grid), which consists of the noise current source in parallel with r_p and the triode load resistance R_L. This circuit is shown in Fig. 5-13 (the conductances indicated are reciprocals of r_p and R_L). The network calculations for noise stemming from triode shot effect thus proceed just as if the fluctuations were a current signal appearing at the plate. The only distinction is that we talk of mean-squared currents (or rms currents) only, with no assigned polarity. We shall have more to say about network calculations after the discussion of thermal-noise effects.

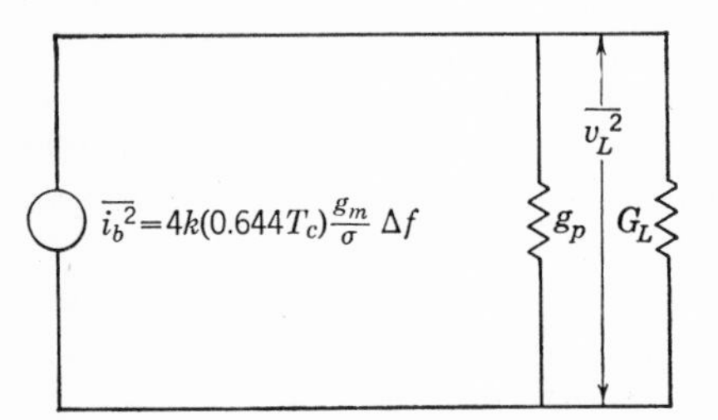

FIG. 5-13. Triode plate circuit for noise calculations (negative grid).

The mean-squared plate noise voltage $\overline{v_L^2}$ can thus be written (if we neglect noise arising in the resistor R_L)

$$\overline{v_L^2} = \frac{\overline{i_b^2}}{(g_p + G_L)^2} \doteq \frac{\overline{i_b^2}}{g_p^2} = \overline{i_b^2} r_p^2 \tag{5-36}$$

if $R_L \gg r_p$.

In the diode case the diode noise current appears across the plate resistance, r_d, and load resistor, and the rms noise voltage generated is proportional to r_d ($R_L \gg r_d$). Triode plate resistances are normally larger than diode plate resistances by the order of μ. (Remember that g_d for the diode is approximately the same as g_m for the triode.) The triode used for the calculation of rms plate noise current in Eq. (5-35) gave 1.33×10^{-9} amp rms. With $r_p = 15$ kilohms (μ is equal to 30) and $R_L = 150$ kilohms, the rms fluctuation voltage at the output is 20 μv rms. (The bandwidth is again 20 kc. The noise generated in the resistor is negligible here, as will be shown in the next section.)

Equation (5-35) gives the mean-squared triode shot-noise current appearing at the plate of the tube. When the tube has a simple resistive load and *the noise due to the resistive element may be neglected*, the mean-squared noise voltage across the load is given by Eq. (5-36). The calculation of noise voltages due to both tubes and resistors depends upon knowledge of noise in resistors. This is discussed in the next section. Calculations for networks with noise sources present are also taken up there and in the following sections.

5-4. Thermal Noise. As was mentioned in the introduction to this chapter on Noise, two basic types of spontaneous fluctuation voltage are present in electric circuits. The first, the so-called shot effect, is due to the random emission of electrons. Shot effect in vacuum tubes has been discussed in previous sections. The second type of spontaneous fluctuation, that due to thermal interaction between the free electrons and vibrating ions in a conduction medium (normally a resistor), is the subject of this section.

In these first sections shot noise and thermal noise are considered to be independently generated in different devices (primarily tubes for shot noise, resistors for thermal noise). However, modern semiconductors (semiconductor diodes, transistors, etc.) have been found to generate both types of noise, as also other types due to other mechanisms. (This might be expected because of current due to impressed fields, just as in the triode, giving rise to shot effect, and to the properties of the solid medium considered as a piece of conducting material, giving rise to thermal noise.) These combined noise effects in junction diodes and transistors will be discussed in Sec. 5-11.

Thermal noise was first thoroughly studied experimentally by J. B. Johnson of Bell Laboratories in 1928. His experiments, together with the accompanying theoretical studies by H. Nyquist, demonstrated that a metallic resistor could be considered the source of spontaneous fluctuation voltages with mean-squared value

$$\overline{v_R^2} = 4kTR\,\Delta f \tag{5-37}$$

where T is the temperature in degrees Kelvin of the resistor, R its resistance in ohms, k the Boltzmann constant already referred to (1.38×10^{-23} joule/°K), and Δf any arbitrary bandwidth. Johnson was able to measure the value of k fairly accurately using this equation and thus demonstrated its validity. He also showed that $\overline{v_R^2}$ was proportional to temperature.

Unlike the shot-noise case with the spectrum cutting off at 1/(transit time), the thermal-noise spectrum has been shown theoretically to be uniform or constant up to extremely high frequencies of the order of 10^{13} cps, where quantum-mechanical effects would be expected to set in (this assumes of course that R is independent of frequency over this tremendous range). The existence of some cutoff frequency would be expected on physical grounds, for a flat or constant spectrum at *all* frequencies would imply infinite noise power generated.

Because of the frequency involved the cutoff is of little practical significance, and for our purposes the noise spectrum may be assumed flat at all frequencies. Noise possessing such a flat spectrum is called *white noise*. (From optics, *white* includes *all* colors or frequencies.) The noise generated in the resistor is thus assumed to have *all* frequencies present, and any band limiting (which determines the Δf to use) is due to the circuitry connected to the resistor.

Nyquist's original derivation of Eq. (5-37)[1] was based on thermodynamic reasoning, assuming temperature equilibrium. The actual mechanism of thermal-noise generation—assumed to be due to the random interaction between the conduction electrons and ions in a metallic conductor—is not necessary for the derivation. Although this at first appears disconcerting, it is actually a blessing in disguise. For using the same thermodynamic reasoning it may be shown that *any linear passive* device, mechanical, electromechanical, microphones, antennas, etc., has associated with it thermal noise of one form or another. In some cases this may be due to random agitation of the air molecules, in others to random electrical effects in the ionosphere and atmosphere, etc. This is so because the $\frac{1}{2}kT$ term occurs generally in thermodynamics as the energy associated with any mode of oscillation (as temperature increases, gas molecules move more rapidly, ions vibrate more violently in a lattice structure, etc.). This was the basis of Nyquist's derivation.

Because of this reasoning the *resistors in the electrical analogue of a passive linear physical device* may be considered *sources of noise voltage* as given by Eq. (5-37). This concept is commonly used in antenna work, acoustics, etc.

Equation (5-37) has also been derived from an assumed model for electrical conduction through a metal.[2] The derivation is somewhat

[1] H. Nyquist, *Phys. Rev.*, no. 32, p. 110, 1928. See also Moullin, *op. cit.*; Van der Ziel, *op. cit.*; Lawson and Uhlenbeck, *op. cit.*

[2] See Lawson and Uhlenbeck, *op. cit.*

similar to our derivation of the temperature-limited shot effect, with a current wave due to one electron expanded into a Fourier series periodic over a long interval of time.

For metallic resistors the mean-squared fluctuation voltage is found to be independent of any applied steady current (due to external sources). The apparent reason for this stems from the fact that the electron velocities associated with random fluctuations are much higher (10^7 cm/sec) than the drift velocities due to steady currents flowing (1 mm/sec).† Granular-type resistors (carbon, carbon microphones, etc.) exhibit larger fluctuations in the presence of steady currents. Equation (5-37) thus applies only to metallic resistors or to the electrical analogues of passive physical systems exhibiting a true thermal noise.

A voltage-model representation of Eq. (5-37) is shown in Fig. 5-14*a*. R is assumed noise-free, with the noise effect lumped into the noise-voltage source shown. An application of Norton's theorem gives the current-source equivalent of Fig. 5-14*b*. (Since $i = v/R$, $\overline{i^2} = \overline{v^2}/R^2 = 4kTG\,\Delta f$; $G = 1/R$.)

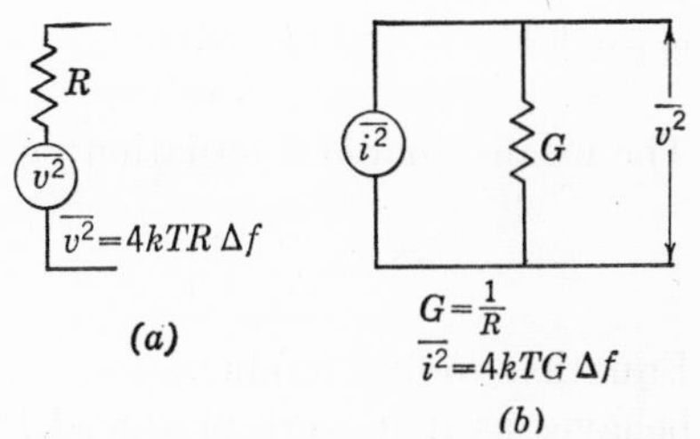

FIG. 5-14. Thermal-noise circuit models. (*a*) Voltage model; (*b*) current model.

Either model may be used, although we shall frequently find the current-source model more convenient, especially when calculating noise voltages across parallel elements. Some typical numbers are again of interest. Let Δf be 5 kc, T equal 293°K (this is normal room temperature, or 20°C), R equal 10 kilohms. Then $\overline{v^2} = 0.75 \times 10^{-12}$ volt^2, or

$$\sqrt{\overline{v^2}} = 0.87\ \mu\text{v rms}$$

$\sqrt{\overline{i^2}} = 0.87 \times 10^{-10}$ amp rms. If the bandwidth is quadrupled to 20 kc, the rms noise voltage and current are doubled to 1.7 μv and 1.7×10^{-10} amp, respectively. The rms noise voltage is proportional to the square root of the resistance and to the square root of the bandwidth.

If the temperature is increased, the resistance value used refers to the new temperature, as does T. Since the derivation of Eq. (5-37) depends on thermal equilibrium, the equation holds only after a steady-state temperature has been reached, not during the heating or cooling period.

5-5. Thermal-noise Network Calculations. Mention was made in the sections on shot noise of the fact that network noise calculations are carried out just asi f the noise source were an ordinary signal source with but one qualification. The one distinction is that noise sources are

† Moullin, *op. cit.*

defined in mean-squared terms only and so have no polarity. Mean-squared values due to two independent noise sources may be added, just as is done in signal-power calculations. *It is incorrect to add rms noise voltages.*[1] (Phase plays no role in noise calculations, having been averaged out in the mean-squared calculation, except when the noise sources are coherent or related.) To demonstrate these statements, consider the output noise voltage due to two resistors R_1 and R_2 connected in parallel (Fig. 5-15).

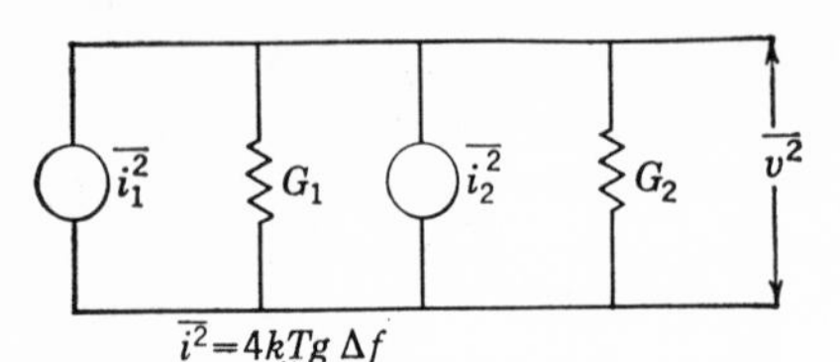

FIG. 5-15. Noise model for two resistors in parallel.

Assume first that the two resistors are at the same temperature. The current-source models are used because of the parallel connection. The mean-squared fluctuation voltage $\overline{v^2}$ is then given by

$$\overline{v^2} = \frac{\overline{i_1^2} + \overline{i_2^2}}{(G_1 + G_2)^2} = \frac{4kT\,\Delta f(G_1 + G_2)}{(G_1 + G_2)^2} = \frac{4kT\,\Delta f}{G_1 + G_2} \tag{5-38}$$

Equation (5-38) produces a very satisfying result: the output voltage behaves as if it were produced by an equivalent resistor given by the parallel combination of the two original resistors. This result depends on the *addition* of *independently generated mean-squared currents* (or voltages). Alternatively we must treat the sources as if we were calculating the total power dissipated in the resistors, necessitating the addition of separate powers. This statement is basic in noise calculations. We *cannot* add $\sqrt{\overline{i_1^2}}$ and $\sqrt{\overline{i_2^2}}$ (that is, rms currents). Mean-squared values only can be added.

Similar results can be obtained for two resistors in series by using the voltage-source models there.

Whenever resistors occur in parallel or in series, then, they may be combined and the mean-squared noise due to the equivalent resistance calculated.

The simple addition of mean-squared voltages or currents is possible, however, only if the quantities being added come from independent sources. Thus, if thermal noise from a given resistor is amplified and the noise voltage then applied to two different circuits, the output voltages of the two circuits are related to one another. If these voltages are now combined, the resulting voltage is obviously not found from the sum of the two mean-squared voltages. Noise voltages related to one another in some manner are said to be *correlated*. Independently generated noise voltages are *uncorrelated*.

[1] If two rms noise voltages are, respectively, 3 and 4 μv, the rms value of the resultant sum is 5 μv ($3^2 + 4^2 = 5^2$), and *not* 7 μv, as obtained by simple addition.

If the resistors are at a different temperature, the sources must be treated separately. The mean-squared fluctuation voltage across the parallel combination then becomes

$$\overline{v^2} = \frac{4k\,\Delta f}{(G_1 + G_2)^2}\,(G_1T_1 + G_2T_2) \tag{5-39}$$

This result was experimentally verified by Dr. F. C. Williams in 1938.[1] [He kept one resistor at the fixed temperature and varied the temperature of the other. The experimental values fitted Eq. (5-39) very closely.]

Now how do we calculate noise voltages in more complicated circuits?

Consider as an example the parallel-resonant circuit of Fig. 5-16*a*. The same circuit with the current-source model and noise-free resistor is shown in Fig. 5-16*b*. The coil and capacitor are assumed dissipationless. (If they are lossy devices, the losses may be assumed lumped with G.)

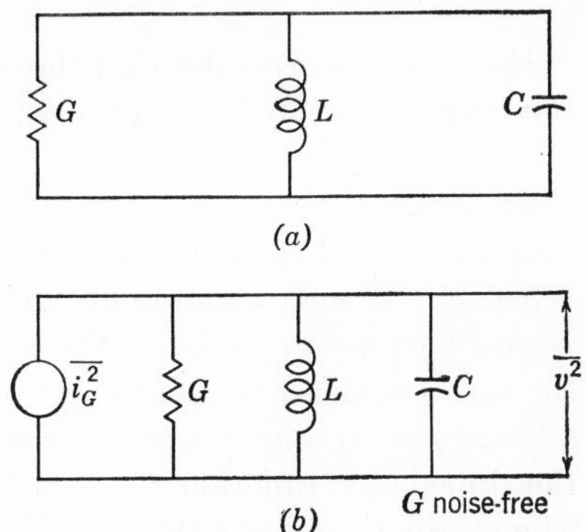

FIG. 5-16. Fluctuation voltage across tuned circuit. (*a*) Original circuit; (*b*) model for noise calculations.

To find $\overline{v^2}$, we proceed as in our usual network calculations. Since $\overline{i_G{}^2}$ depends on bandwidth, however, we assume that Δf is a narrow frequency band centered about some frequency f ($\Delta f \ll f$). (The assumption here is that there will be some filtering ultimately to eliminate noise over the remainder of the frequency spectrum. We thus need not concern ourselves with noise at other frequencies in this case. Alternatively, if the tuned circuit is of high Q and Δf is a band of frequencies centered at the resonant frequency, the circuit itself will serve as the required filter.)

The noise source can then be represented as a nearly sinusoidal source at frequency f, the admittance is very nearly constant over Δf, and

$$\overline{v^2} = \frac{\overline{i_G{}^2}}{\underbrace{|G + j(\omega C - 1/\omega L)|^2}_{Y}} = \frac{4kTG\,\Delta f}{|Y|^2} \tag{5-40}$$

(Since phase is of no significance to us, we must use the *magnitude* of the admittance or impedance function.)

[1] Moullin, *op. cit.*

Now consider the impedance of this network,

$$Z = \frac{1}{G + j(\omega C - 1/\omega L)} = \frac{G - j(\omega C - 1/\omega L)}{|Y|^2} = R(f) + jX(f) \quad (5\text{-}41)$$

Therefore
$$R(f) = \frac{G}{|Y|^2} \quad (5\text{-}42)$$

Comparing Eq. (5-40) and Eq. (5-42), we may write very simply

$$\overline{v^2} = 4kTR(f)\,\Delta f \quad (5\text{-}43)$$

Equation (5-43) states that the mean-squared fluctuation voltage across the two terminals of a narrowband tuned circuit may be found by measuring the resistive part of the impedance across the terminals.

Although derived here for the rather simple case of the narrowband tuned circuit, Eq. (5-43) may be shown to apply to any *linear passive network*. As such it represents an important extension of the fundamental Nyquist equation (5-37). The extended form of Eq. (5-43) states that the mean-squared fluctuation voltage measured across two terminals of a *linear passive network* may be found by determining the resistive part of the impedance function measured looking into the same two terminals. The original proof for this was given by H. Nyquist.

We have been assuming that the sources of noise in linear passive networks are the resistive elements present. It should thus be possible to derive this expression by evaluating the total mean-squared fluctuation voltage at the desired terminal due to all resistors present in the network (this is done by summing up the mean-squared voltages due to each resistor which would appear at the given terminals). Our development is a special case for a very simple network. Dr. F. C. Williams has proved the general relation and verified it experimentally. It holds if all resistors are at the same temperature T.

There are thus two alternative ways for calculating thermal voltages and currents in passive linear networks: (1) Represent each resistor by its appropriate noise source, and then sum the mean-squared voltage (or current) due to each. (2) Find the real part of the impedance function, and calculate the mean-squared voltage by Eq. (5-43).

If $R(f)$ varies appreciably over the frequency range Δf, the contributions over each small frequency interval must be added. Equation (5-43) can then be extended further by writing

$$\overline{v^2} = 4kT \int_{\Delta f} R(f)\,df \quad (5\text{-}44)$$

As an example, consider the simple RC circuit of Fig. 5-17. Let the frequency interval Δf be all frequencies passed by the network itself. The total mean-squared fluctuation voltage is then obtained by summing over all frequencies and is given by

$$\overline{v^2} = \int_0^\infty \frac{4kTG}{G^2 + \omega^2 C^2}\, df = \frac{4kT}{2\pi G} \int_0^\infty \frac{d\omega}{1 + (\omega C/G)^2} \tag{5-45}$$

Defining the half-power frequency $\omega_H = G/C$, and introducing a dimensionless variable $x = \omega/\omega_H$,

$$\overline{v^2} = 4kTR \frac{\omega_H}{2\pi} \int_0^\infty \frac{dx}{1 + x^2} = \frac{kT}{C} \tag{5-46}$$

$\left[\text{since } \omega_H = G/C = 1/RC, \text{ and } \int_0^\infty dx/(1 + x^2) = \pi/2\right]$.

This is the mean-squared voltage that would be read on a thermocouple meter (if it were sensitive enough) if its own frequency-response range were wide compared with ω_H. If a measuring instrument itself acts as a filter, its frequency response must also be included.

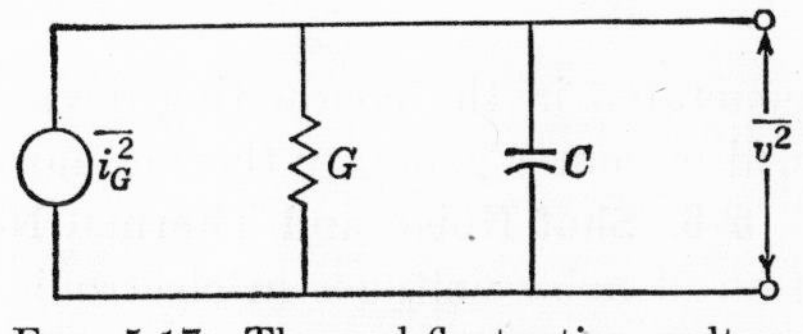

FIG. 5-17. Thermal-fluctuation voltage across RC network.

Equation (5-46) is an example of the application of Eq. (5-44), but it is of interest in its own right. It states that the noise energy (proportional to $\overline{v^2}$) is independent of R and varies with C. Yet the resistor is the assumed source of the noise fluctuations!

This apparent contradiction has disturbed many investigators in the field of noise phenomena.[1] The question is actually much more basic, for if we remember that stored energy in the capacitor is given by $\frac{1}{2}C\overline{v^2}$ the average energy stored is $\frac{1}{2}kT$ by Eq. (5-46). This checks thermodynamically, for, as mentioned previously, each mode of energy storage should have $\frac{1}{2}kT$ joules associated with it. This would seem to imply that the *capacitor* is the source of the noise energy.

The root of the trouble lies in the existence of a sort of gain-bandwidth product as in amplifier circuits. The total mean-squared fluctuation voltage $\overline{v^2}$ defined over *all* frequencies depends not only on the applied noise current (which is dependent upon R) but on the impedance level also. As R increases, the noise in any small frequency interval increases but the over-all bandwidth (ω_H here) decreases at the same time. The total energy included over all frequencies remains constant. This is indicated in Fig. 5-18, with the area under the curve remaining constant as R varies. Equation (5-46) is also obtained for the mean-squared output voltage of a high-Q tuned circuit (as would be expected by a low-pass–high-pass transformation), and similar conclusions hold there.

A simple experiment performed by Dr. F. C. Williams on the noise

[1] *Ibid.*

output of a high-Q circuit demonstrated conclusively that the noise must be associated with the resistor.[1] He varied the temperature of C and showed $\overline{v^2}$ to be independent of this temperature. The T in Eq. (5-46) must thus be associated with the resistor, and thermal noise can be

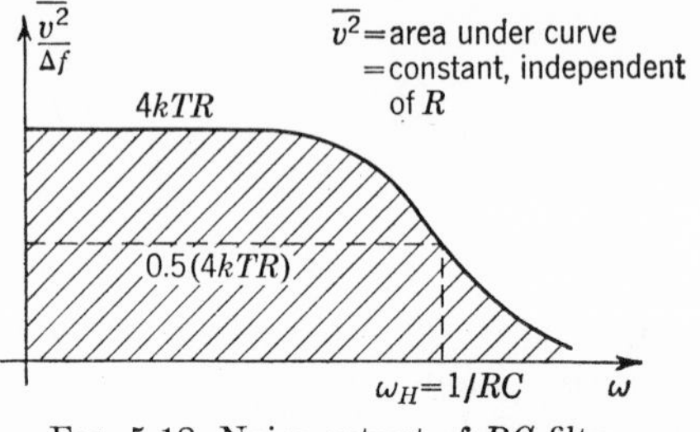

FIG. 5-18. Noise output of RC filter.

generated in the conducting device only. (If the capacitor is leaky, it will of course generate thermal noise also.)

5-6. Shot Noise and Thermal Noise Combined. The actual calculation of noise voltages in electronic systems requires the combination of noise voltages due to shot effect (vacuum tubes in a circuit) and thermal noise (resistors in the circuit). Total noise voltages may be found simply by drawing the appropriate noise-source models and summing mean-squared voltages. We shall demonstrate the procedure by taking a simple example, a space-charge-limited diode with resistive load. We shall then consider examples from triode amplifier circuits and develop some general relations of interest in network noise calculations.

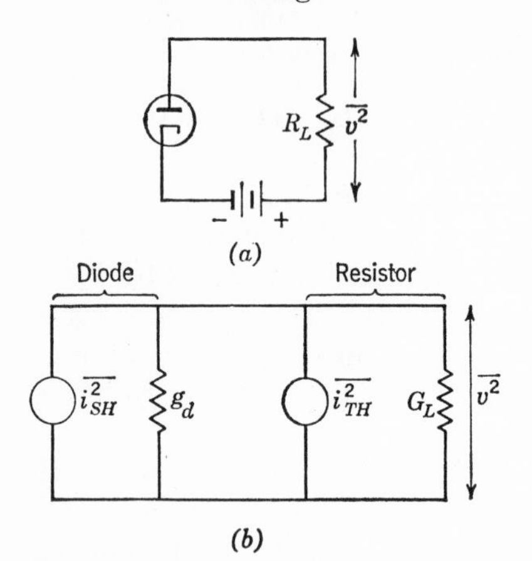

FIG. 5-19. Noise effects in space-charge-limited diode and resistive load. (a) Diode circuit; (b) noise model.

The diode and resistive load are shown in Fig. 5-19a. The linear incremental model (equivalent circuit) appropriate for noise calculations is given in Fig. 5-19b. $\overline{i_{SH}^2}$ is the shot-noise term and $\overline{i_{TH}^2}$ the thermal-noise term. Thus

$$\overline{i_{SH}^2} = 2eI_b\Gamma^2\,\Delta f = 4k(0.644T_c)g_d\,\Delta f \tag{5-47}$$

and

$$\overline{i_{TH}^2} = 4kTG_L\,\Delta f \tag{5-48}$$

Note again that the temperature T represents the temperature of the

[1] *Ibid.*

resistor (normally room temperature), while T_c is the temperature of a diode cathode (usually taken as 1000°K for oxide-coated cathodes). Since independent sources add in a mean-squared sense and the shot and thermal noise are independently generated,

$$\overline{v^2} = \overline{v_{TH}^2} + \overline{v_{SH}^2} = \frac{\overline{i_{TH}^2} + \overline{i_{SH}^2}}{(g_d + G_L)^2} = \frac{4k\,\Delta f}{(g_d + G_L)^2}(0.644T_c g_d + TG_L) \quad (5\text{-}49)$$

It is important to stress again that we do not simply calculate a mean-squared thermal-noise voltage due solely to R_L and add to it a squared voltage term due to the tube. Each device loads down the other, and this must be taken into account. The load impedance seen by each current source is the parallel combination of the diode plate resistance and load resistance.

We can get an idea of the relative contribution of each term by putting some typical numbers in. Let

$$g_d = 2 \times 10^{-3} \text{ mho} \qquad G_L = 10^{-4} \text{ mho}$$
$$T_c = 1000°\text{K} \qquad T = 293°\text{K}$$
$$0.644T_c g_d = 1.3 \qquad TG_L = 0.029$$

The shot noise thus overpowers the thermal noise *in this case.* This is of course due to the much smaller diode resistance (500 ohms) loading down the load resistance (10 kilohms). A choice of 500 ohms for R would have made the thermal-noise term significant. Since $g_d \gg G_L$ here,

$$\overline{v^2} \doteq 4k(0.644T_c)r_d\,\Delta f \quad (5\text{-}50)$$

This explains the assumption made in Sec. 5-2, concerning shot noise in space-charge-limited diodes, that we could neglect thermal noise generated in the load resistor. Again putting numbers in, let

$$\Delta f = 5 \text{ kc}$$
$$g_d = 2 \times 10^{-3} \text{ mho}$$
$$T_c = 1000°\text{K}$$

Then $\quad \overline{v^2} \doteq 0.09 \times 10^{-12} \text{ volt}^2 \qquad \sqrt{\overline{v^2}} = 0.3\ \mu\text{v rms}$

If $\Delta f = 20$ kc, $\sqrt{\overline{v^2}} = 0.6\ \mu$v rms.

The complete equation for shot noise and thermal noise combined [Eq. (5-49)] was checked experimentally by Dr. F. C. Williams.[1]

5-7. Noise Calculations in Triode Amplifiers. The calculation of noise voltages in triode circuits (and generally in all electronic circuits) proceeds directly in the manner just indicated for the space-charge-limited diode.

[1] See *ibid.*

We draw the appropriate noise-source models (a shot-effect current source shunted by r_p as the plate-circuit representation of triode noise, plus the noise-source models for the different resistors in the circuit) and determine the total mean-squared voltages by adding the mean-squared contributions due to each source. (This assumes of course that the different noise voltages are independently generated.)

The actual voltages calculated will depend on the circuit configuration used, as is true for the calculation of signal voltages. Thus, noise output

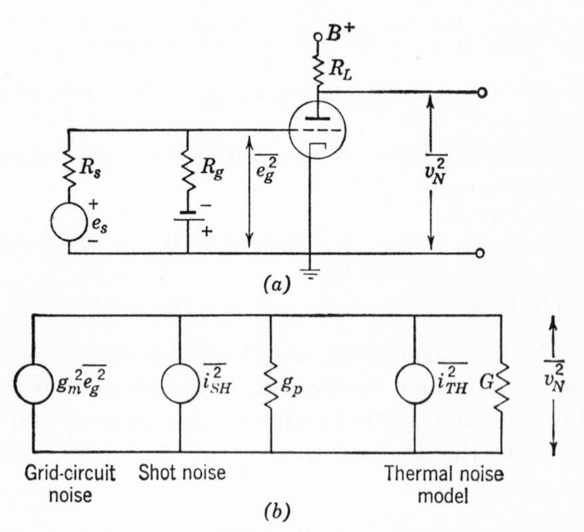

FIG. 5-20. Triode-amplifier noise calculations. (a) Triode amplifier; (b) plate-noise circuit.

voltages will differ for grounded-cathode, cathode-follower, and grounded-grid circuits, as also for more complicated multitube circuits. The procedure used in every case is the same, however.

As a simple example, consider the common triode amplifier of Fig. 5-20a. $\overline{v_N^2}$ is the noise output component. e_s is the rms signal-source voltage with its associated internal impedance R_s. $\overline{e_g^2}$ represents the mean-squared noise voltage at the grid.

The output noise now consists of three components:

1. Noise voltage present in the grid circuit of the tube and amplified like any other voltage in the grid circuit. This noise voltage is in turn due to thermal noise generated in the grid resistor R_g and also consists of any noise brought in with the signal voltage. If the signal voltage is developed from a purely passive network (such linear devices as microphones and antennas are included here), its noise contribution can be assumed to be generated by the internal resistance R_s. *For this special*

case,

$$\overline{e_g^2} = 4kT \frac{R_g R_s}{R_g + R_s} \Delta f \tag{5-51}$$

(R_g and R_s are assumed at the same temperature T.)

2. Triode shot noise appearing in the plate circuit as a current source in parallel with the plate resistance r_p.

$$\overline{i_{SH}^2} = 4k \times 0.644 T_c \frac{g_m}{\sigma} \Delta f \tag{5-52}$$

3. Thermal noise generated in R_L, the plate-load resistor.

$$\overline{i_{TH}^2} = 4kTG_L \Delta f \tag{5-53}$$

The thermal noise due to R_L can normally be neglected in comparison with the shot noise.

The complete model of the triode-amplifier plate circuit for noise calculations is shown in Fig. 5-20*b*. The use of this circuit and Eqs. (5-51) to (5-53) enables us to calculate the over-all output noise. There is an alternative procedure, however, much more commonly utilized in calculating triode noise voltages. This consists in referring the triode shot noise back to the grid circuit. Since incremental changes in plate current may be related to corresponding incremental changes in the grid voltage by the simple relation

$$i_b = g_m e_g \tag{5-54}$$

the shot-noise current may be pictured as having been developed by an equivalent noise-voltage source in the grid. This fictitious voltage source would be given by

$$\overline{e_{g,\,\text{shot noise}}^2} = \frac{\overline{i_{SH}^2}}{g_m^2} = 4k \times 0.644 T_c \frac{1}{\sigma g_m} \Delta f \equiv 4kTR_{eq} \Delta f \tag{5-55}$$

where

$$R_{eq} = \frac{0.644 T_c}{\sigma T} \frac{1}{g_m} \tag{5-56}$$

Equations (5-55) and (5-56) indicate that this fictitious grid noise source may also be looked on as due to an equivalent grid noise resistance R_{eq}.

For the case of *oxide-coated cathodes* $T_c \doteq 1000°\text{K}$. $T = 293°\text{K}$ at normal room temperature. Letting $\sigma = 0.88$ as an average value (and as one contrived to have R_{eq} come out in neat form),

$$R_{eq} = \frac{2.5}{g_m} \tag{5-57}$$

Equation (5-57) is the expression for equivalent grid noise resistance commonly used in practice. Although σ, T_c, and T may vary somewhat from the values chosen above, the noise calculations will not be affected substantially. Equation (5-57) is thus appropriate in most triode calculations.

For typical values of g_m, R_{eq} ranges from 500 to 2,000 ohms.

Since R_{eq} was defined by referring the tube shot noise to the grid circuit, it cannot act as a resistor loading down the noise sources actually present in the grid. For calculation purposes, then, R_{eq} must appear in series with the grid. The appropriate noise model for the triode grid circuit is shown in Fig. 5-21a. The grid noise voltage now includes the effect of R_{eq} and is given by

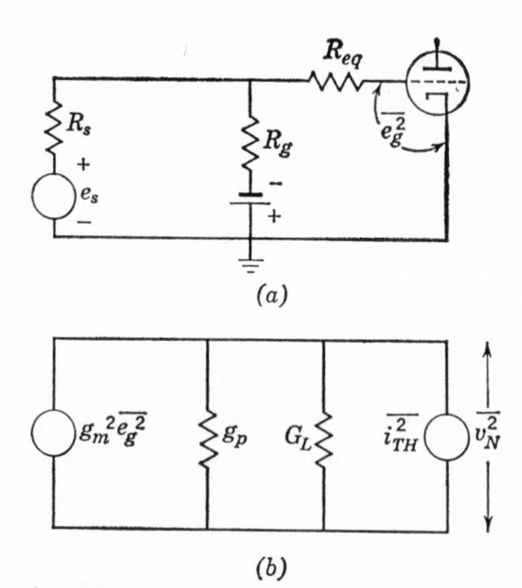

FIG. 5-21. Equivalent grid noise resistance for triode. (a) Triode grid circuit for noise calculations; (b) plate-noise circuit.

$$\overline{e_g^2} = 4kT\left(\frac{R_sR_g}{R_s + R_g} + R_{eq}\right)\Delta f \tag{5-58}$$

The total noise voltage at the tube output is then given, with the help of Fig. 5-21b, by

$$\begin{aligned}\overline{v_N^2} &= \frac{g_m^2\overline{e_g^2} + 4kTG_L\,\Delta f}{(g_p + G_L)^2} \\ &= A_m^2\overline{e_g^2} + \frac{4kTG_L\,\Delta f}{(g_p + G_L)^2}\end{aligned} \tag{5-59}$$

Here $$A_m = \frac{g_m}{g_p + G_L} \tag{5-60}$$

is the usual expression for the mid-band amplification of the circuit.

As stressed previously, then, the grid noise voltage acts just like any other voltage so far as calculations are concerned. Its component across the output resistor is simply found by multiplying by the amplification of the circuit. The one distinction between these noise voltages and our ordinary signal voltages, however, is that they are to be added in the mean-squared sense (assuming the noises independently generated, as is the case here).

Since the grid noise voltage appears multiplied by the circuit amplification, the thermal-noise term due to the plate load resistor is normally negligible (that is, $4kTG_L\,\Delta f \ll g_m^2\overline{e_g^2}$). The plate load resistor R_L must be included in the calculations, however, as a resistance in parallel with r_p.

A simple example of a triode-amplifier noise calculation will clarify the points mentioned above and will also provide us with some idea of the magnitudes of the noise voltages involved. The triode amplifier to be considered is shown in Fig. 5-22.

Coupling and parasitic capacitors are not shown. It is assumed that these plus other reactive elements in circuits connected to this amplifier have fixed the 20-kc bandwidth chosen. Δf is thus the noise equivalent bandwidth of the over-all system. It is also assumed that the cathode impedance is essentially a short circuit over the frequency range of interest.

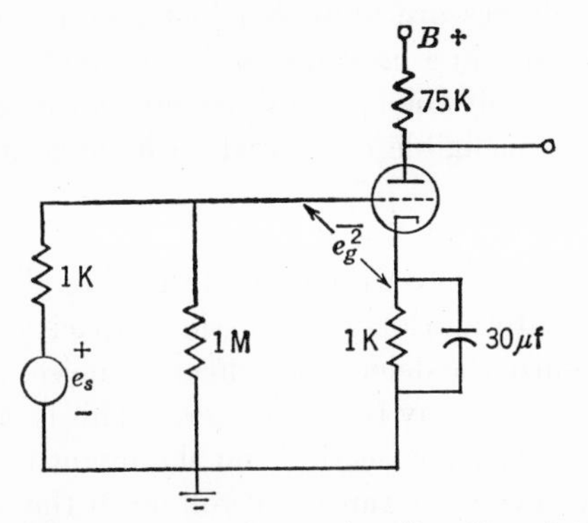

FIG. 5-22. Triode amplifier (e_s = rms input signal). $g_m = 2 \times 10^{-3}$ mho; $r_p = 15$ kilohms; $\mu = 30$; $\Delta f = 20$ kc.

For this triode the equivalent grid noise resistance is

$$R_{eq} = \frac{2.5}{g_m} = 1{,}250 \text{ ohms}$$

The rms grid noise voltage $\sqrt{\overline{e_g^2}}$ is then found from

$$\overline{e_g^2} = 4kT(1{,}000 + 1{,}250)\,\Delta f = (1.62 \times 10^{-20}) \times 2{,}250 \times (20 \times 10^3)$$
$$= 0.73 \times 10^{-12}$$

or

$$\sqrt{\overline{e_g^2}} = 0.85\ \mu\text{v rms}$$

One thousand ohms represents the parallel combination of R_s and R_g, and the circuit is assumed operating at normal room temperature (20°C).

The mean-squared thermal-noise current generated by the 75-kilohm resistor is given by

$$\overline{i_{TH}^2} = 4kTG_L\,\Delta f = 0.43 \times 10^{-20}$$

But $\quad g_m^2\overline{e_g^2} = (4 \times 10^{-6})(0.73 \times 10^{-12}) = 2.9 \times 10^{-18} \gg \overline{i_{TH}^2}$

The noise from the load resistor may thus be neglected in comparison with the amplified grid noise (including the tube shot noise). Since

$$A_m = \frac{g_m}{g_p + G_L} = 25$$

the rms output noise voltage comes out to be

$$\sqrt{\overline{v_N^2}} = 25 \sqrt{\overline{e_g^2}} = 21 \ \mu\text{v rms}$$

Note that, although the load-resistor thermal noise was negligible, the shot noise was comparable to the noise brought in with the signal at the grid ($R_{eq} = 1{,}250$ ohms, $R_s = 1{,}000$ ohms).

Because noise voltages are amplified just like any other voltage, the primary source of noise in a cascaded series of amplifier stages is usually the first stage (or possibly the first and second). The noise introduced in succeeding stages is negligible compared with the amplified noise of the first stages.

5-8. Signal-to-Noise and Noise Figure. We have pointed out previously that noise serves to mask the desired signal in physical systems. It sets a limit on the information-transmission capacity of communication systems. To minimize the deleterious effects of noise, we would normally have to provide a signal many times greater. This is of course the reason for our stress in the past few sections on the quantitative calculation of noise voltages. Knowing the rms noise voltage at the output of a system, one can estimate the minimum value of signal required at that point for the signal to be distinguished properly in the presence of the noise. Alternatively this tells us the signal required at the input of the system for proper transmission in the presence of noise. (Although we have of course stressed throughout this chapter electrical noise or fluctuation voltage, the concept of transmitting signals in the presence of noise is basic to all physical systems.)

Note that whenever we talk of distinguishing signals in the presence of noise we specify the signal relative to the noise voltage. If we could, by redesigning a system, reduce the rms noise voltage by a half, the signal level being transmitted could also be reduced by the same factor (unless of course a certain signal level is required at the output). Because of this it has become common practice in engineering to talk of the *signal-to-noise ratio* required for a particular application.

Since the noise actually fluctuates randomly over a period of time, we cannot talk too readily of instantaneous signal level to instantaneous noise level. Instead we deal with averages over a long period of time and talk of the *mean*-squared signal and *mean*-squared noise. Both signal and noise are measured at the same point in a system and appear across the same impedance. The ratio of mean-squared voltages is thus also the ratio of powers, and so the signal-to-noise power ratio is given by

$$\frac{S}{N} = \frac{v_s^2}{\overline{v_N^2}} \tag{5-61}$$

with v_s and $\sqrt{\overline{v_N^2}}$ the rms voltages at the same point in a system.

In the previous triode-amplifier problem, for example, assume that S/N is required to be 100 at the output. (The actual choice of S/N will depend on the criterion used to distinguish signal from noise, how much signal impairment is to be tolerated, the actual system for which S/N is being calculated, etc.) Since the rms noise voltage at the output was found to be 21 μv,

$$v_s^2 = 100(21\ \mu\text{v})^2$$

or $v_s = 210\ \mu$v rms. At the input to the one-stage amplifier, then, $e_s = 210/25 = 8.5\ \mu$v.

Ideally we would like to deal with systems which introduce no noise additional to that present at the system input. This would imply a constant signal-to-noise ratio throughout the system since both signal and noise voltages are amplified or attenuated by the same amount. (We are assuming, as throughout this book thus far, linear systems.) In practice this is of course impossible, as indicated by the calculations of the past few sections, since any additional tubes or resistors introduce additional noise. S/N must thus continuously decrease throughout a system. (The decrease may be negligible of course if the amplification at the beginning of the system is made large enough so that the additional noise introduced later is negligible.)

The "noisiness" of a particular system or part thereof can thus be measured by comparing S/N at output and input. We call this measure of the noisiness of a system the *noise figure*, F, of the system and define it as follows,

$$\frac{S_o}{N_o} = \frac{1}{F}\frac{S_s}{N_s} \tag{5-62}$$

with S_o/N_o the signal-to-noise ratio at the output and S_s/N_s the signal-to-noise ratio at the input (source). An ideal network is thus one whose noise figure is 1 (that is, no additional noise introduced in the system). As F increases, the "noisiness" of the system increases.

Noise figures are frequently measured in decibels (since F is a ratio of S/N in power), the conversion simply being $10 \log_{10} F$. The concept of noise figure is particularly important for h-f communication, where the circuits presently in use introduce a great deal of noise. Radar receivers in the 1,000-Mc range, for example, have noise figures ranging from 10 to 15 db, or F ranging from 10 to 40. Most of the noise is thus developed in the system (primarily in the crystal converters in use). A decrease of only 3 db in the noise figure of a typical system would cut the power requirements at the radar transmitter in two, so that the question of decreasing system noise figures is of great importance there.

As an example of the calculation of noise figure, consider the triode amplifier discussed in Sec. 5-7. The input S/N, S_s/N_s, is

$$\frac{S_s}{N_s} = \frac{e_s^2}{4kTR_s\,\Delta f} = \frac{e_s^2}{3.2 \times 10^{-13}} \tag{5-63}$$

Since 1 megohm $\gg$ 1 kilohm, the output signal is $A_m e_s = 25e_s$. Since $\overline{v_N^2} = 4.4 \times 10^{-10}$ (the rms noise voltage is 21 μv), the output S/N is

$$\frac{S_o}{N_o} = \frac{A_m^2 e_s^2}{4.4 \times 10^{-10}} = \frac{1}{F}\frac{S_s}{N_s} \tag{5-64}$$

Combining Eqs. (5-64) and (5-63), we find that

$$F = 2.25$$

Actually in this particular example we could have found F much more simply. We noted in Sec. 5-7 that the plate load resistor contributed negligible noise to the output. The primary source of network noise in this example, then, is the tube itself. The tube shot noise can be calculated from the equivalent grid noise resistance R_{eq}. Since the total noise appears in the grid circuit in this problem, the signal voltage for both "output" and "input" S/N is the same, so that F here is simply the ratio of total noise power to input noise power, or

$$F \doteq \frac{R_s + R_{eq}}{R_s} = 2.25 \qquad R_s \ll R_g \tag{5-65}$$

We now ask ourselves the basic question: Is it possible in some manner to reduce the noise figure of this amplifier? One possibility would be to increase the effective source impedance. For as R_s increases, the relative contribution to the total noise by R_{eq} decreases and F decreases. This is shown by Eq. (5-65). We cannot increase R_s too much, however, for eventually R_g begins to load R_s down, and the noise from the source decreases again, as does the signal. We might thus expect an optimum value for R_s.

Arbitrarily increasing the source impedance is not the full answer, however, for this will obviously decrease the signal-to-noise ratio at the input. (More thermal noise is added.) The solution of course is to use a step-up transformer between source and tube circuit. This will keep the signal-to-noise ratio at the tube input unchanged (assuming that the transformer adds negligible noise) but will enable us to optimize the circuit noise figure.

To actually check the possible optimization of F, consider Fig. 5-21a again. The mean-squared noise voltage at the grid is

$$\overline{e_g^2} = \left(\frac{4kT}{G_s + G_g} + 4kTR_{eq}\right)\Delta f \qquad G_s = \frac{1}{R_s},\ G_g = \frac{1}{R_g} \tag{5-66}$$

If R_g and the tube were noiseless devices (ideal network), the mean-squared grid voltage would be

$$\overline{e_g'^2} = \frac{4kTG_s}{(G_s + G_g)^2} \Delta f \tag{5-67}$$

The noise figure F is then

$$F = \frac{\overline{e_g^2}}{\overline{e_g'^2}} = 1 + \frac{G_g}{G_s} + \frac{R_{eq}}{G_s}(G_s + G_g)^2 \tag{5-68}$$

[This result could of course have been obtained by taking the ratio of S/N at the grid to S/N at the input. This should be done as an instructive exercise by the reader and as a check on Eq. (5-68).] Note that Eq. (5-68) does predict an optimum value for F as a function of $G_s(1/R_s)$.

In particular, if $R_g \gg R_s$,

$$F \doteq 1 + \frac{R_s}{R_g} + \frac{R_{eq}}{R_s} \tag{5-69}$$

F will thus increase for either increasing or decreasing R_s. The optimum noise figure is readily found by differentiating F with respect to R_s and setting the derivative equal to zero. This gives

$$F_{\min} = 1 + 2\sqrt{\frac{R_{eq}}{R_g}} \tag{5-70}$$

$$R_s^2 = R_{eq}R_g \qquad R_s \ll R_g \tag{5-71}$$

[Equation (5-70) should be checked by the reader.] As the ratio of equivalent grid noise resistance to grid leak resistance (R_g) is made smaller, the minimum noise figure decreases, approaching the ideal value of 1. (Note that these results apply only to l-f operation of the tube. At higher frequencies, with transit-time effects significant, R_g appears in parallel with an effective resistance due to transit-time loading.)

In the triode circuit of Fig. 5-22, $R_{eq} = 1{,}250$ ohms, $R_g = 10^6$ ohms. Therefore

$$F_{\min} \doteq 1$$

as contrasted with the nonminimal value of 2.25. The effective source resistance must be increased from 1,000 ohms to $\sqrt{R_{eq}R_g} = 35{,}000$ ohms, however.

The lossless transformer used for this purpose would appear as in Fig. 5-23. The signal-to-noise ratio at the output of the transformer (assumed lossless) is the same as at the input (the reader is asked to verify this in one of the problems for this chapter). The effective source impedance R_s is, however,

$$R_s = n^2 R_s' \tag{5-72}$$

The turns ratio for minimum noise figure is thus

$$n^2 = \frac{\sqrt{R_{eq}R_g}}{R_s'} \tag{5-73}$$

from Eq. (5-71).

As an example, if $R_g = 10^6$ ohms, $R_{eq} = 1{,}250$ ohms, and $R_s' = 1{,}000$ ohms, $n = 6$. This would provide the effective source resistance of 35,000 ohms mentioned previously. (Note that this method of optimizing F is possible only at very low signal levels, where the stepped-up voltage is still within the linear region of the tube characteristics.)

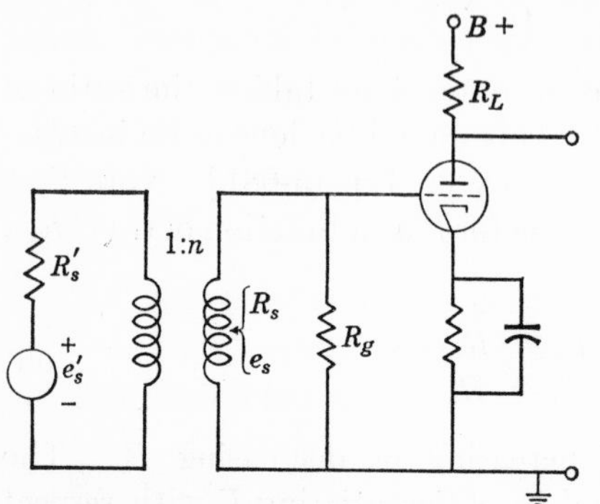

FIG. 5-23. Triode amplifier with input transformer for optimizing noise figure.

This particular problem of optimizing the noise figure of the simple triode amplifier has been discussed in such detail, not because of its exceptional significance, but because it does demonstrate quite simply the concepts of signal-to-noise ratio, noise figure, and noise calculations. The application of these concepts to more complex systems is treated in the next section. The concept of *available gain* is introduced there as a tool in generalizing the discussion.

5-9. Available Gain and Over-all Noise Figure. We are now in a position, based on the specific discussion of the noise figure of the triode amplifier of the previous section, to generalize our approach somewhat. We are ultimately interested in determining the noise figure of a more complete system containing possibly many amplifiers and passive networks. For this purpose it is important to evaluate the relative contribution of each part of the system to the over-all noise output.

In particular, we shall be able to show generally that if successive stages in a system introduce amplification the first stages contribute most to the over-all noise output. This has been mentioned previously and was shown specifically for the triode amplifier of the previous section.

We shall assume that an over-all system consists of a series of cascaded networks. Normally any computation of output signal becomes rather complicated because of the loading effect of each network on the one preceding. In this case we are interested in signal-to-noise ratios, however, with both signal and rms noise appearing across the same impedance. The S/N ratio is thus independent of load (the noise contribution of the next stage is taken into account at the output of that stage) and depends only on the output impedance. In calculating the signal voltage and, ultimately, S/N at a point in the system, then, we can assume any arbitrary load impedance—in particular, a load impedance that will simplify the calculations.

Since the S/N ratios are power ratios, or ratios of mean-squared voltages, the simplest choice of load impedance is the one maximizing the output power. We shall thus assume the load impedance matched to the output impedance. Generalized noise calculations are normally carried out on this basis.

The maximum power available at the output of a system, under matched conditions, is frequently called the *available power*. Thus, for a source represented by an rms signal voltage e_s and output resistance R_s, the available signal power is

$$S_s = \frac{e_s^2}{4R_s} \tag{5-74}$$

(The load resistance is chosen equal to the output resistance.)

Assuming only thermal noise present, the mean-squared noise voltage is

$$\overline{e_n^2} = 4kTR_s\,\Delta f \tag{5-75}$$

The available noise power is thus

$$N_s = \frac{\overline{e_n^2}}{4R_s} = kT\,\Delta f \tag{5-76}$$

The S/N ratio at the source is simply

$$\frac{S_s}{N_s} = \frac{e_s^2}{\overline{e_n^2}} = \frac{e_s^2}{4kTR_s\,\Delta f} = \frac{\text{available signal power}}{\text{available noise power}} \tag{5-77}$$

from Eqs. (5-74) and (5-76).

This of course checks our statement that S/N ratios may be found from the available power and are independent of load impedances.

Now consider this source connected to an arbitrary linear network as shown in Fig. 5-24. e_o is the open-circuit signal output voltage and R_o the output impedance (assumed resistive here).

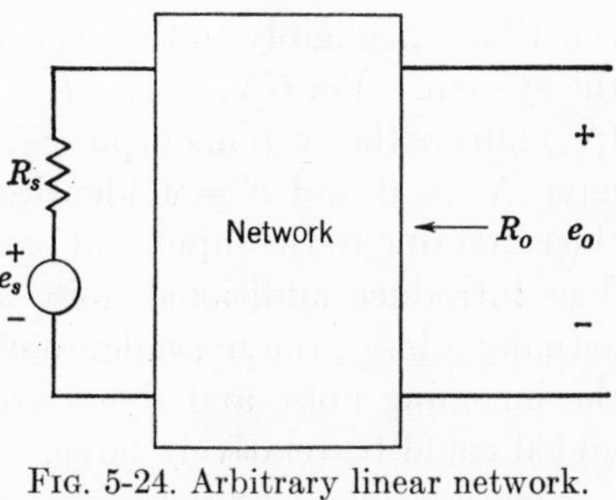

FIG. 5-24. Arbitrary linear network.

The *available power gain G* of this network is defined to be the ratio of available output signal power to available input signal power. (If the network is noiseless, the same ratio will hold for available noise powers.) If the output power is *less* than the input, the gain will actually be a *loss*. Thus

$$S_o = \frac{e_o^2}{4R_o} \qquad S_s = \frac{e_s^2}{4R_s} \tag{5-78}$$

and

$$S_o \equiv GS_s \tag{5-79}$$

The output signal-to-noise ratio S_o/N_o is then given by

$$\frac{S_o}{N_o} = \frac{GS_s}{N_o} = \frac{1}{F}\frac{S_s}{N_s} \tag{5-80}$$

by definition of the network noise figure. The noise figure F can thus be written as

$$F = \frac{N_o}{GN_s} \tag{5-81}$$

Equation (5-81) presents an alternative form for the equation of noise figure (aside from the definition in terms of S/N ratios) and is frequently given as the basic definition of F. Thus F may be defined as the ratio of actual noise power available from a network to that which would be available if the network were noiseless.

The available output noise power N_o can be written in the form

$$N_o = GN_s + N_n \tag{5-82}$$

where GN_s is the available output noise due solely to the input and N_n any additional noise generated in the network itself. Then

$$F = 1 + \frac{N_n}{GN_s} = 1 + \frac{N_n}{GkT\,\Delta f} \tag{5-83}$$

from Eqs. (5-81), (5-82), and (5-76). (Δf is again the effective noise bandwidth of the system.)

Equation (5-83) demonstrates simply the statements made previously that if there is enough amplification in a system the noises added will contribute negligibly to the over-all noise. Here G represents the gain of the system. For $GN_s \gg N_n$, $F \doteq 1$, and the additional noise introduced (N_n) affects the system output S/N negligibly. A noiseless system would have $N_n = 0$ and $F = 1$ identically. The only noise at the output is then that due to the input and passed through the system. If the system does introduce additional noise and $G < 1$ (that is, the power gain is actually a loss), the noise figure of the system may be quite large. Here the incoming noise and signal are both deemphasized so that the noise added could be relatively large.

Now consider two networks cascaded as shown in Fig. 5-25. How does the over-all noise figure depend on the individual noise figures and available gains of the individual networks?

By definition of available power the available gains of the two networks multiply, so that

$$S_o = G_1 G_2 S_s \tag{5-84}$$

The available noise power at the system output is now made up of three parts:

1. That due to the source noise and multiplied by the available gain of the over-all network. This is simply $G_1 G_2 N_s$.

2. That introduced in network 1 and transmitted through network 2. This is simply $G_2 N_{n1}$. But

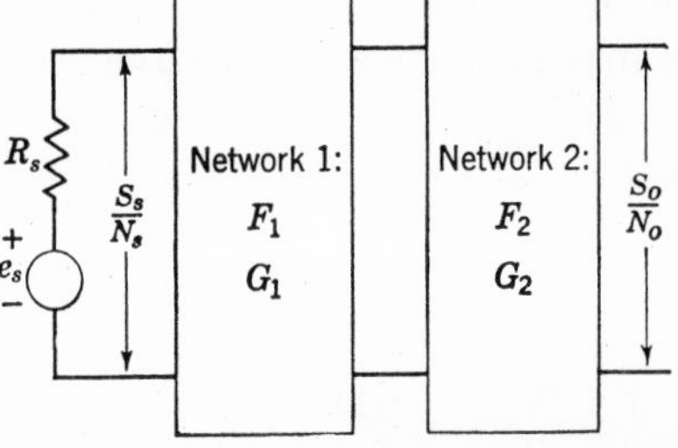

FIG. 5-25. Cascaded linear networks.

$$F_1 = 1 + \frac{N_{n1}}{G_1 N_s}$$

from Eq. (5-83), or

$$N_{n1} = (F_1 - 1) G_1 N_s$$

This component of the output noise is thus

$$G_1 G_2 (F_1 - 1) N_s$$

3. The noise N_{n2} developed in network 2 directly. Again from Eq. (5-83), $N_{n2} = (F_2 - 1) G_2 N_s$.

Upon adding together the three noise components the total available noise power at the output is

$$\begin{aligned} N_o &= G_1 G_2 N_s + G_1 G_2 (F_1 - 1) N_s + G_2 (F_2 - 1) N_s \\ &= G_1 G_2 F_1 N_s + G_2 (F_2 - 1) N_s \end{aligned} \tag{5-85}$$

But the noise figure F of the over-all network is the ratio of total available noise power to that available if the networks were lossless [Eq. (5-81)]. Thus

$$F = \frac{N_o}{G N_s} = \frac{N_o}{G_1 G_2 N_s} = F_1 + \frac{F_2 - 1}{G_1} \tag{5-86}$$

from Eq. (5-85).

Equation (5-86) demonstrates very clearly the relative contribution of two cascaded networks to the over-all noise figure. It can be interpreted exactly as was done for Eq. (5-83). Thus, if the available gain of the first network, G_1, is large enough ($G_1 \gg F_2 - 1$), the second network contributes negligibly to the over-all noise. The over-all noise figure remains at F_1.

These results can be extended quite easily to more cascaded networks. Thus, for three networks in cascade,

$$F = F_1 + \frac{F_2 - 1}{G_1} + \frac{F_3 - 1}{G_1 G_2} \tag{5-87}$$

Obviously, then, in dealing with amplifiers (as in communication or radar receivers), where each stage may have appreciable amplification (and available gain), the first stages determine the S/N properties of the entire system. The noise introduced beyond this point is negligible in comparison with the amplified noise of the first stage or two. (In receivers with mixer circuits the mixer is usually the primary source of noise.) It is of prime importance then that the first stage of an amplifier be a relatively low-noise stage. As will be seen shortly, multielectrode tubes are much noisier than triodes, and for this reason triodes are

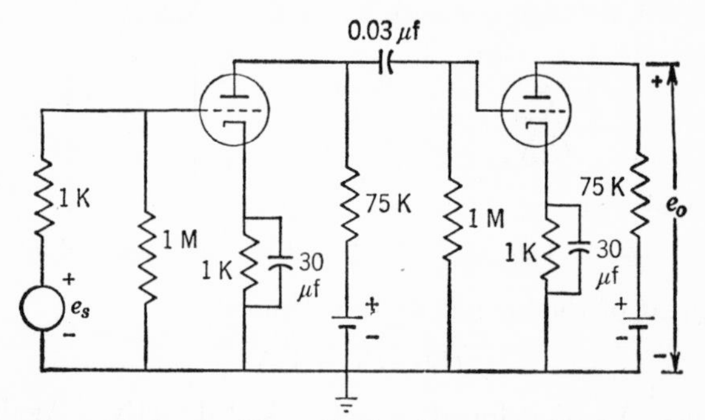

FIG. 5-26. Two-stage triode amplifier. Both tubes: $g_m = 2{,}000$ μmhos; $r_p = 15$ kilohms; $\mu = 30$.

uniformly used in the input or preamplifier stages of communication amplifiers. At high frequencies, however, the parasitic capacitances of the triode ordinarily play havoc with the amplification properties of a triode amplifier. The grounded-grid form of triode amplifier, in which the parasitic effects are less pronounced, has come into use as one form of input stage. The calculation of the noise figure of the grounded-grid triode amplifier is included among the problems for this chapter.

Before proceeding further, it is of interest to pause at this point and calculate the noise figure of a specific circuit. This will enable us to make more concrete the concepts of available gain and will give us some additional practice in noise-figure calculations.

The circuit to be analyzed is the two-stage triode amplifier of Fig. 5-26. Note that each stage individually is identical with the triode amplifier previously discussed. Again we do not actually compute the effect of coupling and bypass capacitors, as well as parasitic capacitors, but assume that these plus other reactive elements in the complete system of which the amplifier is a part have established the effective bandwidth as 50 cps to 20 kc. Δf will thus again be chosen as 20 kc.

To determine the noise figure of the two-stage amplifier, and from this the rms noise output voltage, let us consider the system to be made up of the two networks of Fig. 5-27. (Network 1 is thus taken to the plate of the first tube.)

For network 1 the available input power is $e_s^2/(4 \times 1 \text{ kilohm})$, and the available output power is very nearly $(\mu e_s)^2/(4 \times 15 \text{ kilohms})$, for

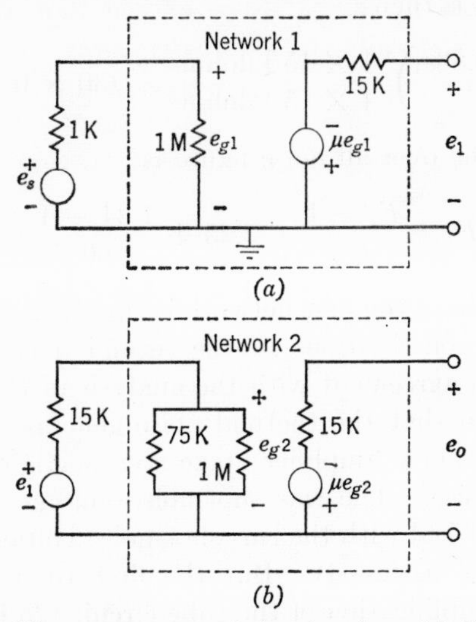

FIG. 5-27. Triode amplifier as two cascaded networks. (a) First stage; (b) second stage.

$e_{g1} \doteq e_s$, since 1 kilohm $\ll 10^6$ ohms. The available gain is thus

$$G_1 = \left(\frac{30e_s}{e_s}\right)^2 \frac{4}{60} = 60 \tag{5-88}$$

From the work of the previous section

$$F_1 \doteq 1 + \frac{G_g}{G_s} + R_{eq}G_s = 2.25 \tag{5-89}$$

The calculations for the second network are similar except that R_g now consists of the 75-kilohm resistor in parallel with 1 megohm and R_s is 15 kilohms (Fig. 5-27b). For this network, then,

$$F_2 = 1 + \frac{G_g}{G_s} + \frac{R_{eq}}{G_s}(G_s + G_g)^2$$

$$= 1 + 15/70 + 1.25 \times 15 \times 10^6 \times \left(\frac{1}{12.4 \times 10^3}\right)^2 = 1.34 \tag{5-90}$$

To find the available gain G_2: The available power in is

$$\frac{(e_1)^2}{4 \times 15 \text{ kilohms}}$$

and

$$e_{g2} = \frac{70}{15 + 70} e_1 = 0.83e_1$$

The available power out is

$$\frac{(30e_{g2})^2}{4 \times 15 \text{ kilohms}} = \frac{(30 \times 0.83e_1)^2}{4 \times 15 \text{ kilohms}}$$

The available gain is then

$$G_2 = \left(\frac{30 \times 0.83e_1}{e_1}\right)^2 \frac{4 \times 15 \text{ kilohms}}{4 \times 15 \text{ kilohms}} = (30 \times 0.83)^2 = 610 \quad (5\text{-}91)$$

From Eq. (5-86) the over-all noise figure is

$$F = F_1 + \frac{F_2 - 1}{G_1} = 2.25 + \frac{1.34 - 1}{60} \doteq 2.25 \quad (5\text{-}92)$$

The available gain of the first network is thus large enough in this case so that the noise contributions of the second network are negligible. This is of course in agreement with the analysis of the previous section, where it was shown that the thermal noise generated in the 75-kilohm load resistor of the first amplifier stage was negligible compared with source and shot noise. The rms shot-noise voltage introduced by the second stage is identical with the rms shot-noise voltage of the first stage (identical tubes are assumed). But the first tube rms shot noise is amplified by the amplification of the tube circuit (25 in this case) before appearing at the grid of the second tube. The shot noise of the second tube is thus negligible in this case.

The S/N at the output can be calculated quite easily now. Using the expression

$$\frac{S_o}{N_o} = \frac{1}{F}\frac{S_s}{N_s}$$

with $S_s/N_s = e_s^2/(3.2 \times 10^{-13})$ from Eq. (5-63) (as calculated previously in Sec. 5-8),

$$\frac{S_o}{N_o} = \frac{e_s^2}{0.73 \times 10^{-12}}$$

If this is to be 100, $e_s = 8.5\ \mu\text{v}$ rms. These results agree with those obtained previously in Secs. 5-7 and 5-8.

We could of course have obtained the same result for S_o/N_o by actually finding the rms output noise voltage. (Since the noise contributions of the load resistors and second stage are negligible, this is simply the rms noise at the grid of the first tube, 0.85 μv rms, multiplied by the over-all amplification, $25^2 = 625$. This gives 560 μv rms noise at the output.) The signal output voltage is simply e_s multiplied by the over-all amplification, or $625e_s$. The ratio of the two voltages squared gives S_o/N_o [$e_s^2/(0.73 \times 10^{-12})$ in this case]. This method of calculating output signal-to-noise ratio is of course almost trivial in this case because the additional noise generated beyond the grid of the first tube is negligible. In other cases this additional noise might not be negligible. Both methods—either by calculation of noise figures and available gain or, directly, by calculation of signal output and noise output voltages—would of course give the same result.

Cathode Follower. As an additional example of noise-figure calculations, it is instructive to calculate the noise figure of the cathode follower. The prototype form of the cathode follower is shown in Fig. 5-28*a*. Other forms of the cathode follower are discussed in books on electronics.[1]

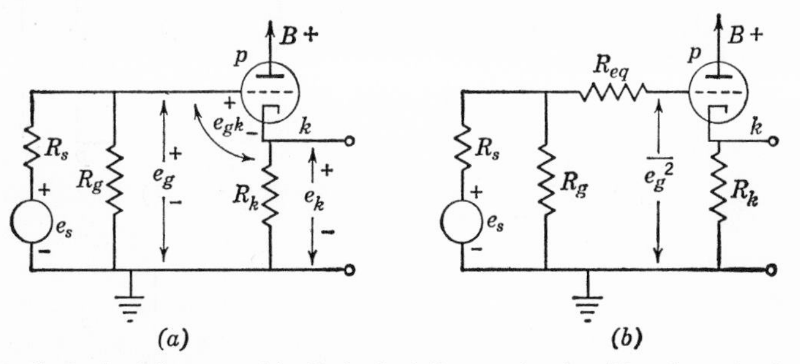

FIG. 5-28. Cathode follower. (*a*) Cathode-follower circuit; (*b*) tube noise included.

The effect of tube shot noise may again be represented by an equivalent noise resistance R_{eq} in series with the grid. As in Eq. (5-57), R_{eq} is given by

$$R_{eq} \doteq \frac{2.5}{g_m}$$

for tubes with oxide-coated cathodes.

Note that the choice and location of this equivalent noise resistor are independent of the external connections of the tube. The effect of the shot noise generated within the tube may be represented by R_{eq} in series with the grid, whether the tube is actually connected in the grounded-cathode circuit of Fig. 5-21 or 5-26, the cathode follower of Fig. 5-28, the grounded-grid circuit, or variations of these circuits.

It is thus apparent from Figs. 5-28 and 5-21 that the noise figure up to the grid is the same for both the grounded-cathode and cathode-follower circuits. We shall show that the noise figure measured to the output of the cathode follower of Fig. 5-28 is essentially that of a grounded-cathode one-stage triode amplifier as well.

To demonstrate this, we focus attention on the output circuit of the cathode follower. Consider first the noise-free case. For linear incremental operation the tube is represented by the usual $g_m e_{gk}$ current gen-

[1] See, e.g., E. J. Angelo, Jr., "Electronic Circuits," p. 274, McGraw-Hill Book Company, Inc., New York, 1958.

erator in parallel with g_p, the plate conductance. These appear shunted by the output conductance $G_k(1/R_k)$. The resulting circuit is shown in Fig. 5-29*a*. This circuit cannot be used directly for calculations since e_{gk} depends on the as yet unknown output voltage e_k. The circuit can be reduced to calculable form, however, by the successive transformations of Fig. 5-29. Since $e_{gk} = e_g - e_k$ from Fig. 5-28, the $g_m e_{gk}$ current source of Fig. 5-29*a* may be split into the two current sources of Fig. 5-29*b*.

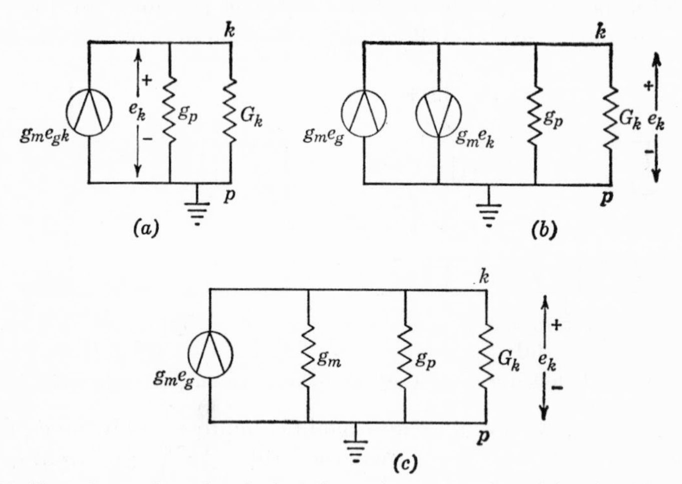

FIG. 5-29. Transformation of cathode-follower incremental model. (*a*) Linear incremental model; (*b*) $e_{gk} = e_g - e_k$, intermediate model; (*c*) final model for output calculations.

The $g_m e_k$ current source may in turn be replaced simply by a conductance g_m, for the current source appears across terminals *kp* with voltage e_k and is of the direction to draw the same current as a conductance g_m. The resultant cathode-follower circuit, valid for calculations at the output terminals, is shown in Fig. 5-29*c*.

This final model provides the well-known results that the output conductance of the cathode follower is $g_m + g_p + G_k$ and that the amplification, or forward voltage-transmission ratio, of the circuit is $A_m = e_k/e_g = g_m/(g_m + g_p + G_k)$. The amplification is thus less than 1 for this circuit.

The calculation of the noise figure of the cathode follower now follows directly from Figs. 5-28*b* and 5-29*c*. Instead of the $g_m e_g$ current source we use the noise current source $g_m^2 \overline{e_g^2}$, which includes both the thermal noise due to R_s and R_g and the shot-noise effect contributed by R_{eq}. The load resistor R_k also contributes additional thermal noise. The resulting noise model for the cathode follower is shown in Fig. 5-30.

Note that the only difference between this model and that of the triode amplifier or grounded-cathode circuit of Fig. 5-21*b* is the addition of the conductance g_m to the output circuit. In practice R_k will be much smaller than the plate load resistor R_L of the triode amplifier, or $G_k \gg G_L$.

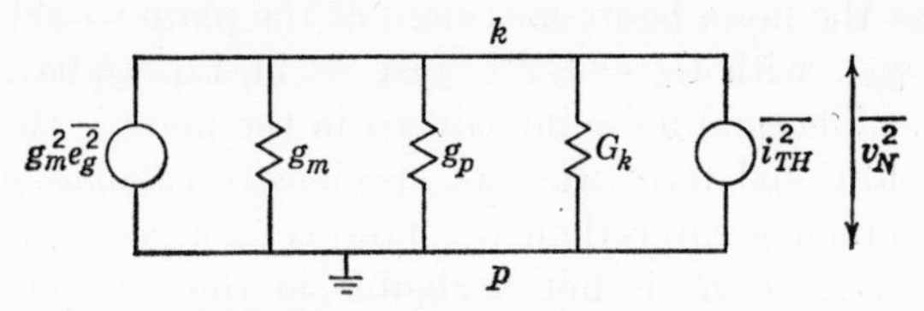

FIG. 5-30. Cathode-follower noise model.

As in the triode-amplifier case,

$$\overline{e_g^2} = 4kT\left(R_{eq} + \frac{R_s R_g}{R_s + R_g}\right)\Delta f \tag{5-93}$$

and

$$\overline{i_{TH}^2} = 4kTG_k\,\Delta f \tag{5-94}$$

The output noise voltage $\overline{v_N^2}$ is given by

$$\overline{v_N^2} = \frac{g_m^2\overline{e_g^2} + \overline{i_{TH}^2}}{(g_p + g_m + G_k)^2} = A_m^2\overline{e_g^2} + \frac{4kTG_k\,\Delta f}{(g_p + g_m + G_k)^2} \tag{5-95}$$

with

$$A_m = \frac{g_m}{g_m + g_p + G_k} \tag{5-96}$$

The noise figure of the cathode follower is given by the ratio of $\overline{v_N^2}$ to the output noise due only to noise brought in by the source resistance R_s. (All other resistors and tubes are assumed noise-free.) The component of $\overline{e_g^2}$ due to R_s only is

$$\overline{e_g'^2} = 4kTR_s\left(\frac{R_g}{R_s + R_g}\right)^2\Delta f$$

$$= \frac{4kTG_s}{(G_s + G_g)^2}\Delta f \tag{5-97}$$

as in Eq. (5-67). The output noise due to R_s is $A_m^2\overline{e_g'^2}$, with A_m the voltage transmission given by Eq. (5-96). The noise figure F is then given by

$$F = \frac{\overline{v_N^2}}{A_m^2\overline{e_g'^2}} = 1 + \frac{G_g}{G_s} + \frac{(G_s + G_g)^2}{G_s}\left(R_{eq} + \frac{G_k}{g_m^2}\right) \tag{5-98}$$

after some manipulation. If $R_g \gg R_s$ or $G_g \ll G_s$, as is generally true,

$$F \doteq 1 + G_s\left(R_{eq} + \frac{G_k}{g_m^2}\right) \tag{5-99}$$

Both Eqs. (5-98) and (5-99) are identical with the equations for noise figure obtained for a plate-loaded triode amplifier of the grounded-cathode type. Thus compare Eq. (5-98) with Eq. (5-68). Since Eq. (5-68) gives the noise figure at the grid of the triode amplifier, it does not include a term involving the plate load resistance R_L. It can be easily verified by the reader that the noise figure measured at the plate would have a term involving G_L/g_m^2, with $G_L = 1/R_L$, just as in Eq. (5-98). Normally, $R_{eq} \gg G_L/g_m^2$. Thermal noise introduced in the plate is thus negligible, and so this additional term was not specifically calculated previously. G_k is usually much greater than G_L, however ($R_k \ll R_L$), so that the thermal noise due to R_k is not negligible in the case of the cathode follower.

As an example, assume the same tube and parameters as in Figs. 5-21 and 5-26. Then $R_s = 1$ kilohm, $R_g = 1$ megohm, $r_p = 15$ kilohms, $g_m = 2{,}000$ μmhos, and $R_{eq} = 1{,}250$ ohms. With $R_k = 2$ kilohms, $A_m = 0.77$, and

$$F \doteq 1 + 10^{-3} \times (1{,}250 + 125) = 2.38$$

as compared with $F = 2.25$ for the triode amplifier. (There, with $R_L = 75$ kilohms, G_L/g_m^2 was negligible compared with R_{eq}.)

Even with this additional term due to R_k included, however, the actual value of the noise figure of the cathode follower does not differ too much from that of the plate-loaded (grounded-cathode) triode amplifier. But the actual value of the output noise, $\overline{v_N^2}$, will be less for the cathode follower (as also the output signal) because of the low amplification (less than 1). The noise contributed by any tubes or resistors following the cathode follower will be comparable with the cathode-follower noise and no longer negligible, as was true in the two-stage amplifier circuit previously discussed. This is due specifically to the low amplification (low gain) of the cathode follower.

The noise figure of a two-stage amplifier using a cathode follower as the first stage will thus be substantially higher than that of the cathode follower alone. This agrees with the discussion based on Eq. (5-86), giving the over-all noise figure of two cascaded networks. (The available gain G_1 of the cathode follower is less than 1.) This differs from the result found for the two-stage amplifier, with a plate-loaded amplifier as the first stage. There the noise contributed by the second stage was negligible compared with the highly amplified noise of the first stage, and the over-all noise figure of the two-stage combination was essentially that of the first stage alone.

A sample calculation of the noise figure of a two-stage amplifier with cathode-follower input is included among the problems for this chapter.

The noise figure of the triode connected for grounded-grid operation again has the same form as that of the grounded-cathode or cathode-follower configurations. The actual calculation of the noise figure of the grounded-grid triode is left for the reader. (It is also included among the problems for this chapter.)

Grounded-grid circuits are frequently used in the input stages of h-f receivers (at 50 Mc or higher), where noise generated must be kept at a minimum. The grounded-cathode triode circuit of Fig. 5-20 has a relatively high input capacitance due to feedback from plate to grid (the Miller effect), leading to parasitic oscillations if used at high frequencies. Multielectrode tubes have for this reason supplanted the triode in many h-f applications since they have a relatively low input capacitance.

The multielectrode tube is inherently much more noisy than the triode, however, as will be shown in the next section. For h-f applications requiring low-noise circuits (such as the input stages of sensitive h-f receivers required to pick up very small signals) both the pentode and the grounded-cathode triode amplifier cannot be used. The grounded-grid circuit overcomes both difficulties, since it has the same noise figure as the grounded-cathode circuit, and has a much smaller input capacitance. The grounded-grid circuit and variations on this such as the *cascode* circuit (combining the grounded-cathode and grounded-grid circuits) have therefore been widely used in low-signal-level h-f circuits.

5-10. Noise in Multielectrode Tubes. We have shown, in the case of diodes and triodes, that the random emission of electrons from the cathode results in a randomly fluctuating cathode current. The fluctuations about the average value of the cathode current tend to obscure any desired variations due to variations in grid and plate voltages (signal). These fluctuations are called shot noise. Although the instantaneous current varies randomly and so can, strictly speaking, be discussed only statistically, the mean-squared variation about the average current does take on a well-defined value dependent on the average current.

The presence of space charge tends to smooth out or decrease these fluctuations, the smoothing effect depending on applied voltages, temperature of emission, and cathode current.

These basic considerations still hold for the case of multielectrode tubes, with additional grids inserted in the cathode-anode space. In the region between cathode and control grid where emission and space-charge smoothing take place the tube still behaves as a diode so that we can write the same equations for mean-squared current fluctuations in both the temperature-limited and space-charge regions of operation, as in the diode or triode cases. If one or more of the additional grids carry current, however, we must be careful to distinguish between cathode current (total space current) and electrode current (such as plate current). If the average *cathode* current is I_t, we can express the mean-squared current fluctuations as

$$\overline{i_t^2} = 2eI_t\,\Delta f \qquad (5\text{-}100)$$

in the temperature-limited case and

$$\overline{i_t^2} = 2e\Gamma^2 I_t \,\Delta f \qquad \Gamma^2 \leq 1 \tag{5-101}$$

in the space-charge case.

These equations are identically the equations written previously for the diode and triode but generalized to any tube structure where fluctuations in *cathode* current only are considered.

It is well-known experimentally, however, that multielectrode tubes tend to be noisier than triodes in circuit applications. Here it is generally the plate current (or some other electrode current) that is of primary interest. This increase in the noise at the plate has been attributed to the presence of one or more additional electrodes carrying current.

To be specific, let us consider the noise characteristics of a pentode. If the tube is operating in the space-charge-limited region (as is normally the case), the space charge has tended to smooth out fluctuations in cathode current due to random emission of electrons. The screen draws a specified fraction of the average cathode current, the anode receiving the rest. The screen current picks up electrons randomly, however, the number intercepted varying from one interval to the next. (The average intercepted over a long period of time is constant and gives the average screen current.) This random interception of electrons by the screen tends to undo the smoothing effect of the space charge and so increases the noise current at both the plate and screen. If more electrodes are present and each draws current, the noise increases further since each electrode intercepts electrons randomly.

This increase in mean-squared noise current at the plate and other electrodes due to random interception of electrons has been called *partition noise.*

D. O. North of RCA Laboratories developed the basic theory for noise phenomena in multielectrode tubes[1] and showed that the equations derived agreed with experimental results. His equations for mean-squared noise fluctuations in the plate and screen currents, respectively, of a pentode are

$$\overline{i_b^2} = 2eI_b \frac{I_{c2} + \Gamma^2 I_b}{I_b + I_{c2}} \Delta f \tag{5-102}$$

and

$$\overline{i_{c2}^2} = 2eI_{c2} \frac{I_b + \Gamma^2 I_{c2}}{I_b + I_{c2}} \Delta f \tag{5-103}$$

where I_b and I_{c2} are the average plate and screen currents, respectively; Γ^2 is the space-charge reduction factor described previously. I_b and I_{c2}

[1] D. O. North, *RCA Rev.*, October, 1940, p. 244.

must sum to give the total space current I_t. Thus

$$I_t = I_b + I_{c2} \tag{5-104}$$

Equations (5-102) and (5-103) may be written in the form

$$\overline{i_b^2} = 2eI_b\Gamma_b^2\,\Delta f \tag{5-105}$$

and

$$\overline{i_{c2}^2} = 2eI_{c2}\Gamma_c^2\,\Delta f \tag{5-106}$$

where the modified space-charge factors Γ_b^2 and Γ_c^2 now include the effect of partition of current among the two electrodes,

$$\Gamma_b^2 = \frac{I_{c2} + \Gamma^2 I_b}{I_b + I_{c2}} = \frac{I_{c2} + \Gamma^2 I_b}{I_t} \tag{5-107}$$

$$\Gamma_c^2 = \frac{I_b + \Gamma^2 I_{c2}}{I_t} \tag{5-108}$$

Equation (5-107) for Γ_b^2 may be rewritten in the form

$$\Gamma_b^2 = \Gamma^2\left(1 + \frac{I_{c2}}{I_t}\frac{1-\Gamma^2}{\Gamma^2}\right) \geq \Gamma^2 \tag{5-109}$$

since $\Gamma^2 \leq 1$. This shows clearly the added noise as contrasted to the ordinary space-charge case [Eq. (5-101)].

Γ_c^2 may similarly be rewritten to show that $\Gamma_c^2 > \Gamma^2$. For the temperature-limited case, however, with $\Gamma^2 = 1$, we get

$$\overline{i_b^2} = 2eI_b\,\Delta f \qquad \overline{i_c^2} = 2eI_{c2}\,\Delta f \tag{5-110}$$

or

$$\overline{i_b^2} + \overline{i_c^2} = 2e(I_b + I_{c2})\,\Delta f = 2eI_t\,\Delta f \tag{5-111}$$

There is thus no additional noise generated in this case. For with a temperature-limited cathode current there is no space-charge smoothing, and the current fluctuations are completely random to begin with. The random interception of the electrons by the screen thus does not add to the mean-squared fluctuations in this case. The mean-squared noise fluctuations in the current of either electrode is, however, greater absolutely than in the space-charge-limited case.

Both Eqs. (5-107) and (5-108) may be rewritten in another instructive form. Adding and subtracting I_b in the numerator of Eq. (5-107), and repeating the same for I_{c2} in Eq. (5-108), we get

$$\Gamma_b^2 = 1 - \frac{I_b}{I_t}(1 - \Gamma^2) \tag{5-112}$$

$$\Gamma_c^2 = 1 - \frac{I_{c2}}{I_t}(1 - \Gamma^2) \tag{5-113}$$

These equations, combined with Eqs. (5-105) and (5-106), indicate that, although current interception by electrodes in a multielectrode tube increases the noise fluctuations in the space-charge case, the mean-squared fluctuations are still less than in the temperature-limited case. (Since $\Gamma^2 < 1$, Γ_b^2 and $\Gamma_c^2 < 1$.)

Equations (5-112) and (5-113) for the pentode may be generalized to any multielectrode tube where the grids intercepting current are not aligned with one another. The general expression for the mean-squared noise fluctuations at the nth electrode is

$$\overline{i_n^2} = 2e\Gamma_n^2 I_n \, \Delta f \tag{5-114}$$

where

$$\Gamma_n^2 = 1 - \frac{I_n}{I_t}(1 - \Gamma^2) \tag{5-115}$$

and I_n is the average current at the nth electrode.

We pointed out toward the beginning of this section that multielectrode tubes were inherently noisier than the equivalent triodes. The justification for the additional partition noise has been presented above and is summarized in Eqs. (5-114) and (5-115). It is of interest to compare the pentode and triode specifically, however, to see just how much noisier the pentode is for the same mode of operation.

To do this, we shall refer the pentode plate-current noise back to the control grid just as we did in Sec. 5-7 for the triode. e_{gp} and g_{mp} will be used to represent pentode grid voltage and transconductance, respectively. e_{gt} and g_{mt} will be the symbols used for the pentode in triode operation. Then, from Eq. (5-102),

$$\overline{e_{gp}^2} = \frac{\overline{i_b^2}}{g_{mp}^2} = \frac{2eI_b}{g_{mp}^2} \frac{I_{c2} + \Gamma^2 I_b}{I_t} \Delta f \tag{5-116}$$

But

$$\overline{e_{gt}^2} = \frac{2eI_t\Gamma^2 \, \Delta f}{g_{mt}^2} \tag{5-117}$$

since the triode plate current is the total space current.

Combining Eqs. (5-116) and (5-117),

$$\frac{\overline{e_{gp}^2}}{\overline{e_{gt}^2}} = \left(\frac{g_{mt} I_b}{g_{mp} I_t}\right)^2 \left(1 + \frac{I_{c2}}{\Gamma^2 I_b}\right) \tag{5-118}$$

But

$$\frac{g_{mt}}{I_t} \doteq \frac{g_{mp}}{I_b} \tag{5-119}$$

for the pentode operated as a triode (i.e., the transconductance is reduced in approximately the same proportion as the plate current, because of the screening effect of the screen grid).

The mean-squared grid noise voltages are thus related in the form

$$\overline{e_{gp}^2} = \left(1 + \frac{I_{c2}}{\Gamma^2 I_b}\right) \overline{e_{gt}^2} \tag{5-120}$$

This expression may be simplified for calculation purposes by recalling that

$$\Gamma^2 I_t = \frac{6(1 - \pi/4)kT_c g_{mt}}{e\sigma}$$
$$\doteq \frac{g_{mt}}{8.7\sigma}\frac{T_c}{1{,}000} \tag{5-121}$$

for the triode.

Using this relation and Eq. (5-119), we get the expression for $\overline{e_{gp}^2}$ developed by North and usually found in the literature,[1]

$$\overline{e_{gp}^2} = \left(1 + 8.7\sigma \frac{I_{c2}}{g_{mp}} \frac{1{,}000}{T_c}\right) \overline{e_{gt}^2} \tag{5-122}$$

If we take $T_c = 1000°K$ (as assumed previously for oxide-coated cathodes) and $\sigma = 0.88$ again,

$$\overline{e_{gp}^2} \doteq \left(1 + \frac{7.7I_{c2}}{g_{mp}}\right) \overline{e_{gt}^2} \tag{5-123}$$

Note that in both Eqs. (5-122) and (5-123) the transconductance referred to is the one for pentode operation.

We can also define the pentode equivalent grid noise as due to an equivalent grid resistance R_{eqp}, as was done for the triode. Thus

$$\overline{e_{gp}^2} = 4kTR_{eqp}\,\Delta f \tag{5-124}$$

and

$$\overline{e_{gt}^2} = 4kTR_{eqt}\,\Delta f \tag{5-125}$$

Equation (5-123) then becomes

$$R_{eqp} = \left(1 + \frac{7.7I_{c2}}{g_{mp}}\right) R_{eqt} \tag{5-126}$$

As an example of relative orders of magnitude of the various quantities defined, assume a tube with the following parameters:

$$I_b = 4 \text{ ma} \qquad I_{c2} = 1 \text{ ma} \qquad I_t = 5 \text{ ma}$$
$$g_{mt} = 2{,}000\ \mu\text{mhos} \qquad g_{mp} = 1{,}600\ \mu\text{mhos} \qquad \frac{I_b}{I_t} \doteq 0.8 = \frac{g_{mp}}{g_{mt}}$$

Then

$$R_{eqt} = 1{,}250 \text{ ohms}$$

as previously, and

$$R_{eqp} = 7{,}250 \text{ ohms}$$

from Eq. (5-126).

The mean-squared grid noise voltage of the pentode is thus almost six

[1] "Reference Data for Radio Engineers," 4th ed., International Telephone and Telegraph Corporation, New York, 1956.

times that of the triode. This is not at all untypical of the increased noisiness of pentode operation.

The noise model of the pentode for use in normal amplifier circuits is identical with that of the triode and so will not be discussed further in this book.

5-11. Noise in Junction Transistors. Electrical currents in junction transistors are due primarily to the flow of minority carriers (holes in the case of the *P-N-P* transistor). Noise, or random current fluctuations, would be expected to arise because of the particle, or granular, nature of the current flow.

The net current flow is determined essentially by two independent processes: diffusion of the minority carriers after crossing a junction (the *P-N* junction in the case of the *P-N-P* transistor), and a recombination process where some of the holes combine with electrons in the base region before reaching the collector. Since very large numbers of carriers are involved in the net current flow, averaging techniques may be employed, just as in the case of current calculations in vacuum tubes, and *average* currents calculated for specified emitter and collector junction voltages. But the rate of diffusion and recombination may be expected to vary randomly about the average, giving rise to fluctuations in the average current. (For example, in the calculation of minority-carrier diffusion an average diffusion time is assumed. Implicit here is the assumption that the number of carriers is so large that average numbers may be used for calculation. Actually the number of carriers involved varies randomly about the average, as does the rate of diffusion. These random variations about the average give rise to mean-squared fluctuations in the current or noise, as in the case of vacuum tubes.)

In addition to these random fluctuations in minority-carrier current (equivalent to the shot noise of vacuum tubes) the pure thermal noise of the semiconducting material, considered as a passive resistance, will contribute to the "noisiness" of the transistors.

Studies of random current fluctuations, or noise, in junction transistors have indicated that there are then basically three sources of noise to be considered:

1. Fluctuations in the diffusion of the minority carriers (holes in the case of *P-N* junctions)
2. Recombination fluctuations in the base region
3. Thermal noise of the base resistance

Transistor noise calculations are thus inherently more complicated algebraically than the calculations for most vacuum-tube circuits, where the tubes are assumed to produce shot noise only, and associated passive elements, thermal noise.

In the case of *P-N-P* transistors the diffusion fluctuations predominate at the emitter-base junction at low frequencies and give rise to an equation identical with the shot-noise equation for vacuum tubes. The recombination fluctuations in the base region give rise to an equation which may also be looked at as a partition-noise term similar to the partition noise in multielectrode tubes. The recombination effect can be represented by the emitter current dividing between base and collector. Random fluctuations in the recombination process can therefore be treated as random variations in the current division between base and collector, or partition noise.

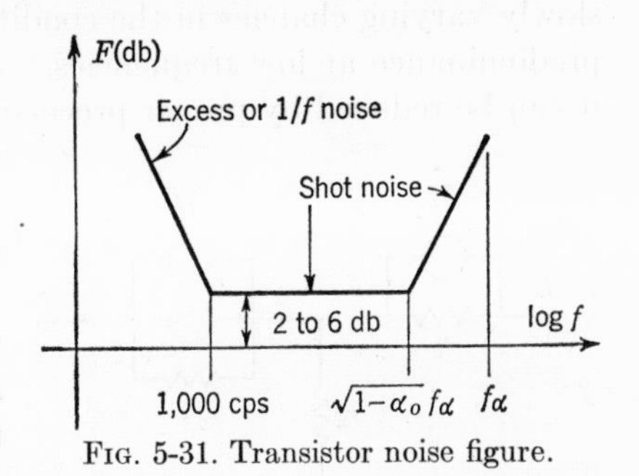

FIG. 5-31. Transistor noise figure.

The transistor thus acts as a source of all three types of noise that we have previously encountered: shot, partition, and thermal noise. (Of course all the noise effects are related in the sense that they are due to the granular, or corpuscular, nature of current flow and to the randomness of the particle motion involved. The distinctions arise from separating out the specific physical phenomena involved.)

In this section we shall first discuss a low-level noise model for the transistor, incorporating the noise sources mentioned, which has been found to agree quite well with experimental data. We shall use this model to calculate the noise figure in Sec. 5-12 of the transistor connected in its three usual configurations. Various conclusions as to ways of minimizing the transistor noise figure can then be drawn from these results. In particular we shall see that a small emitter current I_e, a short-circuit current gain α_0, as close to 1 as possible, α-cutoff frequency f_α as high as possible, and an optimum choice of source resistance all contribute to a minimum noise figure.

We shall then attempt to outline, in Sec. 5-13, the methods used in arriving at the noise model of the junction transistor. This will incidentally also enable us to describe a noise model for the junction (P-N) diode. The reader will be referred to specific papers in the literature for the actual development of the theory of transistor noise.

Transistor Noise Model. A typical experimental curve of transistor noise figure as a function of frequency would appear as in Fig. 5-31.[1] At very low frequencies, typically below 1 kc, the transistor noise figure rises at a rate of 3 db/octave or functionally as $1/f$. The type of noise producing this differs from the types we have previously considered (shot and thermal), which have a flat frequency spectrum. It was originally

[1] E. G. Nielsen, Behavior of Noise Figure in Junction Transistors, *Proc. IRE*, vol. 45, no. 7, pp. 957–963, July, 1957.

the predominant noise term in transistors and was assumed to be due to inhomogeneities in manufacture. More refined methods of design and manufacture have pushed this effect down to very low frequencies so that its contribution to the noise may frequently be assumed negligible over the ordinary range of transistor operation.

A similar type of $1/f$ noise occurs commonly in vacuum-tube work and is there called *flicker effect*. This type of noise phenomenon is due to slowly varying changes in the condition of the cathode surface; hence its predominance at low frequencies. Just as in the case of the transistor it can be reduced by proper processing of the cathode and so is not considered in the class of spontaneous fluctuations such as shot or thermal noise.

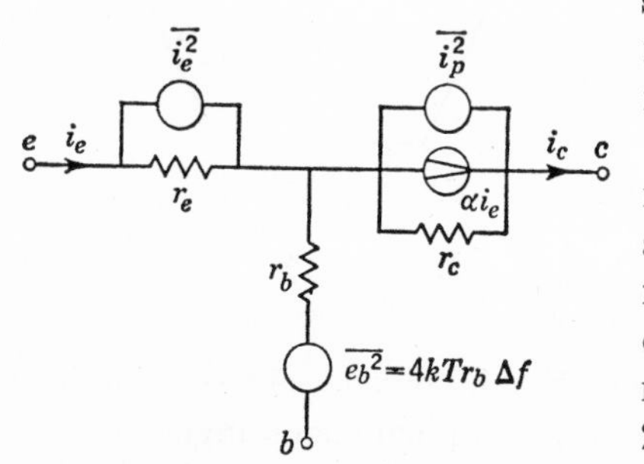

FIG. 5-32. Incremental transistor noise model ($f < f_\alpha$).

At frequencies above 1 kc the noise figure of the transistor may be accounted for by an incremental model incorporating the three sources of noise mentioned previously.[1] This noise figure may typically range from 2 to 6 db for good transistors and is relatively constant up to a frequency in the neighborhood of $\sqrt{1 - \alpha_0}\, f_\alpha$ (f_α is the α-cutoff frequency). Above this frequency the noise figure rises at about 6 db/octave. Again this may be accounted for in the noise model by allowing α to vary with frequency as $\alpha_0/(1 + jf/f_\alpha)$, as in the usual transistor analysis. Calculated noise figures then agree to within 2 db of the experimental noise figure up to frequency f_α.†

The transistor noise model valid below the α-cutoff frequency and above 1 kc (or the frequency at which the $1/f$ noise is assumed to become negligible) is shown in Fig. 5-32. The theoretical justification for the model will be discussed later in this chapter.[2] It is important to note, however, that the model is valid for small-signal operation only. High-level operation is found to produce additional noise.

In this model the emitter noise source is given by

$$\overline{i_e^2} = 2eI_e\,\Delta f \tag{5-127}$$

where I_e is the average emitter current and Δf the effective noise bandwidth of the system. Note that this expression for $\overline{i_e^2}$ is identical with

[1] A. Van der Ziel, Note on Shot and Partition Noise in Junction Transistors, *J. Appl. Phys.*, vol. 25, p. 815, June, 1954; Theory of Shot Noise in Junction Diodes and Junction Transistors, *Proc. IRE*, vol. 43, no. 11, pp. 1639–1646, November, 1955.

† Nielsen, *op. cit.;* G. H. Hansen and A. Van der Ziel, Shot Noise in Transistors, *Proc. IRE*, vol. 45, no. 11, pp. 1538–1542, November, 1957.

[2] Van der Ziel, *op. cit.*

the shot-effect expression in the vacuum diode. At low frequencies this noise term in the emitter circuit is primarily due to diffusion fluctuations.

The noise term in the collector circuit, $\overline{i_p^2}$, is the term due to recombination fluctuations in the base giving rise to additional noise fluctuations in the collector circuit (the partition noise term referred to previously). This noise term appears in the collector in addition to the noise fluctuations carried over from the emitter, as denoted by the current source αi_e. This partition noise term is given by

$$\overline{i_p^2} = 2eI_c\left(1 - \frac{|\alpha|^2}{\alpha_0}\right)\Delta f \qquad I_{c0} \ll I_c(1 - \alpha_0) \tag{5-128}$$

where I_c is the average collector current, I_{c0} is the collector current with zero emitter current, α_0 is the short-circuit current gain at low frequencies, and

$$\alpha = \frac{\alpha_0}{1 + jf/f_\alpha} \tag{5-129}$$

$\overline{i_p^2}$ and $\overline{i_e^2}$ may be assumed to be independent sources at low frequencies $(f < f_\alpha)$, and their effects thus add in quadrature.

Equation (5-128) may also be rewritten, by using Eq. (5-129), as

$$\overline{i_p^2} = 2eI_c(1 - \alpha_0)\,\frac{1 + (f/\sqrt{1 - \alpha_0}\,f_\alpha)^2}{1 + (f/f_\alpha)^2}\,\Delta f \tag{5-130}$$

On a logarithmic plot this equation is seen to have two break frequencies: $\sqrt{1 - \alpha_0}\,f_\alpha$ and f_α.

For $f < \sqrt{1 - \alpha_0}\,f_\alpha$: $\quad \overline{i_p^2} = 2eI_c(1 - \alpha_0)\,\Delta f$
For $f = \sqrt{1 - \alpha_0}\,f_\alpha$: $\quad \overline{i_p^2} = 4eI_c(1 - \alpha_0)\,\Delta f$
For $f > f_\alpha$: $\quad \overline{i_p^2} = 2eI_c\,\Delta f$

The increase in collector noise current at frequencies above $\sqrt{1 - \alpha_0}\,f_\alpha$ accounts for the increase in Fig. 5-31 of noise figure with frequency.

The noise source in the base circuit is a thermal-noise term due to the base spreading resistance r_b. The mean-squared base noise voltage is then

$$\overline{e_b^2} = 4kTr_b\,\Delta f \tag{5-131}$$

5-12. Transistor Noise Figure. The calculation of the noise figure of the transistor in its various configurations is now readily carried out by using the noise model of Fig. 5-32. We shall calculate the noise figure only for the grounded-base circuit. The grounded-emitter and grounded-collector cases will be left to the reader as an exercise in noise-figure calculation. Our calculation will also be for the l-f model case, $f < f_\alpha\sqrt{1 - \alpha_0}$. The extension to the higher-frequency case, using Eqs. (5-128) and (5-129), is then readily carried out.

The incremental noise model for the grounded-base transistor with $f < f_\alpha\sqrt{1 - \alpha_0}$ is shown in Fig. 5-33. R_s is the source resistance. The collector resistance r_c is assumed much larger than any of the circuit resistances and is considered an open circuit.

To find F, the noise figure of this configuration, we would normally calculate the mean noise power at the load due to all noise sources shown, then the noise power at the load due to the input noise ($\overline{v_s^2}$) only, the transistor being assumed noiseless. Since the noise powers at the load are given by $\overline{i_c^2}R_L$, with R_L the load resistance, the noise figure can be found simply by taking the ratio of mean-squared collector current in the

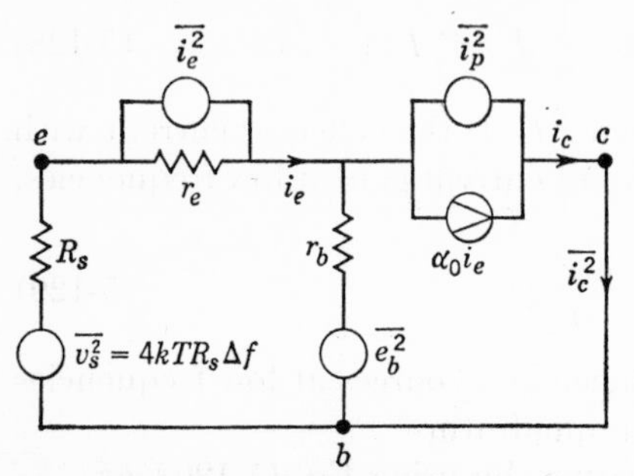

FIG. 5-33. Low-frequency incremental noise model, grounded-base transistor ($f < \sqrt{1 - \alpha_0}\, f_\alpha$).

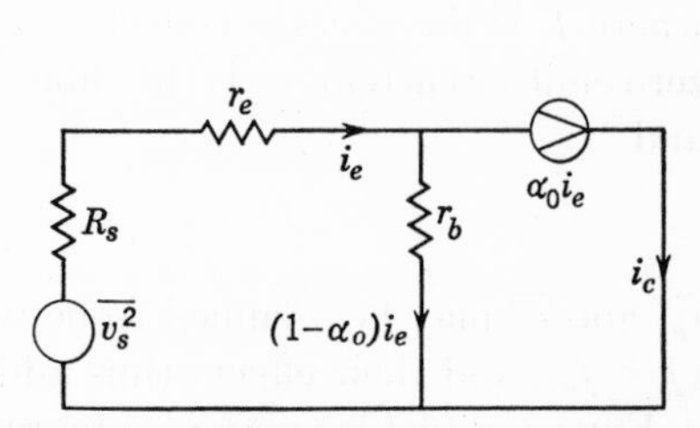

FIG. 5-34. Collector noise due to input only.

two cases. Since we are interested in the transistor only, the noise contribution of R_L does not enter into the calculation. (This is the reason why F could be defined in terms of available noise power in previous sections.) R_L may be considered short-circuited during the calculation of F. This has been done in Fig. 5-33.

Since all the noise sources shown are independent and the circuit is linear, we can determine the output noise due to each source separately and superpose the results.[1] Thus

$$F = \frac{\overline{i_{ct}^2}}{\overline{i_{cs}^2}} = 1 + \frac{\overline{i_{cp}^2} + \overline{i_{cb}^2} + \overline{i_{ce}^2}}{\overline{i_{cs}^2}} \tag{5-132}$$

[1] This could still be done if the sources were dependent, but we would have to treat each source at a particular instant of time as with our usual signal sources. After superposing the instantaneous outputs due to each source we would then square and take the average over a long interval of time. This gives rise to so-called "correlation," or "dependency," terms of the form $\overline{i_p i_e}$ which must be separately evaluated. If i_p and i_e are assumed to vary randomly and independently with time, as is the case here, the average of their products goes to zero. As an example, assume that we add two random sources i_p and i_e after appropriate weighting through some network. We then have $ai_p + bi_e$. Upon squaring and averaging over a long interval we get

$$\overline{(ai_p + bi_e)^2} = a^2\overline{i_p^2} + b^2\overline{i_e^2} + 2ab\overline{i_p i_e}$$

The cross-product term is nonzero if there is some dependence or correlation between i_p and i_e. We shall have occasion to discuss the significance of the correlation later in this book.

where $\overline{i_{ct}^2}$ is the sum of the mean-squared collector noise currents due to all noise sources, $\overline{i_{cs}^2}$ is the contribution to the collector noise due to the input source alone, and the subscripts of the remaining collector noise currents refer, respectively, to the contributions due to $\overline{i_p^2}$, $\overline{e_b^2}$, and $\overline{i_e^2}$.

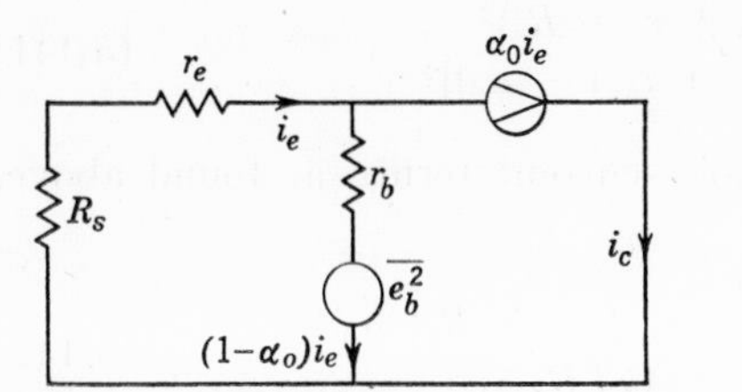

FIG. 5-35. Collector noise due to base thermal noise.

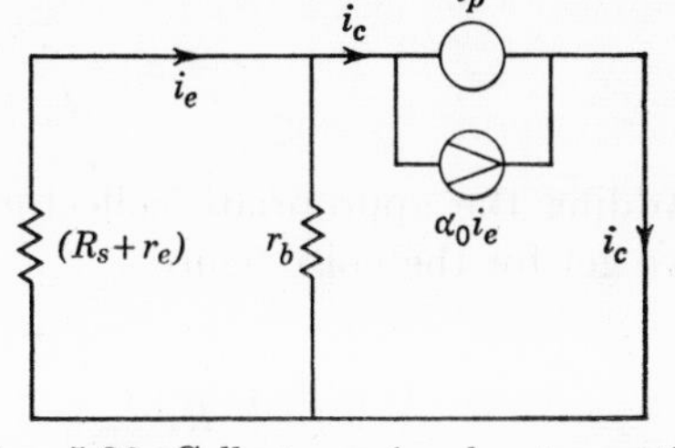

FIG. 5-36. Collector noise due to partition-noise term.

1. First calculating $\overline{i_{cs}^2}$, we use the noise model of Fig. 5-34. Treating v_s first just as an ordinary source and applying Kirchhoff's voltage law, we get

$$v_s = (R_s + r_e)i_e + r_b(1 - \alpha_0)i_e \tag{5-133}$$

Solving for i_e and noting that $i_c = \alpha_0 i_e$, we get

$$i_c = \frac{\alpha_0 v_s}{R_s + r_e + r_b(1 - \alpha_0)} \tag{5-134}$$

On squaring and averaging with time,

$$\overline{i_{cs}^2} = \frac{\alpha_0^2 \overline{v_s^2}}{[R_s + r_e + r_b(1 - \alpha_0)]^2} \tag{5-135}$$

2. $\overline{i_{ce}^2}$, the collector noise contribution due to $\overline{i_e^2}$, is found in identically the same way since $\overline{v_e^2} = r_e^2\overline{i_e^2}$ appears in series with $\overline{v_s^2}$. Therefore

$$\overline{i_{ce}^2} = \frac{\alpha_0^2 r_e^2 \overline{i_e^2}}{[R_s + r_b(1 - \alpha_0) + r_e]^2} \tag{5-136}$$

3. To find $\overline{i_{cb}^2}$, the noise contribution due to $\overline{e_b^2}$, we use the model of Fig. 5-35 (obtained from Fig. 5-33 by letting all other noise sources vanish). Again summing voltages, we have

$$e_b = [R_s + r_e + r_b(1 - \alpha_0)]i_e \tag{5-137}$$

as before. $i_c = \alpha_0 i_e$, so that on squaring and averaging we get

$$\overline{i_{cb}^2} = \frac{\alpha_0^2 \overline{e_b^2}}{[R_s + r_e + r_b(1 - \alpha_0)]^2} \tag{5-138}$$

4. The final noise component, $\overline{i_{cp}^2}$, can be found quite readily from the model of Fig. 5-36. Here

$$i_e = \frac{i_c r_b}{r_b + r_e + R_s} \tag{5-139}$$

by the current-divider relationship. But

$$i_c = i_p + \alpha_0 i_e = i_p + \frac{\alpha_0 i_c r_b}{r_b + r_e + R_s} \tag{5-140}$$

Solving for i_c, squaring, and averaging again,

$$\overline{i_{cp}^2} = \frac{\overline{i_p^2}(r_b + r_e + R_s)^2}{[R_s + r_e + r_b(1 - \alpha_0)]^2} \tag{5-141}$$

Adding the appropriate collector noise-current terms, as found above, we get for the noise figure

$$F = 1 + \frac{r_b}{R_s} + \frac{r_e^2\overline{i_e^2} + [(r_b + r_e + R_s)/\alpha_0]^2\overline{i_p^2}}{4kTR_s\,\Delta f} \tag{5-142}$$

since $\overline{e_b^2} = 4kTr_b\,\Delta f$

and $\overline{v_s^2} = 4kTR_s\,\Delta f$

But $\overline{i_p^2} = 2eI_c(1 - \alpha_0)\,\Delta f \qquad f < \sqrt{1 - \alpha_0}\,f_\alpha$

$\overline{i_e^2} = 2eI_e\,\Delta f$

and $I_c = \alpha_0 I_e + I_{c0} \doteq \alpha_0 I_e$

The noise figure for the grounded-base case thus becomes

$$F = 1 + \frac{r_b}{R_s} + \frac{eI_e}{2kTR_s}\left[r_e^2 + \frac{1 - \alpha_0}{\alpha_0}(r_b + r_e + R_s)^2\right] \tag{5-143}$$

This equation for F may be used for calculation purposes, or it may be put in another useful form.

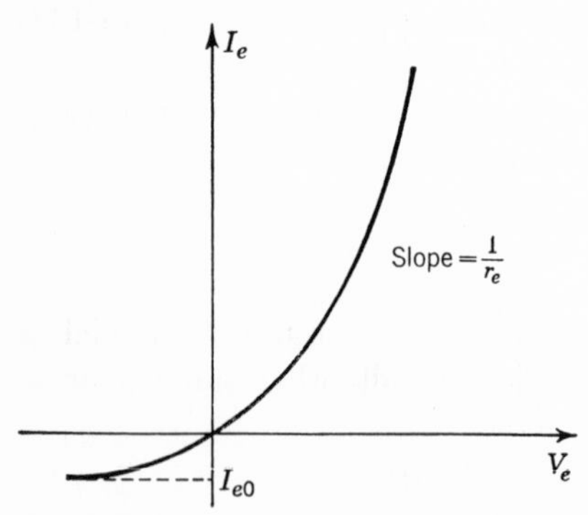

FIG. 5-37. Junction-diode terminal characteristics.

The emitter resistance r_e is simply the dynamic, or incremental, resistance of the emitter-base junction considered as a junction diode. For junction diodes the current and voltage are found to be related by the expression[1]

$$I_e = I_{e0}(e^{eV_e/kT} - 1) \tag{5-144}$$

where V_e is the voltage across the junction and I_{e0} the backward, or saturation, current across the junction when V_e is a very large negative voltage.

Equation (5-144) is shown sketched in Fig. 5-37. The equation is analogous to the Child's-law expression for vacuum diodes. The incre-

[1] A. Van der Ziel, Theory of Shot Noise in Junction Diodes and Junction Transistors, *Proc. IRE*, vol. 43, no. 11, pp. 1639–1646, November, 1955.

mental diode conductance g_e is the slope of the current-voltage curve at a particular current, or

$$g_e = \frac{\partial I_e}{\partial V_e} = \frac{e}{kT}(I_e + I_{e0}) \doteq \frac{e}{kT} I_e \tag{5-145}$$

if $I_e \gg I_{e0}$ (this is true under normal operating conditions). The emitter resistance r_e can thus be written

$$r_e = \frac{1}{g_e} = \frac{kT}{eI_e} = \frac{0.026}{I_e} \tag{5-146}$$

where r_e is given in ohms, I_e in amperes, and 20°C temperature assumed. By using this simple inverse relation between r_e and I_e to eliminate I_e in Eq. (5-143), the noise figure may be written finally as

$$F = 1 + \frac{r_b + r_e/2}{R_s} + \frac{(r_b + r_e + R_s)^2(1 - \alpha_0)}{2\alpha_0 r_e R_s} \tag{5-147}$$

As an example, if $r_b = 200$ ohms, $r_e = 20$ ohms, $\alpha_0 = 0.98$, and $R_s = 1{,}000$ ohms,

$$F = 1.97, \text{ or } 3 \text{ db}$$

The noise figure for the grounded-emitter transistor turns out to be identical with this noise figure for the grounded-base case. This is left as an exercise for the reader.

Some interesting conclusions can be drawn from Eq. (5-147).

First, since $r_e \ll r_b$ normally, F is seen to increase with decreasing r_e. To keep the noise figure as low as possible, then, the emitter current I_e should be kept as low as possible. [This is also seen from the previous equation, Eq. (5-143), with F given in terms of I_e.] Although this might seem to limit the dynamic operating range of a transistor amplifier, it is actually not too stringent a condition. For, as pointed out in previous sections, the first stage of an amplifier is normally the one that would be designed as a low-noise stage and the signal level is low here to begin with. The lowest practical value for I_e is of the order of ⅓ ma. For when I_e is reduced below this value, the short-circuit current gain α_0 also begins to decrease. In addition we must keep in mind our original assumption that $I_{c0} \ll I_e(1 - \alpha_0)$.

Second, α_0 should be as close to 1 as possible to obtain a smaller noise figure. This decreases the number of hole-electron recombinations in the base and decreases the recombination fluctuations as well.

Third, r_b should be reduced as much as possible.

Fourth, just as in the case of the triode amplifier F can be minimized by choosing an optimum source resistance. This is seen by noting that as R_s increases F eventually increases and as R_s decreases F eventually increases. The optimum source resistance can be found quite easily and is given by

$$R_{s,opt} \doteq \left(r_b^2 + \frac{2r_b r_e}{1 - \alpha_0}\right)^{1/2} \qquad r_e \ll r_b \tag{5-148}$$

Using our example with $r_b = 200$ ohms, $r_e = 20$ ohms, and $\alpha_0 = 0.98$, $R_{s,opt} = 660$ ohms.

This optimum value of R_s is not critical. F changes by only 0.5 db for R_s varying from one-half to twice the optimum value and by 2.5 db over a range from $\frac{1}{5}$ to 5 times the optimum value.[1] For example, with $R_{s,opt} = 660$ ohms, $F = 1.92$, as compared with 1.97 with $R_s = 1{,}000$ ohms. $R_{s,opt}$ varies with I_e and is about the same for all three of the usual transistor configurations.

As an interesting point this optimum value of R_s to provide minimum noise figure is close to the value that provides maximum available gain for the grounded-emitter configuration $[r_b + r_e/(1 - \alpha_0)]$. This does not hold true for the grounded-base and grounded-collector configurations.

Noise-figure Variation with Frequency. The previous discussion related to the calculation of noise figure at frequencies below $\sqrt{1 - \alpha_0}\, f_\alpha$. Above this frequency the noise figure begins to rise because of the dependence of α on frequency. By using the frequency-dependent expression for $\overline{i_p^2}$ [Eq. 5-128] the noise figure for the grounded-base and grounded-emitter cases may be shown to have the following frequency-dependent form:

$$F = 1 + \frac{r_b + r_e/2}{R_s} + \frac{(1 - \alpha_0)(R_s + r_b + r_e)^2[1 + f^2/(1 - \alpha_0)f_\alpha^2]}{2\alpha_0 r_e R_s} \tag{5-149}$$

Note again that in deriving this expression as well as the previous l-f one we have assumed r_c very large and $I_{c0} \ll (1 - \alpha_0)I_c$.

The noise figure is thus constant to a frequency in the vicinity of $\sqrt{1 - \alpha_0}\, f_\alpha$ and then begins to increase, eventually approaching a 6 db/octave slope. For example, if the l-f noise figure is 3 db and $\alpha_0 = 0.985$, F increases by 18 db to 21 db at f_α. (f_α and $\sqrt{1 - \alpha_0}\, f_\alpha$ differ by three octaves.) Thus, although reducing $1 - \alpha_0$ reduces the l-f noise, it also decreases the frequency at which F begins to increase. This can be compensated for (or the noise at a given frequency decreased) by increasing f_α.

It is to be noted that the conclusions cited previously for minimizing the transistor noise figure—decreasing r_b and reducing $1 - \alpha_0$, plus the additional conclusion that a high f_α is desirable—correspond to the requirements usually cited for a high-gain wideband transistor amplifier.[1]

[1] Nielsen, *op. cit.*

5-13. Discussion of Transistor Noise Model. Figure 5-32 represents the linear incremental model of the transistor for use in transistor noise calculations.

The previous section was devoted to the calculation of the transistor noise figure and a discussion of the significance of the results obtained. Experimental measurements of the transistor noise figure have demonstrated the validity of the model used. These measurements are described in some of the articles referred to in Sec. 5-12.

We would now like to summarize some of the arguments used in developing the transistor noise model. The detailed derivations and discussions are to be found in two papers: one by Van der Ziel,[1] the other by Guggenbuehl and Strutt.[2] Van der Ziel uses an approach based on the physics of semiconductor operation, while Guggenbuehl and Strutt present a thermodynamic argument for arriving at essentially the same results.

We shall start with a noise model of the junction diode, summarizing *very briefly* the results of calculations carried out in these two papers, then shall proceed to a brief discussion of the transistor noise model itself.

Noise in Junction Diodes. For a *P-N* junction diode the analysis starts by assuming an infinite region of *n*-type material with holes as minority carriers. The diffusion of the holes in the infinite *n*-region is governed by differential equations relating hole concentration and current to the voltage across the junction. These diffusion equations are analogous to the transmission-line equations derived for the case of zero inductance per unit length and can thus be solved in terms of a transmission-line analogue.

With these equations the d-c current I is found to be related to V, the voltage across the junction, by

$$I = I_0 e^{eV/kT} - I_0 \tag{5-150}$$

(Note that the solution appears in the exponential form, just as in the transmission-line case.) I_0 is the backward current of the diode, or the current flowing when V is a large negative voltage, and is found to be given by

$$I_0 = ep_n \left(\frac{D}{\tau}\right)^{1/2} \tag{5-151}$$

where e is the electron charge, p_n the equilibrium hole concentration at the junction (0 voltage), D the hole-diffusion coefficient, and τ the average hole lifetime.

[1] A. Van der Ziel, Theory of Shot Noise in Junction Diodes and Junction Transistors, *Proc. IRE*, vol. 43, no. 11, pp. 1639–1646, November, 1955.

[2] W. Guggenbuehl and M. J. O. Strutt, Theory and Experiments on Semiconductor Junction Diodes and Transistors, *Proc. IRE*, vol. 45, no. 6, pp. 839ff., June, 1957.

Equation (5-150) gives the static diode operating characteristic of Fig. 5-37. The incremental diode conductance at a voltage V (or the incremental conductance across the junction) is

$$g_d = \frac{\partial I}{\partial V} = \frac{e}{kT}(I + I_0) \doteq \frac{eI}{kT} \tag{5-152}$$

($eV \gg kT$ for normal operation, or $I \gg I_0$).

These are the diode equations using an average hole concentration, average hole lifetime, etc. These quantities vary randomly about the average values, however, and give rise to random fluctuations in the current, or noise. In calculating the mean-squared diode current, two independent phenomena must be considered:

1. Fluctuations in the hole concentration throughout the n region, due to diffusion
2. Fluctuations due to recombination

Van der Ziel has calculated these two effects and, adding them quadratically, gets for the mean-squared variation about the average diode current

$$\overline{i_d^2} = 4kTg_d'\,\Delta f - 2eI\,\Delta f \tag{5-153}$$

where g_d' is the a-c conductance of the junction.

$$g_d' = \text{Re}\,[g_d(1 + j\omega\tau)^{1/2}] \tag{5-154}$$

where τ is the average hole lifetime and Re [ ] represents the real part of [ ]. For $\omega \ll 1/\tau$, $g_d' \doteq g_d$, and

$$\overline{i_d^2} = 4kTg_d\,\Delta f - 2eI\,\Delta f \tag{5-155}$$

Equations (5-153) and (5-155) are the fundamental equations to be used in calculating the noise effects of junction diodes. Note that these equations, although derived by Van der Ziel on the basis of the physics of the semiconductor diode, contain a term identical with the Nyquist thermal noise developed by a passive resistor of the same conductance. The second term is a shot-noise term as derived for the vacuum diode. The implication then follows that this expression for the junction-diode noise current might be obtained by an application of thermodynamic reasoning.

Guggenbuehl and Strutt have used this approach in their article previously referred to. The reason that such an approach must always be possible is that both thermal and shot noise relate to fluctuations due to the discrete particle of current flow: in one case the fluctuations are due to particle conduction (the shot-noise case), in the other to thermal agitation.

A difficulty arises in applying thermodynamic reasoning, however, for thermal equilibrium is assumed in the original Nyquist derivation for passive networks, while this is definitely not the case here. To bypass this difficulty, Guggenbuehl and Strutt postulate a condition of quasi-thermal equilibrium. Then, assuming small-signal conditions (i.e., linearity), they superpose the Nyquist thermal effect and a shot-noise effect to arrive at Eq. (5-153).

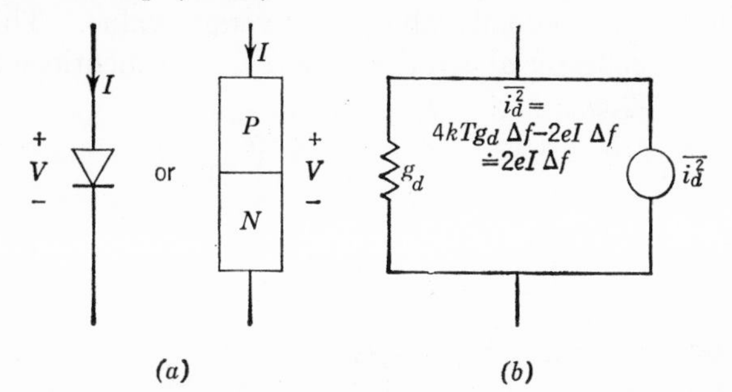

FIG. 5-38. Junction-diode l-f noise model. (a) Diode; (b) model.

Equation (5-155), the l-f equation, may be simplified for calculation purposes by noting from Eq. (5-152) that $g_d = e(I + I_0)/kT$. By using this simple result the diode mean-squared noise current becomes

$$\overline{i_d^2} = 2e(I + 2I_0)\,\Delta f \doteq 2eI\,\Delta f \qquad I_0 \ll I \tag{5-156}$$

This is then in the same form as the shot-effect equation for the vacuum diode.

An l-f noise model for the junction diode would thus be given by Fig. 5-38. (The n region is assumed much greater in extent than the p region in the case of the P-N diode. The model is also valid only for low-level diode operation, i.e., for small currents.)

Junction Transistors. If we now combine two P-N junction diodes back to back in the form of a P-N-P transistor, we get the noise circuit of Fig. 5-39. In the emitter circuit

$$\overline{i_e^2} = 4kTg_e\,\Delta f - 2eI_e\,\Delta f \doteq 2eI_e\,\Delta f \tag{5-157}$$

and

$$g_e \doteq \frac{eI_e}{kT}$$

with the emitter-base junction represented as a junction diode. In the base we get an additional noise term, due to the base spreading resistance, of the form $\overline{e_b^2} = 4kTr_b\,\Delta f$.

The collector-circuit noise model appears rather complicated but can be accounted for in the following fashion:[1]

The collector-base junction has three noise terms associated with it.

[1] H. C. Montgomery and M. A. Clark, *J. Appl. Phys.*, vol. 24, p. 1337, October, 1953; A. Van der Ziel, *J. Appl. Phys.*, vol. 25, p. 815, June, 1954.

One term due to $\overline{i_e^2}$ must be present, for a fraction αi_e of the emitter current appears in the collector circuit ($\alpha < 1$ since some recombination takes place in the base). This term appears of course in the usual transistor circuit and is accounted for by the αi_e current source in the collector circuit. In addition, however, a partition noise term also appears.[1] For the division of the emitter current between base and collector fluctuates randomly about an average value. This increases the noise in the collector above the term $\alpha^2\overline{i_e^2}$ just mentioned. Van der

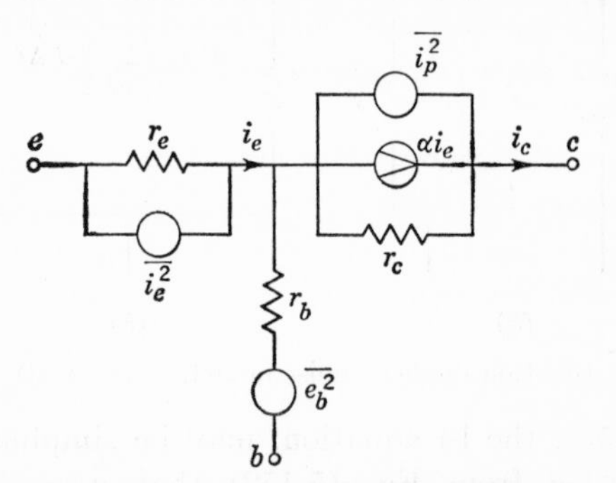

FIG. 5-39. Transistor noise model derived from diode models.

Ziel has shown that this excess noise term is given by $2e\alpha I_e(1 - \alpha)\,\Delta f$. [$I_e(1 - \alpha)$ is the average base current.] This excess noise term is included in source $\overline{i_p^2}$.

With $i_e = 0$ a current I_{c0} flows in the collector. The collector-base junction behaves like a junction diode, there are random fluctuations about I_{c0}, and we get a $2eI_{c0}\,\Delta f$ noise term just as in the junction-diode case. This is incorporated in $\overline{i_p^2}$ also, so that

$$\overline{i_p^2} = 2eI_{c0}\,\Delta f + 2e\alpha I_e(1 - \alpha)\,\Delta f \tag{5-158}$$

Normally, $I_{c0} \ll I_e(1 - \alpha)$, so that we get the model used in Secs. 5-11 and 5-12. $\overline{i_p^2}$ is thus due mainly to recombination fluctuations. (The I_{c0} term is primarily due to diffusion fluctuations.) The model of Fig. 5-39 just described can thus be hypothesized from a knowledge of junction-diode noise and transistor operation. As mentioned previously, this has also been checked experimentally.

A full derivation of the equations of this model and the assumptions made in obtaining it are given in the papers by Van der Ziel and Guggenbuehl and Strutt originally referred to. As pointed out in Secs. 5-11 and 5-12, the model agrees fairly well with experiment up to the α-cutoff frequency f_α if α is assumed to vary as $\alpha_0/(1 + jf/f_\alpha)$. For higher frequencies additional frequency-dependent terms must be considered, and these are treated in the papers mentioned.

[1] Van der Ziel, *ibid.*

5-14. Summary. We have discussed in this chapter the unavoidable presence in communication circuits of two types of fluctuation noise: shot noise and thermal noise. Both types of noise are due to the granular, or particle, nature of current flow. Thermal noise occurs in all conducting media and is attributable to the thermal interaction between free moving charges (electrons or holes) and the vibrating bound ions of the conducting medium. Shot noise, on the other hand, is attributable to nonuniform emission and flow of charged particles (electrons and holes). The concepts of shot noise were originally introduced to describe noise generated in vacuum tubes and have been extended to cover noise in semiconductors also.

We have shown that for both types of fluctuation noise the mean-squared noise voltage or current is proportional to system bandwidth. (In the case of shot noise this is true only for frequencies small compared with the reciprocal of transit time.) Since average power is proportional to mean-squared voltage (or current), we can summarize by saying that mean noise power is proportional to bandwidth. We shall have more to say about noise power in the next chapter.

Using the basic concepts of fluctuation noise, we discussed methods of calculating rms noise voltages (or currents) in systems involving combinations of passive and active elements (tubes, transistors). The concept of noise figure was introduced as an aid in comparing the relative noisiness of different networks. The noise figure was defined essentially to be the ratio of mean noise power out of a system to mean noise power out if the system were noiseless. (The noise power at the output is then that due to the signal source driving the system, as modified by the system properties.)

We showed that in normal communication systems with several stages of amplification included the noise generated in the first stage was the primary factor in determining the system noise figure.

The idea of signal-to-noise ratio as a measure of the distinguishability of signals in the presence of noise was introduced in this chapter. It was defined simply as the ratio of mean signal power to mean noise power, both measured at the same point in a system. The concept is a very useful one in modern information systems and will be utilized throughout the next chapter in comparing the relative efficiency of various communication systems.

We can use the concept of signal-to-noise ratio in enlarging further on the relation for information capacity introduced at the beginning of the book. We assumed there a hypothetical system in which the signals being transmitted were represented by voltage pulses of width τ and of varying amplitude level. The signals were assumed equally likely to occupy any one of n amplitude levels. The average rate of transmission of information, or system capacity, was then shown to be

$$C = \frac{1}{\tau} \log_2 n \qquad \text{bits/sec} \tag{5-159}$$

τ and n are thus parameters limiting the ability of a system to transmit information.

We showed in Chap. 2 that τ, effectively the response time of a linear system, was inversely proportional to the system bandwidth. With B the system bandwidth in cycles per second, C becomes

$$C = B \log_2 n \qquad \text{bits/sec} \tag{5-160}$$

so that bandwidth can be interpreted as one of the factors limiting system information capacity.

The second factor, n, the number of distinguishable amplitude levels, can now be related to the signal-to-noise ratio of a system. For signal amplitude changes can be distinguished only if they are at least comparable to the rms noise level. If we arbitrarily assume, then, that a signal voltage change is distinguishable if it is equal to the rms noise voltage N_v and assume a maximum signal voltage of S_v volts, there will be S_v/N_v distinguishable signal levels. Including 0 volts as an additional possible signal level,

$$n \doteq 1 + \frac{S_v}{N_v} \tag{5-161}$$

where S_v/N_v is the voltage signal-to-noise ratio and is just the square root of our previous power ratio.

The system-capacity expression now becomes

$$C = B \log_2 \left(1 + \frac{S_v}{N_v}\right) \qquad \text{bits/sec} \tag{5-162}$$

Equation (5-162) is similar to a fundamental equation of modern communication theory derived by C. E. Shannon, to which reference is made in the next chapter. It says that we can increase the capacity of a given system obeying this relation by either increasing the bandwidth B or increasing the signal-to-noise ratio. Alternatively, for a fixed capacity required to transmit a particular type of information-bearing signal (determined from considerations such as those in Sec. 1-3), we can "trade" B for S_v/N_v: we can use a smaller bandwidth by increasing the signal-to-noise ratio appropriately. There is of course a limit to this "trade," since we have shown that N_v itself varies with bandwidth. Also, a certain minimum bandwidth is always required to transmit a given type of signal (Chap. 2).

The Shannon equation similar to Eq. (5-162) applies only to a particular type of idealized communication system. We shall have more to say about this in the next chapter and shall discuss a practical pulse-code modulation (PCM) system which approaches this idealized type of system. We shall see, however, that a similar trading of B for S_v/N_v, and vice versa, will appear in investigating the signal-to-noise properties of frequency-modulation (FM) and pulse-position-modulation (PPM) systems. These systems are, however, much less efficient than PCM or the idealized system to which the Shannon equation applies. It is this trade of B for S_v/N_v that explains the noise-level improvement of *wideband* FM over amplitude modulation (AM) and *wideband* PPM over pulse-amplitude modulation (PAM). We shall discuss these ideas in detail in the next chapter.

PROBLEMS

NOTE: All temperatures are assumed to be 20°C except where otherwise noted.

5-1. The diode of Fig. 5-3 is operated in the temperature-limited region. $I_b = 5$ ma, $R_L = 10$ kilohms.

(*a*) Find the rms noise voltage, due to the diode only, across R_L. Assume a bandwidth of 10 kc.

(*b*) Find the rms noise voltage due to the resistive load in a 10-kc bandwidth.

(*c*) Find the *total* rms noise voltage across R_L in a 10-kc bandwidth.

(*d*) $I_b = 0.1$ ma, $R_L = 1$ kilohm, and the bandwidth is 10 kc. Repeat (*c*).

5-2. Calculate the rms noise voltage in a 10-kc bandwidth across a:

(*a*) 10-kilohm resistor.

(*b*) 100-kilohm resistor.

Repeat for a 5-kc bandwidth.

5-3. The resistive load of Prob. 5-1 is replaced by a resistor and capacitor in parallel. $R = 1$ kilohm, $C = 0.02$ μf, $I_b = 5$ ma.

(*a*) Find the *total* rms noise voltage across the RC combination, summing contributions at all frequency ranges.

(*b*) What portion of the total noise energy lies below 30 kc? 15 kc?

5-4. Consider the circuit of Fig. 5-9. The diode is temperature-limited, and its average current is $I_b = 1$ ma. $R = 100$ ohms. The $H(j\omega)$ network shown is an amplifier with a noise-equivalent bandwidth of 5 kc and a voltage amplification of 10^6. Assuming that the amplifier contributes negligible noise, find the rms output voltage.

5-5. The diode in Fig. P 5-5 is operated in the space-charge-limited region. Its incremental plate conductance is $g_d = 1$ millimho. The cathode is oxide-coated, with $T_c = 1000$°K. $R_L = 10$ kilohms, $R = 100$ kilohms. The l-f cutoff frequency due to capacity C is 50 cps. Find the total rms noise voltage across resistor R in a 5-kc bandwidth.

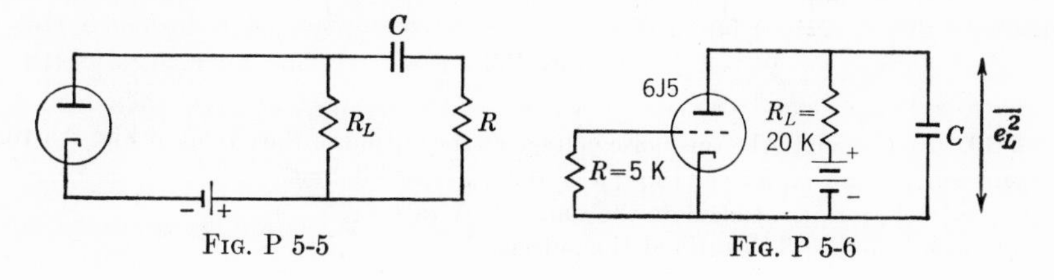

FIG. P 5-5 FIG. P 5-6

5-6. Refer to Fig. P 5-6. Capacitor C is chosen to make the noise equivalent bandwidth 10 kc.

(*a*) Calculate the rms load voltage due to R alone.

(*b*) Calculate the rms load voltage due to the tube. (Assume $T_c = 1000°K$.)

(*c*) Calculate the rms load voltage due to R_L.

(*d*) Calculate the *total* rms load voltage $\sqrt{\overline{e_L^2}}$.

5-7. The noise output of a tube is amplified through a noiseless amplifier of 20 kc bandwidth. A 1-kc-bandwidth meter, connected at the amplifier output, reads 1 volt rms.

(*a*) The amplifier bandwidth is reduced to 5 kc, its voltage amplification remaining the same. What does the meter read?

(*b*) A 500-cps-bandwidth meter is used with the original amplifier. What is the rms output voltage as read by the meter?

5-8. Find the noise figure of the circuit of Fig. P 5-8. The capacitors may be assumed short circuits.

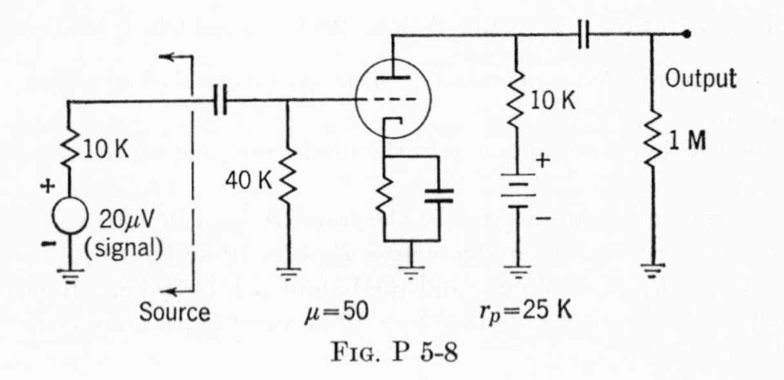

FIG. P 5-8

5-9. Consider the two-stage amplifier of Fig. P 5-9. $g_m = 2.5$ millimhos, and $r_p = 10$ kilohms, for both tubes.

(*a*) List all sources of noise.

(*b*) Calculate the *total* rms voltage e_o at the output. The frequency range of interest is from 50 cps to 20 kc.

(*c*) What rms signal voltage e_s would provide an output S/N power ratio of 50?

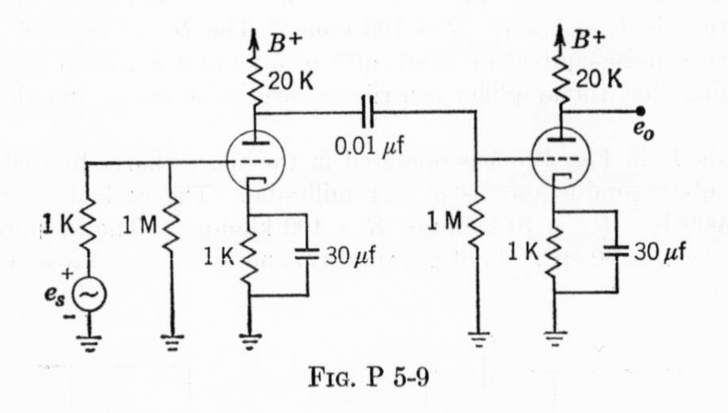

FIG. P 5-9

5-10. (*a*) Calculate the rms noise voltage at the output of the circuit of Fig. P 5-10. Assume $R_{eq} = 2.5/g_m$ for the tube; $\mu = 100$, $r_p = 20$ kilohms.

(*b*) $e_s = 3$ μv rms. Calculate the source S/N ratio.

(*c*) Calculate the S/N ratio at the output.

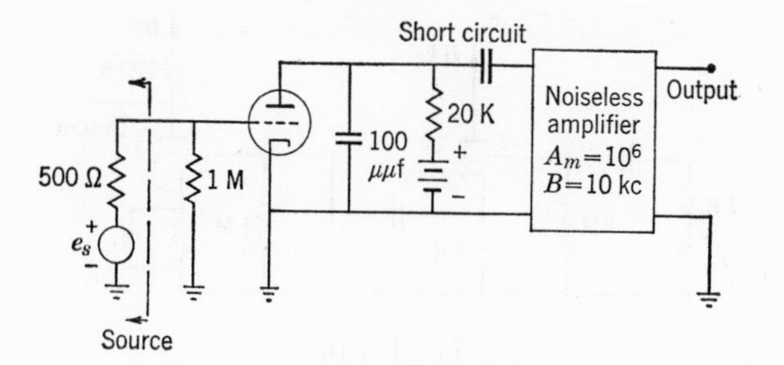

Fig. P 5-10

5-11. A temperature-limited diode noise source is to be used to determine experimentally the noise figure of a given amplifier. The circuit used is shown in Fig. P 5-11. With switch S open the output power is 1 mw. With S closed the output power is 3 mw, and $I_{dc} = 0.3$ ma.

(*a*) What is the amplifier noise figure?

(*b*) What is the decibel gain of the amplifier?

(*c*) What are the rms input and output noise voltages with S open?

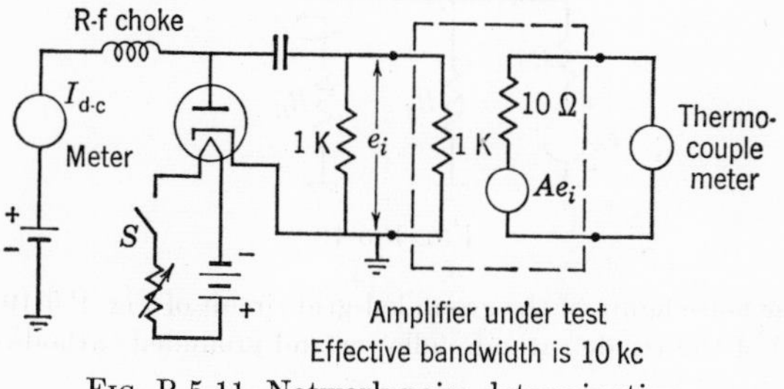

Fig. P 5-11. Network noise determination.

5-12. Find the noise figure of the circuit of Fig. 5-21 by comparing the S/N ratio at the grid to the S/N ratio at the input to the circuit. This result should agree with Eq. (5-68).

5-13. Show that the optimum noise figure for the circuit of Fig. 5-21 is given by Eq. (5-70).

5-14. Show that the S/N ratio at the output of a lossless transformer is the same as the S/N ratio at the input (see Fig. 5-23).

5-15. Derive Eq. (5-87), the noise figure of three networks in cascade.

5-16. Consider the two-stage amplifier with cathode-follower input of Fig. P 5-16. All capacitors are short circuits in the frequency range of interest. The 1-kilohm resistor represents the output impedance of the source (assumed passive). Both triodes are identical, with $\mu = 19$, $r_p = 20$ kilohms, and with an equivalent grid noise resistance $R_{eq} = 2.5/g_m$.

(*a*) What is the rms noise voltage at the output in a 20-kc bandwidth?

(*b*) What is the over-all noise figure for the circuit? Do this two ways: (1) by calculating the available gain and noise figure of each of the tube stages; (2) by computing the S/N ratio at both output and input.

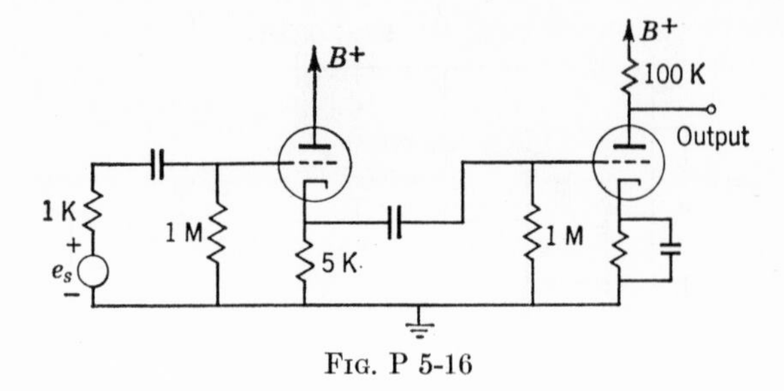

FIG. P 5-16

5-17. The cathode follower of Fig. P 5-16 is replaced by a grounded-cathode amplifier circuit identical with the second tube stage of the circuit. Calculate the over-all noise figure of the two-stage amplifier, and compare with the result of the previous problem.

5-18. Find the noise figure of the amplifier of Fig. P 5-18.

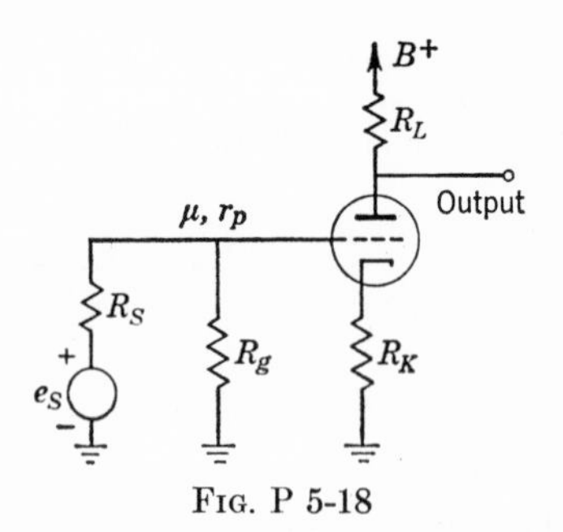

FIG. P 5-18

5-19. Find the noise figure of the grounded-grid circuit of Fig. P 5-19 (compare with the noise figures of the triode cathode-follower and grounded-cathode circuits).

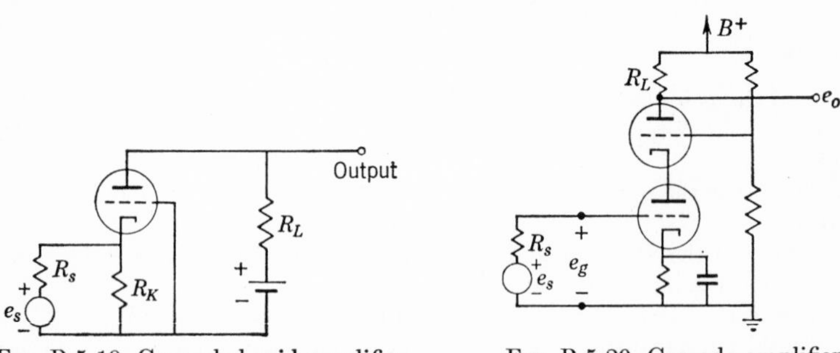

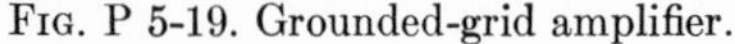

FIG. P 5-19. Grounded-grid amplifier.

FIG. P 5-20. Cascode amplifier.

5-20. Calculate the noise figure of the cascode circuit shown in Fig. P 5-20.

5-21. Using Eqs. (5-119) and (5-126), calculate the equivalent grid noise resistance of each of the following pentodes: 6SJ7, 6SK7, 6AC7, 6AK5. Assume typical operating conditions for the tubes.

5-22. A 6AU6-type pentode is used in an amplifier circuit similar to the triode amplifier of Fig. 5-20. The plate-supply voltage E_{bb} is 300 volts, $E_{c2} = 100$ volts, $E_{c3} = 0$, and $E_{c1} = -1$ volt. The load resistor $R_L = 20$ kilohms, $R_g = 1$ megohm, and $R_s = 10$ kilohms.

(*a*) Calculate the rms output noise voltage.

(*b*) Calculate the noise figure for the circuit.

(*c*) Compare the results of (*a*) and (*b*) with those for the tube operated as a triode under approximately the same operating conditions.

5-23. A 6SJ7 pentode is used in a two-stage amplifier similar to that of Fig. P 5-9. The plate load resistor $R_L = 20$ kilohms as shown. $E_{bb} = 300$ volts, $E_{c2} = 100$ volts, and $E_{c3} = 0$. The cathode bias resistor is chosen to make $E_{c1} = -3$ volts. $R_g =$ 1 megohm, and $R_s = 1$ kilohm.

Calculate the over-all noise figure of the circuit and the output rms noise voltage.

5-24. Using the l-f transistor noise model of Fig. 5-32, find the noise figure of the transistor connected in the grounded-emitter configuration. Show that the noise figure obtained is the same as for the grounded-base case discussed in the text. Assume, as in the text, that $I_{c0} \ll (1 - \alpha_0)I_c$.

5-25. Find the l-f noise figure of the grounded-collector transistor.

5-26. Check the frequency-dependent expression for the noise figure for both the grounded-base and grounded-emitter cases, as given by Eq. (5-149).

5-27. Show that the optimum source resistance providing a minimum noise figure for both the grounded-base and grounded-emitter transistor cases is given by Eq. (5-148).

5-28. Show that the optimum source resistance for maximum gain in the grounded-emitter transistor case is given by $R_s = r_b + r_e/(1 - \alpha_0)$. Compare this result with that of the previous problem.

5-29. (*a*) $R_s = 500$ ohms, $\alpha_0 = 0.975$, $r_b = 300$ ohms, $r_e = 30$ ohms. Find the noise figure F for the grounded-emitter case. Compare with the minimum noise figure found by varying R_s.

(*b*) $f_\alpha = 100$ kc. Sketch F as a function of frequency for the grounded-emitter case.

5-30. (*a*) A test of a transistor with the same characteristics as those of the previous problem shows an excess noise or $1/f$ contribution to the noise figure of 16 db at a frequency of 1 kc. Sketch the total noise figure as a function of frequency.

(*b*) A second transistor with very nearly the same characteristics is found to have an excess noise component of the noise figure of 6 db at 500 cps. Sketch the total noise figure as a function of frequency, and compare with the results of (*a*) of this problem and (*b*) of the previous problem.

5-31. The l-f hybrid π model of the transistor with noise sources included is shown in Fig. P 5-31. The load resistor R_L is assumed zero. The resistor $r_{bb'}$ is comparable to the base spreading resistance r_b in Fig. 5-32. The noise-current sources shown, in addition to the I_{c0} term, are

$$\overline{i_c^2} = 2e\alpha I_c\,\Delta f$$

and

$$\overline{i_r^2} = 2e(1 - \alpha_0)I_e\,\Delta f$$

The resistor $r_{b'e} \doteq r_e/(1 - \alpha_0)$, with r_e the emitter resistance of the transistor model of Fig. 5-32. The constant $g_m \doteq \alpha_0/r_e$. Calculate the noise figure of this transistor model, and show that it agrees with Eq. (5-143) if the I_{c0} term is neglected.

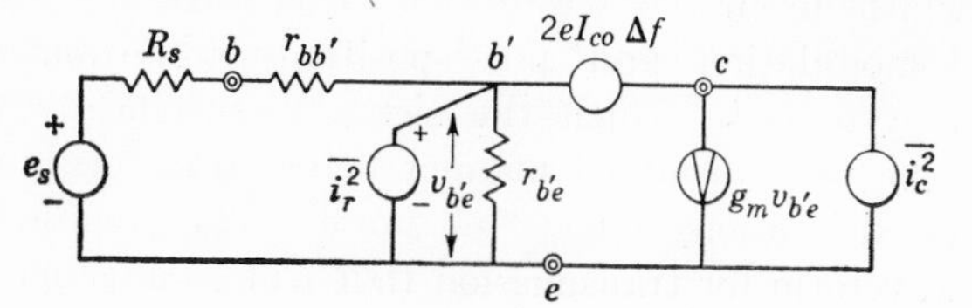

FIG. P 5-31. Hybrid model, transistor.

CHAPTER 6

COMPARATIVE ANALYSIS OF INFORMATION-TRANSMISSION SYSTEMS

We have had occasion to discuss in this book different examples of modern information-transmission systems. These included amplitude-modulation (AM) and frequency-modulation (FM) systems as examples of sine-wave-carrier systems and pulse-amplitude-modulation (PAM) and pulse-position-modulation (PPM) systems as examples of pulse-carrier systems. Primary emphasis was placed on determining the bandwidth requirements and frequency spectra associated with these different systems. No attempt was made to set up any standard of comparison for the systems.

We now propose actually to investigate in some detail the comparative ability of these systems to transmit information. Crucial to this study will again be the concepts of bandwidth and of signal-to-noise ratio, as introduced in the previous chapter. For, as pointed out initially in Chap. 1, there are two basic theoretical limitations to the ability of systems to transmit information: the nonzero time response of information-transmission systems, due to the presence of energy-storage devices, and the inability to distinguish indefinitely small variations in signal. The first limitation was related directly to system bandwidth in Chap. 2, and applications of the bandwidth concept to typical systems were considered in Chaps. 3 and 4. The second limitation was shown in Chap. 5 to be due to the unavoidable presence of noise in systems and to be directly related to the signal-to-noise ratio.

By actually evaluating signal-to-noise ratios for the different systems we shall be able to compare them on the basis of bandwidth and signal-to-noise ratio. We shall see, as pointed out at the end of the last chapter, that such wideband systems as FM and PPM offer signal-to-noise improvement over AM and PAM, respectively, exactly because of the wider bandwidths used.

Frequency-modulation and pulse-position-modulation systems are examples of systems in which the signal is specifically processed or altered in some predetermined manner before transmission in order to minimize the deleterious effects of noise. This requires essentially choosing a waveform for transmission that will be affected only slightly by noise introduced during transmission and at the receiver. We shall see that although FM and PPM systems do function in this manner, they do so less efficiently than so-called "coded-signal" systems, among which pulse-code modulation (PCM) is the principal practical system realized to date.

Although most of this material can be understood quite readily from a knowledge of frequency spectra, bandwidth, and signal-to-noise ratio, a more thorough treatment requires some knowledge of statistics and probability theory. Statistical concepts have become an accepted part of all modern analyses of communication systems, and so we shall take the time to explore some of the simpler ideas of statistics.

A knowledge of statistics is needed for two basic reasons:

1. As noted in Chap. 1, and particularly in Sec. 1-3, signals encountered in practice are never the simple sine wave, step function, or impulse function that we have considered up to now. An actual signal is never known exactly beforehand; otherwise why transmit it? Instead we are frequently given the statistics, or frequency of occurrence, of various signals and are asked to design systems to transmit these types of signals.
2. As pointed out in Chap. 5, noise fluctuations are random in character and must be studied in terms of their statistical properties.

We have been able to study various systems, and develop some important ideas about noise fluctuations as well, using average or mean-squared concepts. We shall continue to use this approach in much of this chapter. Average quantities are themselves examples of statistical parameters, as will become apparent in the next chapter. Any deeper study of communication and control systems must use additional ideas of probability and statistics, however.

6-1. Signal- and Noise-power Spectra. We shall refer frequently in this chapter to the concept of signal-to-noise ratio. It will be necessary for this purpose to calculate mean signal power and mean noise power at various points in a system.

The calculation of mean signal power is simple if the signal is assumed sinusoidal, as in previous chapters of this book. For more realistic signals (nonsinusoidal and defined possibly only by their frequency spectrum), as well as for noise, the power calculation is not so obvious. This section will develop methods of calculating mean signal and noise powers. For this purpose the concepts of *energy spectrum* and *power spectrum* will be introduced.

The power calculations will be found to depend upon the frequency distribution of power (signal or noise) at the input to a system and upon the frequency-selective properties of the system through which the signal or noise is passed. The frequency-selective properties will be described by the system transfer function.

We showed in Chap. 5 that fluctuation noise could be considered white noise when generated, with the mean-squared noise voltage or mean noise power proportional to bandwidth. For example, in the case of pure thermal noise the mean-squared noise voltage generated in a resistor R is $4kTR\,\Delta f$ watts. The available noise power in a bandwidth Δf cps is $kT\,\Delta f$ watts. Similarly the mean noise power generated in a temperature-limited diode and dissipated in a resistance R is $2eI_{dc}R\,\Delta f$ watts. In general, with all noise sources included, the total mean noise power, N watts, in a bandwidth Δf cps, will be

$$N = \eta\,\Delta f \qquad \text{watts} \tag{6-1}$$

where η is a constant. η has the dimensions of watts per cycles per second, or watts per bandwidth, and has the form of a power-density term.

In Chap. 5 we indicated that, if white noise passes through a linear system with frequency transfer function $H(j\omega)$, the output noise power is written

$$N_H = \eta \int_0^\infty |H(j\omega)|^2\,df \tag{6-2}$$

The output noise power is thus distributed with frequency according to $|H(j\omega)|^2$. It will be useful in the work to follow to discuss the distribution of both signal power and noise power with frequency.

We shall discuss this power distribution in terms of a *power spectrum*, obtaining Eq. (6-2) in the course of the discussion. To discuss the concept of *power spectrum*, we consider first a periodic function $f(t)$. $f(t)$ is to be considered either a voltage or a current. Then

$$f(t) = \frac{1}{T}\sum_{n=-\infty}^{\infty} c_n e^{j\omega_n t} = \frac{1}{T}\left[c_0 + 2\sum_{n=1}^{\infty} |c_n| \cos(\omega_n t + \theta_n)\right] \tag{6-3}$$

If this voltage or current is now impressed across a 1-ohm resistor, the average power dissipated will be just the mean-squared value of $f(t)$.

Why the choice of a 1-ohm resistor? Obviously it just serves to normalize our power calculations and enables us to treat both currents and voltages simultaneously. For an actual resistive load anywhere in a system we can always calculate the mean power dissipated from the normalized calculation. In addition, in this book we shall ordinarily be interested in the power signal-to-noise ratio at a given point in a system. This ratio will then just be the same as the ratio of mean-squared voltages or currents.

The average power is then

$$P_{av} = \frac{1}{T}\int_{-T/2}^{T/2} f^2(t)\,dt = \left(\frac{c_0}{T}\right)^2 + \left(\frac{2}{T}\right)^2 \sum_{n=1}^{\infty} \frac{|c_n|^2}{2} \tag{6-4}$$

since

$$\frac{1}{T}\int_{-T/2}^{T/2} \cos\omega_m(t+\theta_m)\cos\omega_n(t+\theta_n)\,dt = 0 \qquad m \neq n$$

$$\frac{1}{T}\int_{-T/2}^{T/2} \cos\omega_m(t+\theta_m)\cos\omega_n(t+\theta_n)\,dt = \tfrac{1}{2} \qquad m = n$$

This is of course just the familiar relation that the total average power may be found by adding up the power contribution due to each sine wave.

Consider now the power associated with a specific frequency $f_n = n/T$. Except for the d-c term this is just $\left(\frac{2}{T}\right)^2 \frac{|c_n|^2}{2} = \frac{1}{T}\left(\frac{2}{T}|c_n|^2\right)$. This can also be interpreted as the power contained in the frequency range f_n to f_{n+1}, or f_n to $f_n + \Delta f$, $\Delta f = 1/T$. (Compare this development with that of the Fourier integral in Sec. 2-6.) We can thus also express this power term as $(2/T)|c_n|^2\,\Delta f$, and the *total average power* becomes

$$P_{av} = \left(\frac{c_0}{T}\right)^2 + \sum_{n=1}^{\infty} \frac{2}{T}|c_n|^2\,\Delta f \tag{6-5}$$

Note that $(2/T)|c_n|^2$ has the dimensions of a power density (watts per cycles per second), just like the noise power density η in Eq. (6-1).

We *define* the power spectral density, or power spectrum, $G(\omega_n)$ to be just this power-density term. Thus

$$G(\omega_n) \equiv \frac{2}{T}|c_n|^2 \tag{6-6}$$

and

$$P_{av} = \left(\frac{c_0}{T}\right)^2 + \sum_{n=1}^{\infty} G(\omega_n)\,\Delta f \tag{6-7}$$

We can plot $G(\omega_n)$ versus ω_n and obtain a graph of power distribution with frequency. This is of course analogous to our plots of amplitude spectrum and phase spectrum in Chap. 2; hence the use of the term *power spectrum*. An example of such a plot is shown in Fig. 6-1*a*.

As in the case of the discussion of complex Fourier series in Chap. 2, the d-c term appears at first sight isolated. We can include c_0 in the summation, as in the Fourier series, by arbitrarily summing over both positive and negative frequencies. Recalling from the discussion of Fourier series in Chap. 2 that

$$c_n^* = c_{-n}$$

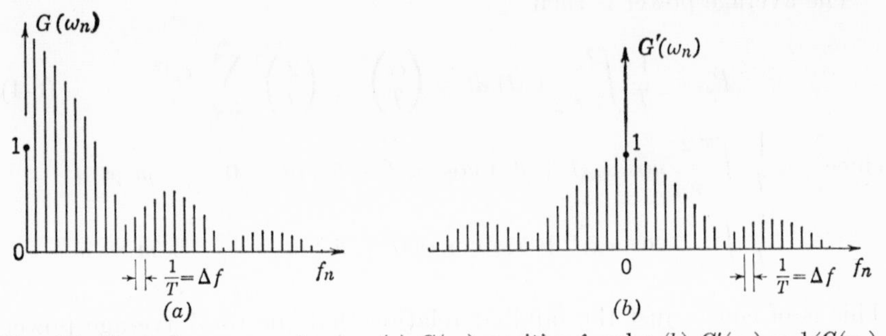

FIG. 6-1. Typical power spectrum. (a) $G(\omega_n)$, positive f_n only; (b) $G'(\omega_n) = \frac{1}{2}G(\omega_n)$, positive and negative f_n.

we can write $|c_n|^2 = c_n c_{-n}$. If we include negative frequencies, half the power at any frequency must be in the positive-frequency term, half in the negative term. We can then define a new power-density function $G'(\omega_n)$, which is summed over positive and negative frequencies.

$$G'(\omega_n) \equiv \frac{G(\omega_n)}{2} = \frac{1}{T}|c_n|^2 \tag{6-8}$$

We now get

$$P_{\text{av}} = \sum_{n=-\infty}^{\infty} \frac{1}{T}|c_n|^2 \Delta f = \sum_{n=-\infty}^{\infty} G'(\omega_n)\,\Delta f \tag{6-9}$$

The d-c term (c_0) is thus included quite naturally as part of the power-spectrum representation (Fig. 6-1*b*). As an example, consider the rectangular-pulse train of previous chapters. Since $c_n = V\tau[\sin(\omega_n\tau/2)/(\omega_n\tau/2)]$,

$$G(\omega_n) = \frac{2}{T}|c_n|^2 = \frac{2}{T}(V\tau)^2\left[\frac{\sin(\omega_n\tau/2)}{\omega_n\tau/2}\right]^2$$

and

$$G'(\omega_n) = \frac{1}{T}(V\tau)^2\left[\frac{\sin(\omega_n\tau/2)}{\omega_n\tau/2}\right]^2 \tag{6-10}$$

These are shown plotted in Fig. 6-2. Note that most of the power in the signal is contained within the bandwidth $1/\tau$ if $\tau \ll T$. This is then another justification for the use of the relation $\Delta f = 1/\tau$ as the bandwidth needed to pass recognizable pulses (see Chap. 2). In particular the average power contained within the bandwidth $1/\tau$ is

$$P_{\text{av}} = \sum_{f_n=-1/\tau}^{1/\tau} G'(\omega_n)\,\Delta f = \sum_{f_n=-1/\tau}^{1/\tau}\left[\frac{V\tau}{T}\frac{\sin(\omega_n\tau/2)}{\omega_n\tau/2}\right]^2 \tag{6-11}$$

The power contained within any other band of frequencies can similarly be calculated. This is one example of the utility of the power-spectrum concept.

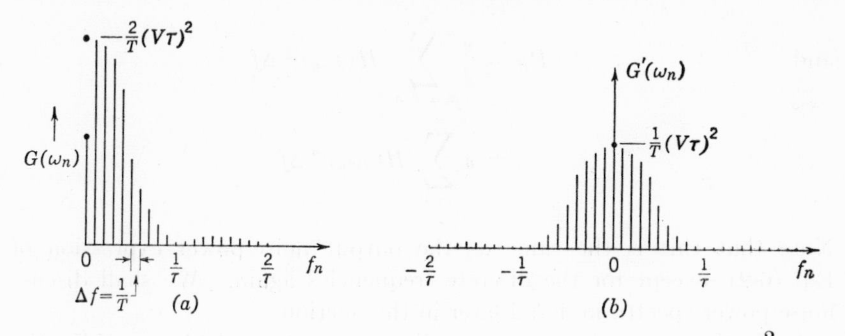

FIG. 6-2. Power spectrum, periodic rectangular pulses ($\tau \ll T$). (a) $G(\omega_n) = \dfrac{2}{T}(V\tau)^2 \left[\dfrac{\sin(\omega_n\tau/2)}{\omega_n\tau/2}\right]^2$; (b) $G'(\omega_n) = \frac{1}{2}G(\omega_n)$.

We now pass $f(t)$ through a system with transfer function $H(j\omega)$ and ask for the power spectrum, or average power distribution, at the output of the system. Since each frequency component is multiplied by $H(j\omega)$, the Fourier coefficient at the output is simply

$$c_{Hn} = -c_n H(j\omega_n) \tag{6-12}$$

and the average power at the output is

$$\begin{aligned} P_H &= \frac{1}{T} \sum_{n=-\infty}^{\infty} |c_{Hn}|^2 \,\Delta f \\ &= \sum_{n=-\infty}^{\infty} G'_H(\omega_n)\,\Delta f \end{aligned} \tag{6-13}$$

where

$$\begin{aligned} G'_H(\omega_n) &= \frac{1}{T}|c_{Hn}|^2 = \frac{1}{T}|c_n|^2 |H(j\omega_n)|^2 \\ &= G'(\omega_n)|H(j\omega_n)|^2 \end{aligned} \tag{6-14}$$

In particular, if the input function $f(t)$ happens to be a periodic sequence of impulses, the power is uniformly distributed over all frequencies and

$$G'(\omega_n) = \frac{\eta}{2} \qquad \text{watts/cps}$$

(We recall from Chap. 2 that the impulse function has a flat, or constant-frequency, spectrum.)

Such an input is then the same as that of our white noise, except that only discrete frequencies are defined. At the network output

$$G'_H(\omega_n) = \frac{\eta}{2}|H(j\omega_n)|^2$$

and
$$P_H = \frac{\eta}{2} \sum_{n=-\infty}^{\infty} |H(j\omega_n)|^2 \, \Delta f$$
$$= \eta \sum_{n=0}^{\infty} |H(j\omega_n)|^2 \, \Delta f$$

Note that this is the same as the output noise-power expression of Eq. (6-2), except for the discrete frequencies again. We shall discuss noise-power spectra in detail later in this section.

As further examples of the application of Eq. (6-14), consider the rectangular-pulse train applied to (1) a simple RC filter; (2) an ideal low-pass filter.

1. In the RC filter case, $H(j\omega) = 1/(1 + j\omega RC)$, and

$$|H(j\omega)|^2 = \frac{1}{1 + (\omega RC)^2} = \frac{1}{1 + (f/f_c)^2} \qquad f_c = \frac{1}{2\pi RC}$$

Then
$$G'_H(\omega_n) = \left(\frac{V\tau}{T}\right)^2 \left[\frac{\sin(\omega_n \tau/2)}{\omega_n \tau/2}\right]^2 \frac{1}{1 + (f_n/f_c)^2}$$

and
$$P_H = \sum_{n=-\infty}^{\infty} G'_H(\omega_n) \, \Delta f$$

2. For the ideal low-pass filter

$$H(j\omega) = Ae^{-jt_0\omega} \qquad |\omega| \le \omega_c$$
$$H(j\omega) = 0 \qquad |\omega| > \omega_c$$

Then
$$|H(j\omega)|^2 = A^2 \qquad |\omega| \le \omega_c$$

and
$$G'_H(\omega_n) = \left[\frac{V\tau}{T} A \frac{\sin(\omega_n \tau/2)}{\omega_n \tau/2}\right]^2 \qquad |\omega_n| \le \omega_c$$
$$G'_H(\omega_n) = 0 \qquad |\omega_n| > \omega_c$$

Thus far we have considered the power-spectrum idea for periodic signals only. We could presumably develop the power spectrum of nonperiodic signals by averaging over all time, or by letting $T \to \infty$ and $\Delta f \to 0$, obtaining (we would hope) a continuous power spectrum. Unfortunately the power-spectrum idea breaks down in general for nonperiodic signals, simply because the power, averaged over an infinite period, goes to zero for normal nonperiodic signals. The idea will still be useful in the case of fluctuation noise and random signal inputs, however, so that we shall follow the limiting procedure anyway.

Assume, therefore, a function $f(t)$ with *zero d-c level and no periodic components*. (These components can be treated separately, if desired, in the manner just indicated.) We can determine the average power in this function by averaging over a very long interval or by letting $T \to \infty$.

Then

$$P_{av} = \lim_{T\to\infty} \frac{1}{T} \int_{-T/2}^{T/2} f^2(t)\, dt$$

$$= \lim_{\Delta f\to 0} \sum_{n=-\infty}^{\infty} G'(\omega_n)\, \Delta f \tag{6-15}$$

In the limit the sum becomes an integral, and we get

$$P_{av} = \int_0^\infty G(\omega)\, df = \int_{-\infty}^{\infty} G'(\omega)\, df \tag{6-16}$$

where

$$G(\omega) = \lim_{T\to\infty} \frac{2}{T} |c_n|^2 = \lim_{T\to\infty} \frac{2}{T} |F(j\omega)|^2$$
$$G'(\omega) = \lim_{T\to\infty} \frac{1}{T} |F(j\omega)|^2 = \frac{G(\omega)}{2} \tag{6-17}$$

We thus get a continuous spectrum instead of a discontinuous spectrum, as expected.

As pointed out above, there is one difficulty, however: For normal signals with well-defined Fourier transforms, $F(j\omega)$ is independent of T in the limit, and both $G(\omega)$ and $G'(\omega)$ go to zero. This occurs because, for normal signals possessing a Fourier transform, $\int_{-\infty}^{\infty} f^2(t)\, dt$ in Eq. (6-15) approaches some finite limiting value. (This is just the energy in the signal, as we shall see shortly.) Then $(1/T) \int_{-\infty}^{\infty} f^2(t)\, dt$, or the average power, goes to zero as $T \to \infty$. (Remember that we exclude d-c or periodic signals; see Fig. 6-3.)

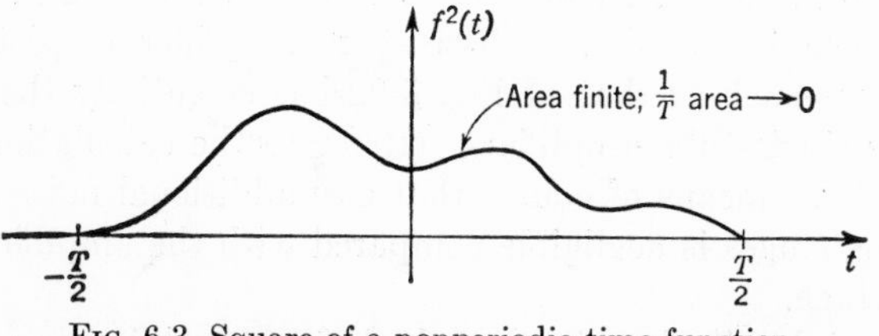

FIG. 6-3. Square of a nonperiodic time function.

The concept of power density *is* useful nevertheless, for we did find in the case of fluctuation noise that mean noise power (or mean-squared noise voltage and current) was proportional to bandwidth. Thus, for a resistor R, the average thermal power generated is

$$4kT\, \Delta f \qquad \text{watts}$$

$4kT$ watts/cps must be the power spectral density, $G(\omega)$. The same holds true for shot noise [$\Delta f \ll 1/(\text{transit time})$]. In general, fluctuation noise has a constant power spectral density or power spectrum,[1]

$$G(\omega) = \eta \tag{6-18a}$$

$$G'(\omega) = \frac{\eta}{2} \tag{6-18b}$$

Such noise, with a *uniform*, or constant, *power spectrum*, is said to be *white noise.* (It is appropriate to note, based on our discussion of Chap. 5, that the spectrum for shot noise is flat only to within the reciprocal transit time. It can be shown from quantum-mechanical considerations that thermal noise also decreases with frequency at very high frequencies. These qualifications are important because a noise spectrum constant to infinite frequency would require infinite average power, a physical impossibility. Since band limiting due to a system normally occurs well within the frequencies at which the noise spectrum ceases to be flat, we can assume a flat noise spectrum in all our calculations.) If this noise is now passed through a *linear* system with transfer function $H(j\omega)$,

$$G_H(\omega) = G(\omega)|H(j\omega)|^2 \tag{6-19}$$

and

$$P_H = \int_0^\infty G_H(\omega)\, df \tag{6-20}$$

as before. Equation (6-20) is of course the same as Eq. (6-2), as used originally in Chap. 5.

As an example of the application of Eqs. (6-18) to (6-20), consider a system in which the triode amplifier of Fig. 5-22 represents the first stage. The rms output noise voltage of this amplifier was found to be 21 μv in a bandwidth of 20 kc. This corresponds to a mean-squared output noise voltage of 440×10^{-12} watt in a 20-kc bandwidth, or 220×10^{-16} watt/cps. As shown in Sec. 5-9, a two-stage amplifier consisting of two identical stages such as that of Fig. 5-22 has essentially the same noise figure as the single-tube amplifier. (Refer to the calculations based on Fig. 5-26.) This means of course that any additional noise contributed by succeeding stages is negligible compared with the amplified noise due to the first stage.

The spectral density in this example, before band limiting takes place, is thus $G(\omega) = \eta = 220 \times 10^{-16}$ watt/cps. This assumes a 1-ohm load resistor. For the actual 75-kilohm load resistor the spectral density is $G(\omega) = (220 \times 10^{-16})/(75 \times 10^3) = 29 \times 10^{-20}$ watt/cps. The power calculation could also be done on the basis of available power. For this calculation the output resistance of the amplifier of Fig. 5-22 is given by the parallel combination of the 75-kilohm load resistor and the dynamic

[1] This is the total fluctuation noise, including all sources. Normally, as pointed out in Chap. 5, this will depend on the input noise to a system and the noise figure of the first section or stages of the system.

plate resistance, $r_p = 15$ kilohms. This gives an output resistance of 12.5 kilohms. The available power, measured at this point, is thus $(440 \times 10^{12})/(4 \times 12.5 \times 10^3) = 88 \times 10^{-16}$ watt in a 20-kc bandwidth, or $G(\omega) = \eta = 44 \times 10^{-20}$ watt/cps, if defined on the basis of available power. The choice of power to be calculated, whether available power, actual power in a load resistor, or power in a 1-ohm resistor, does not matter, since signal-to-noise ratios must ultimately be determined and these are independent of the choice of load resistor. The various values of $G(\omega)$ or η calculated differ only within a constant.

Now assume that the band-limiting effect of the system may be represented by a single RC filter with $|H(j\omega)|^2 = 1/(1 + f/f_c)^2$. The mean output power is

$$P_H = \eta \int_0^\infty \frac{df}{(1 + f/f_c)^2} = \frac{\eta f_c \pi}{2}$$

as found in Chap. 5. This band limiting could be due to shunt capacitance in the plate of the triode amplifier of Fig. 5-22 or to filtering somewhere else in the system. If the over-all system has a voltage amplification of A and behaves again like a single RC section, the power at the output is

$$P_H = \frac{\eta A^2 f_c \pi}{2}$$

In general, assume that the over-all system can be represented by an ideal low-pass filter of bandwidth f_c cps and voltage amplification A. From Eqs. (6-19) and (6-20) the average noise power at the output is given by

$$P_H = \eta A^2 f_c$$

This agrees with the noise-equivalent-bandwidth concept of Eq. (5-18). In particular assume the system to be represented by a low-pass ideal filter of bandwidth $f_c = 10$ kc, with an amplification $A = 10^6$. If the power in a 1-ohm resistor is considered (this is particularly appropriate in voltage-amplifier circuits), $\eta = 220 \times 10^{-16}$ watt/cps. The mean output noise power in a 1-ohm resistor is thus

$$P_H = 220 \times 10^{-16} \times 10^{12} \times 10^4 = 220 \text{ watts}$$

The actual mean output noise power in a 10-kilohm resistor would be 22 mw.

If the mean output noise power within a bandwidth 0 to B cps is desired, rather than the *total* mean noise power over all frequencies, we integrate $G_H(\omega)$ from 0 to B. This gives

$$P_{HB} = \eta \int_0^B |H(j\omega)|^2 \, df \qquad (6\text{-}21)$$

from Eqs. (6-18) and (6-19). We shall use this relation later in calculating the signal-to-noise ratio of FM and AM systems.

The power-spectrum idea is thus useful in noise calculations. But what about calculations involving signals? As mentioned previously, the power-spectrum formulation is meaningless for a well-defined nonperiodic $f(t)$ with a specific Fourier transform. In practice, however, signals are ordinarily not well-defined functions but random functions. (These are the only ones that carry information, as pointed out in Chap. 1.) We shall see in Chap. 7 that the power spectra of such functions can be defined. The power-spectrum concept has found widespread use in system analysis for such signals.

For the nonperiodic and nonrandom $f(t)$ we can use an energy formulation instead of the power formulation. To show this, we again take first the case of periodic $f(t)$. The energy dissipated over a period (assuming a 1-ohm resistor again) is

$$E = \int_{-T/2}^{T/2} f^2(t)\,dt = \frac{1}{T}\left(c_0^2 + 2\sum_{n=1}^{\infty} |c_n|^2\right)$$

$$= \left(c_0^2 + 2\sum_{n=1}^{\infty} |c_n|^2\right)\Delta f \tag{6-22}$$

If we include positive *and* negative frequencies,

$$E = \int_{-T/2}^{T/2} f^2(t) = \sum_{n=-\infty}^{\infty} |c_n|^2\,\Delta f \tag{6-23}$$

Now let $f(t)$ be nonperiodic (we again exclude d-c and periodic components). If we calculate the energy contained within $f(t)$ as $T \to \infty$,

$$E = \int_{-\infty}^{\infty} f^2(t)\,dt = \int_{-\infty}^{\infty} |F(j\omega)|^2\,df = 2\int_0^{\infty} |F(j\omega)|^2\,df \tag{6-24}$$

since $|F(j\omega)|$ is an even function of frequency. $|F(j\omega)|^2$ has the dimensions of an *energy spectral density*, and we can write

$$E = \int_0^{\infty} E(\omega)\,df = \int_0^{\infty} 2|F(j\omega)|^2\,df \tag{6-25}$$

where $E(\omega) = 2|F(j\omega)|^2$, the energy spectral density. Using $E(\omega)$, we can calculate the distribution of energy with frequency. For example, the energy contained between frequencies f_1 and f_2 is

$$E = \int_{f_1}^{f_2} E(\omega)\,df = 2\int_{f_1}^{f_2} |F(j\omega)|^2\,df \tag{6-26}$$

Some examples are of interest at this point.

1. Assume that $f(t)$ is a rectangular pulse of width τ and height V and is impressed across a resistor R ohms. The total energy dissipated is

$$\frac{1}{R}\int_{-\infty}^{\infty} f^2(t)\,dt = \frac{V^2\tau}{R} \qquad \text{watt-sec}$$

But

$$F(j\omega) = V\tau\,\frac{\sin(\omega\tau/2)}{\omega\tau/2}$$

or

$$E(\omega) = 2(V\tau)^2\left[\frac{\sin(\omega\tau/2}{\omega\tau/2}\right]^2$$

The total energy contained in all frequencies is thus

$$\frac{1}{R}\int_0^{\infty} E(\omega)\,d\omega = \frac{2(V\tau)^2}{R}\int_0^{\infty}\left[\frac{\sin(\omega\tau/2)}{\omega\tau/2}\right]^2 df$$

$$= \frac{2}{R}\,V^2\tau\,\frac{1}{\pi}\int_0^{\infty}\frac{\sin^2 x}{x^2}\,dx \qquad x \equiv \frac{\omega\tau}{2} = \pi f\tau$$

Since $\int_0^{\infty} [(\sin^2 x)/x^2]\,dx = \pi/2$, the total energy is again $V^2\tau/R$ watt-sec, checking the first calculation.

The energy spectrum for this pulse is of course $\lim_{T\to\infty} 2TG'(\omega_n)$, with $G'(\omega_n)$ as defined previously. The power-spectrum plots of Figs. 6-1 and 6-2 may thus be interpreted as energy-spectrum plots if the line spacing approaches zero (i.e., the curves become continuous).

2. $f(t) = e^{-a|t|}$, shown in Fig. 6-4*a*. Then $F(j\omega) = 2a/(a^2 + \omega^2)$ (Fig. 6-4*b*). The energy spectrum is

$$E(\omega) = 2|F(j\omega)|^2 = \frac{8}{a^2}\left[\frac{1}{1 + (\omega/a)^2}\right]^2$$

$E(\omega)$ is sketched in Fig. 6-4*c*.

The *total* energy is then

$$E = \int_0^{\infty} E(\omega)\,df = \frac{8}{a^2}\int_0^{\infty}\left[\frac{1}{1 + (\omega/a)^2}\right]^2 d\left(\frac{\omega}{2\pi}\right)$$

Integrating,

$$E = \frac{4}{a\pi}\,\frac{\pi}{4} = \frac{1}{a}$$

From the time function itself

$$\int_{-\infty}^{\infty} f^2(t)\,dt = 2\int_0^{\infty} e^{-2at}\,dt = \frac{1}{a}$$

checking the spectrum calculation.

Note from Fig. 6-4*b* that $\omega = a$ might be considered a measure of the radian bandwidth of this signal. How much of the energy is contained within this bandwidth? Actually integrating $E(\omega)$ from $f = 0$ to $f = a/2\pi$ cps, we find that about 80 per cent of the signal energy lies within this bandwidth. (The details are left to the reader as an exercise.)

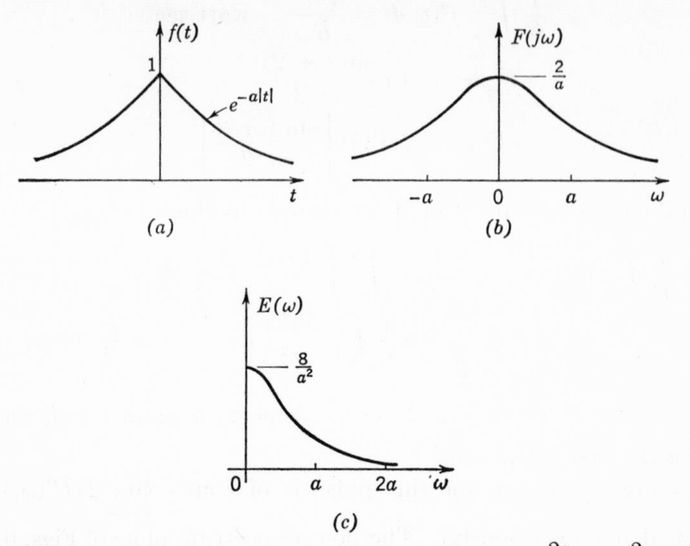

FIG. 6-4. Energy spectrum. (a) $f(t) = e^{-a|t|}$; (b) $F(j\omega) = \dfrac{2a}{a^2 + \omega^2} = \dfrac{2}{a}\dfrac{1}{1 + (\omega/a)^2}$; (c) energy spectrum $E(\omega) = 2|F(j\omega)|^2 = \dfrac{8}{a^2}\left[\dfrac{1}{1 + (\omega/a)^2}\right]^2$.

Equation (6-24) relates energy-time calculations to energy-frequency calculations. Repeating the equation here,

$$\int_{-\infty}^{\infty} f^2(t)\, dt = \int_{-\infty}^{\infty} |F(j\omega)|^2\, df \tag{6-24}$$

This relation, obtained directly from the Fourier-series expansion of a periodic function, is a basic theorem in Fourier-integral theory, and is frequently called Plancherel's theorem. We can prove this theorem in an alternative and instructive way by using the convolution theorem developed in Chap. 2.

We recall that we showed there that if

$$G(j\omega) = F(j\omega)H(j\omega) \tag{6-27}$$

$$g(t) = \int_{-\infty}^{\infty} f(\tau)h(t - \tau)\, dt \tag{6-28}$$

In particular, assume that

$$H(j\omega) = F^*(j\omega) \tag{6-29}$$

But

$$F(j\omega) = \int_{-\infty}^{\infty} f(t)e^{-j\omega t}\, dt \tag{6-30}$$

Then

$$F^*(j\omega) = \int_{-\infty}^{\infty} f(t)e^{j\omega t}\, dt = F(-j\omega) \tag{6-31}$$

[$f(t)$ assumed real]. Note that $F^*(j\omega) = F(-j\omega)$ is just an extension of the relation $c_n^* = c_{-n}$ from the complex Fourier series. We can also write

$$F(-j\omega) = \int_{-\infty}^{\infty} f(t)^{j\omega t}\, dt = \int_{-\infty}^{\infty} f(-t)e^{-j\omega t}\, dt \tag{6-32}$$

Thus

$$h(t) = f(-t)$$

from Eqs. (6-29), (6-31), and (6-32).

The convolution integral now becomes, for this *special case*,

$$g(t) = \int_{-\infty}^{\infty} f(\tau)f(\tau - t)\, dt \tag{6-33}$$

In particular, if we let $t = 0$ in Eq. (6-33),

$$g(0) = \int_{-\infty}^{\infty} f^2(\tau)\, d\tau = E \tag{6-34}$$

But

$$g(t) = \frac{1}{2\pi}\int_{-\infty}^{\infty} G(j\omega)e^{j\omega t}\, d\omega = \int_{-\infty}^{\infty} F(j\omega)H(j\omega)e^{j\omega t}\, df$$

$$= \int_{-\infty}^{\infty} |F(j\omega)|^2 e^{j\omega t}\, df \tag{6-35}$$

in this special case. In particular

$$g(0) = \int_{-\infty}^{\infty} |F(j\omega)|^2\, df = \int_{-\infty}^{\infty} f^2(t)\, dt \tag{6-36}$$

using Eq. (6-34).

Plancherel's theorem serves to relate further the time and frequency representations of real functions. It is of course simply a statement of the equality of the energy term in either one of the two representations. We shall use the convolution theorem again in later work to prove some further relations in power-spectrum analysis.

We return briefly now to our formulation of the power spectrum. We showed that if a signal contained no d-c or periodic components the average power could be written

$$P_{\text{av}} = \int_{-\infty}^{\infty} G'(\omega)\, df \qquad G'(\omega) = \lim_{T\to\infty} \frac{|F(j\omega)|^2}{T}$$

For periodic signals we had also

$$P_{\text{av}} = \sum_{n=-\infty}^{\infty} G'(\omega_n)\, \Delta f \qquad G'(\omega_n) = \frac{|c_n|^2}{T}$$

where $G'(\omega_n)\, \Delta f$ is the average power associated with frequency $f_n = \omega_n/2\pi$.

How do we now treat the case of a signal which has both aperiodic and periodic (or d-c) components? In particular can we define a power spectrum for this function which will show the existence of power at discrete frequencies (the periodic components) and power density at continuous frequencies?

We can do this by letting $\Delta f \to 0$ in the power expression for periodic signals. Since $G'(\omega_n)\,\Delta f$ represents the power at a discrete frequency ω_n, it must remain constant as $\Delta f \to 0$, or $G'(\omega_n)$ must become very large. In fact $G'(\omega_n)$ becomes just the impulse function discussed in Chap. 2.

We can check this by noting that for a single sine wave at frequency ω_n, given by

$$f(t) = A_n \cos(\omega_n t + \theta_n) = \frac{2|c_n|}{T} \cos(\omega_n t + \theta_n) \tag{6-37}$$

the average power is

$$P_{av} = \frac{A_n^2}{2} = \frac{2|c_n|^2}{T}\frac{1}{T} = \frac{2|c_n|^2}{T}\,\Delta f \tag{6-38}$$

This is of course exactly the form we used in defining the power spectral density for periodic functions.

We can arbitrarily associate half this power with frequency ω_n, half with $-\omega_n$. At each frequency, then, we have $A_n^2/4 = (|c_n|^2/T)\,\Delta f$ watts. If we let $T \to \infty$, the term $|c_n|^2/T = T(A_n^2/4)$ goes to infinity also, since $A_n^2/4$ must remain constant. This gives the impulse function at *each* frequency, ω_n and ω_{-n}.

$$\begin{aligned} \lim_{T\to\infty} \frac{|c_n|^2}{T} &= \frac{A_n^2}{4}\,\delta(\omega - \omega_n) \\ \lim_{T\to\infty} \frac{|c_n|^2}{T} &= \frac{A_n^2}{4}\,\delta(\omega + \omega_n) \end{aligned} \tag{6-39}$$

$$G'(\omega) = \frac{A_n^2}{4}\,[\delta(\omega - \omega_n) + \delta(\omega + \omega_n)] \tag{6-40}$$

The continuous power-spectrum concept developed for nonperiodic functions can thus be extended to periodic functions also if we introduce delta functions.

As an example, assume that a sine wave $A \cos(\omega_n t + \theta)$ is added to fluctuation noise with spectral density $G'(\omega) = \eta/2$ watts/cps. The spectral density of the combination is then

$$G'(\omega) = \frac{A^2}{4}\,[\delta(\omega - \omega_n) + \delta(\omega + \omega_n)] + \frac{\eta}{2} \tag{6-41}$$

if both positive and negative frequencies are included, and

$$G(\omega) = \frac{A^2}{2}\,\delta(\omega - \omega_n) + \eta \tag{6-42}$$

if only positive frequencies are considered.

Both cases are shown in Fig. 6-5.

The average power contained within a bandwidth 0 to B is then

$$
\begin{aligned}
P_{av} &= \int_{-B}^{B} G'(\omega)\, df \\
&= \frac{A^2}{2} + \eta B \qquad B > f_m \\
P_{av} &= \eta B \qquad\qquad B < f_m
\end{aligned}
\tag{6-43}
$$

using the definition of impulse functions introduced in Chap. 2.

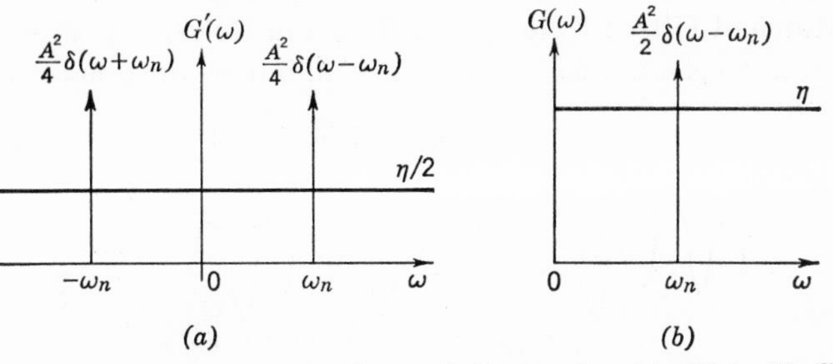

FIG. 6-5. Power spectrum, noise plus periodic signal. (a) $G'(\omega)$; (b) $G(\omega)$.

As a second example, assume that a periodic signal

$$
f(t) = A_1 \cos(\omega_1 t + \theta_1) + A_2 \cos(\omega_2 t + \theta_2) \tag{6-44}
$$

is added to fluctuation noise that has been passed through an RC network. Then the over-all spectral density $G(\omega)$, defined for positive frequencies only, is

$$
G(\omega) = \frac{A_1^2}{2}\,\delta(f - f_1) + \frac{A_2^2}{2}\,\delta(f - f_2) + \frac{\eta}{1 + (f/f_c)^2} \tag{6-45}
$$

This is shown in Fig. 6-6.

How do we now include a d-c component in a signal? The power contributed must be A_0^2 watts (a 1-ohm resistor again) if the d-c voltage is A_0 volts. If we include positive and negative frequencies in our power spectrum, the d-c contribution is represented by $A_0^2\,\delta(f)$.

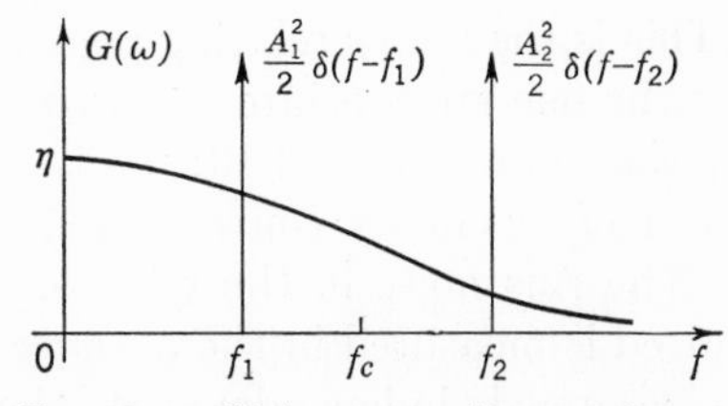

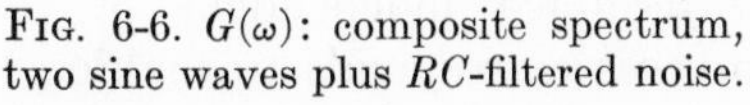
FIG. 6-6. $G(\omega)$: composite spectrum, two sine waves plus RC-filtered noise.

In general, for a signal containing a d-c component, periodic components, and a nonperiodic component, the power spectrum $G'(\omega)$, defined over both positive and negative frequencies, becomes

$$
G'(\omega) = \underbrace{A_0^2\,\delta(f)}_{\text{D-c term}} + \underbrace{\sum_n \frac{A_n^2}{4}\,[\delta(f - f_n) + \delta(f + f_n)]}_{\text{Periodic components}} + \underbrace{\lim_{T\to\infty} \frac{|F(j\omega)|^2}{T}}_{\text{Continuous spectrum}} \tag{6-46}
$$

We shall have occasion to discuss these concepts further in later sections.

In the next section we shall apply the idea of power spectrum to the determination of a system transfer function that will maximize signal-to-noise ratio under certain desired conditions. The results obtained are utilized in the radar field, in PAM transmission, and in PCM systems to be described later. We shall also use the power-spectrum relations in a discussion of FM signal-to-noise ratio in Sec. 6-3.

6-2. Matched Filter: Detection of Signal in Noise. As an application of our power-spectrum ideas we consider an important practical problem.

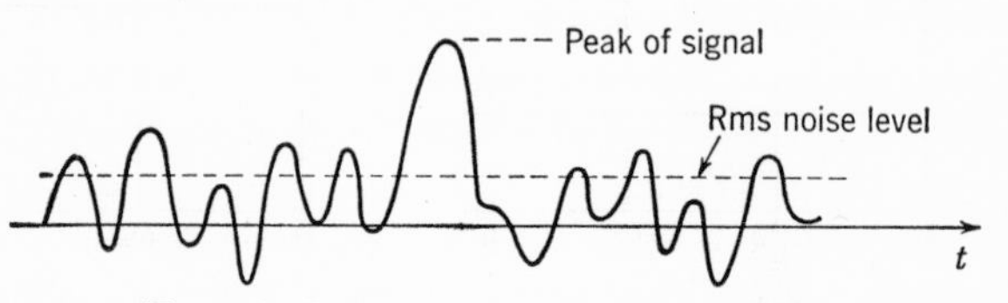

FIG. 6-7. Pulse signal embedded in noise.

A pulse signal $f(t)$ plus additive noise is transmitted through a linear system. How do we design the system, i.e., filter the combination of signal and noise, so as to maximize the ratio of peak signal voltage to rms noise at the system output? (Although we assume throughout this section that the signal is a video pulse, the results obtained apply also to the case of a pulse carrier, with the envelope of the carrier corresponding to the video pulse. The system frequency function is assumed centered about the carrier and of bandwidth narrow compared with the carrier frequency.)

Although the signal-to-noise ratio to be maximized in this case involves the peak, or maximum, amplitude of a signal pulse, it differs only by a constant factor from the rms signal-to-noise ratio introduced in Chap. 5. (This is the factor relating peak and rms values.) This ratio happens to be the one appropriate to the problem at hand. The word *pulse* is used in the sense of Sec. 2-10: $f(t)$ is assumed to have a definable width, with most of its energy concentrated over a specified time interval.

The rms noise in the ratio of signal voltage to rms noise to be maximized is measured in the absence of a signal. The output signal voltage is assumed independent of the noise. Physically, this maximizing process corresponds to making the signal amplitude as high above the surrounding noise level as possible. An example of a pulse signal embedded in noise is shown in Fig. 6-7.

The results of the analysis to follow are obviously useful in designing PAM systems, where the question to be asked might well be: Given rectangular-pulse samples of the signal to be transmitted, how should these be filtered so as to have maximum signal-to-rms-noise ratio at the output of the system? We might alternatively state this: How shall we shape our rectangular pulses (by filtering them) so that the signal-to-noise ratio will be maximized?

A similar problem is encountered in radar systems, where it is required to detect the presence of a signal echo embedded in fluctuation noise. The amplitude of the signal relative to the noise should thus be maximized if possible.

We shall see later on that our results are useful in PCM systems also, where it is important to know whether or not a pulse is present in a given time interval.

In all these examples we are not specifically interested in maintaining fidelity of pulse shape. We are primarily interested in improving our ability to "see" or recognize a pulse signal in the presence of noise. This ability to see the pulse is assumed to be related to the ratio of peak signal to rms noise. In PPM systems the time of occurrence of the pulse is of prime significance. (This is also true in many tracking radars.) Fidelity, or sharpness, of pulse rise time is thus of much greater significance there, and the concept of designing the system frequency characteristic to maximize peak signal-to-noise ratio has no meaning in that case.

This is an important point that bears stressing: the analysis to follow is of significance only in those communication systems in which the peak signal amplitude is of primary interest and is to be maximized relative to the noise. The signal shape is of secondary interest.

How do we know that the peak signal-to-noise ratio can be maximized by properly choosing the filter characteristic? This is simply answered from our discussions of Chaps. 2 and 5.

Assume, for simplicity's sake, that $f(t)$ is a rectangular pulse of width τ sec. The system is assumed to have the idealized filter characteristics of Sec. 2-7, with a variable bandwidth f_c cps.

For very small bandwidth ($f_c \ll 1/\tau$) the peak of the output signal is small and increases with bandwidth. This is shown by the curves of Fig. 2-23. It is also indicated by the curve of Fig. 6-8a, showing the familiar $(\sin x)/x$ spectrum with the filter cutoff frequency (f_c) superimposed. The output-signal amplitude is proportional to the area under the curve. For $f_c \ll 1/\tau$ the frequency spectrum is flat, so that the output signal increases linearly with f_c. [This is also apparent from the Fourier integral of Eq. (2-66).]

The rms noise is proportional to $\sqrt{f_c}$ and so increases at a smaller rate than the signal for small bandwidth.

As the bandwidth increases, approaching $f_c = 1/\tau$, the signal amplitude begins to increase less rapidly with f_c. For $f_c > 1/\tau$ the signal remains approximately at the same amplitude as at $f_c = 1/\tau$ (Fig. 2-23). (Recall from Chap. 2 that increasing the bandwidth beyond $f_c = 1/\tau$ just served to fill out the fine details of the pulse. For a recognizable pulse a bandwidth $f_c = 1/\tau$ was all that was necessary.) The rms noise keeps increasing with bandwidth, however, so that the ratio of peak signal to rms noise begins to decrease inversely as $\sqrt{f_c}$. We would thus expect an optimum ratio at about $f_c = 1/\tau$. This will be borne out in the analysis to follow.

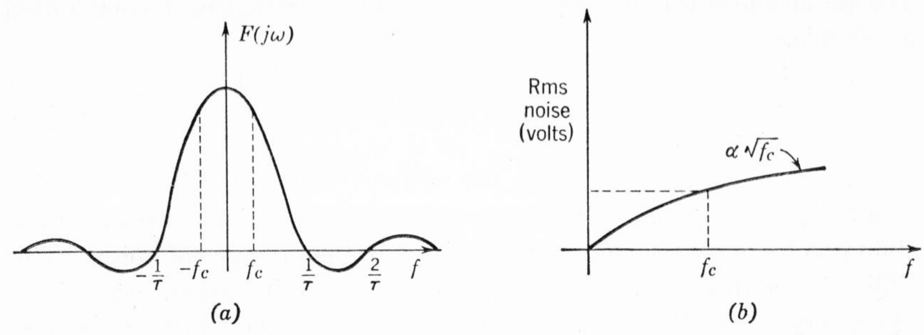

FIG. 6-8. Rectangular pulse and noise passed through ideal filter. (a) Signal pulse spectrum, with filter cutoff superimposed; (b) rms noise output.

Note that this result for optimum f_c agrees with the time-bandwidth relation ($f_c\tau = 1$) demonstrated in Chap. 2.

In general, not only the filter bandwidth but the shape of the filter characteristic can be adjusted to optimize the peak signal-to-noise ratio. To show this, consider $f(t)$ impressed across a linear filter with frequency transfer function $H(j\omega)$. Defining $F(j\omega)$ to be the Fourier transform of $f(t)$,

$$F(j\omega) = \int_{-\infty}^{\infty} f(t)e^{-j\omega t}\,dt \tag{6-47}$$

The output signal $g(t)$ is given by

$$\begin{aligned} g(t) &= \frac{1}{2\pi}\int_{-\infty}^{\infty} F(j\omega)H(j\omega)e^{j\omega t}\,d\omega \\ &= \int_{-\infty}^{\infty} F(j\omega)H(j\omega)e^{j\omega t}\,df \qquad \omega = 2\pi f \end{aligned} \tag{6-48}$$

The magnitude of $g(t)$ at any specified time t_0 is

$$|g(t_0)| = \left|\int_{-\infty}^{\infty} F(j\omega)H(j\omega)e^{j\omega t_0}\,df\right|$$

The time t_0 will be chosen specifically as the time at which $|g(t)|$ is a maximum (peak).

The power spectrum of the white noise at the filter input is taken as

$$G'(\omega) = \frac{\eta}{2} \qquad \text{watts/cps} \tag{6-49}$$

as in the previous section. [$G'(\omega)$ is again the *two-sided spectrum* defined for both positive and negative frequencies.] The two-sided power spectrum at the filter output is then

$$G'_H(\omega) = \frac{\eta}{2} |H(j\omega)|^2 \tag{6-50}$$

and the average output noise power (or mean-squared noise voltage across a 1-ohm resistor) is

$$N_H = \frac{\eta}{2} \int_{-\infty}^{\infty} |H(j\omega)|^2 \, df \tag{6-51}$$

$\sqrt{N_H}$ is the rms output noise in the absence of a signal.

We would now like to choose $H(j\omega)$ such that the ratio $|g(t_0)|/\sqrt{N_H}$ is maximized. This is the same as maximizing the square of the ratio, or $|g(t_0)|^2/N_H$. This squared ratio is just the ratio of instantaneous peak signal power at $t = t_0$ to mean noise power and differs from the ratio of mean signal power to mean noise power of Chap. 5 by a constant factor.

Since the input signal $f(t)$ is assumed given, its energy content, E watt-sec, is a constant and is given by

$$E = \int_{-\infty}^{\infty} f^2(t) \, dt = \int_{-\infty}^{\infty} |F(j\omega)|^2 \, df \tag{6-52}$$

from the previous section.

Dividing the peak signal power to mean noise power by the constant E will obviously not affect the determination of the maximum ratio. So we can take as our problem that of maximizing the ratio

$$\frac{|g(t_0)|^2}{EN_H} = \frac{\left| \int_{-\infty}^{\infty} F(j\omega)H(j\omega)e^{j\omega t_0} \, df \right|^2}{(\eta/2) \int_{-\infty}^{\infty} |F(j\omega)|^2 \, df \int_{-\infty}^{\infty} |H(j\omega)|^2 \, df} \tag{6-53}$$

This is readily done by means of *Schwarz's inequality*, relating the integral of products of complex functions:

$$\left| \int_{-\infty}^{\infty} X(\omega)Y(\omega) \, d\omega \right|^2 \leq \int_{-\infty}^{\infty} |X(\omega)|^2 \, d\omega \int_{-\infty}^{\infty} |Y(\omega)|^2 \, d\omega \tag{6-54}$$

Schwarz's inequality for integrals of complex functions is just an extension of an inequality for real integrals, given by

$$\left[\int_{-\infty}^{\infty} f(t)g(t) \, dt \right]^2 \leq \int_{-\infty}^{\infty} g^2(t) \, dt \int_{-\infty}^{\infty} f^2(t) \, dt \tag{6-55}$$

It might be termed a generalization of the familiar distance relation among vectors that the magnitude of the sum of two vectors is less than or equal to the sum of the magnitudes of the two vectors:

$$|\bar{a} + \bar{b}| \leq |\bar{a}| + |\bar{b}| \tag{6-56}$$

In the vector case the equality is satisfied if $\bar{a} = K\bar{b}$, or $\bar{a}$ and $\bar{b}$ are collinear. Similarly in Eq. (6-55) the equality is satisfied if $f(t) = Kg(t)$. In the case of complex functions the equality is satisfied if

$$Y(\omega) = KX^*(\omega) \tag{6-57}$$

K is a real number.

Schwarz's inequality is readily proved by considering the integral

$$I = \int_{-\infty}^{\infty} d\omega \int_{-\infty}^{\infty} |X(\omega)Y(y) - Y(\omega)X(y)|^2 \, dy \geq 0 \tag{6-58}$$

where X and Y are complex functions. I is necessarily positive and real because it is the integral of the absolute value of a function. The quantity inside the vertical bars may be multiplied out and expanded to give four terms. Thus

$$|X(\omega)Y(y) - Y(\omega)X(y)|^2 = |X(\omega)|^2|Y(y)|^2 + |Y(\omega)|^2|X(y)|^2 \\ - Y(\omega)Y^*(y)X^*(\omega)X(y) - Y^*(\omega)Y(y)X(\omega)X^*(y)$$

Integrating term by term, the integrals of the first two terms are identical, as are the last two integrals. (ω and y are both dummy variables in any one integral.) Upon replacing y with ω in the first two terms and interchanging ω and y in the last term, the over-all integral becomes

$$I = 2\int_{-\infty}^{\infty} |X(\omega)|^2 \, d\omega \int_{-\infty}^{\infty} |Y(\omega)|^2 \, d\omega \\ - 2\int_{-\infty}^{\infty} Y(\omega)X^*(\omega) \, d\omega \int_{-\infty}^{\infty} Y^*(y)X(y) \, dy$$

But $\left|\int_{-\infty}^{\infty} X(\omega)Y(\omega) \, d\omega\right|^2 = \int_{-\infty}^{\infty} X(\omega)Y(\omega) \, d\omega \int_{-\infty}^{\infty} X^*(y)Y^*(y) \, dy$

ω being replaced by y in the last integral. Equation (6-58) finally becomes

$$\frac{I}{2} = \int_{-\infty}^{\infty} |X(\omega)|^2 \, d\omega \int_{-\infty}^{\infty} |Y(\omega)|^2 \, d\omega - \left|\int_{-\infty}^{\infty} X(\omega)Y(\omega) \, d\omega\right|^2 \geq 0 \tag{6-59}$$

This proves the inequality stated as Eq. (6-54).

How do we apply Schwarz's inequality to our problem of maximizing peak signal-to-noise ratio?

Note that the ratio of Eq. (6-53) contains exactly the integrals of Eq. (6-54) if we let

$$X(\omega) = F(j\omega)e^{j\omega t_0} \qquad Y(\omega) = H(j\omega)$$

The ratio $\dfrac{\eta}{2}\dfrac{|g(t_0)|^2}{EN_H}$ must then be less than or equal to 1, and

$$\left|\int_{-\infty}^{\infty} F(j\omega)H(j\omega)e^{j\omega t_0} \, df\right|^2 \leq \int_{-\infty}^{\infty} |F(j\omega)|^2 \, df \int_{-\infty}^{\infty} |H(j\omega)|^2 \, df \tag{6-60}$$

In particular, the ratio is a *maximum* when the equality holds, or

$$H(j\omega) = K[F(j\omega)e^{j\omega t_0}]^* = KF^*(j\omega)e^{-j\omega t_0} \tag{6-61}$$

As an example, if $f(t)$ is the rectangular pulse of width τ and height V, $F(j\omega) = V\tau\{[\sin(\omega\tau/2)]/(\omega\tau/2)\}$ and

$$H(j\omega) = K\frac{\sin(\omega\tau/2)}{\omega\tau/2}e^{-j\omega t_0}$$

for maximum ratio of peak signal to rms noise. The linear holding circuit of Fig. 4-21 has a transfer function of the $(\sin x)/x$ type.

Filters possessing the characteristic of Eq. (6-61) are said to be *matched filters*. The response at the output of such a filter, to $f(t)$ applied at the input, is

$$\begin{aligned} g(t) &= \int_{-\infty}^{\infty} F(j\omega)H(j\omega)e^{j\omega t}\,df \\ &= K\int_{-\infty}^{\infty} |F(j\omega)|^2 e^{j\omega(t-t_0)}\,df \end{aligned} \tag{6-62}$$

In particular $g(t)$ will have maximum amplitude (peak value) when $t = t_0$: $|g(t_0)| = K\int_{-\infty}^{\infty} |F(j\omega)|^2\,df$.

The peak value of $g(t)$ is thus independent of the choice of t_0. This time of occurrence of the peak value of $g(t)$ can be varied at will by adjusting the $e^{-j\omega t_0}$ phase term in the matched-filter characteristic.

If the input time function $f(t)$ is symmetrical in time $[f(t) = f(-t)]$, $F(j\omega)$ will be a real function of frequency (see Sec. 2-9). From Eq. (6-61) $H(j\omega) = KF(j\omega)e^{-j\omega t_0}$ for this case. This means that the impulse response $h(t)$ is $h(t) = Kf(t - t_0)$. The impulse response of a filter matched to a symmetrical input is a delayed replica of such an input.

If $f(t)$ is not symmetrical, $F(j\omega)$ is complex. By using the Fourier-integral relations it may be shown that

$$h(t) = Kf[-(t - t_0)] \tag{6-63}$$

in general. The proof is left to the reader as an exercise since it is identical to the procedure used to prove Plancherel's theorem in the last section. Since $f(t)$ is normally defined for positive t, $h(t)$ in the general case will be defined for negative t. As pointed out in Chap. 2, such a filter is physically not realizable. In the general case, then, the matched filter is *not realizable.*

Of what value then is this entire analysis leading to the matched-filter result? Just as in the case of the ideal filter of Chap. 2, we can approximate the matched-filter characteristics by those of an actual filter. We can also compare practical filters with the matched filter so far as the ratio of peak output signal to noise is concerned and can optimize their shape and bandwidth as far as practicable. This is the procedure we shall follow in the remainder of this section.

The input time function $f(t)$ is assumed to be a rectangular pulse of width τ sec and height V. We assume $V\tau = 1$. With $f(t)$ symmetrically located about $t = 0$, $F(j\omega) = [\sin(\omega\tau/2)]/(\omega\tau/2)$, a real function as noted above. The impulse response of the matched filter is then also a rectangular pulse of τ sec duration. [$H(j\omega) = F(j\omega)$ here.] The response of this matched filter to the rectangular pulse will then be the convolution of two rectangular pulses. This was worked out in Chap. 2 as an example of the convolution integral and, as was shown there, gave a triangular-pulse output. We can check this by noting that for the matched filter $F(j\omega)H(j\omega) = \{[\sin(\omega\tau/2)]/(\omega\tau/2)\}^2 e^{-j\omega t_0}$ ($V\tau = 1$). This is just the Fourier transform of a triangular pulse of width 2τ sec, as shown in Chap. 2. This output pulse is τ sec wide at the half-amplitude points.

Note that such a triangular pulse is not too different in shape from the output of the ideal low-pass filter of Sec. 2-7, with $f_c = 1/\tau$ (see Fig. 2-23). In fact the ideal-filter output for $f_c = 1/\tau$ could very well have been approximated by such a triangle. If the bandwidth of the matched filter is assumed to be the frequency of the first zero in its amplitude characteristic, the bandwidth is also just $1/\tau$ ($\sin \omega\tau/2 = 0$; $\omega\tau/2 = \pi$; $f = 1/\tau$).

This is an interesting point, for it agrees with our previous results that for producing a recognizable pulse a filter bandwidth of the order of $f_c = 1/\tau$ should be used. We actually assumed bandwidths of the order of $1/\tau$ in our discussion of PAM in Chap. 4. We shall see below that for an ideal low-pass filter $f_c\tau = 0.7$ actually gives maximum signal-to-noise ratio.

Just how significant the shape of the filter characteristic and bandwidth are in determining the output peak signal-to-noise ratio for a rectangular-pulse input can be found by applying Eq. (6-53) to various filters. The resulting signal-to-noise ratio can then be compared with that for the optimum matched filter. We shall actually calculate $[(\eta/2)|g(t_0)|^2]/EN_H$ so that the optimum value is normalized to 1. In all cases the rectangular-pulse input is assumed to have unit area ($V\tau = 1$), so that

$$F(j\omega) = \frac{\sin(\omega\tau/2)}{\omega\tau/2}$$

1. Ideal low-pass filter, variable bandwidth. Here

$$\begin{aligned} H(j\omega) &= e^{-j\omega t_0} \qquad |\omega| \le \omega_c \\ H(j\omega) &= 0 \qquad |\omega| > \omega_c \end{aligned} \tag{6-64}$$

The square of the peak S/N ratio or the power ratio for this case, as obtained from Eq. (6-53), becomes

$$\frac{\left|\int_{-\omega_c}^{\omega_c} \frac{\sin(\omega\tau/2)}{\omega\tau/2}\,d\omega\right|^2}{\int_{-\infty}^{\infty}\left[\frac{\sin(\omega\tau/2)}{\omega\tau/2}\right]^2 d\omega \int_{-\omega_c}^{\omega_c} d\omega} = \frac{\left(\frac{2}{\tau}\int_{-a}^{a}\frac{\sin x}{x}\,dx\right)^2}{\frac{2}{\tau}\int_{-\infty}^{\infty}\left(\frac{\sin x}{x}\right)^2 dx\; 2\omega_c}$$

with $x \equiv \omega\tau/2$ and $a = \omega_c\tau/2$.

Using the relation $\int_{-\infty}^{\infty} [(\sin x)/x]^2\,dx = \pi$ and recalling the sine integral definition, $\text{Si}\,a = \int_0^a [(\sin x)/x]\,dx$, the ratio squared becomes

$$\frac{2}{\pi a}(\text{Si}\,a)^2$$

This expression may be plotted by using tables of the sine integral[1] and is found to have a maximum at $a = \omega_c\tau/2 = 2.2$. This corresponds to

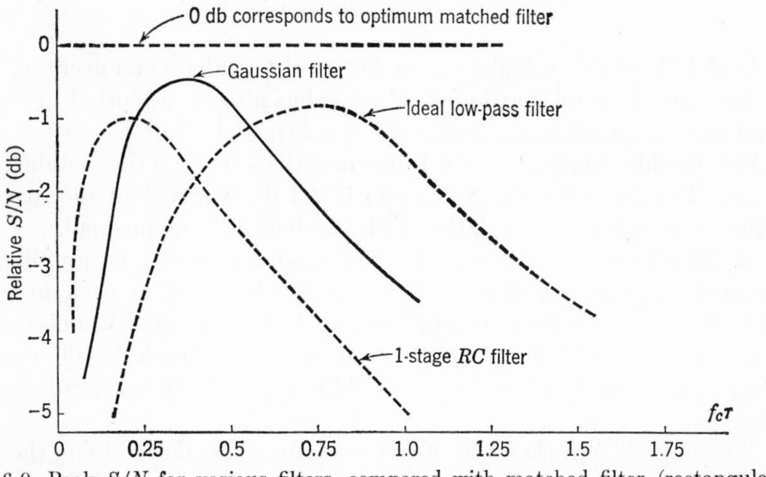

FIG. 6-9. Peak S/N for various filters, compared with matched filter (rectangular-pulse input).

$f_c\tau = 2.2/\pi = 0.7$. At this bandwidth the S/N peak power ratio is found to be 0.83, as compared with 1 for the optimum filter. This corresponds to a relative deterioration of 0.8 db.

The ideal-low-pass-filter case is plotted in Fig. 6-9 as a function of $f_c\tau$. The decibel scale used is relative to the 0-db case for the optimum matched filter. Although the maximum ratio is found for $f_c\tau = 0.7$, the maximum is very broad and varies less than 1 db from $f_c\tau = 0.4$ to $f_c\tau = 1$.

[1] S. Goldman, "Frequency Analysis, Modulation, and Noise," McGraw-Hill Book Company, Inc., New York, 1948; E. Jahnke and F. Emde, "Tables of Functions," Dover Publications, New York, 1945.

For a pulsed carrier signal the bandwidth would be twice the bandwidth shown here, so that $f_c\tau = 1.5$ would be optimum for a rectangular filter.

2. One-stage RC filter, variable bandwidth.

$$H(j\omega) = \frac{1}{1 + j\omega RC} \tag{6-65}$$

with $\omega_c = 1/RC$ the 3-db bandwidth. The response of this filter to a rectangular-pulse input is plotted in Fig. 2-10. The peak output occurs at $t = \tau$ and is given by

$$g(\tau) = 1 - e^{-\tau/RC}$$

[This procedure is much simpler then the frequency-response method of Eq. (6-48) in this case.] The normalized signal-to-noise peak power ratio becomes for this case, after some manipulations,

$$\frac{(1 - e^{-2a})^2}{a} \qquad a = \frac{\tau}{2RC} = \frac{\omega_c\tau}{2}$$

The details of this calculation are left to the reader as an exercise.

The signal-to-noise ratio for this case has also been plotted in Fig. 6-9 and shows a maximum value at $f_c\tau = 0.2$ ($f_c = 1/2\pi RC$). At this bandwidth the filter output is only 1 db worse than that for the matched-filter case. For $f_c\tau = 0.5$ the S/N ratio is 2.3 db worse than the matched-filter case so that the variation with bandwidth is again small.

3. Multistage RC filters. A signal would normally be amplified by several stages of amplifiers, with filtering included in each amplifier. It is thus of interest to compare the matched-filter signal-to-noise output with that of a multistage amplifier. We assume a simple RC filter in each stage. (For a pulsed carrier we would use a single-tuned circuit for each stage.)

The peak S/N ratio could of course be found by determining the over-all frequency response of the multistage amplifiers. This becomes unwieldy mathematically. It can be shown,[1] however, that the transfer function of a large number of isolated RC sections approaches the form

$$H(j\omega) = e^{-0.35(\omega/\omega_c)^2}e^{-jt_0\omega} \tag{6-66}$$

where $f_c = \omega_c/2\pi$ is the 3-db bandwidth of the *over-all* filter. This is the mathematical expression for the so-called gaussian, or normal, error curve, encountered very frequently in the field of statistics.

The gaussian filter response curve has a characteristic "bell" shape and is symmetrical about $\omega = 0$. It is shown sketched in Fig. 6-10. We

[1] C. Cherry, "Pulses and Transients in Communication Circuits," p. 311, Chapman & Hall, Ltd., London, 1949, Dover Publications, New York, 1950.

shall have a great deal to say about this gaussian curve in our discussion of probability in Chap. 7.

We can again use Eq. (6-53) to calculate the peak power S/N ratio for a rectangular pulse applied to a network with this amplitude characteristic. The result will then approximate the output of a multistage RC amplifier. The analysis is identical to that carried out for the ideal filter. The details will not be presented here, but the results are plotted in Fig. 6-9, again compared with the optimum matched-filter case.

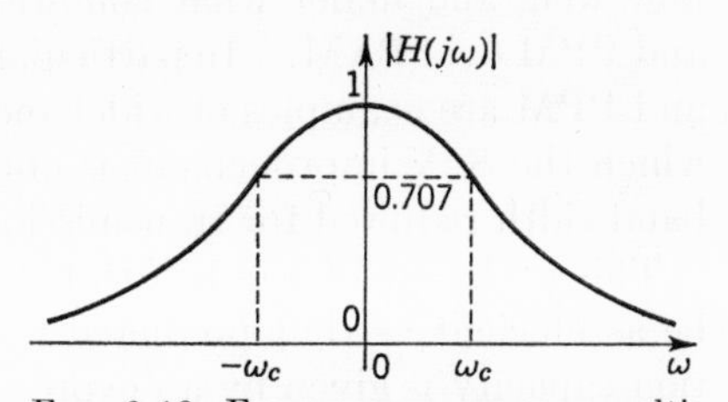

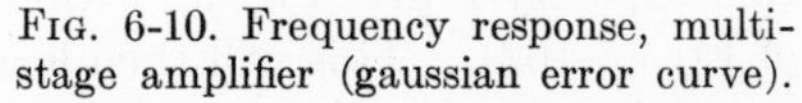

FIG. 6-10. Frequency response, multistage amplifier (gaussian error curve).

Actual calculations[1] for two and three stages of amplification with RC filtering included produce results which do not differ substantially from those for the gaussian filter, so that the gaussian-error-curve analysis will be a good approximation to a multistage RC amplifier with two or more stages.

Note that the peak S/N ratio occurs in this case for $f_c\tau = 0.4$. (For a two-stage amplifier the peak occurs at $f_c\tau = 0.3$.) The maximum is quite broad, however, varying by no more than 1 db from $f_c\tau = 0.2$ to $f_c\tau = 0.7$.

At the maximum the ratio is only 0.5 db less than that for the optimum matched filter. This would be quite negligible in most practical applications. The over-all filter characteristic of a multistage amplifier will thus be close to optimum for transmission of rectangular pulses, with the over-all bandwidth chosen as $f_c = 0.5/\tau$.

In radar systems the bandwidth used is actually the bandwidth at a high carrier frequency, and so twice this bandwidth, or $f_c = 1/\tau$, would be optimum there. Such a bandwidth choice is common practice in the design of pulse radars.

In most cases the actual design or approximation of a matched filter would not be economical, since the gaussian-shaped characteristic provided by ordinary amplifier circuits works almost as well.

The gaussian-shaped characteristic converts a rectangular pulse into a pulse of approximately cosinusoidal shape. This filter characteristic has been used in an experimental PCM system designed at Bell Telephone Laboratories.

6-3. Signal-to-Noise Ratios in FM and AM. Using the concepts of power spectrum and signal-to-noise ratio (S/N), we are now in a position actually to compare quantitatively various information-transmission

[1] A. M. Fine, Optimum Filters for Pulsed Signals in Noise, master of electrical engineering thesis, Polytechnic Institute of Brooklyn, June, 1957.

systems as to their relative noise-rejection properties and information-handling capacity.

We alluded, in Chap. 3, to the fact that wideband FM gives a significant improvement in noise or interference rejection over AM. Similarly wideband PPM was stated to provide noise-rejection improvement over PAM. We would now like to demonstrate these statements and see just how well, and under what conditions, FM is an improvement over AM and PPM over PAM. In particular we shall see specifically that both FM and PPM are examples of wideband information-transmission systems in which the S/N improvement is obtained at the expense of the increased bandwidth required for transmission.

This exchange of bandwidth for S/N ratio in these two cases will not be as efficient as that predicted for an idealized system whose information capacity is given by an expression similar to the capacity expression of Eq. (5-162). This will then lead us into a discussion of PCM, a modern pulse system whose exchange of bandwidth for S/N is much more efficient than that of FM or PPM, and whose capacity expression may in fact be written in a form similar to that of Eq. (5-162).

We shall first compare FM and AM,[1] then take up, very briefly, PPM and PAM. For the purpose of comparison of FM and AM we shall assume the same carrier power and mean noise spectral density at the input to each system. We shall then calculate S/N ratios at the system outputs and compare.

As indicated in the previous section (6-2) on the matched-filter criterion the actual definition of S/N is arbitrary and depends on the application for which it is intended. There we were interested in maximizing a peak signal with respect to the surrounding noise level and defined our S/N ratio accordingly. Here we revert to the definition of S/N introduced in Chap. 5. This is taken to be the ratio of mean signal power to mean noise power, the signal power measured in the absence of noise, the noise power in the absence of signal (i.e., the carrier is unmodulated). Such a mean S/N power ratio differs of course only by a constant from the peak ratio of the previous section.

Why this definition here? First, because of its relative simplicity and because it does lead to significant conclusions; second, because in the usual AM or FM system the noise *is* more noticeable in the absence of a signal. (This refers to a supposedly quiet channel.)

In other communication systems, such as those mentioned in connection with Sec. 6-2, the problem is somewhat different: there we may want to rate the system on the basis of *both* signal and noise present. We shall show, in Chap. 7, that for high S/N ratio, however, the mean

[1] H. S. Black, "Modulation Theory," chap. 14, D. Van Nostrand Company, Inc., Princeton, N.J., 1953.

signal and noise powers may be assumed to add linearly, and signal power measured in the absence of noise does not differ substantially from that measured with noise present.

For high S/N ratio, then, we can determine the mean signal power at the output of the receiver (FM or AM) with noise assumed absent, then repeat for the case of noise with signal absent. The ratio of these two quantities will be defined to be our mean S/N ratio.

Amplitude Modulation. A typical AM receiver to be analyzed is shown in Fig. 6-11.

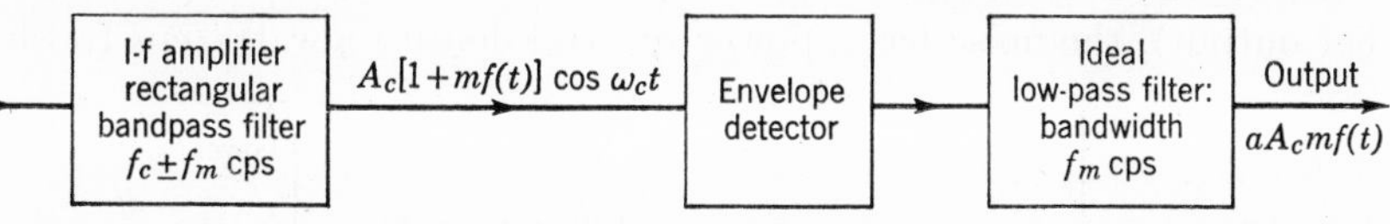

FIG. 6-11. Idealized AM receiver.

The amplitude-modulated carrier at the input to the envelope detector has the form

$$f_c(t) = A_c[1 + mf(t)] \cos \omega_c t \qquad |mf(t)| \leq 1 \tag{6-67}$$

if noise is assumed absent. A_c is the unmodulated carrier amplitude measured at the same point.

If the desired signal $f(t)$ is band-limited to f_m cps, the intermediate-frequency amplifier preceding the detector should have a bandwidth of at least $2f_m$ cps, centered about f_c cps. The amplifier is assumed to have the characteristics of an ideal rectangular filter.

This AM signal is now envelope-detected and passed through an ideal filter f_m cps wide. As shown in Sec. 3-6 the output of the envelope detector $f_d(t)$ will be proportional to $f(t)$, or

$$f_d(t) = aA_c mf(t) \tag{6-68}$$

where a is a constant of proportionality of the filter. The average signal output power, measured across a 1-ohm resistor, is then

$$S_o = (aA_c m)^2 \frac{1}{T} \int_0^T f^2(t)\, dt \tag{6-69}$$

where T is the basic repetition period of $f(t)$ (assumed periodic). In particular, if $f(t)$ is a sinusoidal test signal, $f(t) = \cos \omega_m t$,

$$S_o = \tfrac{1}{2} m^2 a^2 A_c^2 \tag{6-70}$$

The case of 100 per cent modulation, or $m = 1$, gives maximum output power.

But the average unmodulated carrier power at the input to the detector is

$$S_c = \tfrac{1}{2} A_c^2 \tag{6-71}$$

again measured across a 1-ohm resistor. In terms of the average unmodulated carrier power the average output signal power for a sinusoidal signal may be written

$$S_o = m^2a^2S_c \tag{6-72}$$

Now consider noise added on top of the unmodulated carrier (this is the zero-signal case). This noise may have been introduced in the transmission path from transmitter to receiver, the first stages of the receiver, and the mixer of the receiver. We assume this noise to be fluctuation noise (both thermal and shot noise). At the *detector input* (or i-f amplifier output), the noise has a power spectral density η watts/cps (positive

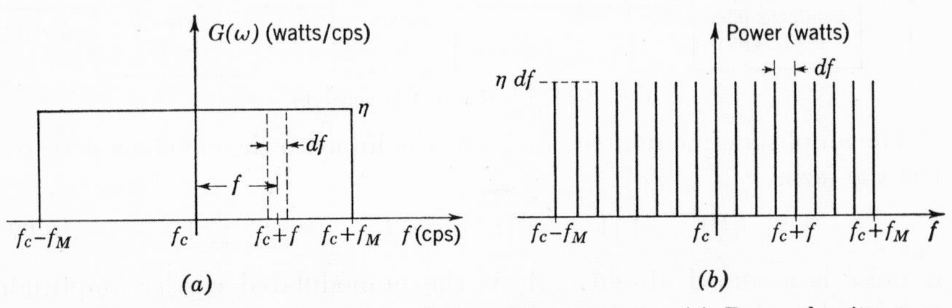

FIG. 6-12. Noise-power spectrum at i-f amplifier output. (*a*) Power-density spectrum; (*b*) power spectrum, discrete approximation.

frequencies only). The noise power is assumed measured across the same 1-ohm resistor as was the signal.

Because of the rectangular bandpass filter characteristics assumed for the i-f amplifier, the *total* mean noise power at the input to the detector is

$$N_c = 2f_m\eta \qquad \text{watts} \tag{6-73}$$

The actual value of the power density η will depend on the over-all noise figure of the entire receiver measured up to the detector. It is calculated as in the example of Sec. 6-1, following Eq. (6-20). This noise will perturb the unmodulated carrier in a random fashion and will effectively appear as an amplitude-modulated signal that will be detected and emerge as a disturbing crackle at the system output.

We can show this in the following simple way: The noise has a continuous power-density spectrum distributed uniformly with a magnitude η watts/cps over the range $f_c \pm f_m$ cps. We can approximate this spectrum by breaking it up into many narrow intervals df cps wide ($df \ll f_m$). The noise appearing at frequency $f_c + f$ and covering a width df cps (Fig. 6-12*a*) can then be approximated by a sine wave of the same average power and the same frequency. Such a sine wave at frequency $f_c + f$ is given by

$$n(t) \doteq A_n \cos(\omega_c + \omega)t \tag{6-74}$$

with $A_n^2/2 = \eta\, df$ the average power of the sine wave. We have thus replaced a continuous power-density spectrum by an equivalent discrete power spectrum of the same total power (Fig. 6-12*b*). Alternatively we have assumed that we can approximate the noise by a sum of sinusoids of the same total power as the noise. Basic to this is the implicit assumption that the noise component in any one bandwidth df cps wide is independent of the noise in another band of the same width. All have the same mean power, however, and the powers add directly. [Actually the amplitude of the noise term of Eq. (6-74) will fluctuate randomly. We approximate it by a constant-amplitude term of the same rms value.]

Any one component of the noise will add directly to the carrier to give

$$\begin{aligned} A_c \cos \omega_c t + A_n \cos (\omega_c + \omega)t & \\ &= A_c \cos \omega_c t + A_n(\cos \omega_c t \cos \omega t - \sin \omega_c t \sin \omega t) \\ &= (A_c + A_n \cos \omega t) \cos \omega_c t - A_n \sin \omega t \sin \omega_c t \\ &= \sqrt{A^2 + B^2} \cos (\omega_c t + \theta) \end{aligned} \tag{6-75}$$

where

$$A = A_c + A_n \cos \omega t$$

$$B = A_n \sin \omega t$$

and

$$\theta = \tan^{-1} \frac{A_n \sin \omega t}{A_c + A_n \cos \omega t}$$

The sum of this one noise component at frequency $f_c + f$ and the carrier at frequency f_c thus gives rise to a carrier whose amplitude and phase are *both* modulated by the noise.

We shall discuss the phase term in analyzing FM noise. Here we focus attention on the amplitude since it is this term which will be detected by the envelope detector. If the mean noise power is assumed small compared with the mean carrier power, or

$$N_c \ll S_c$$

the noise-component amplitude will obviously be small compared with the carrier amplitude,

$$A_n \ll A_c$$

With this assumption we can approximate the envelope term by

$$\sqrt{A^2 + B^2} \doteq A_c \left(1 + \frac{A_n}{A_c} \cos \omega t\right) \qquad \frac{A_n}{A_c} \ll 1 \tag{6-76}$$

But this is just the form of the envelope of an amplitude-modulated wave. Since $\cos \omega t$ lies within the passband of the filter following the envelope detector (Fig. 6-11), a noise term will appear at the receiver output. As in the case of the signal the detected noise term will be of the form

$$aA_n \cos \omega t$$

where a is the detector constant. This term is just at the difference frequency between the noise component $n(t)$ at $f_c + f$ and the unmodulated carrier at f_c cps. The mean power contributed by this term at the output is then

$$\frac{a^2 A_n{}^2}{2} = a^2 \eta \, df \qquad \text{watts}$$

Each noise component within the passband of the i-f amplifier will give rise to such an output-power term. Since these terms are assumed independent, the powers add and the total mean noise power at the output of the final filter will be

$$N_o = a^2(2f_m\eta) = a^2 N_c \qquad \text{watts} \tag{6-77}$$

(This is under the assumption that $N_c \ll S_c$.)

We could of course have obtained this result by noting that the detector, as a nonlinear device, produces at its output all sum and difference frequencies of the terms present at the input. These terms at the input consist of the unmodulated carrier at f_c cps plus noise terms at frequencies ranging from $f_c - f_m$ to $f_c + f_m$. The filter, with a passband extending to f_m cps, then selects all the sum and difference frequencies within that range. These will consist generally of two types of terms:

1. Those due to each of the noise components within $\pm f_m$ cps of the carrier frequency mixing with the carrier term.

2. Those due to the different noise components mixing with each other and producing difference frequencies within the filter passband. For example, a noise term at frequency $f_c - f_m$ will produce difference frequencies within the filter passband when mixed with any of the noise terms from $f_c - f_m$ to f_c.

Because of our assumption of large carrier-to-noise ratio ($S_c \gg N_c$), the total mean power of the terms in the second category will be negligible compared with the power in the terms of the first category. The mean power of the terms in the first category is then just that of Eq. (6-77),

$$N_o = a^2(2f_m\eta) \qquad \text{watts} \qquad N_c \ll S_c$$

The complete analysis of the output power spectrum of various nonlinear devices with noise and carrier applied at the input is in general quite cumbersome. Rice of Bell Telephone Laboratories has summarized his own work and that of other investigators in a classic paper on noise published in 1944–1945. He discusses there the output power spectrum for various nonlinear devices and has in particular sketched the form of the output spectrum for the two cases of a square-law detector and a piecewise-linear detector.[1] (These are the two types of nonlinear devices

[1] S. O. Rice, Mathematical Analysis of Random Noise, *Bell System Tech. J.*, vol. 24, pp. 46–156, pt. 4, January, 1945.

considered here in Sec. 3-3.) In general this spectrum contains the two categories mentioned. For large carrier-to-noise ratio the output components due to noise beating against noise become negligible, and the terms due to the noise beating with the carrier are the primary ones contributing to the output noise.

The low-frequency (l-f) output spectrum of the piecewise-linear detector, as obtained from Rice, has been sketched in Fig. 6-13. It is

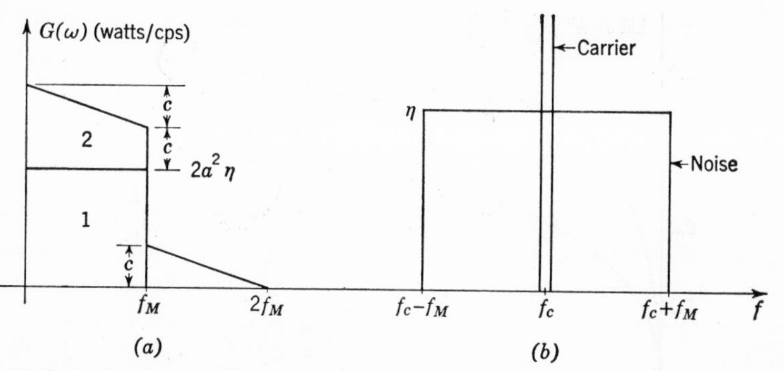

FIG. 6-13. Low-frequency power spectrum, noise plus carrier, at output of piecewise-linear detector. (a) Output spectrum; (b) input spectrum. (*S. O. Rice, Mathematical Analysis of Random Noise, Bell System Tech. J., vol.* 24, *pp.* 46–156, *pt.* 4, *fig.* 9, *January,* 1945, *by permission.*)

there compared with the input spectrum centered about f_c. The output spectrum of the square-law detector is of the same form, but with different constants. The two parts of the output spectrum below f_m cps that are comparable with the two types of terms mentioned are indicated by the numerals:

1. Noise beating with the carrier
2. Noise beating with noise

The parameters c and a shown depend on carrier-to-noise power ratio, or S_c/N_c, as indicated in Fig. 6-14. For $S_c > 4N_c$

$$c = 2\left(\frac{1}{\pi}\right)^2 \eta \frac{N_c}{16S_c}$$

and

$$a = \frac{1}{\pi}$$

So, even for $S_c/N_c = 4$, the No. 1 category predominates. For smaller values of S_c/N_c the curves of Fig. 6-14 may be used to obtain c and a.

Upon using Eqs. (6-77) and (6-72), the output-power signal-to-noise ratio becomes

$$\frac{S_o}{N_o} = \frac{a^2m^2S_c}{a^2N_c} = m^2\frac{S_c}{N_c} \tag{6-78}$$

For $m = 1$ (100 per cent modulation) the output signal-to-noise ratio is just the input carrier-to-noise ratio.

We have assumed the i-f bandwidth to be $2f_m$ cps and the output filter bandwidth to be f_m cps. These are the bandwidths required to pass the desired signals assumed band-limited to f_m cps. If we were to widen the bandwidth of the i-f amplifier, more noise power would appear at the system output, while the signal power would remain unchanged. The

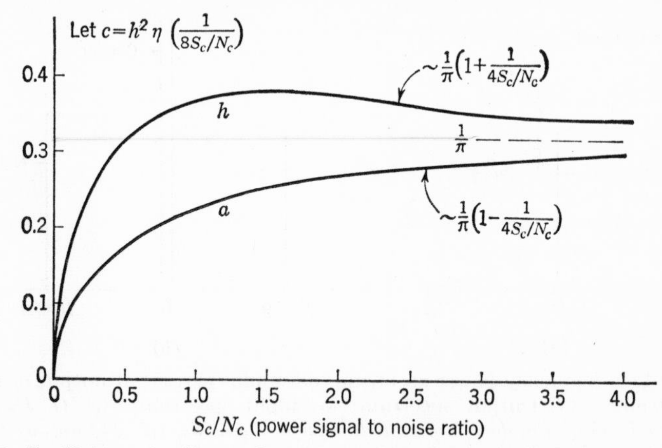

FIG. 6-14. Coefficients for linear detector output shown in Fig. 6-13. (*S. O. Rice, Mathematical Analysis of Random Noise, Bell System Tech. J., vol.* 24, *pp.* 45–156, *pt.* 4, *fig.* 10, *January,* 1945, *by permission.*)

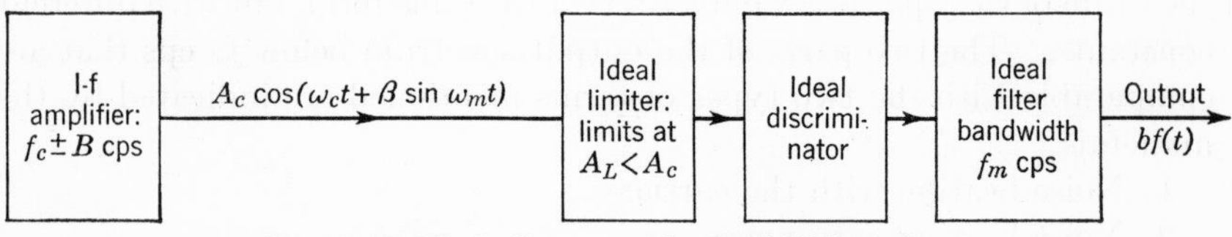

FIG. 6-15. Block diagram, idealized FM receiver.

S_o/N_o ratio would thus decrease. The AM bandwidth is thus limited to just the bandwidth needed to transmit the signal.

Note that the analysis of the previous Sec. 6-2 does not apply in this case, for we are not simply interested in maximizing a peak S/N ratio. Here a minimum bandwidth is required in order to ensure signal fidelity.

Frequency Modulation. For the case of FM we shall again define the S/N ratio as the ratio of mean signal power with noise absent to the mean noise power in the presence of an unmodulated carrier. Again the analysis will be confined to the case of large carrier-to-noise ratio.

We shall show that, contrary to the AM case, widening the transmission bandwidth (as is required for wideband FM) *does* improve the S/N ratio.

The idealized FM receiver to be discussed here is shown in Fig. 6-15.

A frequency-modulated signal of transmission bandwidth $2B$ cps is first passed through an ideal limiter which removes all amplitude variations. The limiter output, after filtering, goes to the discriminator, assumed to give an output directly proportional to the instantaneous frequency of the signal, and then to an ideal low-pass filter of bandwidth f_m cps ($f_m < B$). f_m is the maximum bandwidth of the actual information signal, $f(t)$, being transmitted.

Assuming, as in Chap. 3, a sine-wave signal of the form

$$f(t) = \Delta\omega \cos \omega_m t \tag{6-79}$$

the frequency-modulated carrier measured at the *output* of the *i-f amplifier* is given by

$$f_c(t) = A_c \cos (\omega_c t + \beta \sin \omega_m t) \tag{6-80}$$

Noise is assumed absent here. $\beta = \Delta\omega/\omega_m = \Delta f/f_m$ is the modulation index and $\Delta f = \Delta\omega/2\pi$ the maximum frequency deviation.

The average power of the FM wave is simply

$$S_c = \tfrac{1}{2}A_c^2 \tag{6-81}$$

independent of the modulating signal.

The instantaneous frequency is given by

$$\begin{aligned} \omega = \frac{d\theta}{dt} &= \omega_c + \beta\omega_m \cos \omega_m t = \omega_c + \Delta\omega \cos \omega_m t \\ &= \omega_c + f(t) \end{aligned} \tag{6-82}$$

The discriminator output is proportional to the instantaneous frequency deviation away from ω_c, or $\omega - \omega_c$. This frequency deviation is just $f(t)$. The output signal is then

$$f_d(t) = b\,\Delta\omega \cos \omega_m t = bf(t) \tag{6-83}$$

where b is a constant of the discriminator.

The discriminator output must be filtered to eliminate higher-frequency distortion terms. Filtering will also reduce the output noise when present. The filter bandwidth is chosen as f_m cps in order to pass all frequency components of $f(t)$.

From Eq. (6-83) the average output signal power is simply

$$S_o = \frac{b^2(\Delta\omega)^2}{2} \quad \text{watts} \tag{6-84}$$

if a 1-ohm normalized load resistor is assumed.

The case of noise plus unmodulated carrier (signal absent) can now be treated in a manner directly analogous to that for AM. We again assume fluctuation noise of spectral density η watts/cps uniformly distributed at the output of the i-f amplifier. The i-f amplifier bandwidth is $2B$ cps ($B > f_m$), as required for a wideband FM signal. As in the AM case we replace the continuous noise spectrum by an equivalent set of discrete spectral lines of the same mean power. This corresponds to assuming that the noise may be represented by a discrete number of sine waves, spaced df cps apart, each sine wave having $\eta\, df$ watts average power. In particular the noise component at frequency $f_c + f$ will be given by

$$n(t) = A_n \cos (\omega_c + \omega)t \qquad \frac{A_n^2}{2} = \eta\, df \tag{6-85}$$

Again, by adding this noise term to the unmodulated carrier, the noise plus carrier at the output of the amplifier becomes

$$A_n \cos (\omega_c + \omega)t + A_c \cos \omega_c t = A(t) \cos (\omega_c t + \theta) \tag{6-86}$$

The amplitude-varying term, $A(t)$, was considered in the AM case [Eq. (6-75)]. $\theta(t)$, the phase term, is given by

$$\theta = \tan^{-1} \frac{A_n \sin \omega t}{A_c + A_n \cos \omega t} \tag{6-87}$$

Note that in general, then, the noise introduces both AM and FM.

The ideal limiter and associated filter remove all amplitude variations, providing at the limiter output a constant-amplitude phase-modulated signal given by

$$A_L \cos (\omega_c t + \theta) \qquad A_L \text{ a constant } (A_L \leq A_c)$$

For large carrier-to-noise ratio, as will be assumed here, Eq. (6-87) may be simplified considerably. For, with $A_n \ll A_c$, θ becomes

$$\theta \doteq \frac{A_n}{A_c} \sin \omega t \qquad A_n \ll A_c \tag{6-88}$$

The limiter output is then

$$A_L \cos \left(\omega_c t + \frac{A_n}{A_c} \sin \omega t \right)$$

Note that this is exactly in the form of a *narrowband* FM signal, with the effective modulation index β given by $A_n/A_c \ll 1$.

The noise fluctuations, superimposed on the carrier, thus serve to produce a frequency-modulated signal and will consequently appear at the receiver output. *But* (and this is the crucial point), for a noise level much less than the carrier level (as assumed here), the *noise* at the FM output will be *narrowband*. With a desired *signal* arranged to produce *wideband* FM the noise effect will be reduced. As the signal deviation (or the FM bandwidth) is increased, the noise effect will become increasingly smaller. This observation, based on our simple analysis thus far, serves as the key to the understanding of the "noise-improvement" property of wideband FM.

The rotating vectors of Chap. 3 serve as a simple graphical demonstration of this result. With $\omega_c t$ as a reference phase angle, $A_c \cos \omega_c t + A_n \cos (\omega_c + \omega)t$ may be represented by the two vectors of Fig. 6-16.

For $A_n \ll A_c$, θ, the angle of the resultant vector, may be represented by

$$\theta \doteq \frac{A_n}{A_c} \sin \omega t$$

just as in Eq. (6-88). The total phase swing due to noise is thus very small and the noise-modulated carrier, given by the amplitude-limited resultant of Fig. 6-16, will rock back and forth with small variations about the unmodulated carrier. Phase variations due to a large deviation (wideband) signal will run into many radians, however, and so are much more readily distinguishable.

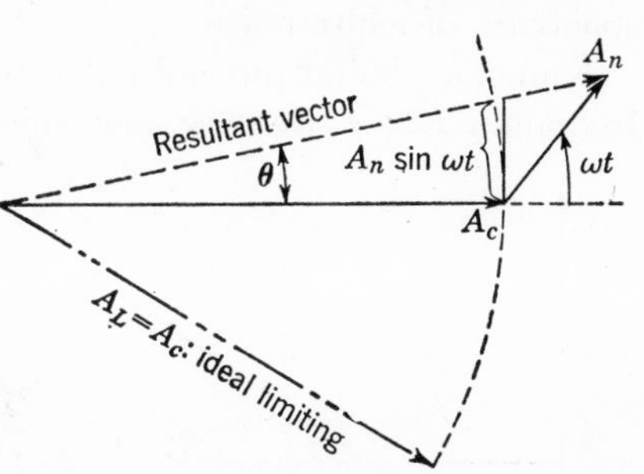

FIG. 6-16. Carrier plus noise in FM system ($A_n \ll A_c$).

With the phase angle θ given by Eq. (6-88), the noise output of the ideal discriminator is

$$f_d(t) = b\,\frac{d\theta}{dt} = b\omega\,\frac{A_n}{A_c} \cos \omega t \qquad A_n \ll A_c \tag{6-89}$$

with b again the discriminator constant.

The amplitude $b\omega(A_n/A_c)$ of this noise term is proportional to f, the frequency difference between the input noise term at $f_c + f$ and the unmodulated carrier at frequency f_c cps (Fig. 6-12). The noise terms in the i-f amplifier which are farther away from the carrier produce a greater frequency deviation and hence a larger voltage at the output of the discriminator.

The mean noise power at the discriminator output, due to this one noise component, is simply

$$dN_o = \frac{b^2\omega^2}{2}\left(\frac{A_n}{A_c}\right)^2 \tag{6-90}$$

Since $A_n^2/2 = \eta\, df$ by assumption,

$$dN_o = \left(\frac{b\omega}{A_c}\right)^2 \eta\, df \tag{6-91}$$

where dN_o/df represents the power spectral density of FM noise at the discriminator output and is quadratic in f. This is to be contrasted with the constant spectral density (white noise) assumed at the i-f amplifier output. This is of course true only for large carrier-to-noise ratio.

The spectrum of the rms noise voltage is directly proportional to f and so is frequently referred to as being triangular in shape. The rms noise spectrum is shown sketched in Fig. 6-17. Also shown is the rms spectrum of white noise.

Knowing the output noise due to one noise component at i-f amplifier frequency $f_c + f$, we may now compute the *total* mean noise power at the output of the FM receiver. This total noise power is that contained within the passband, f_m, of the ideal low-pass filter which follows the discriminator. Because of the nonlinear properties of frequency modulation this power is in general difficult to compute. Under our assumption of large carrier-to-noise ratio, however, the frequency deviation due to any one noise component has been found to be very small. This narrowband-noise FM can be handled as a linear system (see Chap. 3), and superposition applies.

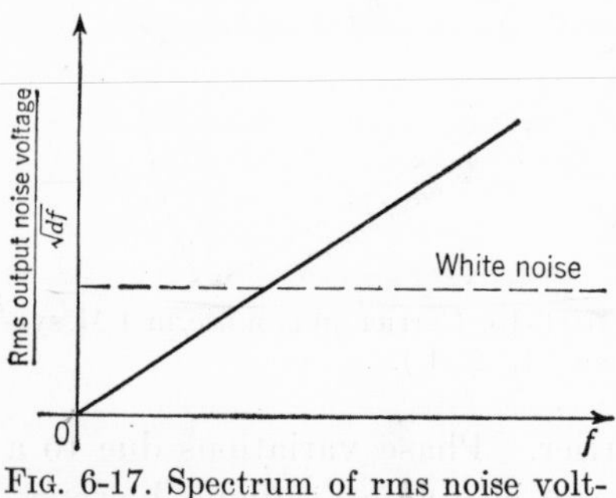

FIG. 6-17. Spectrum of rms noise voltage, output of FM discriminator.

We can thus determine the total output noise power by summing the power contributions of the input noise components. Again as in the AM case both sidebands about the carrier contribute equally, and the different noise components are assumed independent. We are essentially neglecting output noise due to the modulation of one noise component by another. We assume that for large carrier-to-noise ratio the only significant noise components in the output are those due to the modulation of the carrier by the noise.

The total noise power at the output is then given by

$$N_o = \int_{-f_m}^{f_m} dN_o = \eta \left(\frac{b}{A_c}\right)^2 \int_{-f_m}^{f_m} \omega^2 \, df \tag{6-92}$$

from Eq. (6-91). f varies from $-f_m$ to f_m because of equal contributions from both sidebands. Because of the low-pass filter only those input noise components within $\pm f_m$ cps of f_c contribute to the output.

Integrating (6-92), we get

$$N_o = \frac{2\eta}{3}\left(\frac{b}{A_c}\right)^2 (\omega_m)^2 f_m \qquad \omega_m = 2\pi f_m \tag{6-93}$$

But $A_c^2/2 = S_c$ is the mean carrier power [Eq. (6-81]. The mean output noise power can thus be written

$$N_o = \frac{\eta b^2}{3S_c} (\omega_m)^2 f_m \qquad (6\text{-}94)$$

By using Eq. (6-84), the expression for the output signal power (the signal is assumed to be a cosine wave with noise absent), the mean S/N power ratio at the output becomes

$$\frac{S_o}{N_o} = 3 \left(\frac{\Delta\omega}{\omega_m}\right)^2 \frac{S_c}{2\eta f_m} \qquad (6\text{-}95)$$

But $2\eta f_m = N_c$, the average noise power in the AM sidebands, and $\beta = \Delta\omega/\omega_m$ is the modulation index. Then

$$\frac{S_o}{N_o} = 3\beta^2 \frac{S_c}{N_c} \qquad (6\text{-}96)$$

Note that S_c/N_c corresponds to the carrier-to-noise ratio of an *AM system* with the same carrier power and noise spectral density. The total noise power over the transmission bandwidth $2B$ of the FM system is greater than N_c since $B > f_m$.

For a specified carrier amplitude and noise spectral density at the i-f amplifier output Eq. (6-96) shows that the output S/N increases with the modulation index or the transmission bandwidth. This is in contrast to the AM case, where increasing the bandwidth beyond $2f_m$ was found only to deteriorate the output S/N.

We may specifically compare the FM and AM systems by assuming the same unmodulated carrier power and noise spectral density η for both. (These quantities are measured here at the output of the i-f amplifier.) For a 100 per cent modulated AM signal we have

$$\left(\frac{S_o}{N_o}\right)_{\text{AM}} = \frac{S_c}{N_c}$$

Equation (6-96) may thus be modified to read

$$\left(\frac{S_o}{N_o}\right)_{\text{FM}} = 3\beta^2 \left(\frac{S_o}{N_o}\right)_{\text{AM}} \qquad (6\text{-}97)$$

For large modulation index (this corresponds to a wide transmission bandwidth; for, with $\beta \gg 1$, the bandwidth approaches $2\,\Delta f$) we can presumably increase S_o/N_o significantly over the AM case. As an example, if $\beta = 5$, the FM output S/N is 75 times that of an equivalent AM system. Alternatively for the same S/N at the output in both receivers the power of the FM carrier may be reduced 75 times. But this requires increasing the transmission bandwidth from $2f_m$ (AM case) to $16\,f_m$ (FM case; see Fig. 3-27). Frequency modulation thus provides a substantial improvement in S/N, but at the expense of increased bandwidth. This, we shall see, is a characteristic of all noise-improvement systems.

Can we keep increasing the output S/N indefinitely by increasing the frequency deviation and hence the bandwidth? If we keep the transmitter power fixed, S_c is fixed. With the noise power per unit bandwidth (η) fixed and the audio signal bandwidth f_m fixed, N_c presumably remains constant, *but*, as the frequency deviation increases and the bandwidth with it, more noise must be accepted by the limiter. Eventually the noise power at the limiter becomes comparable to the signal power. The above simplified analysis, which assumes large carrier-to-noise power ratios, does not hold any more, and noise is found to "take over" the system.

This effect is found to depend very sharply upon FM carrier-to-noise ratio and is called a *threshold* effect. For this ratio greater than a specified threshold value FM functions properly and shows the significant improvement in S/N predicted by Eq. (6-97).[1] For the ratio below this threshold level the noise improvement is found to deteriorate rapidly, and Eq. (6-97) no longer holds. The actual threshold level depends upon the FM carrier-to-noise ratio and upon β. For large β the level is usually taken as a carrier-to-noise ratio of 20:1, or 13 db.

This *threshold* phenomenon is a characteristic of all wideband noise-improvement systems. We shall encounter it again in discussing PCM.

Two conditions must thus ordinarily be satisfied for an FM system to show significant noise-"quieting" properties:

1. Frequency-modulation carrier-to-noise ratio > 13 db to avoid the threshold effect.

2. With FM carrier-to-noise ratio > 13 db, $\beta > 1/\sqrt{3}$ if $S_o/N_o > S_c/N_c$ [see Eq. (6-97)].

But $\beta > 1\sqrt{3} \doteq 0.6$ corresponds to the transition between narrowband and wideband FM. *Narrowband FM thus provides no S/N improvement over AM.* This is of course as expected, for the improvement is specifically the result of restricting the noise phase deviations of the carrier to small values, while the signal variations are assumed to be large.

Experimental studies of FM noise characteristics show the threshold phenomenon very strikingly and also bear out the validity of Eq. (6-97) above the threshold value. Figure 6-18 is taken from some experimental work of M. G. Crosby[2] and shows a comparison of AM and FM receivers for $\beta = 4$ and $\beta = 1$. Note that for $\beta = 4$ the FM signal-to-noise ratio deteriorates rapidly for $S_c/N_c < 15$ db. In fact, for $S_c/N_c < 8$ db, the

[1] Black, *op. cit.;* M. G. Crosby, Frequency Modulation Noise Characteristics, *Proc. IRE*, vol. 25, pp. 472–514, April, 1937.

[2] Crosby, *ibid.*, fig. 10.

AM system becomes superior. For $S_c/N_c > 15$ db, however, the FM system shows an improvement of 14 db. For $\beta = 4$ we would expect the theoretical improvement to be $3\beta^2 = 48$, or 17 db. For $\beta = 1$ the threshold level is experimentally found to occur at 2 db. Above this value of AM carrier-to-noise ratio the FM improvement over AM is 3 db. The theoretical improvement would be expected to be $3\beta^2 = 3$, or 4.8 db.

Signal-to-Noise Improvement through Deemphasis. We showed, in Chap. 3, that the transmission bandwidth of an FM system is determined

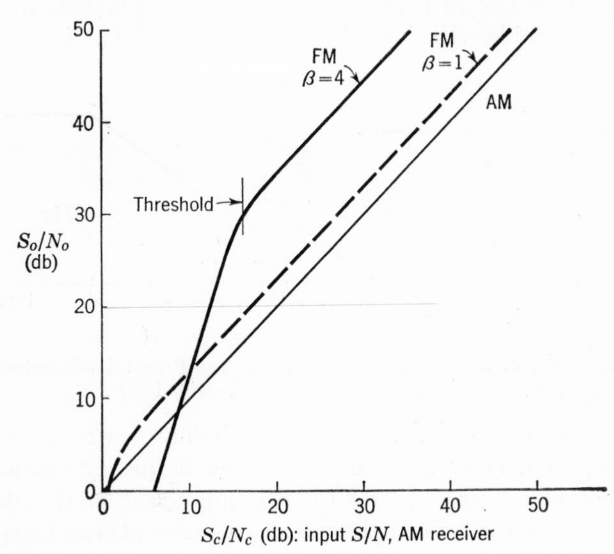

FIG. 6-18. Measured characteristics, FM and AM receivers. (*Adapted from M. G. Crosby, Frequency Modulation Noise Characteristics, Proc. IRE, vol. 25, pp. 472–514, fig. 10, April, 1937, by permission.*)

by the maximum frequency deviation Δf produced by the highest modulating frequency f_m to be transmitted. In particular, for $f_m = 15$ kc and a maximum frequency deviation Δf of 75 kc, we found that the required bandwidth was 240 kc.

In practice the higher-frequency components of the modulating signal rarely attain the amplitudes needed to produce a 75-kc frequency deviation. Audio signals of speech and music are found to have most of their energy concentrated in the lower-frequency ranges. The instantaneous signal amplitude, limited to that required to give the 75-kc deviation, is due most of the time to the lower-frequency components of the signal. The smaller-amplitude high-frequency (h-f) components will, on the average, provide a much smaller frequency deviation. The FM signal thus does not fully occupy the large bandwidth assigned to it.

The spectrum of the noise introduced at the receiver does, however, occupy the entire FM bandwidth. In fact, as we have just noted, the noise-power spectrum at the output of the discriminator is emphasized at the higher frequencies. (The spectrum is proportional to f^2 for large carrier-to-noise ratio.)

This gives us a clue as to a possible procedure for improving the S/N ratio at the discriminator output: we can artificially *emphasize* the h-f components of our input audio signal at the transmitter, *before the noise is introduced*, to the point where they produce a 75-kc deviation most of the time. This *equalizes* in a sense the l-f and h-f portions of the audio spectrum and enables the signal fully to occupy the bandwidth assigned.

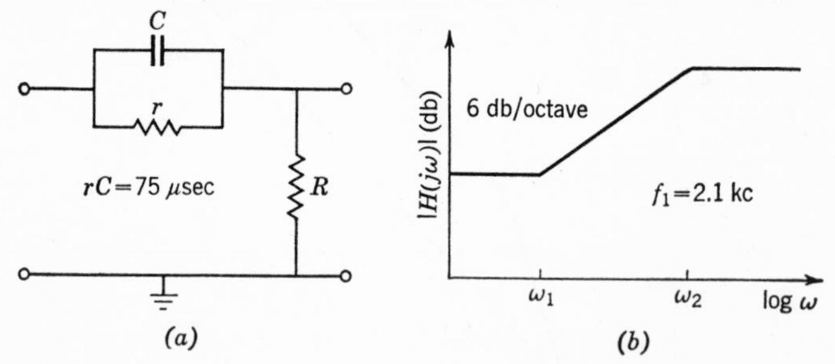

FIG. 6-19. Example of a preemphasis network. (*a*) Preemphasis network, $r \gg R$, $rC = 75$ μsec; (*b*) asymptotic response, $\omega_1 = 1/rC$, $\omega_2 \doteq 1/RC$.

Then, at the output of the receiver discriminator, we can perform the inverse operation, or *deemphasize* the higher-frequency components, to restore the original signal-power distribution. But in this deemphasis process we reduce the h-f components of the noise also and so effectively increase the S/N ratio.

Such a preemphasis and deemphasis process is commonly used in FM transmission and reception and provides, as we shall see, 13 to 16 db of noise improvement. Note that this procedure is a simple example of a signal-processing scheme which utilizes differences in the characteristics of the signal and the noise to process the signal more efficiently. The entire FM process is itself an example of a much more complex processing scheme in which use is made of the fact that random noise alters the instantaneous frequency of a carrier much less than it does the amplitude of the carrier (for large carrier-to-noise ratio). The noise-improvement properties of PPM and PCM, considered later in this chapter, are again due to differences in the characteristics of random noise and signal.

A simple frequency transfer function that emphasizes the high frequencies and has been found very effective in practice is given by

$$H(j\omega) = 1 + j\frac{\omega}{\omega_1} \tag{6-98}$$

An example of an RC network that approximates this response very closely is shown in Fig. 6-19a. The asymptotic logarithmic amplitude-frequency plot for this network is shown in Fig. 6-19b.

With $r \gg R$ the amplitude response has two break frequencies given by $\omega_1 = 1/rC$ and $\omega_2 \doteq 1/RC$. Signals in the range between ω_1 and ω_2 are thus emphasized. (Actually the higher-frequency components are passed unaltered, and the lower-frequency components are attenuated. The attenuation can of course be made up by amplification.) The choice of $f_1 = \omega_1/2\pi$ is not critical, but 2.1 kc is ordinarily used in practice

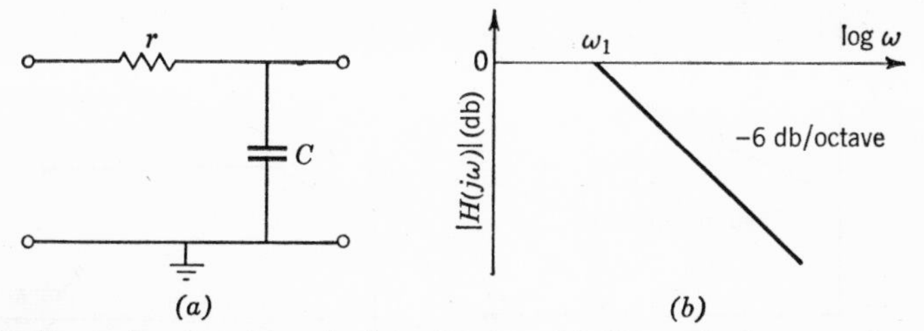

FIG. 6-20. Example of a deemphasis network. (a) Deemphasis network, $rC = 75$ μsec; (b) asymptotic response, $f_1 = 2.1$ kc.

($rC = 75$ μsec). $f_2 = \omega_2/2\pi$ should lie above the highest audio frequency to be transmitted. $f_2 \geq 30$ kc is a typical number. In the range between these two frequencies $|H(j\omega)|^2 \doteq 1 + (f/f_1)^2$, and all audio frequencies above 2.1 kc are increasingly emphasized.

The receiver deemphasis network, following the discriminator, must have the inverse characteristic given by

$$H(j\omega) = \frac{1}{1 + jf/f_1} \tag{6-99}$$

with $f_1 = 2.1$ kc as before. This then serves to restore all signals to their original relative values. The simple RC network of Fig. 6-20 ($rC = 75$ μsec) provides this deemphasis characteristic. (Note incidentally that the two networks are identical with the lead and lag networks, respectively, of the servomechanisms and feedback amplifier fields.)

How much does the deemphasis network improve the S/N ratio at the discriminator output?

From Eq. (6-91) of the FM noise analysis, the two-sided noise spectral density at the discriminator output can be written (for large carrier-to-noise ratio)

$$G'(\omega) = \frac{dN_o}{df} = \frac{b^2\eta\omega^2}{A_c^2} = \frac{b^2\eta\omega^2}{2S_c} \tag{6-100}$$

where b is the discriminator constant, η the input noise spectral density,

A_c the carrier amplitude, and $S_c = A_c^2/2$ the mean carrier power at the discriminator input.

If this noise is now passed through the RC deemphasis network of Fig. 6-20, the modified spectral density at the network output is

$$G'_H(\omega) = G'(\omega)|H(j\omega)|^2 = \frac{b^2\eta\omega^2}{2S_c}\frac{1}{1+(f/f_1)^2} \tag{6-101}$$

The original noise-power spectrum $G(\omega)$ at the output of the discriminator and the modified spectrum $G_H(\omega)$ are shown sketched in the

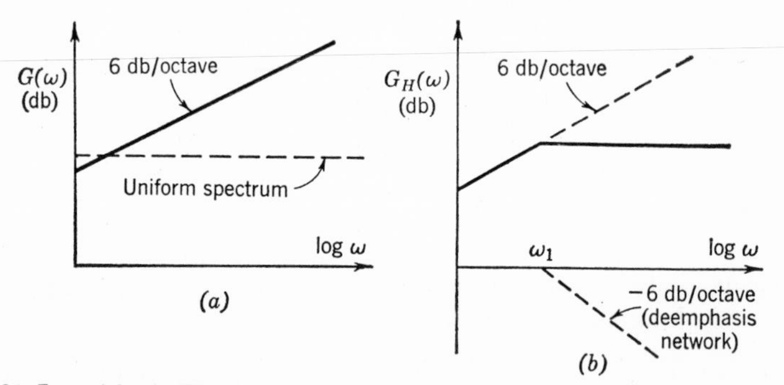

FIG. 6-21. Logarithmic FM noise-power spectrum: output of discriminator ($S_c \gg N_c$). (*a*) Spectrum without deemphasis; (*b*) spectrum with deemphasis.

logarithmic plots of Fig. 6-21. (Only the one-sided spectra, defined for positive f only, are shown because of the logarithmic plots.)

Note that for $f > f_1$ the noise spectrum with deemphasis included becomes a uniform spectrum: the deemphasis network has canceled out the ω^2 (increasing noise frequency) factor of Eq. (6-100).

The total mean noise power at the output of an ideal low-pass filter of bandwidth f_m cps is given by

$$\begin{aligned} N_{oD} &= \int_{-f_m}^{f_m} G'_H(\omega)\,df \\ &= \int_{-f_m}^{f_m} \frac{b^2\eta\omega^2}{2S_c}\frac{df}{1+(f/f_1)^2} \end{aligned} \tag{6-102}$$

where N_{oD} represents the mean noise power with the deemphasis network included, as compared with the symbol N_o used previously for the noise power with no deemphasis network.

Equation (6-102) is readily integrated to give

$$N_{oD} = \frac{\eta b^2}{2\pi S_c}\,\omega_1^3\left(\frac{f_m}{f_1} - \tan^{-1}\frac{f_m}{f_1}\right) \tag{6-103}$$

Multiplying numerator and denominator by $3/\omega_m^3$, and recalling from

Eq. (6-94) that $N_o = \frac{\eta b^2}{2\pi S_c} \frac{\omega_m{}^3}{3}$, the mean noise power can be written in the form

$$N_{oD} = N_o D \tag{6-104}$$

where

$$D = 3\left(\frac{f_1}{f_m}\right)^3 \left(\frac{f_m}{f_1} - \tan^{-1}\frac{f_m}{f_1}\right) \tag{6-105}$$

The parameter D represents the effect of the deemphasis network and is readily seen to be less than or equal to 1 in value. The deemphasis network thus reduces the output noise. For $f_m \ll f_1$ (the deemphasis effect is then introduced beyond the range of the low-pass filter) $D \to 1$, as is to be expected. For $f_m \gg f_1$, $\tan^{-1}(f_m/f_1) \to \pi/2$, and

$$D \to 3\left(\frac{f_1}{f_m}\right)^2 \qquad f_1 \ll f_m \tag{6-106}$$

The output noise power thus decreases rapidly with increasing f_m.

Increasing f_m indefinitely provides no *absolute* improvement in the output noise, however, for N_o increases as $f_m{}^3$. The output filter bandwidth f_m should thus be restricted to just the bandwidth required to pass the highest audio frequency and no more.

With $f_1 = 2.1$ kc, as noted previously, and $f_m = 15$ kc, $D = 1/20$. The noise is thus reduced by a factor of 20, or 13 db. If $f_m = 10f_1 = 21$ kc, the improvement due to the deemphasis network is 16 db.

The signal power at the output of the discriminator is $S_o = b^2(\Delta\omega)^2/2$ [Eq. (6-84)], for a single sine wave, independent of the preemphasis and deemphasis procedure. The S/N ratio with deemphasis is thus

$$\frac{S_o}{N_{oD}} = \frac{1}{D}\frac{S_o}{N_o} = \frac{3\beta^2}{D}\frac{S_c}{N_c} \tag{6-107}$$

The signal-to-noise improvement in decibels is the same as the noise reduction: 13 db for $f_m = 15$ kc, 16 db for $f_m = 21$ kc.

Preemphasis and deemphasis techniques are obviously not restricted to FM only. They are possible because the audio signals to be transmitted in practice are concentrated at the low end of the spectrum. All modulation systems can thus use deemphasis techniques to improve the S/N ratio at the receiver output.

As an example, consider AM. Here we showed that for large carrier-to-noise ratio ($S_c \gg N_c$) the noise-power spectrum at the detector output was uniform (Fig. 6-13). In particular

$$G'(\omega) = a^2\eta \qquad \text{watts/cps} \tag{6-108}$$

at the detector output, where a is the detector constant and η the input spectral density.

Using the preemphasis and deemphasis networks of the FM analysis,

$$G'_H(\omega) = G'(\omega)|H(j\omega)|^2 = \frac{a^2\eta}{(1 + f/f_1)^2} \tag{6-109}$$

is the spectral density at the output of the deemphasis network. Both $G(\omega)$ and $G_H(\omega)$ are sketched in Fig. 6-22. The total mean noise power at

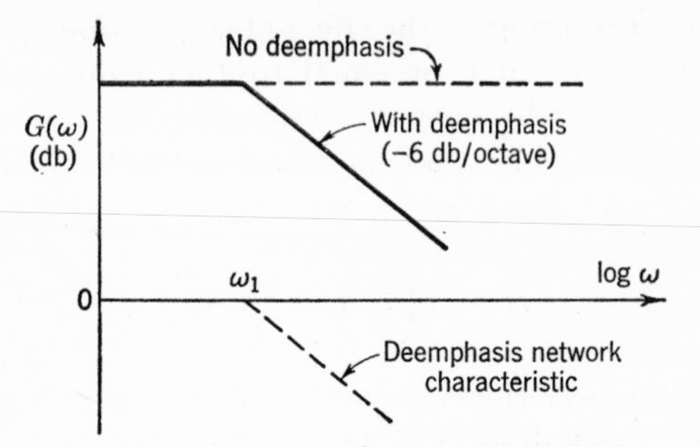

FIG. 6-22. Amplitude-modulation spectral density, detector output ($S_c \gg N_c$).

the output of an ideal low-pass filter of bandwidth f_m is

$$\begin{aligned} N_{oD} &= \int_{-f_m}^{f_m} G'_H(\omega)\, df \\ &= 2a^2\eta f_1 \tan^{-1}\frac{f_m}{f_1} \\ &= N_o D' \end{aligned} \tag{6-110}$$

where $N_o = a^2\eta(2f_m)$ is again the mean noise power with no deemphasis network and

$$D' = \frac{f_1}{f_m}\tan^{-1}\frac{f_m}{f_1} \tag{6-111}$$

is the improvement factor due to deemphasis in the AM case.

For $f_m \ll f_1$, $D' \rightarrow 1$, so that there is no improvement in this case (the filter bandwidth is well within the deemphasis range). For $f_m/f_1 \gg 1$, $\tan^{-1}(f_m/f_1) \doteq \pi/2$, and

$$D' \doteq \frac{\pi}{2}\frac{f_1}{f_m} \qquad \frac{f_m}{f_1} \gg 1 \tag{6-112}$$

The noise power thus decreases inversely with the filter bandwidth f_m. In the FM case the noise power decreased inversely as the square of the bandwidth [Eq. (6-106)], so that the *RC* deemphasis network provides relatively greater improvement for FM than for AM.

As an example, if $f_1 = 2.1$ kc and $f_m = 15$ kc, D' is 6 db for the AM case and D is 13 db for the FM case. With $f_m = 21$ kc, D' is 8 db for AM, while D is 16 db for FM. For $f_m = 5$ kc, $D' = 3$ db.

Although this deemphasis technique is not as efficient for AM as for FM, it still would provide some S/N improvement. Why then has it not been adopted for AM systems? Several reasons can be listed:[1] Its use would require modification of all existing receivers. Emphasizing the higher-frequency sidebands would increase interference between adjacent AM channels. An increase in m, the modulation factor, at higher audio frequencies would put severe requirements on detector design.

Deemphasis networks are commonly used in FM receivers, however, with the corresponding preemphasis networks built into the audio section of FM transmitters. The same "equalization" principle is also used quite commonly in sound recording to reduce "scratch."

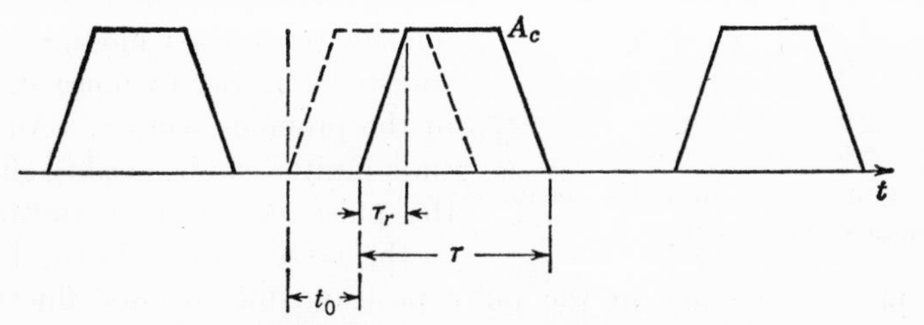

FIG. 6-23. Pulse-position-modulation pulse train.

6-4. Signal-to-Noise Ratio in PPM. The PPM system described qualitatively in Sec. 4-9 can be considered the pulse-modulation analogue of a phase-modulation or frequency-modulation system. Here information is transmitted by displacement of the positions of the train of pulses constituting the carrier. Since the pulses are maintained at fixed width and amplitude, the positional information is also carried by the location of the leading edge of a pulse or by the point of zero crossing of the leading edge.

A train of unmodulated trapezoidal pulses is shown in Fig. 6-23 (compare with Figs. 4-28 and 4-30). A_c represents the fixed amplitude of these pulses. (This corresponds to the constant amplitude of the carrier in FM.) τ is the pulse width, τ_r the pulse rise time. In the Federal Telephone Laboratories PPM system described in Sec. 4-9 a pulse width of 0.8 μsec and pulse rise time of 0.15 μsec are used. t_o represents the maximum modulation displacement in any one direction away from the unmodulated position of the pulse. The maximum displacement in the Federal Telephone Laboratories system is 1 μsec (see Fig. 4-28). Thus, if the modulating signal is a sinusoidal test signal of frequency f_m cps and of maximum amplitude, the corresponding position of the pulse will vary sinusoidally in time about the unmodulated pulse location following

[1] L. B. Arguimbau and R. D. Stuart, "Frequency Modulation," p. 5, Methuen & Co., Ltd., London, 1956.

the equation $t_0 \cos \omega_m t$. This corresponds of course to a sinusoidal phase modulation of the carrier in a phase-modulation system, or to the $\Delta\omega \cos \omega_m t$ frequency displacement in FM.

For such a sinusoidal test signal the rms time displacement of the pulse (or its leading edge) is $t_0/\sqrt{2}$ sec. An ideal converter in the output of a PPM receiver converts these pulse-position variations to voltage variations given by $Kt_0 \cos \omega_m t$, with K a constant of proportionality of the converter.

If noise is now superimposed on the pulse, the pulse amplitude and the point of zero crossing will both be perturbed (Fig. 6-24). This corresponds to the amplitude and frequency (or phase) modulation of a sinusoidal carrier by noise, discussed in the previous section. An amplitude limiter can be used to eliminate the pulse-amplitude variations due to the noise, just as in the FM system. The uncertainty in the pulse position due to noise fluctuations remains, however, and gives rise to a noise voltage at the output of the converter.

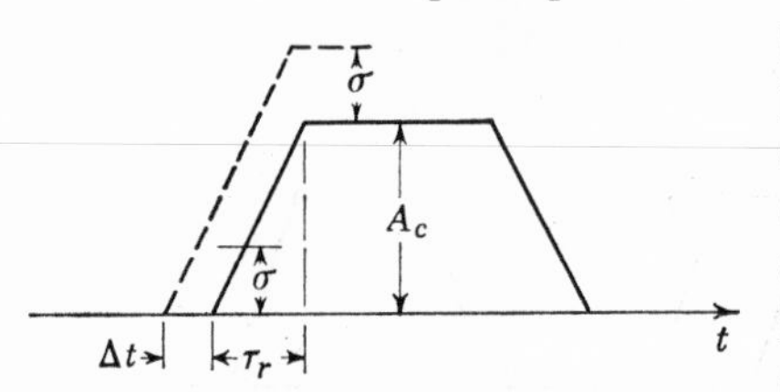

FIG. 6-24. Variation in pulse position due to noise or interference.

If the mean noise power is small compared with the average pulse power and the noise varies slowly over the rise-time portion of the pulse, the pulse perturbation may be represented as in Fig. 6-24. Since we are eventually interested in a mean signal-to-noise ratio at the converter output, we represent the amplitude of the noise voltage over the time interval shown by the rms noise voltage σ and assume this voltage constant over the pulse rise time. The corresponding rms error in determining the pulse location will be Δt sec. (This is of course the same procedure adopted in the previous section, where, for large carrier-to-noise ratio, we approximated the fluctuating noise voltage by a constant-amplitude voltage of the same rms value. The actual noise voltage will normally vary randomly about a zero average value, as pointed out in Chap. 5. The rms noise voltage, evaluated over a long time interval, then serves as a measure of the amount of noise present.)

Figure 6-24 indicates that the rms positional error Δt may be reduced by increasing the slope of the pulse leading edge. For a given mean noise power the noise effect may be minimized by using pulses with sharply defined leading edges. But this requires either decreasing the rise time, correspondingly *widening* the transmission *bandwidth*, or increasing the pulse amplitude A_c. We thus see that, just as in the FM case, an exchange of input signal to noise for bandwidth is possible: here decreasing the rise time (or increasing bandwidth) enables a smaller amplitude pulse to be used for a given rms positional error. This is obviously not possible in a PAM system, where the amplitude alone carries the signal information.

We can obtain a simple expression for output signal-to-noise ratio by assuming the same conditions as in the FM-AM analysis: the mean output noise power is evaluated in the absence of a signal and under the assumption of large carrier-to-noise ratio. The output signal power is calculated under noise-free conditions and for a sinusoidal test signal of maximum amplitude. The signal-to-noise ratio is then defined to be the ratio of these two quantities.

The rms output signal voltage is simply $Kt_0/\sqrt{2}$ in terms of the preceding notation. The rms output noise voltage due to the rms positional displacement Δt will similarly be $K\,\Delta t$ at the output of the converter. The S/N power ratio at the converter output is then

$$\frac{S_o}{N_o} = \left(\frac{t_0/\sqrt{2}}{\Delta t}\right)^2 \tag{6-113}$$

From Fig. 6-24 we get the simple relation

$$\frac{\Delta t}{\tau_r} = \frac{\sigma}{A_c} \tag{6-114}$$

valid for $A_c \gg \sigma$, and in the absence of a signal. Substituting for Δt in Eq. (6-113), the output S/N is given by

$$\frac{S_o}{N_o} = \frac{1}{2}\left(\frac{t_0}{\tau_r}\right)^2\left(\frac{A_c}{\sigma}\right)^2 \tag{6-115}$$

But $(A_c/\sigma)^2$ is the ratio of peak pulse power to mean noise power and is analogous to the carrier-to-noise power ratio of the previous section. Using the same symbols as used there,

$$\frac{S_c}{N_c} \equiv \left(\frac{A_c}{\sigma}\right)^2$$

and

$$\frac{S_o}{N_o} = \frac{1}{2}\left(\frac{t_0}{\tau_r}\right)^2\frac{S_c}{N_c} \tag{6-116}$$

The term S_c/N_c may also be considered the effective signal-to-noise ratio of a PAM system.

Equation (6-116) indicates very simply the improvement in S_o/N_o possible in a PPM system by decreasing the pulse rise time τ_r or correspondingly widening the transmission bandwidth.

If the relation $B = 1/\tau_r$,† as developed in Chap. 2, is used to represent the system bandwidth necessary to pass the trapezoidal pulses chosen,

† This is the video bandwidth. A sinusoidal carrier amplitude-modulated with these pulses would require twice this bandwidth.

the output S/N ratio becomes

$$\frac{S_o}{N_o} = \tfrac{1}{2} t_0^2 B^2 \frac{S_c}{N_c} \tag{6-117}$$

The power ratio S_o/N_o is thus proportional to B^2, just as in the FM case [Eq. (6-97)]. If $B = \tfrac{1}{2}\tau_r$ is used instead,

$$\frac{S_o}{N_o} = 2 t_0^2 B^2 \frac{S_c}{N_c} \tag{6-118}$$

As an example, we can evaluate the S/N improvement possible for the Federal Telephone Laboratories PPM system of Sec. 4-9 as compared with a PAM system. With $t_0 = 1$ μsec and $\tau_r = 0.15$ μsec, $S_o/N_o = 22 S_c/N_c$. With these numbers the S/N is improved by 13 db. The bandwidth required is correspondingly increased, however.

A PAM system incorporating the same 24 channels, each sampled at the same 8-kc rate, could conceivably utilize the full 5 μsec between samples for each channel pulse. The minimum bandwidth required for the system would then be approximately 200 kc. For the PPM system 2.8 Mc is specified as the system bandwidth. The improvement in S/N has thus been obtained at the expense of increased bandwidth, just as in the FM case. (Note again that the bandwidths referred to are the bandwidths required to transmit the d-c pulses. Intermediate-frequency amplifiers of twice these bandwidths would be required if the pulses amplitude-modulated a sinusoidal carrier.)

Assuming the system bandwidth unlimited, can we improve S_o/N_o indefinitely? As previously, the noise power introduced at the receiver increases with bandwidth. Eventually the noise becomes comparable to the signal, the zero crossings become completely erratic, and the noise "takes over," or "recaptures," the system. A threshold level thus also exists, just as in the FM case. The carrier-to-noise ratio S_c/N_c must be much larger than the threshold value for the wideband improvement to work. This threshold level is usually taken as $A_c/\sigma = 2$, or $S_c/N_c = 4$ (6 db).

Again as in the FM case equalizing networks may be utilized to improve further the S/N properties of PPM systems designed to transmit speech and music.

6-5. Wideband Noise-improvement Systems: Coded and Uncoded Types. We have shown that for both FM and PPM an improvement in output S/N is possible by increasing the transmission bandwidth. The actual expressions for output-power S/N were found to be

1. FM:
$$\frac{S_o}{N_o} = 3\beta^2 \frac{S_c}{N_c} \tag{6-119}$$

2. PPM:
$$\frac{S_o}{N_o} = \frac{1}{2}\left(\frac{t_0}{\tau_r}\right)^2 \frac{S_c}{N_c} \tag{6-120}$$

The FM modulation index β is proportional to the frequency deviation Δf, which in turn is one-half the i-f bandwidth for large β. The bandwidth required in a PPM system is proportional to $1/\tau_r$, so that for both FM and PPM the improvement in the power S/N ratio is proportional to the square of the bandwidth. The voltage S/N ratio improves linearly with bandwidth in both cases. This linear improvement in voltage S/N with bandwidth may be emphasized more specifically, and the S/N expressions for FM and PPM written in comparable form, by writing $\beta = \Delta f/f_m = 2B/2f_m$ ($\beta \gg 1$) in the FM case and $1/\tau_r = B$ in the PPM case. B is then the frequency bandwidth (in cycles per second) required for PPM transmission, and $2B$ cps for FM transmission. In addition, for a *single-channel* PPM system, the minimum spacing between pulses is the Nyquist sampling interval $1/2f_m$, with f_m the maximum-frequency component of the signal to be transmitted. For this *single-channel* system the maximum modulation displacement t_0 is just one-half the sampling interval, assuming $t_0 \gg \tau$, the pulse width, and assuming no guard time between pulses. Thus

$$t_0 \doteq \frac{1}{4f_m} \tag{6-121}$$

In terms of bandwidth, the rms-voltage S/N ratios at the system output become

1. FM:

$$\frac{S_{ov}}{N_{ov}} = \sqrt{3}\,\frac{\beta S_{cv}}{N_{cv}} = \frac{2\sqrt{3}B}{2f_m}\,\frac{S_{cv}}{N_{cv}} \tag{6-122}$$

2. Single-channel PPM:

$$\frac{S_{ov}}{N_{ov}} = \frac{t_o/\sqrt{2}}{\tau_r}\,\frac{S_{cv}}{N_{cv}} = \frac{B}{4\sqrt{2}f_m}\,\frac{S_{cv}}{N_{cv}} \tag{6-123}$$

[$S_o/N_o = (S_{ov}/N_{ov})^2$; $S_c/N_c = (S_{cv}/N_{cv})^2$. Also, $S_{cv} = A_c$, $N_{cv} = \sigma$ in the PPM case.] For the normal multichannel system t_0 would be defined differently.

In both cases, then, the output-voltage S/N is linearly proportional to the ratio of transmission bandwidth to signal bandwidth, f_m. The larger the ratio of B/f_m, the greater the S/N improvement, *provided* that the input S/N always exceeds a specified threshold level.

The wide transmission bandwidths required (compared with f_m) are specifically the result of processing the signal in such a manner as to enable it to be better detected in the presence of noise. The two distinct bandwidths required, f_m cps for initially passing the signal at the transmitter input and for filtering it back out at the receiver output and B cps (or $2B$ cps for the FM signal) for actually transmitting the processed or modulated signal, with $B > f_m$, are characteristic of wideband noise-improvement systems in general. A simple block diagram summarizing the general characteristics of a wideband information-transmission system is shown in Fig. 6-25.

The signal initially requires f_m cps bandwidth. After processing or modulation the bandwidth required for transmission is B cps. (For an FM signal, or a PPM signal amplitude-modulating a sinusoidal carrier, this would be $2B$ cps.) Noise is introduced during transmission and reception, and S_c/N_c represents the receiver signal-to-noise ratio. Detection of the signal and filtering, again with a bandwidth of f_m cps, reproduce the original signal with noise added. S_o/N_o is the signal-to-noise ratio at this point. The narrowband filtering ($f_m < B$) reduces the noise effect, so that $S_o/N_o > S_c/N_c$.

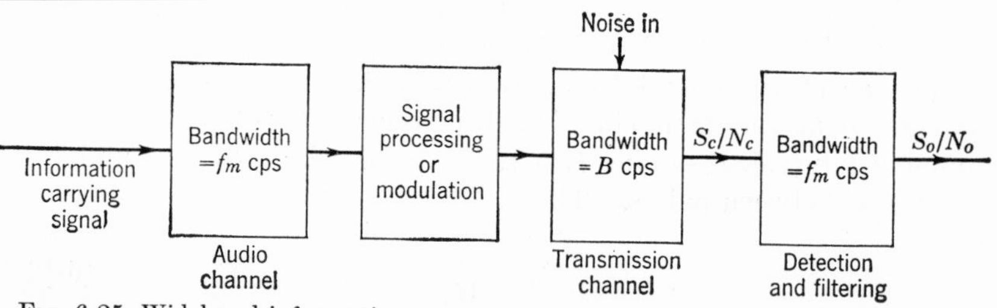

FIG. 6-25. Wideband information-transmission system. $B > f_m$; $S_0/N_0 > S_c/N_c$.

For AM and PAM systems $B = f_m$ [or $2f_m$ if radio-frequency (r-f) bandwidths are considered], and no noise improvement with bandwidth is possible. For both these cases $S_o/N_o = S_c/N_c$.

Both FM and PPM systems are examples of *uncoded*, or analogue-type, signal-transmission systems with a one-to-one correspondence between the input signal and the modulated carrier eventually transmitted. The rms noise improvement is linearly proportional to B/f_m in both cases, and we may write

$$\frac{S_{ov}}{N_{ov}} = K\frac{B}{f_m}\frac{S_{cv}}{N_{cv}} \tag{6-124}$$

where K is a constant, for both systems.

Information transmission is also possible by so-called *coded*, or digital-type, transmission systems. Pulse-code modulation is an example of such a system, as we shall see shortly. For these coded systems bandwidth widening also improves the output signal-to-noise ratio, but the improvement is *exponential* with bandwidth, rather than linear as expressed by Eq. (6-124). Such systems are thus inherently capable of better transmission efficiency than the uncoded types, as represented by FM, PPM, and other examples. In these coded systems the signal voltage, usually continuous in form, must first be converted into discrete or digital form. A discrete signal voltage can then be coded or transformed into a number of signal symbols uniquely representing the signal.

The representation of a signal by a discrete number of voltage levels in Chap. 1 is an example of such a coding process. We can demonstrate the exponential improvement of S_{ov}/N_{ov} with bandwidth for such a hypothetical system quite simply.[1] We shall then go on to a discussion of PCM as an example of an actual system utilizing coding techniques for transmission.

In Chap. 1 we developed a relation for the rate of information transmission, or the information capacity, of a system. For signals given in the form of equally likely voltage levels (Fig. 1-2) we showed that the capacity could be defined by the expression

$$C = \frac{1}{\tau} \log_2 n \qquad \text{bits/sec} \tag{6-125}$$

where τ is the minimum response time of the system and n the number of distinguishable voltage levels. As indicated in Sec. 5-14 n can be related to the voltage signal-to-noise ratio and τ to the system bandwidth. The capacity expression can then be written, as shown in Eq. (5-162), in the form

$$C = B \log_2 \left(1 + \frac{S_v}{N_v}\right) \tag{6-126}$$

where B is the system bandwidth and S_v/N_v the voltage signal-to-noise ratio.

Now assume that such a sequence of discrete voltage levels are transmitted through the system of Fig. 6-25. The capacity of the system, in bits per second, is assumed everywhere the same (there is no "pile-up" of information anywhere), or the information per second emerging at the system output is the same as that going in.

We assume that initially, when first introduced into the system, the sequence of voltage levels requires f_m cps bandwidth for transmission. Before actually transmitting the different levels, however, we assume that they are encoded in some form so as to require B cps for transmission. We shall demonstrate a rather simple way of doing this in the section on PCM that follows. With an rms noise voltage, N_{cv} volts, introduced during transmission and reception the capacity at the receiver is given by

$$C = B \log_2 \left(1 + \frac{S_{cv}}{N_{cv}}\right) \qquad \text{bits/sec}$$

from Eq. (6-126).

At the output of the receiver the coded signals must be encoded back into the original voltage levels and passed through a filter of f_m cps band-

[1] W. G. Tuller, *Proc. IRE*, vol. 37, p. 468, 1949; M. Leifer and W. F. Schreiber, Communication Theory, summary chapter in L. Marton (ed.), "Advances in Electronics," vol. III, pp. 305–343, Academic Press, Inc., New York, 1951.

width. After doing this an rms-voltage signal-to-noise ratio S_{ov}/N_{ov} results. The rate of information transmission at this point is now given by

$$C = f_m \log_2 \left(1 + \frac{S_{ov}}{N_{ov}}\right) \qquad \text{bits/sec}$$

Under our assumption of equal information capacity throughout the system we may equate the two expressions for system capacity to give

$$C = B \log_2 \left(1 + \frac{S_{cv}}{N_{cv}}\right) = f_m \log_2 \left(1 + \frac{S_{ov}}{N_{ov}}\right) \tag{6-127}$$

Solving for the output S/N,

$$1 + \frac{S_{ov}}{N_{ov}} = \left(1 + \frac{S_{cv}}{N_{cv}}\right)^{B/f_m} \tag{6-128}$$

or, for $S_{ov}/N_{ov} \gg 1$ and $S_{cv}/N_{cv} \gg 1$,

$$\frac{S_{ov}}{N_{ov}} \doteq \left(\frac{S_{cv}}{N_{cv}}\right)^{B/f_m} \tag{6-129}$$

If $B > f_m$, the output S/N increases exponentially with the ratio of the bandwidths. A hypothetical system of the type described thus gives theoretically much better S/N improvement with bandwidth than the FM or PPM systems. We shall return to a comparative discussion of the uncoded and coded types of systems after a discussion of the principles of PCM.

6-6. Pulse-code Modulation as an Example of a Coded System. Pulse-code modulation represents a practical embodiment of the rather hypothetical and somewhat vague system transmitting discrete voltage levels that was first introduced in Chap. 1 and referred to again in Chap. 5 and in the previous section.

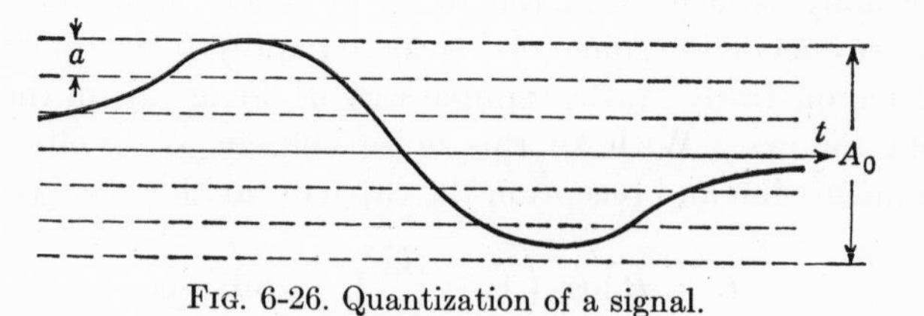

FIG. 6-26. Quantization of a signal.

In the two examples of pulse-modulation systems previously discussed —PAM and PPM—a signal to be transmitted was sampled and its instantaneous value at the sampling times used to modulate a train of pulses. Actually there is no need to transmit all possible signal amplitudes. Because of noise introduced during transmission and at the receiver the demodulator or detector circuit will not be able to distinguish fine variations in signal amplitude. In addition the ultimate recipient of the information, our ears in the case of sound or music, or our eyes in the case of a picture, is limited as to the fine gradation of signal it can distinguish.

Pulse-code modulation makes use of this ultimate limitation in distinguishing between all possible signal amplitudes by first breaking the signal up into a prescribed number of discrete amplitude levels. This is called the *quantization* process and produces a *quantized* signal. An example of a quantized signal is shown in Fig. 6-26. The levels are assumed separated a volts apart. (Pulse-code-modulation systems with variable level separation have been described in the literature and may be shown to give some S/N improvement. This is similar to the preemphasis and deemphasis technique discussed previously. We shall concentrate on uniform quantization, however.) For a total amplitude variation of A_0 volts there will be $s = A_0/a$ quantizing levels.

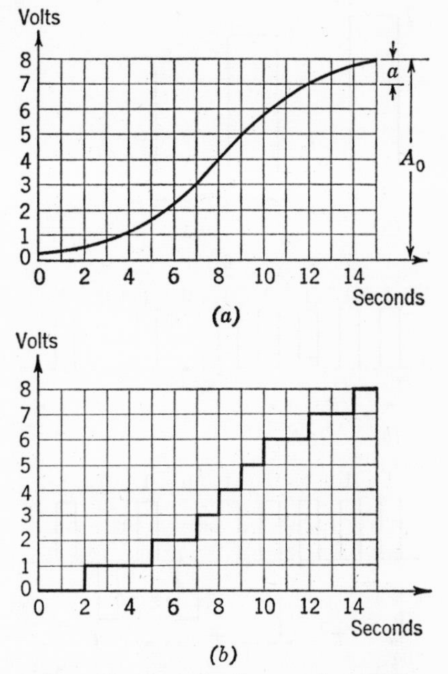

FIG. 6-27. Quantization and sampling. (*a*) Given signal; (*b*) quantized and sampled version.

In the example of Fig. 6-27 the interval between levels is 1 volt, and there are eight amplitude levels (excluding zero), corresponding to a maximum amplitude excursion of 8 volts. The quantized and sampled version of this signal, sampled at 1-sec intervals, is shown in Fig. 6-27*b*. All voltages ranging between $\pm a/2$ volts of a particular level are referred to that level. For example, in Fig. 6-27*a*, the voltage at sampling interval 6 is 2.3 volts. The corresponding quantized voltage is 2 volts and is so indicated in Fig. 6-27*b*. The voltage at interval 9 is 4.9 volts and is thus shown as 5 volts in Fig. 6-27*b*.

Obviously the quantizing process introduces some error in the eventual reproduction of the signal. The demodulated signal will differ somewhat from the desired signal. The over-all effect is as if additional noise had been introduced into the system. We shall have more to say about this *quantization noise* later, but it is apparent that the noise may be reduced by decreasing the level separation, a, or increasing the number of levels, s, used.

Experiment has shown[1] that 8 to 16 levels are sufficient for good intelligibility of speech, and at least 32 are required for commercial use. An experimental PCM system built at the Bell Laboratories uses 128 levels.[2] (This system uses variable level separation.)

If the quantized signal samples were transmitted directly as pulses of varying (although quantized) heights, the resultant system would be a modified form of PAM. But with discrete or numbered voltage levels each level can be coded in some arbitrary form before transmission. It is this possibility of *coding discrete sample levels* that gives quantized signals much greater flexibility in transmission than the continuous-wave (c-w) shapes previously considered. In particular the information capacity of a coded system is greater than that of an uncoded system, or, as we have seen, S/N and bandwidth are exchanged in a much more efficient way. (A coded system makes much more efficient use of bandwidth widening to increase the output S/N than does an uncoded system.)

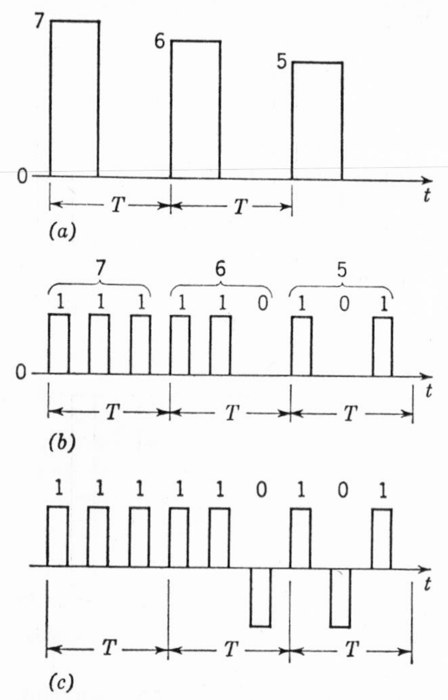

FIG. 6-28. Binary coding of samples. (*a*) Given signal (already sampled and quantized); (*b*) coded samples; (*c*) another form of binary code.

The coding scheme of PCM is particularly simple. The Bell PCM system mentioned converts the quantized and sampled signal pulse into an equivalent group or packet of binary (on-off or plus-minus) pulses of fixed amplitude. This is an example of binary coding similar to that described in Secs. 1-2 and 4-8. Since more than one pulse must now be transmitted in the sampling interval originally allotted to one quantized sample, the pulse widths are decreased and the bandwidth goes up. The S/N goes up exponentially with the bandwidth increase, however, just as in Eqs. (6-128) and (6-129). An example of this coding process is shown in Fig. 6-28.

[1] H. F. Mayer, Pulse Code Modulation, summary chapter in Marton (ed.), *ibid.*, pp. 221–260.

[2] L. A. Meacham and E. Peterson, An Experimental Multichannel Pulse Code Modulation System of Toll Quality, *Bell System Tech. J.*, vol. 27, no. 1, pp. 1–43, January, 1948.

A binary code is just one special case of the coding theoretically possible in a PCM system. In general any one quantized signal sample may be coded into a group of m pulses, each with n possible amplitude levels. These m pulses must be transmitted in the original sampling interval allotted to the quantized sample. Since the information carried by these m pulses is equivalent to the information carried by the original s amplitude levels ($s = A_0/a$), the number of possible amplitude combinations of the m pulses must equal s. Thus

$$s = n^m \tag{6-130}$$

(Recall from Chap. 1 that m pulses, each with n possible heights, may be combined in n^m different ways. Each combination must correspond to one of the original s levels.) If there are two possible levels, $n = 2$, we have the binary code just mentioned. With $s = 8$, three binary pulses are necessary. If $n = 3$, a ternary code results. Obviously, if $m = 1$, $n = s$ and we are back to our original uncoded but quantized samples. As the number of levels, n, chosen for the coded pulses increases, m decreases, as does the bandwidth required for transmission.

A simple binary-code table, relating eight possible signal levels to three on-off (or plus-minus equal-amplitude) pulses, can be drawn up, just as in Sec. 4-8. Such a table is shown below. The pulses of Fig. 6-28 correspond to the relations given in this table.

BINARY CODE

Amplitude level	On-off pulses	Plus-minus pulses
0	000	−1 −1 −1
1	001	−1 −1 1
2	010	−1 1 −1
3	011	−1 1 1
4	100	1 −1 −1
5	101	1 −1 1
6	110	1 1 −1
7	111	1 1 1

Why does this coding of the quantized signal enable us to improve the system capacity, or make more efficient use of the increased bandwidth?

Consider the transmission of a binary pulse group as an example. All we have to do at the receiver is to recognize the absence or presence of a pulse, or the polarity (plus or minus) of a pulse, and then decode into the original quantized form to reconstruct the signal. The pulse shape or exact amplitude is not significant as it was in the PPM and PAM systems, respectively. By originally transmitting binary pulses of high enough amplitude we can ensure correct detection of the pulses in the presence of noise with as low an error rate (or possibility of mistakes) as required. A yes-no decision as to the presence or absence of a pulse is more readily accomplished in the presence of a specified amount of noise power than a determination of the pulse height or the time of its zero crossing. So, qualitatively at least, we would expect an improvement in output signal-to-noise ratio.

But we are now sending m binary pulses instead of 1 multilevel pulse and require essentially m times the bandwidth. We have thus improved the output S/N considerably, but at the expense of increased bandwidth. We can of course reduce the bandwidth required by using a ternary ($n = 3$) or higher-order code. m then decreases, as does the bandwidth

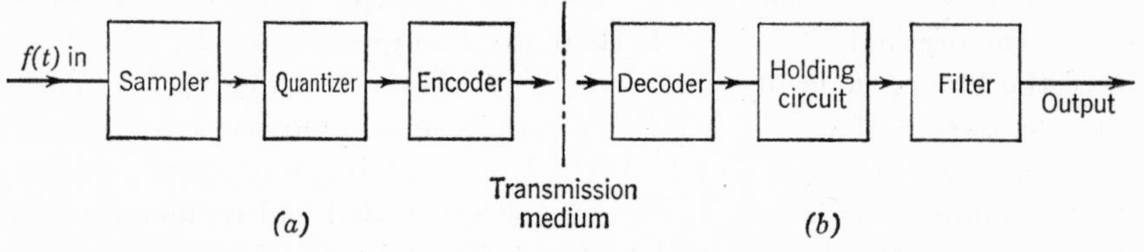

FIG. 6-29. One-channel PCM system. (a) Transmitter; (b) receiver.

required. But for the same noise rejection the average signal power must be greater (as n increases, the highest amplitude level must be increased also to enable the lowest level to be detected). So we cut the bandwidth, but at the expense of increased signal power. We can thus exchange S/N for bandwidth, just as in FM and PPM. The exchange is much more efficient here, however, as pointed out previously, and as will be shown in a somewhat different manner shortly.

Since the decoder at the receiving end must recognize the absence or presence of a particular pulse, rather than shape, the over-all system filtering should be such as to maximize the ratio of pulse peak amplitude to noise. But this is just the criterion used to develop the matched filter of Sec. 6-2. The ideal system frequency response for transmitting rectangular PCM pulses would then be of the $(\sin x)/x$ type. As shown in Sec. 6-2, a cascaded series of RC amplifiers (or equal-tuned i-f amplifiers for r-f pulses) approximates the signal-to-noise output of the matched filter very well. The over-all response of such a system approaches a gaussian-shaped amplitude response, as pointed out in Sec. 6-2. The Bell PCM system uses the gaussian-shaped response for its transmission characteristic.[1]

From the preceding discussion we can envisage a simple form of PCM system as having the same form as a PAM system, with the addition of a quantizer and encoder at the transmitter and a decoder at the receiver. A simple block diagram of a one-channel PCM system is shown in Fig.

[1] *Ibid.*

6-29. Details of the Bell PCM system actually constructed can be found in the article by Meacham and Peterson.

The expression for information capacity of a PCM system can be derived quite simply.[1]

Assume that we have encoded our quantized signal of s discrete levels into a group of m pulses, each with n possible levels. The spacing between these levels must be chosen so that the decoder at the receiver will be able to distinguish between adjacent levels with as little error as desired. By taking σ volts as the rms noise voltage at the input to the decoder the spacing will be some constant, K, times the rms noise voltage, or $K\sigma$. As K increases, the chance of an error obviously decreases. In the next chapter, after some discussion of the elements of probability, we shall relate the actual chóice of K to the average error rate. We shall show there the existence of a threshold (an abrupt change in the error rate above a certain value of K) just as in the other wide-band systems considered. Figure 6-30 defines the terminology used.

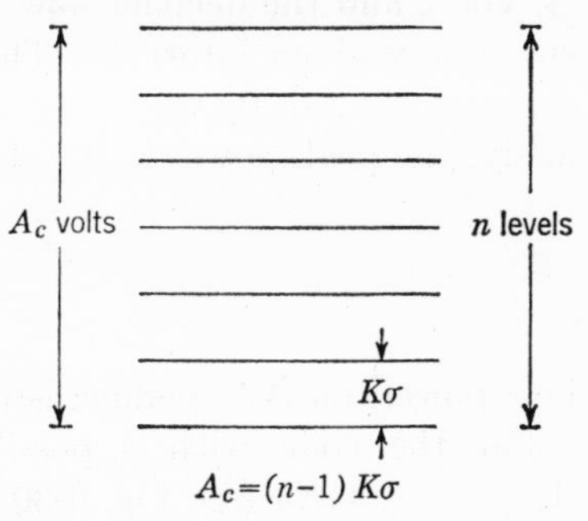

FIG. 6-30. Input to the PCM decoder.

If the *total* voltage swing at the decoder is A_c volts (Fig. 6-30), what is the average signal power required? This will be useful in evaluating the information capacity of the system.

For the binary pulse group, $n = 2$, there are two possibilities (Fig. 6-31):

1. With on-off signals used the on signal is a pulse of A_c volts amplitude, and the off signal is zero. The decoder converts the binary pulse

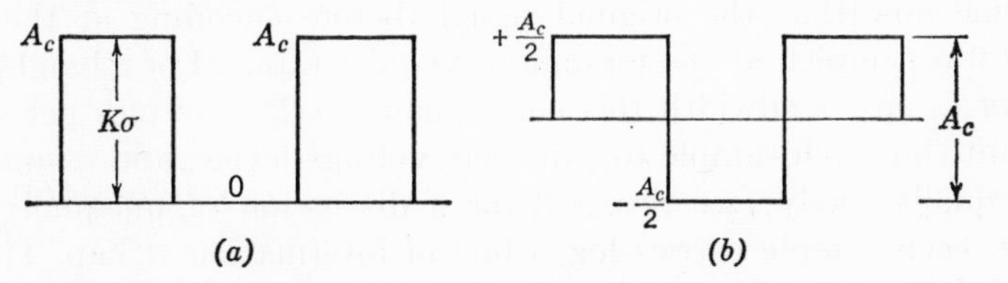

FIG. 6-31. Binary-code pulses at the decoder. (*a*) On-off pulses; (*b*) plus-minus pulses.

group back to the original s levels by determining whether a pulse is present or not. This it does by checking to see whether or not the voltage (signal plus noise) in a given interval exceeds $A_c/2$ volts. If the signal is

[1] B. M. Oliver, J. R. Pierce, and C. E. Shannon, The Philosophy of PCM, *Proc. IRE*, vol. 36, p. 1324, November, 1948.

assumed equally likely to be on or off, the peak power is A_c^2 and the average power is

$$S_c = \frac{A_c^2}{2} \tag{6-131}$$

(signal on half the time, off half the time, on the average; 1-ohm resistor assumed).

2. If plus or minus pulses are sent instead, the pulses will be of amplitude $+A_c/2$ and $-A_c/2$, respectively. The total voltage swing is still A_c volts, and the decoder now must judge the polarity of the pulse present in any given interval. This it does by determining whether or not the pulse exceeds 0 volts. Again assuming either polarity of pulse equally likely, the peak power is $A_c^2/4$ and is the same as the average power,

$$S_c = \frac{A_c^2}{4} \tag{6-132}$$

Less power, on the average, is thus required to send plus-minus pulses.

For the code with n possible levels, each spaced $K\sigma$ volts apart, $A_c = (n - 1)K\sigma$ (see Fig. 6-30). For double-polarity pulses the various pulse heights possible will be $\pm K\sigma/2$, $\pm 3K\sigma/2$, . . . , $\pm(n - 1)K\sigma/2$. Again assuming the different levels equally likely, the average power over a large time interval will be

$$\begin{aligned} S_c &= \frac{2}{n}\left\{\left(\frac{K\sigma}{2}\right)^2 + \left(\frac{3K\sigma}{2}\right)^2 + \cdots + \left[\frac{(n-1)K\sigma}{2}\right]^2\right\} \\ &= (K\sigma)^2\,\frac{n^2 - 1}{12} \end{aligned} \tag{6-133}$$

(The reader should check this relation for himself.)

Assume now that the original signal (before encoding at the transmitter) was sampled at the minimum Nyquist rate. For a band-limited signal of f_m cps bandwidth this corresponds to $2f_m$ samples per second. By quantizing each sample to s discrete voltage levels, and assuming all levels equally likely (see Sec. 1-3 for a discussion of unequally likely signals), each sample carries $\log_2 s$ bits of information (Chap. 1). The rate of information transmission, or system capacity, must thus be

$$C = 2f_m \log_2 s \qquad \text{bits/sec} \tag{6-134}$$

(multiplying the number of samples per second by the information per sample). This is of course just Eq. (1-3) rewritten with different symbols.

The encoding process does not change the rate of transmission of information but only converts the s quantized levels to a code group of m pulses of n levels each. The capacity can therefore be written, with $s = n^m$,

$$\begin{aligned} C &= 2mf_m \log_2 n \\ &= mf_m \log_2 n^2 \qquad \text{bits/sec} \end{aligned} \tag{6-135}$$

Alternatively we can say that we now send m pulses for each previous pulse sample. The pulse rate at the output of the encoder is thus $2mf_m$ pulses per second. But with n equally likely levels in each pulse the average information content of each pulse is $\log_2 n$ bits. The capacity is the number of pulses per second times the average number of bits per pulse, or $C = 2mf_m \log_2 n$ bits/sec, as before.

Equations (6-134) and (6-135) also check, to within a constant, the capacity relations discussed in the previous section for a hypothetical *coded* information-transmission system. We recall that we assumed a signal bandwidth of f_m cps required before processing and a transmission bandwidth B cps after processing or encoding ($B > f_m$; Fig. 6-25). At the receiver we assumed that the voltage S/N ratio was S_{cv}/N_{cv} and used for our capacity relation

$$C = B \log_2 \left(1 + \frac{S_{cv}}{N_{cv}}\right) \tag{6-136}$$

At the output of the decoder the signal was again filtered to f_m cps bandwidth. With an output voltage S/N of S_{ov}/N_{ov} we then wrote

$$C = f_m \log_2 \left(1 + \frac{S_{ov}}{N_{ov}}\right) \tag{6-137}$$

In this present case of the PCM system f_m again represents the input and output signal bandwidth. The encoding process converts one pulse sample to a group of m pulses. Since these m pulses are squeezed into the space previously allotted to the one sample, they are reduced in width by $1/m$. Conserving the peak pulse amplitude is of primary interest here, rather than pulse shape, so that the bandwidth is determined by the pulse width. With pulse widths reduced to $1/m$ of the original width the transmission bandwidth must increase by a factor of m, or

$$B = mf_m$$

The PCM system is thus a *coded* wideband system, in which the transmission bandwidth is purposely widened from f_m to B cps to increase the effective S/N ratio at the system output.

Equations (6-134) and (6-135) for the PCM system are equivalent to Eqs. (6-137) and (6-136), respectively, for our hypothetical coded system, first introduced in Chap. 1. s and n, the number of voltage levels before and after coding in the PCM case, can be related to appropriate S/N ratios, just as in Eqs. (6-136) and (6-137).

To show this, we have from Eq. (6-133)

$$n^2 = 1 + \frac{12S_c}{(K\sigma)^2} \tag{6-138}$$

By introducing this into Eq. (6-135) and letting $N_c = \sigma^2$, the mean noise power in a 1-ohm load resistance, we get

$$C = mf_m \log_2 \left(1 + \frac{12S_c}{K^2N_c}\right) \qquad \text{bits/sec} \tag{6-139}$$

Shannon has shown[1] that the maximum possible rate of transmission of binary digits is

$$C = B \log_2 \left(1 + \frac{S_c}{N_c}\right) \qquad \text{bits/sec} \tag{6-140}$$

This is theoretically possible with the error rate made to approach zero as closely as possible but requires an extremely complicated encoder and results in indefinitely large time delays in transmission. Note that the PCM system-capacity expression resembles this ideal expression quite closely.

The PCM expression involves the parameter K, however, dependent upon the separation between levels desired. As K increases, the system error rate decreases. (An error occurs when a noise pulse is mistaken for a signal pulse or a signal pulse is not detected because of the noise.) We shall show in the next chapter that the transmission of binary digits, with an average error rate of 1 digit in 10^5 digits, requires a peak signal-to-rms-noise voltage ratio of 9.2. The plus-minus pulses must then have a peak signal-to-rms-voltage ratio of 4.6 ($A_c/2\sigma$). Increasing the signal above this value reduces the error rate quite rapidly.

Since $A_c = K\sigma$ for the binary pulses (Fig. 6-31), K must have the value 9.2 for an average error rate of 10^{-5}. For this value of K

$$\frac{12}{K^2}\frac{S_c}{N_c} = \frac{S_c}{7N_c}$$

[1] C. E. Shannon, Communication in the Presence of Noise, *Proc. IRE*, vol. 37, pp. 10–21, January, 1949.

Upon comparing Eqs. (6-139) and (6-140) the PCM system transmitting binary digits requires 7 times as much power (8.5 db) as the ideal system for the same channel capacity.

The PCM system, as an example of a coded wideband system, is much more efficient than the uncoded systems (FM or PPM, for example) but is still 8.5 db less efficient than Shannon's ideal binary transmission system.

6-7. Quantization Noise and S/N in PCM. We have already alluded to the fact that the noise improvement of PCM, as a coded information-transmission system, increases exponentially with transmission bandwidth. This is in contrast with FM, PPM, and other types of uncoded wideband systems in which the improvement is only linear with bandwidth. The improvement is of course measured in terms of output signal-to-noise ratio.

We can demonstrate this property of PCM in another instructive way, in terms of the quantization noise.[1]

As has been pointed out already, fluctuation noise introduced during transmission and at the receiver may cause errors in recognition of the code symbols being transmitted. If the signal pulses transmitted are above a specified threshold level, however (about which we shall have more to say in the next chapter), the average error rate can be kept quite low. Aside from causing errors occasionally, fluctuation noise will have no other effect on the output signal. This is to be contrasted with the modulation systems previously considered—AM, FM, PAM, PPM—in which the noise affected the output signal continuously. This is the basic reason for transmitting coded signals: the problem becomes one of recognizing the presence or absence of a pulse (binary code) or of the amplitude level of a pulse ($n > 2$). So long as the noise does not cause a 0 symbol to be mistaken for a 1 symbol, for example, the effect of fluctuation noise can be completely removed. With the signal power great enough, mistakes can be made to occur rather infrequently. So, aside from these occasional errors, fluctuation noise does not appear at the output.

But, in order to code a continuous signal, we must first quantize it into discrete steps of amplitude. Once quantized, the instantaneous values of the continuous signal can never be restored exactly. This, as we have pointed out previously, gives rise to random error variations which are called *quantization noise.* Instead of fluctuation noise we now have the artificially introduced quantization noise to concern us. This noise can be reduced to any desired degree, however, by choosing the quantum steps

[1] Oliver, Pierce, and Shannon, *op. cit.;* Mayer, *op. cit.*

or level separations fine enough. The output S/N will be a function of the quantization noise or the number of quantum steps used.

To calculate the rms quantization noise, and from this the output S/N, assume equal spacing between levels. Let the signal at the transmitter be

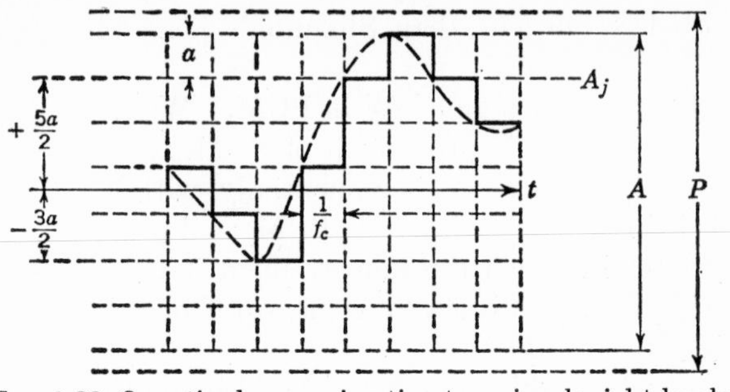

FIG. 6-32. Quantized approximation to a signal: eight levels.

initially quantized into s levels, with a the spacing in volts between adjacent levels. With a maximum plus-minus signal excursion of P volts

$$a = \frac{P}{s} \tag{6-141}$$

(The continuous signal is assumed to have 0 average value, or no d-c component.) The quantized amplitudes will be at $\pm a/2$, $\pm 2a/2$, $\pm 3a/2$,

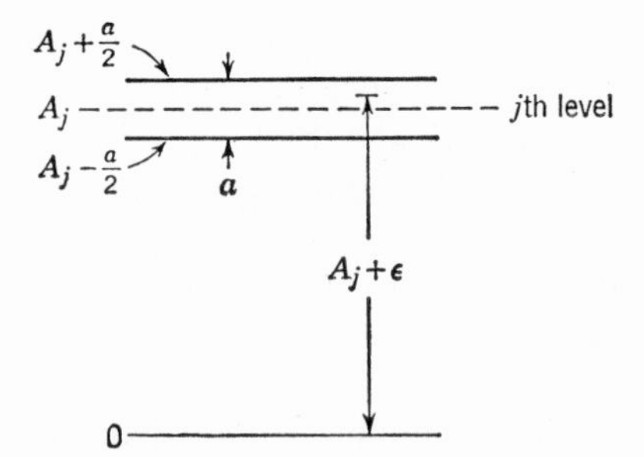

FIG. 6-33. Region of uncertainty at system output.

$\ldots, \pm(s-1)(a/2)$, and the quantized samples will cover a range

$$A = (s-1)a \qquad \text{volts}$$

[See Fig. 6-32. Do not confuse this with the previous discussion of the *coded* samples, leading to Eq. (6-133), and illustrated by Fig. 6-30.]

The quantization process introduces an irreducible error, since a sample appearing at the receiver output at quantized voltage A_j volts could have been due to any signal voltage in the range $A_j - a/2$ to $A_j + a/2$ volts. This region of uncertainty is shown in Fig. 6-33. So far as the ultimate recipient of the message is concerned, this region of uncertainty could just as well have been due to fluctuation noise masking the actual signal level. The one difference is that fluctuation noise, as we mentioned in Chap. 5, could theoretically take on all possible voltage values. The quantization noise, on the other hand, is limited to $\pm a/2$ volts. The distinction between these two will become clearer in Chap. 7.

We can calculate a mean-squared error voltage due to quantization and treat this just like our previous mean-squared noise voltages, or mean noise powers. To do this, assume that over a long period of time all voltage values in the region of uncertainty eventually appear the same number of times. The instantaneous voltage of the signal will be $A_j + \epsilon$, with $-a/2 \leq \epsilon \leq a/2$. ϵ represents the error voltage between the instantaneous (actual) signal and its quantized equivalent. Under our assumption all values of ϵ are equally likely. The mean-squared value of ϵ will then be

$$\overline{\epsilon^2} = \frac{1}{a} \int_{-a/2}^{a/2} \epsilon^2 \, d\epsilon = \frac{a^2}{12} \tag{6-142}$$

The average value of the error is zero with the assumption made. The rms error is then $a/\sqrt{12} = a/(2\sqrt{3})$ volts, and this represents the rms "noise" at the system output.

The output S/N, after the decoder, can now be calculated. We shall define two different S/N ratios, one in terms of the peak signal excursion, P volts, the other in terms of the mean signal power, $S_o = [(s^2 - 1)a^2]/12$ [by comparison with Eq. (6-133)].

1. Peak signal. Since $P = as$ is the peak signal excursion, the ratio of peak signal voltage to rms noise will be

$$\frac{S_{ov}}{N_{ov}} = \frac{P}{a/(2\sqrt{3})} = 2\sqrt{3}\, s \tag{6-143}$$

The corresponding power ratio is

$$\frac{S_o}{N_o} = 12s^2 \tag{6-144}$$

or, in decibels,

$$\left(\frac{S_o}{N_o}\right)_{db} = 10.8 + 20 \log_{10} s \tag{6-145}$$

The power ratio thus goes up as the square of the number of levels. The S/N decibel improvement with s is given in the accompanying table. Also indicated is the relative bandwidth as obtained from the discussion following.

QUANTIZATION S/N IMPROVEMENT WITH NUMBER OF LEVELS

S_0/N_0, db	s	Relative bandwidth
17	2	1
23	4	2
29	8	3
35	16	4
41	32	5
47	64	6
53	128	7

Since s, the number of levels used, determines the number of pulses into which the quantized signal is encoded before transmission, increasing s increases the number of code pulses and hence the bandwidth. We can thus relate S/N to bandwidth. This is easily done by noting that $s = n^m$, with m the number of pulses in the code group and n the number of code levels. With this relation, Eqs. (6-144) and (6-145) become, respectively,

$$\frac{S_o}{N_o} = 12n^{2m} \tag{6-146}$$

and

$$\left(\frac{S_o}{N_o}\right)_{db} = 10.8 + 20m \log_{10} n \tag{6-147}$$

In particular, for a binary code ($n = 2$),

$$\left(\frac{S_o}{N_o}\right)_{db} = 10.8 + 6m \tag{6-148}$$

Since the bandwidth is proportional to m, the number of pulses in the code group, the output S/N increases exponentially with bandwidth. The decibel S/N increases linearly with bandwidth [Eq. (6-148)]. These results check with our previous discussion of coded wideband systems. For a 128-level system such as the one developed by the Bell Laboratories,

$S_o/N_o = 53$ db, and seven-pulse binary-code groups are transmitted, requiring a sevenfold bandwidth increase. (The Bell PCM system uses variable level spacing so that the S/N results are not quite applicable to that system.)

2. Mean signal power. Essentially similar results are obtained upon defining a mean power S/N. With a quantized level spacing of a volts and signal swings of $\pm P/2$ volts the mean signal power is

$$S_o = \tfrac{1}{12}(s^2 - 1)a^2$$

assuming all signal levels equally likely. [This result is obtained in the same way as Eq. (6-133). Recall that Eq. (6-133) gave the mean power in the transmitted code group. The present calculation refers to the original quantized signal both at the transmitter, before being encoded, and at the receiver, after decoding.]

Since $N_o = a^2/12$, the mean power output S/N is

$$\frac{S_o}{N_o} = s^2 - 1 \tag{6-149}$$

For $s \gg 1$ this differs only by a constant from the peak S_o/N_o relation given by Eq. (6-144). For a system with 128 levels the quantization S/N is 42 db. A binary-code group requires seven pulses ($2^7 = 128$), or seven times the bandwidth of the original quantized signal.

To summarize, PCM provides an exponential increase of output S/N with bandwidth. This differs from the linear increase found previously for noncoded wideband systems (FM and PPM). Alternatively we may reduce the bandwidth by providing larger S/N ratios at the input. This exchange of S/N for bandwidth, and vice versa, has recently led to interesting conjectures for narrowband communication systems.

For example, if noise is no problem in a particular system, we may combine two or more successive quantized samples of the original signal and code them into one sample with more than s levels. This is the reverse of the encoding process considered up to now. Sending fewer samples corresponds of course to *decreasing* the bandwidth. The increased number of quantum steps or levels in the encoded signal corresponds to requiring a larger S/N ratio.

Oliver, Pierce, and Shannon, in the article on PCM previously referred to, discuss in some detail the distinction between the coded and uncoded noise-improvement (wideband) communication systems. They compare specifically FM and PCM. They explain the distinction between coded and uncoded systems as analogous to the relation between analogue and digital computers. In the analogue-computer case increased precision dictates a proportional increase in the range of the physical variable used. (For example, if the precision is to be doubled, the voltage representing the variable must be doubled.) Also, small errors accumulate and cannot be eliminated. This is analogous to FM, for example, where to improve S/N (equivalent to improving precision), the audio signal amplitude must be increased. This increases the frequency deviation and hence the bandwidth required. S/N is thus proportional to bandwidth.

The precision of a digital computer, on the other hand, increases *exponentially* with the number of digits used and hence with the size of the computer. If we double the number of digits used, for example from three to six, the precision is squared instead of being doubled. In addition, small errors do not accumulate. This is analogous to the situation in PCM: once the signal to fluctuation noise is above a specified threshold value, fluctuation noise has no effect on the signal—except to introduce errors occasionally. The coding of the signal has reduced the chance of error considerably.

In FM (or PPM) doubling the bandwidth improves S/N by a factor of 2. In PCM doubling the bandwidth allows twice as many pulses to be used and so squares the number of distinguishable amplitude levels.

Any further discussion of PCM, or other information systems for that matter, requires some knowledge of probability theory. For this reason we defer further quantitative considerations of PCM to Chap. 7 after introducing some elementary aspects of probability theory and noise statistics. We shall at that time be able to discuss the threshold effect quantitatively.

6-8. Summary. Central to this chapter has been the underlying concept first introduced in Chap. 1, that noise and bandwidth constitute the two basic limitations to the transmission of information.

The concept of system bandwidth and its inverse relationship to system time response was first introduced in Chap. 2 and applied in the discussion of various types of information-transmission systems in Chaps. 3 and 4. The significance of the term *noise*, examples of its origin in physical devices, and the calculation of the signal-to-noise ratio at various points in a system were all discussed in Chap. 5.

In this chapter we attempted to tie together some of these ideas introduced in previous chapters. In particular how do noise and bandwidth combine to limit the information-handling capabilities of the various systems discussed in Chaps. 3 and 4? Although we did not attempt to put down a definitive answer to this question, we did show that the so-called "wideband" modulation systems, with FM and PPM as the prime examples, provide an improvement over such systems as

AM and PAM in the ability to transmit information. In particular, in both FM and PPM systems, an increase in bandwidth provides a proportional increase in output signal-to-noise ratio, effectively suppressing the noise more and more relative to the signal. Alternatively, for a given output S/N ratio, a linear exchange is possible between input S/N and system bandwidth. As the bandwidth is increased the input S/N ratio may, within limits, be reduced for the same output S/N. Such an S/N-bandwidth trade is not possible in AM and PAM systems.

This noise-improvement property of the wideband systems can be enhanced considerably by first coding the signals to be transmitted. For coded wideband systems, with PCM as the specific practical example discussed, the output S/N was found to increase exponentially with increases in system bandwidth. In the case of PCM we found it possible to write a specific expression for the system information capacity. This expression appears in the form of the capacity expression first written intuitively in Chap. 1 and is similar to the equation for the maximum capacity of an ideal coded communication system derived by C. E. Shannon. The capacity relation again indicated the possibility of an exchange between bandwidth and signal-to-noise ratio.

In the comparative discussion of the different communication systems we found it necessary first to introduce the ideas of power and energy spectra for both signals and noise. As an example of the usefulness of the spectrum idea, we discussed the important problem of detecting a signal in the presence of noise. In the special case where the signal information is carried only by the absence or presence of a signal pulse (the signal shape is secondary) it was shown possible to maximize the signal-to-noise ratio by using a so-called "matched filter," or by designing the system frequency-response characteristics to match those of the pulse to be transmitted. The matched-filter criterion is of importance in PAM, PCM, and search radar systems, among others.

Any further discussion of information-transmission systems requires a knowledge of the theory of probability. Some of the topics from probability theory pertinent to the study of information transmission are discussed in the next chapter, with applications drawn from the areas of noise statistics, radar signal detection, PCM error analysis, etc.

PROBLEMS

6-1. A rectangular-pulse train has a repetition rate of 10,000 pulses per second. Each pulse has an amplitude of 10 volts and a width of 10 μsec.

Plot both the single-sided and double-sided spectral densities $G(\omega_n)$ and $G'(\omega_n)$, respectively, including frequency components out to 200 kc.

What is the average power dissipated if these pulses are impressed across a 50-ohm load?

6-2. The periodic pulses of Prob. 6-1 are applied to an oscilloscope with frequency response approximated by an ideal low-pass filter cutting off at 100 kc.

What fraction of the power represented by the input pulses is actually utilized in driving the oscilloscope?

6-3. Consider the periodic pulses of Figs. P 2-5 and P 2-6.

(*a*) Plot the two power spectral densities, $G(\omega_n)$ and $G'(\omega_n)$, for all four cases, and compare.

(*b*) In each case the peak amplitude A is 10 volts, the pulse width τ is 10 μsec, and the period is 100 μsec. What fraction of the total average power is contained within a bandwidth of 100 kc? Compare with the result of Prob. 2-5.

6-4. A 10-mv rectangular-pulse train is applied to a single-stage grounded-cathode triode amplifier with a voltage amplification of 20. The pulses have a duty cycle τ/T of 0.01 and are repeated at the rate of 20,000 pulses per second.

Sketch the signal power spectrum at the output of the amplifier if the amplifier frequency response is representable by a single RC section with a half-power frequency of 500 kc.

6-5. Repeat Prob. 6-4 if the amplifier consists of two stages, each identical to the single-stage amplifier of that problem.

6-6. Consider the circuit of Fig. P 5-6. Calculate the total noise power dissipated in the resistor R_L if $C = 20\ \mu\mu$f. What fraction of this power is in the frequency range 0 to 400 kc? 0 to 1.2 Mc?

6-7. A single signal pulse is given by $f(t) = e^{-a|t|}$. Show that approximately 80 per cent of the signal energy is contained within the radian-frequency bandwidth $\omega = 0$ to $\omega = a$ radians/sec. (See Fig. 6-4.)

6-8. Consider the two-stage amplifier of Fig. P 5-9. The plate-to-cathode and grid-to-cathode capacitances are each 5 $\mu\mu$f for each tube. The output of the second stage is connected to a load consisting of a 1-megohm resistor in parallel with 5 $\mu\mu$f.

Calculate the output noise power in the frequency range up to 1 Mc. Repeat for 2.4 Mc and 4 Mc. Wiring capacitance is assumed negligible. (It could be added in with the capacitances given. Note also that the effects of the blocking and cathode bypass capacitors may be neglected in this case.)

What is the *total* output noise power if the effect of Miller capacitance from grid to plate is ignored?

6-9. Write an expression for the output spectral density of the circuit of Prob. 6-8 if the effect of the 0.01-μf blocking capacitor is also to be included. Assume that the cathode bypass capacitors are effectively short circuits. Why was it possible to neglect the effect of the blocking capacitor in Prob. 6-8?

6-10. A rectangular pulse of amplitude V volts and width τ sec is applied to a matched filter. Show that the output is a triangular-shaped pulse. Find the peak value of this pulse. Calculate the total noise power at the output of the filter (assumed noiseless) if white noise of spectral density η volts^2/cps is applied at the input. Calculate the output signal-to-noise ratio at the peak of the signal pulse if signal and noise appear together at the filter input.

6-11. (*a*) The signal pulse of Prob. 6-10 is applied to a single RC section, with $RC = \frac{2}{3}\tau$. Sketch the output pulse, and compare with that of Prob. 6-10. Calculate the total output noise power if white noise of spectral density η volts^2/cps is again added to the input signal. Calculate the peak S/N ratio at the output, and compare with the result of Prob. 6-10, checking a point on the appropriate curve of Fig. 6-9 in the text.

(*b*) Let the pulse width τ vary, and repeat (*a*). Calculate the peak S/N ratio at the output, and plot as a function of τ. Compare with the appropriate curve of Fig. 6-9.

6-12. A signal pulse of unit peak amplitude and half-power width τ is given mathematically by the so-called "gaussian" error curve $f(t) = e^{-0.35(2t/\tau)^2}$. Added to the signal pulse is white noise of spectral density η volts²/cps. The signal plus noise is applied to a filter.

Show that the optimum filter characteristic for maximizing the peak S/N ratio at the filter output is given by a gaussian curve in frequency,

$$|H(j\omega)| = \sqrt{\frac{\pi}{1.4}}\,\tau e^{-(\omega\tau)^2/5.6}$$

(See Prob. 7-42 and the discussion of the gaussian curve in Sec. 7-4. Note that $\int_{-\infty}^{\infty} e^{-x^2}\,dx = \sqrt{\pi}$.)

Sketch $f(t)$ and $|H(j\omega)|$.

6-13. The gaussian pulse and white noise of Prob. 6-12 are passed through an ideal low-pass filter of cutoff frequency ω_c radians/sec. Show that the maximum peak S/N ratio at the output occurs at $\omega_c\tau = 2.4$. Show that this maximum value of the peak S/N ratio is only 0.3 db less than that found by using the optimum filter characteristic of Prob. 6-12.

6-14. (*a*) Prove that the impulse response of a matched filter is given in general by Eq. (6-63).

(*b*) A signal pulse given by $f(t) = e^{-at}$, $t \geq 0$, is mixed with white noise of spectral density η volts²/cps. Find the impulse response of the matched filter, and compare with $f(t)$.

6-15. The i-f section of a radar receiver consists of four identical tuned amplifiers with an over-all 3-db bandwidth of 1 Mc. The center frequency is 15 Mc. The amplifiers represent the bandpass equivalent of RC-coupled amplifiers. The input to the i-f strip consists of a 1-μsec rectangular signal pulse plus fluctuation noise generated primarily in the r-f stage and mixer of the receiver. Calculate the relative difference in decibels of the peak S/N ratio at the receiver output for the amplifier given, as compared with an optimum matched filter. Repeat for over-all amplifier bandwidths of 500 kc and 2 Mc.

6-16. An FM receiver consists of an ideal bandpass filter of 225 kc bandwidth centered about the unmodulated carrier frequency, an ideal limiter and frequency discriminator, and an ideal low-pass filter of 10 kc bandwidth in the output. The ratio of average carrier power to total average noise power at the input to the limiter is 40 db. The modulating signal is a 10-kc sine wave that produces a frequency deviation Δf of 50 kc.

(*a*) What is the signal-to-noise ratio S_o/N_o at the output of the low-pass filter?

(*b*) A deemphasis network with a time constant $rC = 75$ μsec is inserted just before the output filter. Calculate S_o/N_o again.

(*c*) Repeat (*a*) and (*b*) if the modulating signal is a 1-kc sine wave of the same amplitude as the 10-kc wave. Repeat with the amplitude reduced by a factor of 2. (The carrier amplitude and filter bandwidths are unchanged.)

6-17. An audio signal is to be transmitted by either AM or FM. The signal consists of either of two equal-amplitude sine waves: one at 50 cps, the other at 10 kc. The amplitude is such as to provide 100 per cent carrier modulation in the AM case and a frequency deviation $\Delta f = 75$ kc in the FM case.

The average carrier power and the noise power density at the detector input are the same for the AM and FM systems.

(*a*) Calculate the transmission bandwidth and output filter bandwidth required in the AM case and the FM case. The carrier-to-noise ratio is 30 db for the AM system. Calculate the output S_o/N_o for each sine wave for each of the systems. (Preemphasis and deemphasis networks are not used.)

(*b*) Repeat (*a*) if the amplitude of the 10-kc wave is reduced by a factor of 2.

6-18. The ratio of average carrier power to noise spectral density, S_c/η, at the detector input is 4×10^6 for both an FM and an AM receiver. The AM carrier is 100 per cent modulated by a sine-wave signal, while a sine-wave signal produces a maximum deviation of 75 kc of the FM carrier.

Calculate and compare the output signal-to-noise ratios for both the FM and the AM receivers if the bandwidth f_m of the low-pass filter in each receiver is successively 1, 10, and 100 kc. Deemphasis networks are not used. (Assume that the r-f bandwidths are always at least twice the low-pass bandwidth.)

6-19. The low-pass filter bandwidth of an AM and an FM receiver is 1 kc. The ratio of average carrier power to noise spectral density, S_c/η, is the same in both receivers and is kept constant. The AM carrier is 100 per cent modulated.

Calculate the relative S/N improvement of the FM over the AM system if the frequency deviation Δf of the FM carrier is 100 cps; 1 kc; 10 kc.

6-20. The time constant of an RC deemphasis network is chosen as 75 μsec. Plot the improvement in output S/N due to the deemphasis network for both FM and AM detectors as a function of the bandwidth of the output low-pass filter (assume that S_c/η is the same and constant in both cases). What is the minimum filter bandwidth to be used if audio signals from 0 to 10 kc are to be passed?

6-21. The signal pulses in a PPM system have a peak amplitude of 1 volt. The pulse rise time is 0.15 μsec. The maximum modulation displacement is 1 μsec. Noise of value 0.1 volt rms is added to these pulses during transmission. Compare the S/N ratio after demodulation with the S/N ratio during transmission. What bandwidth is required for transmission?

6-22. Check Eq. (6-133).

6-23. A single information channel carries voice frequencies in the range 50 to 3,300 cps. The channel is sampled at an 8-kc rate, and the resulting pulses are transmitted over either a PAM system or a PCM system.

(*a*) Calculate the over-all bandwidth of the PAM system if the peak S/N ratio at the system output is to be a maximum. The system filtering effect may be represented by four cascaded and isolated RC amplifier stages.

(*b*) In the PCM system the sampled pulses are quantized into eight levels and transmitted as binary digits. Find the transmission bandwidth of the PCM system, and compare with that of (*a*) if the peak S/N ratio at the input to the decoder is to be a maximum. The system filtering effect is the same as in (*a*).

(*c*) Repeat (*b*) if 128 quantizing levels are used. Compare the rms quantization noise in the two cases, if the peak-to-peak voltage swing at the quantizer is 2 volts.

6-24. Repeat Prob. 6-23 for the case of 12 voice channels, each carrying frequencies of 50 to 3,300 cps, which are sampled and time-multiplexed. Include block diagrams of both the PAM and PCM systems.

6-25. The sinusoidal voltage $10 \sin 6{,}280t$ is sampled at $t = 0.33$ msec and thereafter periodically at a 3-kc rate. The samples are then quantized into eight voltage levels and coded into binary digits.

Draw the original voltage and below it to scale the outputs of the sampler, the quantizer, and the encoder. Calculate the rms quantization noise.

6-26. A signal voltage in the frequency range 100 to 4,000 cps is limited to a peak-to-peak swing of 3 volts. It is sampled at a uniform rate of 8 kc, and the samples are quantized to 64 evenly spaced levels. Calculate and compare the bandwidths and ratios of peak signal to rms quantization noise if the quantized samples are transmitted either as binary digits or as four-level pulses.

6-27. Calculate the capacity in bits per second of the PCM systems of Probs. 6-23*b* and *c*, 6-24, and 6-26.

CHAPTER 7

STATISTICAL METHODS IN ANALYSIS OF INFORMATION-TRANSMISSION SYSTEMS

Reference has been made in the past two chapters to the *statistical* properties of noise. We have thus far managed to avoid introducing explicitly material from the theory of probability, the mathematical discipline dealing with random phenomena, by concentrating on the average or mean-squared values of such parameters as voltage, current, power, etc. This has enabled us to develop some understanding of the role noise plays in limiting the transmission of information, without becoming lost in a welter of mathematical symbolism.

Any thorough study of the effects of noise in systems must eventually utilize aspects of probability theory, however, and we shall attempt to lay some of the groundwork in this chapter. The reader is referred to some excellent articles and books for a deeper study of the statistical analysis of noise in communication and control systems than will be possible in this book.[1]

The study of probability theory is also extremely important for an understanding of information-transmission systems because of the inherently statistical nature of signal messages to be transmitted. The statistical structure of signal messages was discussed in an elementary fashion in Chap. 1. In particular we were able to calculate, in Sec. 1-3, the average information in bits of a message composed of symbols with a prescribed probability for each. As mentioned previously we shall not have occasion to pursue the subject of information content of signals further in this book. Interested readers can refer to the books and articles on information theory mentioned in Chap. 1.

It is appropriate at this point, because of the statistical nature of both signals and noise, to spend some time studying the elementary concepts of the theory of probability. We shall review the concept of probability

[1] S. O. Rice, Mathematical Analysis of Random Noise, *Bell System Tech. J.*, July, 1944; January, 1945. W. R. Bennett, Methods of Solving Noise Problems, *Proc. IRE*, vol. 44, no. 5, pp. 609–638, May, 1956. W. B. Davenport, Jr., and W. L. Root, "Introduction to Random Signals and Noise," McGraw-Hill Book Company, Inc., New York, 1958. J. H. Laning, Jr., and R. H. Battin, "Random Processes in Automatic Control," McGraw-Hill Book Company, Inc. New York, 1956.

as the relative frequency of occurrence of specified events, as first introduced in Sec. 1-3, then extend it to the study of various interesting problems in noise theory. Further analyses of pulse-code-modulation (PCM) systems, radar, etc., will then be given as examples of the statistical procedures studied.

Our approach will in general be nonrigorous. We shall define some statistical properties of noise (or signals) in an intuitive sense. Our goal is to develop a feeling for the terms used and the ability to utilize the theory of probability in studying various communication systems.

7-1. Introduction to Probability.[1] The need for statistical analysis arises in many branches of science.

In many cases measurements of various parameters may be deterministic in nature. They follow classical laws, and results may presumably be predicted exactly if all pertinent information is known. If a great many variables are involved, however, it frequently becomes extremely difficult to analyze the problem exactly. Instead various *average* properties may be defined.

For example, if we are interested in investigating various properties of a gas trapped in a container, we could conceivably do this analytically by following the path of each molecule as it moves along, colliding with its neighbors, with the walls of the container, etc. Application of the simple laws of mechanics would presumably tell us all we want to know about each gas molecule, and therefore about the gas as a whole. But with millions of molecules to treat simultaneously, each moving with a possibly different velocity from the next, this theoretically possible calculation becomes practically impossible. Instead, because we deal with *large numbers* of molecules, we can determine average values for the velocity, force, momentum of the molecules, etc., and from these determine such *average* properties of the gas as temperature and pressure. (We shall define the concept of average more precisely later on, but we rely on our intuition now.)

The crucial point here is the phrase large numbers. Whenever we deal with large numbers of variables (whether the millions of gas molecules in a small container, the millions of possible messages in a particular language to be transmitted, or the millions of different pictures that could possibly be seen on a small TV screen), we can talk about the *average* properties, obtained by applying statistical concepts to the variables in question.

[1] T. Fry, "Probability and Its Engineering Uses," D. Van Nostrand Company, Inc., Princeton, N.J., 1928; W. Feller, "An Introduction to Probability Theory and Its Applications," 2d ed., vol. 1, John Wiley & Sons, Inc., New York, 1957; A. M. Mood, "Introduction to the Theory of Statistics," McGraw-Hill Book Company, Inc., New York, 1950; H. Cramér, "Mathematical Methods of Statistics," Princeton University Press, Princeton, N.J., 1951.

These large numbers we deal with and the statistics based on them can be generated in different ways. For example, we could conceivably set up 1,000 blackboards and ask 1,000 persons to start simultaneously writing anything that came into their minds. If at a given instant we scanned the particular letter being written by each, we could determine the relative frequency of occurrence of letters in the language (say English) being used. (This assumes that the persons were selected randomly, have no connection with one another, were not briefed beforehand, etc.) Alternatively we could watch one typical person writing and perhaps pick out the first letter in each new paragraph as he writes. This, too, could be used to determine the relative frequency of occurrence of letters in the language. But we would need many paragraphs of writing here (say 1,000 or more) to get a good approximation to our desired frequencies. The same type of experiments could be used to determine the average properties of a gas: either measure simultaneously the velocity of each molecule in a container or follow one molecule about over a long period of time, and from this determine its average velocity and other statistical properties.

The distinction between these two methods of determining average or statistical properties of a particular quantity will be considered later on. Now we simply emphasize that they both involve dealing with large numbers of events.

How do we now make use of large numbers of measurements to determine the statistical properties of a particular occurrence?

Assume, as the simplest type of experiment, that we are engaged in repeatedly tossing a coin. Can we determine whether heads or tails will appear in any particular throw? Of course, given enough information about the way in which the coin is dropped, initial velocity, etc., we could predict heads or tails. But this is extremely difficult. Instead we say ordinarily that we *do not know exactly* which side will appear on any one throw but that the odds are 50-50 either way; i.e., in the *long run* (large number of tries), as many heads will appear as tails. Either event (heads or tails) is equally likely.

How do we arrive at this conclusion? We may perhaps say intuitively that by virtue of complete symmetry, assuming an unloaded coin, there can be no preference as to heads or tails. Or perhaps we have come to the same conclusion after long experience with coin tossing (a valuable and instructive use of time!).

Thus, although in only a few throws the frequency of occurrence of heads or tails may not be the same, we feel sure that, over many repetitions (tosses) of the experiment, either event will occur very nearly the same number of times. If we plotted, for example, the ratio of the number of heads (H) to the total number of tosses (N), we might obtain the curve of Fig. 7-1.

Initially (N small) H/N takes on greatly differing values. As N increases, however, H/N approaches 0.5 more and more closely. For large N, then, we are presumably justified in saying that heads will occur as often as tails. We then generalize by saying that in the next throw there is a 50 per cent chance of heads occurring.

The same conclusions would of course be drawn from an experiment with signals consisting just of on-off pulses. If a long series of tests with all types of messages show that pulses appear as frequently as spaces (no

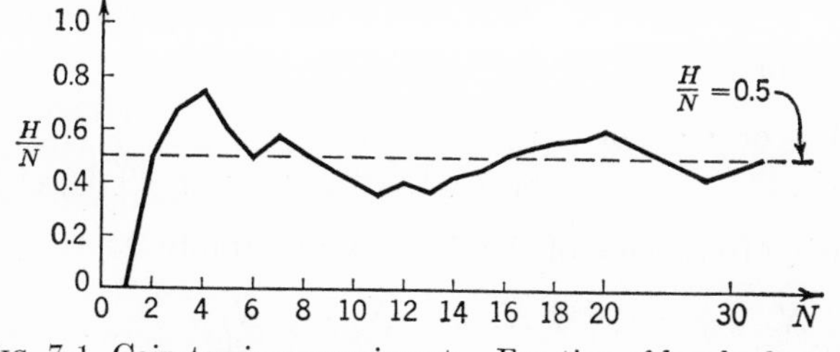

FIG. 7-1. Coin-tossing experiment. Fraction of heads thrown.

pulses), we would presumably say there is a 50 per cent chance of getting a pulse (or a space) in any one interval. The pulses and spaces are then equally likely.

We can consider similarly the tossing of a die: we feel intuitively, or might perhaps demonstrate by actual tosses of a die, that in many tosses each face should come up very nearly as often as any other. We say that, with six faces, each face has a $\frac{1}{6}$ chance of coming up on any one toss. Any two faces have a $\frac{1}{3}$ chance; any three faces, a $\frac{1}{2}$ chance; etc.

These intuitive ideas of chance as associated with many repetitions of an experiment may be formalized somewhat, as in Sec. 1-3, by defining the probability of one event out of several possible occurring as follows: Say there are n possible outcomes of an experiment given by A_1, A_2, A_n. (In the case of the coin A_1 is H, A_2 is T, n is 2. In the case of the die n is 6, and the A's represent different faces of the die.) If the experiment is repeated N times and the relative frequency of occurrence of event A_K is found to approach a limiting value for N much larger than n, this limiting value is defined to be the probability of occurrence, $P(A_K)$, of event A_K. Thus

$$P(A_K) = \frac{\text{number of times } A_K \text{ occurs in } N \text{ tries}}{N} \qquad N \gg n \qquad (7\text{-}1)$$

If the occurence of any one event excludes the occurrence of any others (a head excludes the occurrence of a tail), the events are said to be *mutually exclusive*. Then, if all possible events A_1 to A_n are included,

$$P(A_1) + P(A_2) + \cdots + P(A_n) = 1 \tag{7-2}$$

Equation (7-2) is an obvious statement of the fact that some one of the n events must occur in the N tries, and the sum of all the events must be equal to N. In probability terms, then, the probability of *any* event occurring is 1. (The probability of a head or a tail is 1; the probability of any one of the six faces of a die coming up is 1; etc.)

We can now generalize our definition of probability a bit. If the n events are mutually exclusive, the probability of one of K events of the n occurring ($K \leq n$) must be the sum of the probabilities of each event occurring. Thus

$$P(A_{j+1} \text{ or } A_{j+2} \text{ or } \cdots \text{ or } A_{j+K}) = P(A_{j+1}) + P(A_{j+2}) + \cdots + P(A_{j+K}) \leq 1 \tag{7-3}$$

For the relative frequency of the K events is simply

$$\frac{N_{j+1} + N_{j+2} + \cdots + N_{j+K}}{N} = \frac{N_{j+1}}{N} + \frac{N_{j+2}}{N} + \cdots + \frac{N_{j+K}}{N}$$

or the sum of the probabilities, as above.

The simplest examples of the calculation of probabilities relate to games of chance. We shall refer to some of these as we proceed, for the very same ideas involved appear in the calculation of noise and signal statistics.

As an example, assume that a box contains three white and seven black balls. What is the probability of drawing a white ball? If we were repeatedly to draw one ball at a time from the box, replacing each ball after it was drawn, we would again expect intuitively to find the white balls appearing 30 per cent of the time, the black balls 70 per cent of the time. There are thus two possible events here: A_1 is a white ball, A_2 is a black ball, and $P(A_1) = 0.3$, $P(A_2) = 0.7$.

Alternatively we could tag each white and black ball separately. Any one ball would thus appear very nearly $\frac{1}{10}$ of the time in many ($N \gg 10$) drawings of a ball. But we can lump together the chances of drawing any one of the three white balls and get a probability of 0.3 of drawing a white ball. (Here we could also say that each ball is equally likely to be drawn. Any one ball must thus have a $\frac{1}{10}$ chance of being drawn.) This latter approach is simply one example of adding the probabilities of each of a group of mutually exclusive events to determine the probability of occurrence of the over-all group.

For another example, consider two dice to be thrown. What is the probability of getting a 6? Again two approaches are possible:

1. Since each die has six faces, a total of $6 \times 6 = 36$ possible outcomes exists. Each possibility is equally likely to occur (as determined by experiment or, more probably, by intuition) so that the probability of drawing any combination of two faces is $\frac{1}{36}$. But there are five different face combinations that give a 6 (5, 1; 4, 2; 3, 3; 2, 4; 1, 5). The probability of the over-all event is $\frac{1}{36} + \cdots + \frac{1}{36} = \frac{5}{36}$.
2. More directly, of 36 possible outcomes, 5 are the favorable ones corresponding to a 6 occurring. We can call the drawing of a 6 the desired event rather than the drawing of any one of the combinations giving 6 as above. Then 6 will occur $\frac{5}{36}$ of the time in many repeated tosses. [As a check, $P(2) = \frac{1}{36}$, $P(3) = \frac{2}{36}$, $P(4) = \frac{3}{36}$, $P(5) = \frac{4}{36}$, etc. Then $P(2) + P(3) + \cdots + P(11) + P(12) = 1$, as expected.]

For the third example, say two coins are thrown. What is the probability of one head and one tail? Here there are four possible outcomes: H,H; H,T; T,H; T,T. Each outcome is equally likely and has a probability of $\frac{1}{4}$ of appearing. Head-tail can occur in two ways if no distinction is made as to which coin turns up head. So

$$P(H,T) = \frac{1}{4} + \frac{1}{4} = \frac{1}{2}$$

Alternatively we can say that the head-tail combination is one of three possible: H-T, T-T, H-H. But in many throws we would expect H-T to come up 50 per cent of the time.

Note that from our definition of probability as the relative frequency of occurrence of a specified event we have gradually and almost unconsciously moved to another interpretation of probability:

We enumerate the total number r of possible outcomes of an experiment that are *equally likely* and *mutually exclusive* (i.e., in a long series of repetitions of the experiment each outcome would occur on the average as often as any other). Then the probability of one of these events occurring is simply $1/r$. Our specified event could be just one of these equally likely events, in which case its probability of occurrence would be $1/r$. Or it might comprise a group, say K ($K < r$), of the r events. Its probability would then be K/r by summing the probabilities of the mutually exclusive events.

For example, in the case of the two dice thrown, all face combinations are equally likely. Then $r = 36$, and the probability of any one face combination occurring is $\frac{1}{36}$. But of these 36 combinations $K = 5$ constitute our desired event (a 6 appearing); so $\frac{5}{36}$ is the probability of throwing a 6.

By reducing the calculation of probability to the determination of the equally likely events first we can often avoid the necessity of actually performing an experiment many times to determine relative frequencies of occurrence. Thus, in calculating the probabilities of getting various head-tail combinations in the tossing of a coin, there is usually no need actually to carry out a coin-tossing experiment. We know intuitively that tossing a head or a tail on an unbiased coin is equally likely and begin our calculations from that point.

This is not possible in many cases, however. The calculation of the probability of occurrence of the different letters in the English alphabet cannot be based on any "equally likely" argument. We must actually calculate the relative frequency of occurrence of a particular letter in a long series of trials.

Where the "equally likely" approach is fruitful, however, use can sometimes be made of some of the fundamental notions of permutations and combinations. As an example, say a set of 2 cards is to be drawn from a deck of 52. What is the probability of drawing 1 spade and 1 heart?

The total number of ways in which 2 successive cards may be drawn is obviously 52×51. (For each card drawn, 51 remain. But 52 different cards may be drawn on the first try.) This number is just the permutations of 52 elements taken 2 at a time. Each one of these 52×51 possibilities or permutations is equally likely, so that the probability of drawing any one pair of cards is $1/(52 \times 51)$. But 13 different spades could have been drawn as the first card and for each such spade 13 different hearts as the second card. 13×13 is thus the number of spade-heart possibilities. But a heart followed by a spade would have done just as well; so $2(13 \times 13)$ is the number of favorable possibilities of the 52×51 possible outcomes. The probability of a spade and a heart is thus $2(13 \times 13)/(52 \times 51)$.

In general we may have n items (say, n books, n symbols of an alphabet, n voltage levels, etc.) which can be selected. m of these items are to be selected successively, with no duplication allowed. Thus, if a particular book or symbol is selected as the first of m selections, it can no longer be used in further selections. (If the 2-volt level is picked in the first interval, it can no longer be chosen in the second or later intervals.) What is the probability of selecting a particular symbol combination, book combination, or voltage-level combination? This probability will depend on the number of permutations or combinations of n items, m at a time.

If we pay attention to the *order* of the selection, the number of ways of picking m of n events is the number of *permutations* of n items taken m at a time. Thus, if two of the letters a, b, c, d, e are to be selected and *order* is important, ab differs from ba.

The number of ways of selecting m of n events is called the number of *combinations* if the order is unimportant. Thus, if an a and a b are all that are desired, ab is the same as ba.

If the m elements selected are *ordered*, the first may be selected in n ways, the second in $(n - 1)$ ways, etc. (Remember that once a particular item is chosen it cannot be selected again.) Then the number of possible selections is $P_{n,m}$ (number of permutations of n items taken m at a time).

$$P_{n,m} = n(n-1)(n-2) \cdots [n-(m-1)] = \frac{n!}{(n-m)!} \tag{7-4}$$

As an example, if two of the five letters a, b, c, d, e are to be selected, there are $5 \times 4 = 20$ possibilities, with order important. (The reader may wish to tabulate these to convince himself of this result.) In particular, if n selections are made,

$$P_{n,n} = n! \tag{7-5}$$

For example, there are $3! = 6$ permutations of the three letters a, b, c selected in three successive tries: *abc*, *acb*, *bac*, *bca*, *cab*, *cba*.

How do we now find the number of unordered selections or combinations? Call this number $C_{n,m}$. Then, for example, *abcd* and *abce* are different combinations, but *abcd* and *abdc* are not to be distinguished. There are $m!$ ways of obtaining each particular combination of m units, or, alternatively, $m!$ ways of rearranging a combination of m items, once obtained. (For example, *abc* can be rearranged in $3! = 6$ ways.) Then $C_{m,n}m!$ must equal the total number of possible selections of $P_{n,m}$.

$$C_{n,m} = \frac{P_{n,m}}{m!} = \frac{n!}{m!(n-m)!} \tag{7-6}$$

The card problem we discussed previously is a good example of using permutations and combinations to calculate probabilities: We draw 2 cards from a 52-card pack. The number of combinations possible is $C_{52,2} = (52 \times 51)/2$. Each of these is equally likely. But of these the possible number of ways for a spade-heart to appear is 13×13. Then $P(\text{heart,spade}) = [2(13 \times 13)]/(52 \times 51)$, as before.

Alternatively there are $P_{52,2} = 52 \times 51$ permutations of the cards taken two at a time. Of these, $2(13 \times 13)$ represent possible ways of getting a spade and a heart, and we get the same result for the probability of getting a spade and a heart.

7-2. Conditional Probability and Statistical Independence. Up to this point we have discussed the probability of one particular event occurring: a head or a tail in coin tossing, a particular number in the tossing of dice, a particular letter (say e or g, for example) in the English alphabet, etc. We shall have occasion in future sections to discuss the probability of occurrence of two or more events, and it is appropriate at this point to extend our definition of probability as the relative frequency of occurrence to include the *joint probability* of two or more events occurring.

One possible example that we shall discuss later in this chapter concerns the probability that the noise voltage at the output of an amplifier exceeds a specified voltage (say 4 volts) at one instant of time, t_1, and another voltage (say 5 volts) some time, t_2, later (see Fig. 7-2). We shall relate such joint probabilities to the noise-power spectrum at that time.

In Sec. 1-3 we indirectly hinted at the need for determining such probabilities. There we pointed out that, in determining the statistical structure of a language such as English, a count of the relative frequency of occurrence of different letters of the alphabet does not provide full information about the language statistics. Letters commonly occur in pairs (for example, *qu*, *th*, *tr*, *st*) or even in groups of three or more.

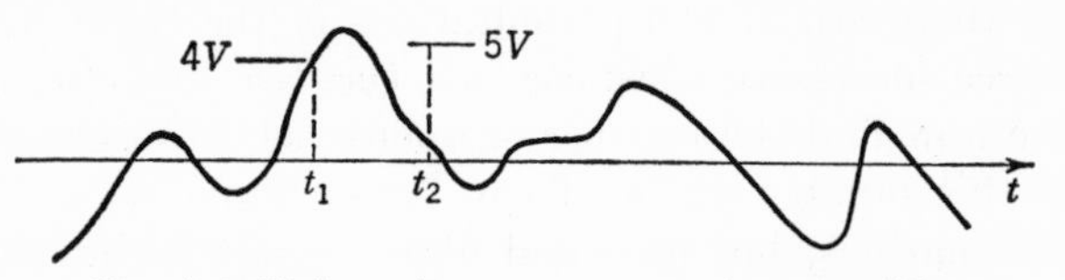

FIG. 7-2. Noise voltage at output of an amplifier.

Some word combinations occur more frequently than others. All these joint occurrences affect the over-all statistics and must be included in an accurate determination, for example, of the language information content.

The fact that some events occur *jointly* indicates that there may be some dependence of one event on another: the letter u obviously follows q much more frequently than does the letter e, for example. So we should be able to determine the independence of several events by measuring the frequency of joint occurrence. We shall restrict ourselves here to two events, A and B, only. The reader is referred to the literature on probability and noise statistics previously cited for an extension to more than two events of interest.

A simple example of the calculation of a joint probability will clarify these ideas and enable us to generalize quite readily. We determined previously, as an example in the calculation of probability, the chance of drawing a heart and a spade from a deck of cards. Using permutations and combinations, we were able to show that

$$P(\text{heart,spade}) = \frac{2(13 \times 13)}{52 \times 51} = 2\left(\frac{13}{4 \times 51}\right)$$

Although we considered the heart-spade drawing at that time to be a single event of interest, we could just as well have treated it as a problem in joint probability: what is the probability that in the drawing of two cards one will be a heart, the other a spade?

To answer this question, consider first the case in which we are interested in drawing a heart as the first card, a spade as the second. Let A

represent the drawing of a heart, B the drawing of a spade. Then $P(AB)$ represents the desired probability of drawing first a heart, then a spade.

The chance of drawing a heart as the first card is $P(A) = 1/4$, since 13 of the 52 cards are hearts. The probability of drawing a spade as the second card is not $1/4$, however, but $13/51$, since 51 cards are left. The second drawing is thus dependent upon, or *conditioned* by, the first drawing. We designate this possible dependence of the second of the two events on the first by the symbol $P(B/A)$: the probability of event B occurring, it being known that A has occurred. This is called a *conditional probability*. Here $P(B/A) = 13/51$. [Had the first card been replaced, we would have had $P(B) = 1/4$, independent of the first card.]

The chance of drawing the desired sequence heart-spade (AB) is then

$$P(AB) = 1/4 \times 13/51 = P(A)P(B/A)$$

since, for every heart we draw ($1/4$ of the time on the average), there is a $13/51$ chance of drawing a spade.

But we could just as well have asked for a spade first, then a heart in this particular problem. (The original problem specified not a particular sequence of cards, but merely a heart and a spade.) This sequence obviously gives $P(BA) = 1/4 \times 13/51 = P(B)P(A/B)$ again. Since the probabilities of the two sequences are mutually exclusive (*either* a heart *or* a spade is drawn as the first card), the chance of a heart-spade combination being drawn is the sum of the two probabilities, or

$$1/4 \times 13/51 + 1/4 \times 13/51 = 2 \times 1/4 \times 13/51$$

This agrees of course with the result using permutations and combinations. To recapitulate, there we considered the heart-spade drawing as the one desired event and calculated the corresponding probability of this event occurring from a consideration of its relative frequency of occurrence. Here we have chosen to treat it as two events (one dependent on the other in this case).

We can now generalize the concepts of joint and conditional probability and their relation to the dependence of two events on one another. Assume that we perform an experiment and look for the occurrence of two events A and B in that order. We repeat this experiment many times and measure the relative frequency of occurrence of each event separately and as a pair (AB). (We shall actually give an example of such an experiment, and calculations based on it, shortly.)

Our problem is to determine the relative dependence (or independence) of B on A. The conditional probability $P(B/A)$, or the probability of B occurring, given A having occurred, will serve as a measure of this dependence. How do we then determine $P(B/A)$ from our measurements?

Let n_{AB} represent the number of times in n repetitions of the experiment that the combination AB appears. For n a "large number," the joint probability of first A and then B occurring is

$$P(AB) = \frac{n_{AB}}{n} \tag{7-7}$$

by using our previous definition of probability. In the same n trials the outcome A is found to appear n_A times, the outcome B n_B times. n_A must include n_{AB}, since some of the times that A appears it is followed by a B. The ratio $n_{AB}/n_A \leq 1$ represents the relative frequency of occurrence of B preceded by the event A and is just the desired conditional probability $P(B/A)$ (n_A "large" enough). Thus

$$P(B/A) = \frac{n_{AB}}{n_A} \leq 1 \tag{7-8}$$

As an example, n might represent a large number of drawings of two successive cards, n_A the number of times a heart appears, n_B the number of times a spade appears, n_{AB} the number of times a heart is followed by a spade. Dividing the numerator and denominator of Eq. (7-8) by n, we get

$$P(B/A) = \frac{n_{AB}/n}{n_A/n} = \frac{P(AB)}{P(A)} \tag{7-9}$$

from Eq. (7-7) and the definition of $P(A)$. Equation (7-9) is the defining equation relating conditional and joint probabilities. Multiplying through by $P(A)$ we get

$$P(AB) = P(A)P(B/A) \tag{7-10}$$

This is the relation used in the two-card problem given as an example.

Now assume that $P(B/A) = P(B)$. This implies that the probability of event B happening is independent of A. Such a situation would be true in the two-card problem if the first card were immediately replaced after having been drawn. In this case Eq. (7-10) gives

$$P(AB) = P(A)P(B) \tag{7-11}$$

We thus multiply the two separate probabilities together to find the probability of the event AB, if B is independent of A.

Equation (7-11) can also be written

$$P(AB) = P(B)P(A)$$

This implies that $P(AB)$ is independent of the order of occurrence of A and B in this case. It must thus be the same as $P(BA)$, the probability of A following B. But we also write

$$\begin{aligned} P(BA) &= P(B)P(A/B) \\ &= P(B)P(A) \end{aligned} \tag{7-12}$$

in this case. Then $P(A/B) = P(A)$, and A is independent of the occurrence of B.

Two events A and B are said to be *statistically independent* if their probabilities satisfy the equations

$$P(AB) = P(BA) = P(A)P(B) \tag{7-13}$$

and

$$P(B/A) = P(B) \qquad P(A/B) = P(A) \tag{7-14}$$

Some examples of conditional probability are in order at this point.

1. Consider an urn containing two white balls and three black balls. Two balls are drawn in succession, the first one not being replaced. What is the chance of picking two white balls in succession? (Note that this is similar to the two-card problem.)

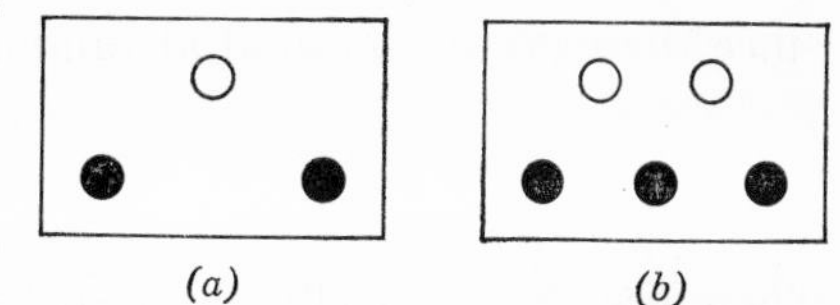
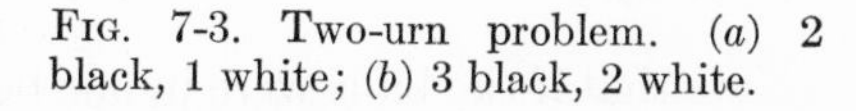
(a) (b)

FIG. 7-3. Two-urn problem. (a) 2 black, 1 white; (b) 3 black, 2 white.

Letting event A represent a white ball on draw 1, event B a white ball on draw 2,

$$P(AB) = P(A)P(B/A) = \frac{2}{5} \times \frac{1}{4} = \frac{1}{10}$$

Here two of the five balls are white so that the chances of drawing a white are $\frac{2}{5}$. Once a white is drawn, however, only one white ball remains among the four balls left. The chance of drawing a white ball now, assuming a white drawn on the first try, is $\frac{1}{4}$.

Alternatively we can say that there are $C_{5,2} = 5!/3!2! = 10$ possible combinations of five balls arranged in groups of two. Of these only one combination, two white balls, is of interest. The chance of drawing this combination is thus $P(AB) = 1/C_{5,2} = \frac{1}{10}$ again. (Combinations are used here instead of permutations because the two white balls drawn cannot be distinguished from one another.)

If the first ball were replaced before drawing the second, the two events would be *independent:*

$$P(AB) = P(A)P(B) = \left(\frac{2}{5}\right)^2 = \frac{4}{25}$$

2. Two urns contain white and black balls. Urn A contains two black balls and one white ball; urn B contains three black balls and two white balls (Fig. 7-3). One of the urns is selected at random, and one of the balls in it chosen. What is the probability $P(W)$ of drawing a white ball?

There are two ways of satisfying the desired event W—the drawing of one white ball:

a. Pick urn A; draw W.
b. Pick urn B; draw W.

These two subevents are mutually exclusive, so that

$$P(W) = P(AW) + P(BW)$$

But
$$P(AW) = P(A)P(W/A) = \frac{1}{2} \times \frac{1}{3} = \frac{1}{6}$$

Thus the probability of drawing a white ball from urn A is the probability $P(A) = 1/2$, of first picking A, times the probability $P(W/A) = 1/3$, that a white ball will be selected once A is chosen. [$P(A) = P(B) = 1/2$, since the urns are selected at random.] Similarly

$$P(BW) = P(B)P(W/B) = \frac{1}{2} \times \frac{2}{5} = \frac{1}{5}$$

Therefore
$$P(W) = 1/6 + 1/5 = 11/30$$

[Note that if the balls were in one box $P(W)$ would be $3/8$. Because of the two urns the balls are not equally likely to be drawn.]

3. Color blindness.[1] Assume that 5 men out of 100 and 25 women out of 10,000 are color-blind. A color-blind person is chosen at random from a representative sample of 10,000 men and 10,000 women. What is the probability that he will be male?

It may be assumed that 500 men and 25 women of this sample are color-blind. This gives a total of 525 color-blind persons. The probability that the person chosen will be male is thus $500/525 = 20/21$.

Alternatively let $N = 20{,}000$, $N_M = N_W = 10{,}000$ be the number of men or women in the sample, $N_C = 525$ be the total number of color-blind persons. $N_{MC} = 500$ represents the number of color-blind men. Then the conditional probability that a man is selected if a color-blind person is chosen is

$$P(M/C) = \frac{N_{MC}}{N_C} = \frac{500}{525}$$

As a check, let $P(MC)$ be the probability of selecting a color-blind man, $P(C)$ the probability of selecting a color-blind person.

$$P(MC) = P(C)P(M/C) = \frac{525}{20{,}000}\frac{500}{525} = \frac{500}{20{,}000}$$

as expected. We could also determine the probability of selecting a color-blind man by first picking a man at random. The chance of doing this is $P(M) = 1/2$. Once a man is selected, the probability that he is color-blind is $P(C/M) = 5/100$. The probability of picking a color-blind man is again $5/200$.

[1] Feller, *op. cit.*, chap. 5, p. 130, prob. 7.

4. Statistics of three-letter alphabets. Suppose that we have an alphabet containing three letters A, B, C. We wish to determine the statistics of messages using this alphabet. In particular what is the relative frequency of occurrence, or probability, of each letter, and the probability of two-letter groups such as AA, AB, BC, CA, etc., occurring? From this we can determine the statistical dependence (or independence) of successive letters.

We take a typical example of a message using this three-letter alphabet and proceed to count the frequency of occurrence of the individual letters and groups of two successive letters. This is then an example of the repeated experiment mentioned previously as a method of determining the different probabilities of interest. A typical message of 50 letters appears as follows:

CBACABCABABCCBBABBCABAAAACACCBBCC
ACCBBBBACCAACBABC

Letting n = the total number of letters, n_A the number of A's, n_B the number of pairs (diads) of AA, n_{AB} the number of pairs of AB, n_{BA} the pairs of BA, etc., we get $n = 50$: $n_A = 16$, $n_B = 17$, $n_C = 17$, and

$$\begin{array}{lll} n_{AA} = 4 & n_{AB} = 6 & n_{AC} = 6 \\ n_{BA} = 6 & n_{BB} = 6 & n_{BC} = 5 \\ n_{CA} = 6 & n_{CB} = 5 & n_{CC} = 5 \end{array}$$

From the almost equal number of times that the different letters appear we can conclude that the letter probabilities are equal. The different letters are thus equally likely in this particular three-letter language.

$$P(A) = \frac{n_A}{n} = 0.32 \qquad P(B) = 0.34 = P(C)$$

are the calculated probabilities, and 0.33 would be the actual probabilities if the letters were equally likely to occur.

The conditional probabilities can be calculated quite easily from the number of times the different pairs appear. For example,

$$P(B/A) = \frac{P(AB)}{P_A} = \frac{n_{AB}}{n_A} = \frac{6}{16}$$

Thus $P(B/A)$ represents the number of times that an A is followed by a B. Repeating this calculation for the different pair combinations—nine in number—we get the following conditional-probability table.[1]

[1] C. E. Shannon, A Mathematical Theory of Communication, *Bell System Tech. J.*, vol. 27, pp. 379–423, July, 1948.

CALCULATED PROBABILITIES

$P(j/i)$		j		
		A	B	C
i	A	$4/16$	$6/16$	$6/16$
	B	$6/17$	$6/17$	$5/17$
	C	$6/17$	$5/17$	$5/17$

THEORETICAL PROBABILITIES, ASSUMING STATISTICAL INDEPENDENCE

$P(j/i)$		j		
		A	B	C
i	A	$1/3$	$1/3$	$1/3$
	B	$1/3$	$1/3$	$1/3$
	C	$1/3$	$1/3$	$1/3$

Both the table and the list of the number of times each pair appears lead us to conclude that the letters in the pair combinations are *statistically independent.* For statistical independence $P(j/i) = P(j)$, or the probability of occurrence of any letter is independent of the letter preceding. Here, theoretically, we would expect all the $P(j/i)$'s to be $1/3$. Because of the relatively short length of the message used (small sample, small number of experiment repetitions) the actual frequencies calculated differ somewhat.

C. E. Shannon has published an example of a three-letter alphabet in which any letter in a particular sequence is dependent on the letter immediately preceding.[1] (There is no dependence on letters before that one.) This alphabet consists of the letters A, B, C with the following probability tables:

i	$P(i)$
A	$9/27$
B	$16/27$
C	$2/27$

$P(j/i)$		j		
		A	B	C
i	A	0	$4/5$	$1/5$
	B	$1/2$	$1/2$	0
	C	$1/2$	$2/5$	$1/10$

The letter B should thus occur most frequently, the letter C only occasionally. The letter A has 0 probability of being followed by another A, as is true also for C following a B. Each time A appears there is a $4/5$ probability that a B will follow, a $1/5$ probability that a C will follow. A C is followed by a B $2/5$ of the time, by an A $1/2$ of the time, by another C $1/10$ of the time.

A typical message given by Shannon for this three-letter language is

ABBABABABABABABBBABBBBBAB
ABABABABBBACACABBABBBBABB
ABACBBBABA

[1] *Ibid.*

Calculating the number of times each letter and each pair of letters occurs, just as we did previously, we get $n = 60$:

$$\begin{array}{lll} n_A = 22 & n_B = 35 & n_C = 3 \\ n_{AA} = 0 & n_{AB} = 18 & n_{AC} = 3 \\ n_{BA} = 19 & n_{BB} = 16 & n_{BC} = 0 \\ n_{CA} = 2 & n_{CB} = 1 & n_{CC} = 0 \end{array}$$

Again calculating a conditional probability table based on the actual relative frequencies, we get:

CALCULATED

$P(j/i)$		j: A	j: B	j: C
i	A	0	$18/22$	$3/22$
	B	$19/35$	$16/35$	0
	C	$2/3$	$1/3$	0

THEORETICAL

$P(j/i)$		j: A	j: B	j: C
i	A	0	$4/5$	$1/5$
	B	$1/2$	$1/2$	0
	C	$1/2$	$2/5$	$1/10$

Note again that the calculated probabilities, based on relative frequencies of occurrence, and the theoretical probabilities agree reasonably well. The reader should check these results for himself. He should also calculate the joint probabilities $P(ij)$ and compare for both the theoretical and actual cases.

7-3. Discrete and Continuous Probability Distributions. In this introductory discussion of probability we have thus far been primarily concerned with calculating the probability of occurrence of a finite number of discrete events. For instance, in the coin-tossing example there were two possible events: head or tail. In the case of a die we might be interested in the probability of one of the six possible faces coming up. In the case of the English alphabet there are 26 letters, and we may ask for the probability that one of them, say f, will occur.

In all these examples we can represent the different possible outcomes by a discrete variable x. If x has n distinct values $x_1, x_2, \ldots, x_n$, each of which has probability $P_1, P_2, P_3, \ldots, P_n$, x is called a discrete chance variable, or discrete stochastic variable, or *discrete random variable.* As an example, say that we toss two dice. Let x represent the number coming up on any throw. Then x takes on the discrete values 2, 3, 4, . . . , 12, each one with its associated probability.

If the variable x is now allowed to take *any* value in a whole interval, however, and to each subinterval in the over-all interval there is associated a probability of occurrence, x is called a *continuous random variable.* For example, if we start a pointer on a wheel spinning, the pointer will stop at *any* position on the wheel's circumference. It is not limited to discrete positions only.

We shall be primarily concerned with continuous chance variables because of our interest in the statistics of noise and signals in noise. If we were to plot the noise voltage at the output of an amplifier, for example, it might have the continuous appearance of the curve of Fig. 7-2. *All* values of voltage are possible, not just discrete values.

How do we now compute probabilities in the case of continuous chance variables?

We shall start by using the relative-frequency approach of the past two sections. In dealing with continuous variables we shall find it convenient to introduce a *probability-density function.* We shall compare this probability-density function with the analogous mass density with which we are presumably quite familiar. Charge-density functions occur of course in electric-field problems also and are used to compute the field due to a continuous, or smoothed-out, array of charge, rather than discrete charges.

As an example of the determination of probability for continuous chance variables, say that we are interested in determining the distribution of height among American males. The height of a man may take on *any* value within a specified interval and thus represents a *continuous* random variable. Once we have such a height distribution, we may use this to calculate the probability that the height of a given male will lie between 5 ft 7 in. and 5 ft 9 in. We may use this to determine an average height, etc.

Assume that we select for this determination a representative sample of 1,000 men. We measure their heights (this is an example of the repeated experiment of Secs. 7-1 and 7-2) and group them according to the nearest even inch (5 ft 0 in., 5 ft 2 in., 5 ft 4 in., etc.). All heights from 4 ft 11 in. to 5 ft 1 in. will, for example, be grouped in the 5 ft 0 in. category. The relative frequency of men found in each height interval is then the number grouped in that interval divided by the total number (1,000). A typical plot of such a height distribution is shown in Fig. 7-4. x represents the height, n_x/n the relative number of men grouped in the interval Δx in. about x. n is the 1,000-man sample here. Since all heights in a 2-in. interval about the even heights are grouped together, they are shown as horizontal lines covering the 2-in. grouping. For a large enough sample we can say that n_x/n represents the probability $P(x_j)$ that the height of an American male will lie between $x_j - \Delta x/2$ and $x_j + \Delta x/2$.

This probability $P(x_j)$ obviously depends on the choice of interval size Δx (2 in. here). For if we decrease Δx, say to 1 in., the number of men in this height interval decreases also. In particular, if we begin using smaller and smaller intervals, the ordinate will become smaller and smaller also. Eventually, if the height intervals are made very small (0.1 in., for example), very few men will be found in any one interval. The plot of relative distribution vs. height approaches zero and is of little value to us. Recall in Sec. 6-1 that, for nonperiodic time functions with continuous frequency spectra, the power (or energy) at any one frequency was zero. The energy contained within a specified frequency interval

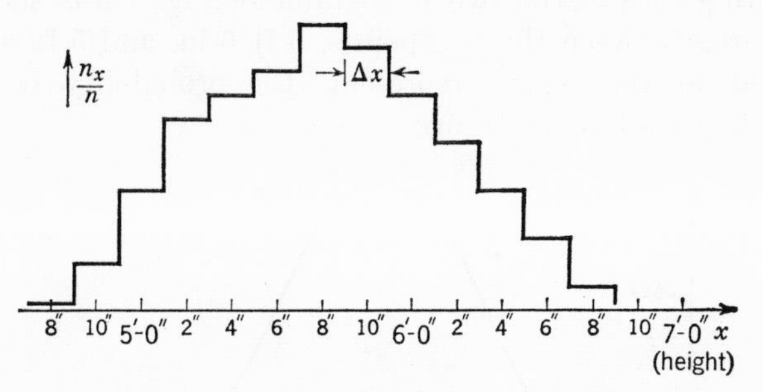

FIG. 7-4. Relative distribution of heights.

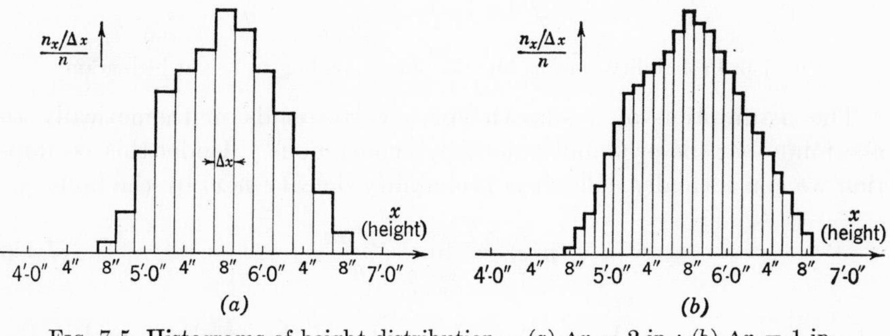

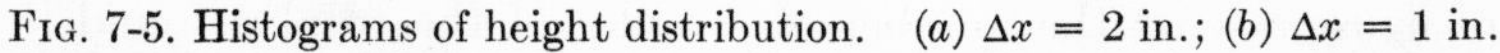

FIG. 7-5. Histograms of height distribution. (a) $\Delta x = 2$ in.; (b) $\Delta x = 1$ in.

was nonzero, however, and led us to define a spectral-density function as a limiting function.

Here too, because heights are continuously distributed, the chance of a man having a specific height given to three or four significant figures is negligible. But the chance of a man having a height somewhere within a 1-in. or 2-in. interval can be calculated.

To do away with the dependence on the size of the interval Δx chosen for the height distribution, we represent the height distribution, at a particular height and of interval Δx, by a rectangle of area n_x/n. The height of this rectangle will be $(1/\Delta x)(n_x/n)$, its width Δx. Such a relative-frequency curve is called a *histogram*. Two histograms for the height example used here are shown in Fig. 7-5*a* and *b*, one for $\Delta x = 2$ in., the other for $\Delta x = 1$ in. For a large enough sample size the probability that a man's height will lie between two given heights, 5 ft 7 in. and

5 ft 9 in., for example, will now be the area of the histogram between these two limits.

If the histogram approaches a smooth curve as $\Delta x \to 0$, the ordinate takes on the form of a *probability-density function*, with the *area* under the curve between two points giving the probability that the height will be found between these two points. The probability-density function as the limiting case of the two histograms of Fig. 7-5 is shown in Fig. 7-6. The area between the two points, 5 ft 6 in. and 5 ft 8 in., shown crosshatched in the figure, represents the probability that a man's height will be found in that range.

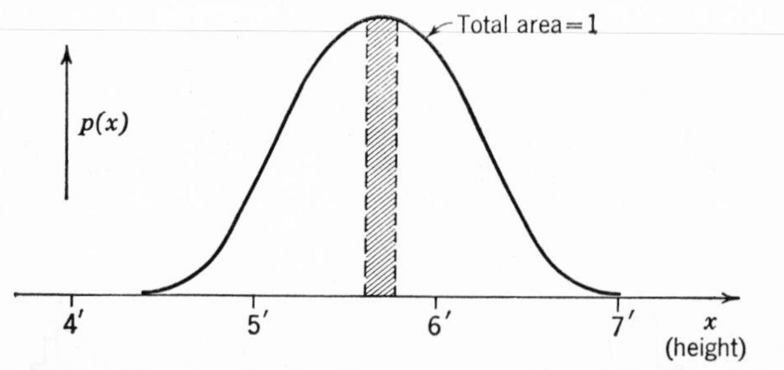

FIG. 7-6. Probability-density function corresponding to height histogram.

The assumption of a smooth curve corresponds mathematically to assuming that the probability density is continuous. Under this assumption we can formally define the probability density $p(x)$ by the limit

$$p(x) = \lim_{\substack{\Delta x \to 0 \\ n \to \infty}} \frac{n_x/\Delta x}{n} \tag{7-15}$$

where n_x represents the number of samples of the total n found in the range $x - \Delta x/2$ to $x + \Delta x/2$. The probability that the variable x will lie in the range x_1 to x_2 is then the area under the $p(x)$ curve, or

$$\text{Prob } (x_1 < x < x_2) = \int_{x_1}^{x_2} p(x)\, dx \tag{7-16}$$

In particular the probability that x will lie somewhere in its allowable range of variation must be 1. In general x can range from $-\infty$ to ∞ (the voltage at the output of an amplifier is an example). In special cases it may range only between 0 and ∞ (the variation of height, for example) or between 0 and 2π (for example, the rotation of a pointer on a wheel). For the general case of x ranging between $-\infty$ and ∞

$$\int_{-\infty}^{\infty} p(x)\, dx = 1 \tag{7-17}$$

The histogram, or probability-density curves, must be normalized to have unity area.

From the definition of probability density $p(x)$ must be a function which is always positive. Thus

$$p(x) \geq 0 \tag{7-18}$$

Equations (7-17) and (7-18) represent two conditions that must be satisfied by any probability-density function, as, for example, the one of Fig. 7-6.

To emphasize the fact that $p(x)$ represents only a probability-*density* function, with $p(x)\,dx$ the probability that x will be found in the range $x \pm dx/2$, we define another important function, the *cumulative distribution function* $P(x)$. (For conciseness this will often be referred to as the distribution function.) This is defined to be the probability that the variable will be less than some value x. Since all values of x are mutually exclusive (a noise voltage can have only one value at any instant; a pointer may stop only at one point), $P(x)$ must be the sum of all the probabilities from $-\infty$ to x. This is just the area under the $p(x)$ curve from $-\infty$ to x. $P(x)$ is thus given by

$$P(x) = \int_{-\infty}^{x} p(x)\,dx \tag{7-19}$$

Equation (7-19) is the indefinite integral of $p(x)$. If $P(x)$ possesses a first derivative, we have

$$p(x) = \frac{dP(x)}{dx} \tag{7-20}$$

Equations (7-19) and (7-20) relate the probability-density function and the distribution function.

Since $p(x) \geq 0$ and $\int_{-\infty}^{\infty} p(x)\,dx = 1$, $P(x)$ must satisfy the inequality

$$0 \leq P(x) \leq 1 \tag{7-21}$$

$P(x)$ is a continuously or monotonically increasing function, going from 0 to 1. A typical density function and its corresponding distribution function are shown in Fig. 7-7. $P(x)$ corresponds to the crosshatched area of Fig. 7-7*a*. It is left to the reader to show very simply that the probability that x will lie somewhere between x_1 and x_2 can be found from the distribution function by the relation

$$\text{Prob}\,(x_1 < x < x_2) = \int_{x_1}^{x_2} p(x)\,dx = P(x_2) - P(x_1) \tag{7-22}$$

The rotating pointer on a wheel serves as a good example of these different relations. Intuitively we feel that a freely rotating pointer has an equally likely chance of stopping anywhere on the wheel. The probability that it will stop at any one angle θ is zero since there is an infinity of points, but the probability of its stopping within some angular range $d\theta$ is proportional to $d\theta$ and independent of the particular value of θ (Fig. 7-8a). Since this probability must be $p(\theta)\,d\theta$, with $p(\theta)$ the density function, $p(\theta)$ must be a constant K for this example. The constant is found by invoking the specification that the area under the $p(\theta)$ curve must be 1.

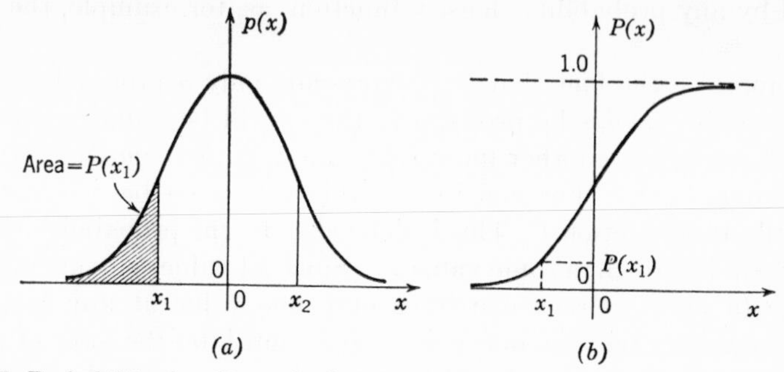

FIG. 7-7. Probability-density and -distribution functions. (a) $p(x)$ = density function; (b) $P(x)$ = distribution function.

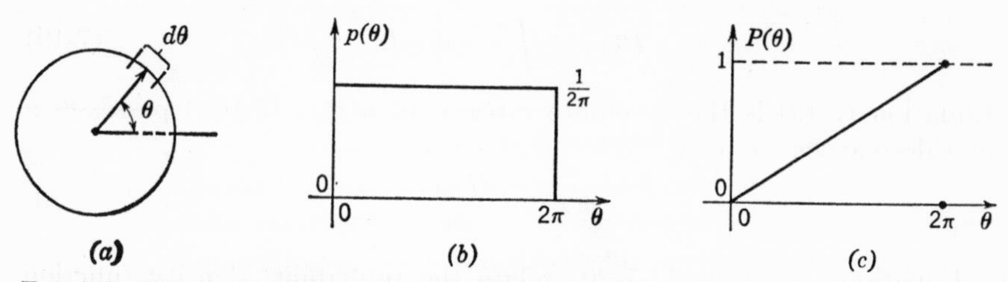

FIG. 7-8. Rotating pointer and probability functions. (a) Rotating pointer; (b) probability-density function; (c) distribution function.

(The pointer will obviously stop somewhere on the wheel rim.) Thus

$$\int_0^{2\pi} p(\theta)\,d\theta = 1 = K\int_0^{2\pi} d\theta = 2\pi K \tag{7-23}$$

and

$$p(\theta) = \frac{1}{2\pi} \tag{7-24}$$

This serves to normalize $p(\theta)$ properly. $p(\theta)$ in this case is one example of the rectangular density function to which we shall have occasion to refer in more detail later.

The cumulative distribution function $P(\theta)$ is the probability that the variable will be less than θ. In this case the lower limit of θ is 0, and

$$P(\theta) = \int_0^{\theta} p(\theta)\,d\theta = \frac{\theta}{2\pi} \tag{7-25}$$

This agrees with our intuitive feeling that all values of θ are equally likely. Both $p(\theta)$ and $P(\theta)$ are shown sketched in Fig. 7-8. The probability that θ will be less than $\pi/4$, for example, is $\frac{1}{8}$. The probability that it will be less than π is $\frac{1}{2}$.

The probability that θ will lie between $\pi/2$ and π is

$$P(\pi) - P\left(\frac{\pi}{2}\right) = \frac{\pi}{4\pi} = \frac{1}{4}$$

as is to be expected.

We have been discussing the probability-density function, $p(x)$, for continuous variables. Can we also define such a function for discrete variables? This will be of particular interest in problems where a variable may have both discrete and continuous ranges. We shall now show

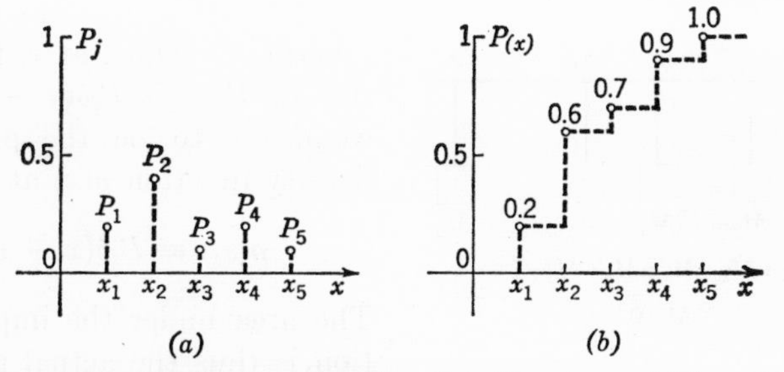

FIG. 7-9. Probability-distribution function for discrete variable. (a) Individual probabilities; (b) cumulative distributive function.

that the impulse, or delta, function serves to connect the discrete and continuous cases. This is similar to the power-spectrum analysis of Sec. 6-1, where we considered the spectrum of combined periodic and nonperiodic voltages.

We can develop the required relationship quite simply from the cumulative distribution function. Assume a discrete random variable x with values $x_1, x_2, \ldots, x_n$. Corresponding to each value of x is a probability $P_1, P_2, \ldots, P_n$. An example is depicted in Fig. 7-9a. Since the values of x are mutually exclusive and some one value of x must occur,

$$P_1 + P_2 + \cdots + P_n = 1 \tag{7-26}$$

The probability that x will be less than some value x_j can again be defined as a cumulative distribution function $P(x)$. Since all values of x are mutually exclusive, $P(x_j)$ will be equal to the sum of the probabilities $P_1 + P_2 + \cdots + P_{j-1}$. Thus

$$P(x_j) = P_1 + P_2 + \cdots + P_{j-1} \tag{7-27}$$

For example, assume that x represents the number given by the toss of two dice. The numbers possible are $x = 2, 3, \ldots, 8, \ldots, 12$, and the corresponding probabilities are $\frac{1}{36}, \frac{2}{36}, \ldots, \frac{5}{36}, \ldots, \frac{1}{36}$, respectively. (The reader can check this for himself.) The probability that a number less than 5 will come up is then the sum of the probabilities of the numbers 2, 3, 4, or $\frac{1}{36} + \frac{2}{36} + \frac{3}{36} = \frac{1}{6}$.

Since the individual probabilities P_1, P_2, etc., are all greater than or equal to 0, the distribution function $P(x)$ must monotonically increase with x, just as in the case of the continuous random variable. Although it is defined only at the points $x_1, x_2, \ldots, x_n$, we may arbitrarily draw it as a series of ascending steps, as in Fig. 7-9b. The jump at step x_2 is just $P_2 = 0.4$, for example.

Although the derivative of $P(x)$ for the discrete variable does not exist in the usual sense (limit of ratio $\Delta P/\Delta x$ as $\Delta x \to 0$), we may define the derivative in terms of impulse functions. Thus, at x_j the derivative of $P(x)$ is $P_j\delta(x - x_j)$. This we *define* to be the probability-density function $p(x)$ at $x = x_j$.

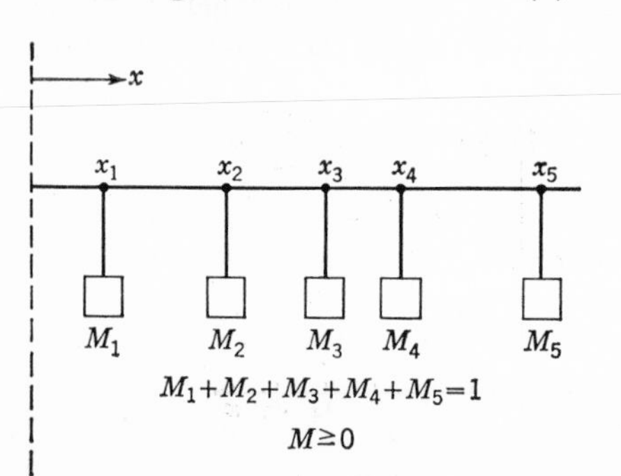

FIG. 7-10. Discrete mass distribution.

$$p(x_j) \equiv P_j\delta(x - x_j) \qquad (7\text{-}28)$$

The area under the impulse function is thus the actual probability at the point in question. In terms of this impulse-type density function the sum representation of the distribution function $P(x)$ given by Eq. (7-27) becomes the integral

$$P(x) = \int_{-\infty}^{x} p(x)\,dx \qquad (7\text{-}29)$$

where

$$p(x) = \sum_{j=1}^{n} P_j\delta(x - x_j) \qquad (7\text{-}30)$$

We thus generalize our concept of probability density to include discrete random variables as well as continuous random variables by utilizing the delta function. This is of course exactly analogous to the generalization of power spectral density in Chap. 6 to include periodic time functions.

Mass Analogy. It is instructive to relate the concepts of density and distribution functions to the analogous and familiar relations involving the distribution of mass. (Another analogy is that involving charge distributions.)

Consider first a weightless bar as shown in Fig. 7-10 with masses $M_1, M_2, \ldots, M_n$ suspended at distances $x_1, x_2, \ldots, x_n$ from the left end. The weights are normalized to a total weight of 1 lb, so that

$$M_1 + M_2 + \cdots + M_n = 1$$

The masses are then analogous to the probabilities at different values of the discrete variable and could be plotted as in Fig. 7-9*a*.

The cumulative mass distribution $M(x_j)$ can be defined to be the tota mass to the left of x_j and is obviously

$$M(x_j) = M_1 + M_2 + \cdots + M_{j-1} \leq 1$$

$M(x_j)$ would plot in the manner of $P(x_j)$ in Fig. 7-9*b*.

Now consider a second bar with no hanging weights, but with a mass density $m(x)$, or (mass)/(unit length), varying in some manner along the bar. The *total* mass is still normalized to be 1. If the total length of the bar is l ft, $m(x)$ must satisfy the relation

$$\int_0^l m(x)\,dx = 1$$

Between any two infinitesimally separated points the mass included is $m\,dx$ lb. For example, if the mass is uniformly distributed, $m(x)$ is a constant equal to $1/l$ lb/ft. A sketch of $m(x)$ would be similar to the $p(\theta)$ function shown in Fig. 7-8*b*.

The cumulative distribution function $M(x)$, or the mass of the bar included at all points less than x, is

$$M(x) = \int_0^x m(x)\,dx = \frac{x}{l} \qquad \text{lb}$$

for the uniformly distributed case. This corresponds to the sketch of $P(\theta)$ in Fig. 7-8*c*.

In all cases we must have $m(x) \geq 0$ and $0 \leq M(x) \leq 1$ is a monotonically increasing function. The mass included between two points x_1 and x_2 is given by

$$\int_{x_1}^{x_2} m(x)\,dx = M(x_2) - M(x_1)$$

All these relations are obviously identical with those set down for the probability-density and distribution functions. Just as in the probability case we must remember that $m(x)$ is a mass *density*, that only $m(x)\,dx$ represents mass (in particular, the mass between $x - dx/2$ and $x + dx/2$), and that the mass at any *one* point is zero if the mass is distributed smoothly throughout the bar.

Another example of a mass-density function might be one in which the density progressively increases along the bar. For example, let $m(x) = Kx$ lb/ft. With the total weight maintained at 1 lb the constant K is given by

$$\int_0^l m(x)\,dx = 1 = K\int_0^l x\,dx = \frac{Kl^2}{2}$$

Then $K = 2/l^2$, and $m(x) = 2x/l^2$ lb/ft. The mass-distribution function is now

$$M(x) = \int_0^x m(x)\,dx = \frac{x^2}{l^2}$$

Both $m(x)$ and $M(x)$ for this example are shown sketched in Fig. 7-11.

We can of course extend this analogy, just as in the probability case, to include a bar with both discrete weight and distributed mass. The mass-density function would now include delta functions corresponding to the discrete masses.

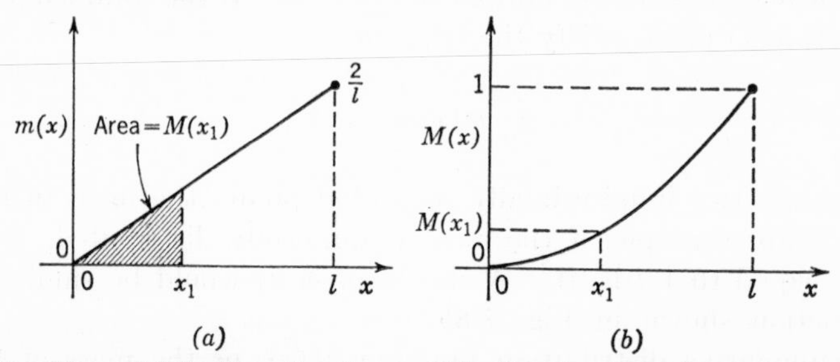

FIG. 7-11. Mass-distribution functions. (a) Density function; (b) distribution function.

7-4. Statistical Averages and Examples of Density Functions. The probability-density functions discussed in the previous section provide us with information as to the probability or chance that a random variable will occupy a specified portion of its range. As such, they may also be interpreted as *weighting functions*, analogous to the weighting functions discussed in Chap. 2. Because of this weighting property the density function also provides us with information as to the *average* value of a given random variable.

To demonstrate this, assume first that we have a discrete variable x, whose average value we would like to calculate. x can take on the values $x_1, x_2, \ldots, x_n$. We again perform repetitions of a hypothetical experiment, measuring the number of times N_1 that x_1 appears, the number of times N_2 that x_2 appears, etc. The total number of trials N is

$$N_1 + N_2 + \cdots + N_n = N \tag{7-31}$$

The arithmetic average of x is then found in the usual way by *weighting* each value of x by the number of times it appears, summing the weighted values of x, and dividing by the total number of trials N. Thus, av x, the average value of x, is simply

$$\text{av } x = \frac{x_1N_1 + x_2N_2 + \cdots + x_nN_n}{N} \tag{7-32}$$

For a large enough number of trials, however, N_1/N is just the relative frequency of occurrence of x, or its probability P_1. (The expression "large enough number of trials" is taken to mean in an intuitive sense the number of trials beyond which we can detect no significant difference in the calculation of N_1/N and of av x.) We can thus write

$$\text{av } x = \sum_{j=1}^{n} P_j x_j \qquad \sum_{j=1}^{n} P_j = 1 \tag{7-33}$$

In a similar way we could find the average of the square of x, the average of the square root of x, etc. In general, if we are interested in the average value of some function $F(x)$, we determine it in the same manner and write

$$\text{av } F(x) = \sum_{j=1}^{n} P_j F(x_j) \tag{7-34}$$

Note that the individual probabilities P_j behave like weighting parameters; those values of x most likely to occur (i.e., those with the highest probabilities) are weighted most heavily in determining the average value. As a special case, if x_5 has a probability $P_5 = 1$ of occurring and all other values of x have zero probability, av $F(x) = F(x_5)$, as expected.

The calculation of the average value of x or of some function $F(x)$ is carried out in the same way for continuous variables. Assume that we perform a hypothetical series of measurements on x. We choose x at Δx intervals, just as in the previous section, for determining the histogram of x. From these measurements we calculate av x or av $F(x)$ as a straight arithmetic average. Alternatively we can utilize the information that $p(x)\,\Delta x$ is the probability that x will be found in the range $x \pm \Delta x/2$. From Eq. (7-34), then,

$$\text{av } F(x) = \sum_{j} F(x_j)p(x_j)\,\Delta x$$

In the limit, as $\Delta x \to 0$,

$$\text{av } F(x) = \int_{-\infty}^{\infty} F(x)p(x)\,dx \tag{7-35}$$

As a special case the average value of x is

$$\text{av } x = \int_{-\infty}^{\infty} xp(x)\,dx \tag{7-36}$$

in agreement also with Eq. (7-33).

The average value of x, av x, is frequently also called the *first moment*, m_1, of x by analogy with the concept of moments in mechanics. In mechanics the first moment of a group of masses is just the average location of the masses, or their center of gravity. For example, the center of gravity of the masses $M_1, M_2, \ldots$ in Fig. 7-10 can be found simply by taking moments about $x = 0$. The average value of x, or the center of gravity, is

$$\text{av } x = \frac{M_1x_1 + M_2x_2 + \cdots}{M_1 + M_2 + \cdots}$$

identical with the form of Eq. (7-32). If the mass is not concentrated at discrete points but is smeared out over the bar, we can calculate the center of gravity by considering a differential mass $m(x)\,dx$ [with $m(x)$ the linear mass density] located x units from the origin. The center of gravity is then found by summing all the mass contributions. This sum again becomes an integral, and we have

$$\text{av } x = \int_0^l xm(x)\,dx$$

just as in Eq. (7-36).

The second moment in mechanics is just the moment of inertia of a mass or the turning moment of a torque about a specified point. By analogy with mechanics the second moment of a random variable is the average value of the square of the variable. For discrete variables this is given by

$$m_2 = \text{av } x^2 = \sum_{j=1}^{n} P_jx_j^2 \tag{7-37}$$

as a special case of Eq. (7-34). For a continuous variable we have

$$m_2 = \text{av } x^2 = \int_{-\infty}^{\infty} x^2p(x)\,dx \tag{7-38}$$

as a special case of Eq. (7-35).

We can continue defining higher moments if we wish. In general the nth moment of x, or av x^n, is given by

$$m_n = \text{av } x^n = \int_{-\infty}^{\infty} x^np(x)\,dx \tag{7-39}$$

The density function $p(x)$ plays the role of a weighting function throughout. If some particular range of x, say in the vicinity of x_j, occurs most frequently, the probability-density function will be highly peaked about that point. The nth moment will then be very nearly x_j^n. In particular, if

$$p(x) = \delta(x - x_j) \tag{7-40}$$

$$m_n = \int_{-\infty}^{\infty} x^n\delta(x - x_j)\,dx = x_j^n \tag{7-41}$$

Here x_j is the only point weighted, to the exclusion of all other points.

The delta function is one example of a probability-density function. It enables us to include the case of a variable defined to have one value only. If x is a discrete variable, the density function may be written as a sum of weighted impulse functions as in Eq. (7-30). Thus

$$p(x) = \sum_{j=1}^{m} P_j \delta(x - x_j) \tag{7-42}$$

and

$$m_n = \text{av } x^n = \int_{-\infty}^{\infty} x^n \left[\sum_{j=1}^{m} P_j \delta(x - x_j) \right] dx$$

$$= \sum_{j=1}^{m} P_j x^n \tag{7-43}$$

checking Eq. (7-34).

What is the significance of these moments?

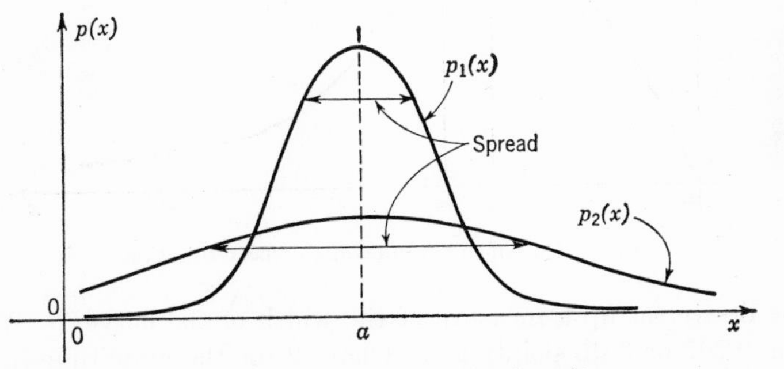

FIG. 7-12. Two possible density functions.

We shall see later on in signal and noise problems that m_1 gives just the d-c voltage or current. m_2 will be found to give the mean-squared voltage (current) or the mean power. These quantities can easily be measured with meters, and they are just the mean values used in Chap. 6 to calculate signal-to-noise ratios. Since m_1 and m_2 can be determined from the probability-density function $p(x)$, it should be possible in turn to say something about $p(x)$, given the measured values of m_1 and m_2.

Consider, for example, the two possible probability-density functions shown in Fig. 7-12. What are the distinguishing characteristics of these two density functions? Obviously $p_1(x)$ is more highly peaked about point a. $p_2(x)$ is more squat and spread out over a larger range of x. A wider range of values of x will thus appear in the case of $p_2(x)$, while in the case of $p_1(x)$ values close to a will appear much more frequently than those somewhat removed. We would expect that the average value of x would be close to, or equal to, a in both cases.

In this particular case the curves happen to have two distinguishing parameters: the location of the peak (a in this case), and the width, or spread, of the curves. We would probably agree intuitively that the first moment m_1 serves as some measure of the location of the peak in this case. (If the curve is symmetrical and unimodal, i.e., one peak, the peak will occur at m_1.) In general m_1 is one possible measure of the location of the range of most probable values of x. Other measures used and, in general, providing results not too different from m_1 are the median, or point at which the cumulative distribution $P(x)$ is 0.5, and the mode, or actual value at which the peak occurs if a single peak exists. Figure 7-13 shows one example of an unsymmetrical density function that we shall encounter later. Here $m_1 >$ modal point.

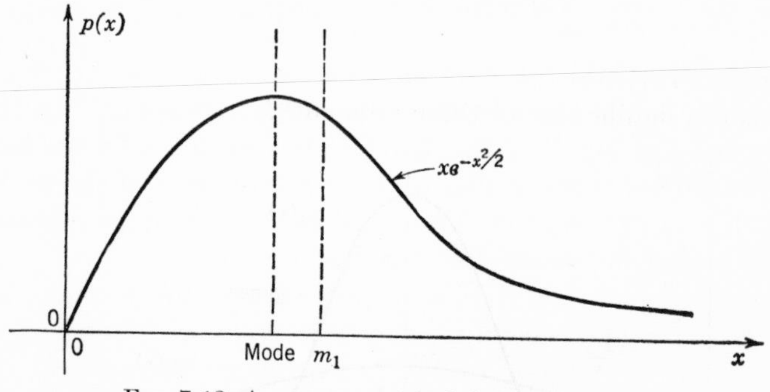

FIG. 7-13. An unsymmetrical density function.

How do we set up a measure of the width of the curves? We could use the 0.707 or 3-db points as in Chap. 2 for the amplitude-frequency response curves. We could also use a specified percentage of the total area about point a as a measure of this spread. In general the measure of the width or criterion used to define a spread parameter is completely arbitrary. One possible measure of the width of the curve about a is the mean-squared variation about a:

$$s = \text{spread} \equiv \int_{-\infty}^{\infty} (x - a)^2 p(x)\, dx \tag{7-44}$$

Because of the squared term, values of x to either side of a are equally significant in measuring variations away from a. If $p(x)$ happens to be a broad function such as $p_2(x)$ in Fig. 7-12, values of x far removed from a will still have sufficiently large values of $p_2(x)$ to be weighted strongly and provide a large value of spread, as desired. If $p(x)$ is a narrow function, such as $p_1(x)$, only those values of x close to a will be weighted significantly, and the spread will be correspondingly smaller.

In general this measure of the width of the curve $p(x)$ will vary with the value of a chosen. Although a was picked as the peak location in Fig. 7-12, it could have been chosen anywhere else, with Eq. (7-44) defined to be the spread about that point. The value of a for which the spread is a minimum is of interest. To find this point, differentiate

Eq. (7-44) with respect to a. This gives

$$\frac{ds}{da} = 0 = -2 \int_{-\infty}^{\infty} (x - a)p(x)\,dx$$
$$= 2a \int_{-\infty}^{\infty} p(x)\,dx - 2 \int_{-\infty}^{\infty} xp(x)\,dx \tag{7-45}$$

But $p(x)\,dx = 1$ and $m_1 = \int_{-\infty}^{\infty} xp(x)\,dx$ by definition. Then

$$a = m_1 = \int_{-\infty}^{\infty} xp(x)\,dx$$

or the point about which this mean-squared measure of the curve width is a minimum is just the average value, or first moment. In the symmetrical curves of Fig. 7-12 this happens to coincide with the peak. In the unsymmetrical curve of Fig. 7-13 it is to the right of the peak. The fact that $a = m_1$ gives a minimum and not a maximum is shown very simply by taking the second derivative of Eq. (7-44).

The spread about m_1, or the mean-squared variation about m_1, is called the *variance* or second central moment μ_2.

$$\mu_2 \equiv \int_{-\infty}^{\infty} (x - m_1)^2 p(x)\,dx = \text{av } (x - m_1)^2 \tag{7-46}$$

The square root of this term is called the *standard deviation* and is frequently given the symbol σ. We shall use σ as the measure of the spread of the density function about m_1. Thus

$$\mu_2 = \sigma^2$$

Multiplying out the squared term in the integral of Eq. (7-46) and integrating term by term, we get

$$\mu_2 = \sigma^2 = \int_{-\infty}^{\infty} (x - m_1)^2 p(x)\,dx$$
$$= \int_{-\infty}^{\infty} x^2 p(x)\,dx - 2m_1 \int_{-\infty}^{\infty} xp(x)\,dx + m_1^2 \int_{-\infty}^{\infty} p(x)\,dx$$
$$= m_2 - m_1^2 \tag{7-47}$$

from Eq. (7-36).

The variance is thus the second moment less the square of the first moment. m_2 represents the spread of the curve about $x = 0$, μ_2 about $x = m_1$. Equation (7-47) is analogous to the parallel-axis theorem of mechanics, with m_2 the moment of inertia about the origin, μ_2 the moment of inertia about the center of gravity. In terms of mean-squared voltages and mean power, μ_2 or σ^2 will be considered later on to be the mean a-c power and σ the rms a-c voltage.

The equivalent relation for μ_2 for the discrete-variable case is left to the reader as an exercise.

We now consider two typical distribution functions as illustrative examples of the above ideas.

1. Rectangular distribution. Assume that the random variable x is uniformly distributed with density function $p(x) = K$ between $x = a$ and $x = b$ (Fig. 7-14). The pointer problem of the previous section is one example of this density function. (There we had $a = 0$, $b = 2\pi$.) The PCM quantization error discussed in Sec. 6-7 was assumed to be uniformly distributed and hence has this form of density function. The variable x has no values less than a and greater than b and is equally likely to be found anywhere from a to b.

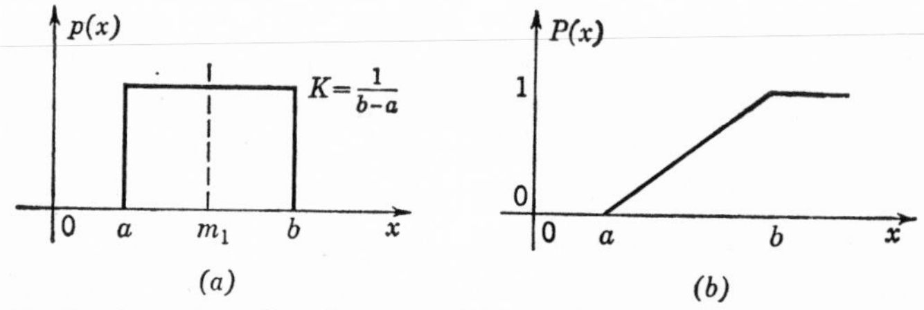

FIG. 7-14. Rectangular distribution. (a) Probability density; (b) distribution function.

Judging from the curve of Fig. 7-14, we should expect the average value to be halfway between a and b, or at $m_1 = (a + b)/2$. The width of the curve should obviously be related to $b - a$.

Since $p(x)$ must be normalized to have unity area [the probability that x lies somewhere between a and b is $\int_a^b p(x)\,dx = 1$], the constant K must be $1/(b - a)$. m_1 is given by

$$m_1 = \int_a^b xp(x)\,dx = \frac{1}{b-a}\int_a^b x\,dx = \frac{a+b}{2} \tag{7-48}$$

as expected. The second moment m_2 is given by

$$\begin{aligned} m_2 &= \int_a^b x^2p(x)\,dx = \frac{1}{b-a}\int_a^b x^2\,dx = \frac{b^3 - a^3}{3(b-a)} \\ &= \frac{b^2 + ab + a^2}{3} \end{aligned} \tag{7-49}$$

The variance is then

$$\sigma^2 = m_2 - m_1^2 = \frac{(b-a)^2}{12} \tag{7-50}$$

This result could have been obtained just as well by finding σ^2 directly from Eq. (7-46). The standard deviation σ is then

$$\sigma = \frac{b-a}{2\sqrt{3}} \tag{7-51}$$

It thus appears in terms of $b - a$, as expected.

Note that if the width of the curve, $b - a$, is made smaller, the height $1/(b - a)$ increases correspondingly. The variable x is constrained to lie within a narrower range of variation and has a greater probability of doing so. Ultimately, as $b - a \to 0$, by letting b approach a, the height $\to \infty$, but with the area under the curve always equal to 1. In the limit $p(x) \to \delta(x - a)$, and the variable has only one possible value, $x = a$, with a probability of 1.

As an example of the use of the rectangular distribution, we can let the variable x be the PCM quantization error ϵ of Sec. 6-7. This error was the error due to quantization of continuous voltages measured within a specified range about a particular voltage level. If all voltages about this level are assumed equally likely to occur, ϵ will be uniformly distributed with zero average value. The voltage separation between adjacent levels is just the $b - a$ variation here. If this is set equal to a volts, as in Sec. 6-7, the rms quantization error is the standard deviation σ, or $a/(2\sqrt{3})$ volts. This was exactly the result obtained in Chap. 6 [Eq. (6-142)].

As pointed out by Bennett,[1] these results are applicable in general to quantizing noise arising when analogue signals are converted to their quantized digital form and are not limited to the PCM problem alone.

The cumulative distribution function, or the probability that x will be less than some specified value, is found to be

$$\begin{aligned} P(x) &= 0 && x < a \\ P(x) &= \frac{x - a}{b - a} && a < x < b \\ P(x) &= 1 && x \geq b \end{aligned} \tag{7-52}$$

2. Gaussian or normal distribution. The gaussian function that we have previously encountered in our discussion of frequency spectra as the limiting expression for the amplitude-frequency transfer function of a large number of cascaded RC amplifier stages happens also to be one of the most important density functions in probability theory and statistics. The gaussian function for one variable is given by the equation

$$p(x) = \frac{e^{-(x-a)^2/2\sigma^2}}{\sqrt{2\pi\sigma^2}} \tag{7-53}$$

When plotted, it has the characteristic bell-shaped curve of Fig. 7-15. The curve is symmetrical about the point $x = a$ and has a width proportional to σ. This is apparent from Eq. (7-53), for if we pick the point $x - a = \sqrt{2}\,\sigma$ at which the exponential is unity and let σ increase, $x - a$ increases correspondingly. Intuitively we would expect a to be

[1] *Op. cit.*

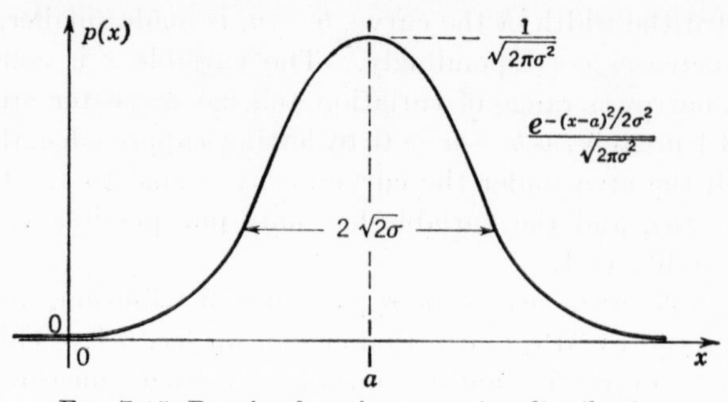

FIG. 7-15. Density function, gaussian distribution.

just the first moment, or average value of x, for this distribution. We can check this by actually performing the required integration. Thus

$$m_1 = \int_{-\infty}^{\infty} xp(x)\,dx = \int_{-\infty}^{\infty} \frac{xe^{-(x-a)^2/2\sigma^2}\,dx}{\sqrt{2\pi\sigma^2}} \tag{7-54}$$

Upon changing variables by letting $y = (x - a)/\sqrt{2\sigma^2}$, $dx = \sqrt{2}\,\sigma\,dy$. The limits of integration remain $-\infty$ and ∞, so that we get

$$m_1 = \int_{-\infty}^{\infty} \frac{(\sqrt{2}\,\sigma y + a)e^{-y^2}}{\sqrt{\pi}}\,dy$$

But

$$\int_{-\infty}^{\infty} ye^{-y^2}\,dy = 0$$

(either by direct integration, or by noting that the function is odd), and

$$\int_{-\infty}^{\infty} e^{-y^2}\,dy = \sqrt{\pi}$$

from any table of definite integrals. This gives us immediately

$$m_1 = a \tag{7-55}$$

for this particular function.

In a similar manner we can show by integration that σ^2 in Eq. (7-53) is the second central moment or variance μ_2 of this distribution.

$$\mu_2 = \int_{-\infty}^{\infty} \frac{(x-a)^2 e^{-(x-a)^2/2\sigma^2}\,dx}{\sqrt{2\pi\sigma^2}} = \sigma^2 \tag{7-56}$$

The actual calculation is left as an exercise for the reader.

Since σ in Eq. (7-53) has been shown to be a measure of the width of the gaussian curve, this result agrees with our interpretation of the standard deviation as a measure of the spread or width of a probability-density curve.

That $p(x)$ as given by Eq. (7-53) is properly normalized can be shown by direct integration. Thus

$$\int_{-\infty}^{\infty} p(x)\,dx = \int_{-\infty}^{\infty} \frac{e^{-(x-a)^2/2\sigma^2}}{\sqrt{2\pi\sigma^2}}\,dx = 1 \tag{7-57}$$

This integration is also left as a simple exercise for the reader.

This gaussian curve weights values of x near a most heavily. The value of $p(x)$ at the peak is $1/\sqrt{2\pi\sigma^2}$, so that, as the width σ decreases, the height of the curve in the vicinity of $x = a$ increases. Ultimately, for $\sigma \rightarrow 0$, this curve approaches the delta function $\delta(x - a)$, and the variable x becomes a constant a with a probability of 1.

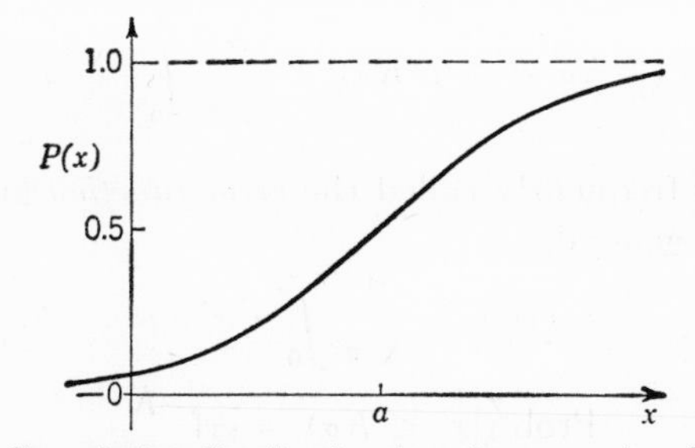

FIG. 7-16. Cumulative-distribution function, gaussian distribution.

The cumulative distribution function, or the probability that the variable will be less than some value x, is

$$P(x) = \int_{-\infty}^{x} \frac{e^{-(x-a)^2/2\sigma^2}}{\sqrt{2\pi\sigma^2}}\,dx \tag{7-58}$$

Since the $p(x)$ curve is symmetrical about $x = a$, half the area is included from $-\infty$ to a. The probability that $x < a$ is thus 0.5, or

$$P(a) = 0.5 \tag{7-59}$$

As mentioned before, the 0.5 probability point is called the median of a statistical distribution. For the gaussian function the median, the average value, and the modal point [peak of $p(x)$] all coincide.

$P(x)$ is shown plotted in Fig. 7-16. The curve is symmetrical about the point $x = a$.

The probability distribution of fluctuation noise is of the gaussian form, as we shall note in the next section. The average value of the noise is 0 volts, however, so that the curve is symmetrical about the origin. σ then represents the rms value of the noise voltage. A question frequently asked is: What is the probability that the noise voltage will be less than some prescribed $K\sigma$ (K a constant)? (Positive and negative voltages are included.) Letting x represent the instantaneous noise voltage, we can answer the question by writing

$$\text{Prob}\,(-K\sigma < x < K\sigma) = \int_{-K\sigma}^{K\sigma} p(x)\,dx$$

$$= \int_{-K\sigma}^{K\sigma} \frac{e^{-x^2/2\sigma^2}}{\sqrt{2\pi\sigma^2}}\,dx \tag{7-60}$$

This integral cannot be evaluated in closed form. Instead the integrand must be expanded in a power series and the resultant integral evaluated term by term. It can be put into a form more convenient for tabulation by letting $y = x/\sqrt{2}\sigma$. Doing this, and utilizing the symmetry of $p(x)$, we get

$$\text{Prob}\,(-K\sigma < x < K\sigma) = \frac{2}{\sqrt{\pi}} \int_0^{K/\sqrt{2}} e^{-y^2}\,dy \tag{7-61}$$

This integral is frequently called the *error function* and is abbreviated erf $(K/\sqrt{2})$. In general,

$$\text{erf}\, x \equiv \frac{2}{\sqrt{\pi}} \int_0^x e^{-y^2}\,dy \tag{7-62}$$

and

$$\text{Prob}\,(|x| < K\sigma) = \text{erf}\,\frac{K}{\sqrt{2}} \tag{7-63}$$

The error function is tabulated in various books of mathematical tables[1] and in books on probability and statistics. Using these tables, we find that, for $K = 1$,

$$\text{erf}\,\frac{1}{\sqrt{2}} = 0.683$$

and, for $K = 2$,

$$\text{erf}\,\frac{2}{\sqrt{2}} = 0.955$$

The probability that the noise voltage will be less than σ volts in magnitude is thus 0.68. The probability that the voltage will be less than twice the rms noise voltage (2σ) is 0.95.

Although we have used fluctuation noise as an example here, these results are more general. Thus it is easy to show that, for any variable which has a gaussian probability-density function, the probability that the variable will deviate from the average value by less than σ is 0.68, while the chance of a deviation greater than 2σ is $1 - 0.95 = 0.05$. For example, assume that 100,000 resistors are to be manufactured with 100 kilohms nominal resistance. Owing to variations in the raw material and in the manufacturing process used the resistors will actually vary

[1] See, for example, B. O. Peirce, "A Short Table of Integrals," Ginn & Company, Boston, 1929.

about the 100-kilohm nominal value. Assume that the variations away from this value follow a gaussian curve with a standard deviation of 10 per cent of the average value. σ is then 10 kilohms, and 68 per cent of the group of 100,000, or 68,000 resistors, should on the average have resistances within ± 10 kilohms of the 100-kilohm rated value. On the average 95 per cent, or 95,000, should lie within ± 20 kilohms of the rated value.

The cumulative probability distribution of Eq. (7-58) can be related quite simply to the error function defined by Eq. (7-62). It is left as an exercise to the reader to show that

$$P(x) = \tfrac{1}{2}\left(1 + \operatorname{erf}\frac{x - a}{\sqrt{2}\,\sigma}\right) \tag{7-64}$$

7-5. Measurement of the Statistical Properties of Noise. The gaussian, or normal, probability distribution has been discussed in some detail because of its extreme importance in probability theory in general and because of its particular application to our study of the statistics of noise and of signals in the presence of noise.

The importance of the gaussian distribution can be inferred from the central-limit theorem of probability theory, which states essentially that the distribution of the sum of a large number of independent random variables will approach the gaussian distribution under certain rather broad conditions. Thus, if $x_1, x_2, \ldots, x_n$ are independent variables, $x = x_1 + x_2 + \cdots + x_n$ has a probability-density function approaching the gaussian function. This is true no matter what the distribution of the individual variables. We shall give an example of such an approach to the gaussian distribution later in this chapter.

In our discussion of shot noise in Chap. 5 we assumed a large number of independent and overlapping current pulses. Because of the random occurrence of these individual current pulses the total current fluctuates about a specified average value. The total current is in this case the sum of a large number of independent random variables, and we might expect the probability distribution of the current to approach the gaussian distribution, in view of the central-limit theorem.

S. O. Rice and other investigators have shown that fluctuation noise in general does follow the gaussian distribution if the noise can be represented as a large number of independent overlapping current or voltage pulses. A proof of this result appears in the article by Rice to which reference has been made,[1] as also in some of the other previous references.[2]

If the fluctuation noise has zero average value, the probability density

[1] Rice, *op. cit.*

[2] See Davenport and Root, *op. cit.*, for example.

of the noise voltage (or current) will be of the form

$$p(v) = \frac{1}{\sqrt{2\pi\sigma^2}} e^{-v^2/2\sigma^2} \tag{7-65}$$

where σ is the standard deviation and v the instantaneous noise voltage. If the instantaneous voltage fluctuates about some d-c or average value V (as in the case of the shot-noise current or in the presence of some signal of average value V), the distribution of the *total* instantaneous voltage will be the same gaussian distribution, but with V as average value.

$$p(v) = \frac{1}{\sqrt{2\pi\sigma^2}} e^{-(v-V)^2/2\sigma^2} \tag{7-66}$$

Equations (7-65) and (7-66) are sketched in Fig. 7-17*a* and *b*, respectively.

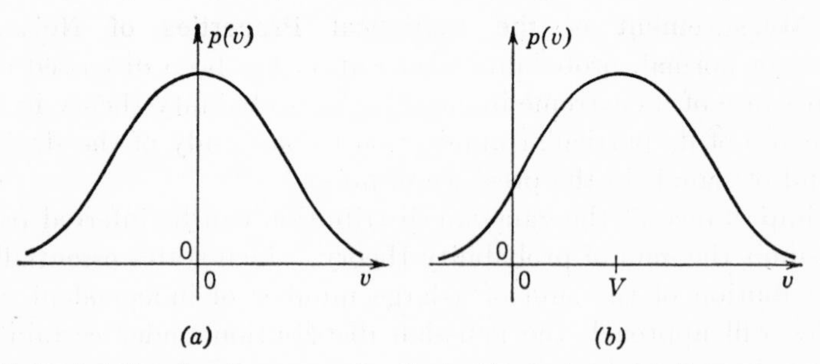

FIG. 7-17. Probability-density curves for fluctuation noise. (*a*) Zero average value; (*b*) average value = V.

The standard deviation σ will actually be the rms voltage fluctuation about the average value and σ^2 the mean-square fluctuation or mean-squared noise power (1-ohm resistor) about the average value (Fig. 7-19*b*). We can demonstrate these simple relations in terms of the histogram approach to probability density.

Assume that we have available a pen recording of the instantaneous voltage at the output of a specified noise source. This could, for example, be the amplified output of a temperature-limited diode, or perhaps the noise output of an entire communication system. One such recording is shown in Fig. 7-18.

How do we experimentally measure the probability-density function of the voltage, the standard deviation, the mean value, etc.? Proceeding as in the past sections, we can divide the voltage scale into small increments Δv volts apart (this is shown as 1 volt in Fig. 7-18) and then measure the fraction of time the voltage is found in each voltage level Δv volts wide. Normalizing this fraction to Δv and plotting versus v, we obtain a histogram of the noise voltage. For Δv small enough and the measurements taken over a large enough interval we would presumably obtain a good approximation to a gaussian-shaped probability-density curve.

Alternatively we could sample the curve. (We shall show later that this must be done at intervals greater than the reciprocal of the system bandwidth to ensure independent measurements.) The number of times a particular voltage level is occupied at the time of sampling gives us again a relative-frequency count from which the probability-density curve can be found. For example, in Fig. 7-18, $v = 4$ volts is occupied once in the four sampling times shown. Obviously this number of samples is

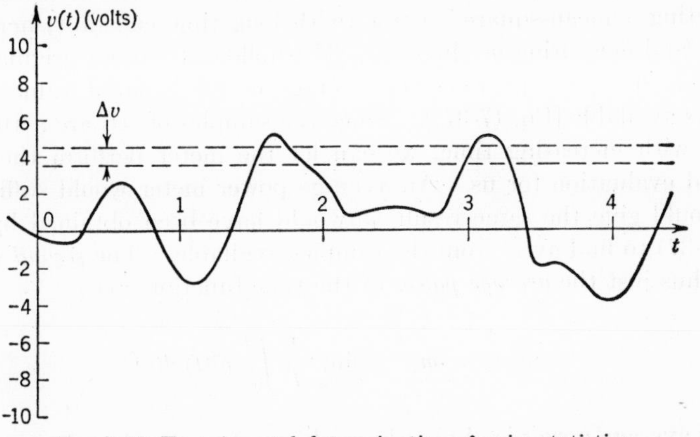

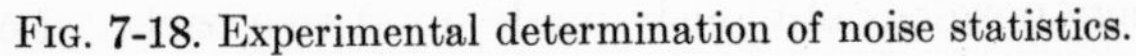
FIG. 7-18. Experimental determination of noise statistics.

too small to provide a reliable histogram and probability-density curve of $v(t)$. But if we were to continue this procedure over a long enough time interval, we would find the relative frequency of occurrence of the different voltage levels settling down to fairly constant, unchanging values.

Plotting the smoothed-out probability-density curve from these counts, we would get the bell-shaped curve characteristic of the gaussian function. For noise with zero average value the curve would resemble Fig. 7-17*a*. For noise with a constant signal of V volts superimposed the curve would be that of Fig. 7-17*b*.

From such a curve we could then proceed to find the moments m_1, m_2, etc., and the variance σ^2, if desired. It is, however, much simpler to find these parameters directly from the data. In particular we can determine m_1, m_2, and σ^2 by using readily available meters. To demonstrate this, we recall that the first moment m_1 of the probability distribution is just the limit of the arithmetic average of a large number of samples of a continuous variable as the number of samples gets very large and the sample level spacing $\Delta v \to 0$. In this particular case our samples of $v(t)$ are obtained by sampling in time. This is the same as averaging $v(t)$ in time, or

$$\text{av } v = m_1 = \lim_{T\to\infty} \frac{1}{T} \int_0^T v(t)\, dt \tag{7-67}$$

This is just the average value as given by an averaging voltmeter with a long time constant. The average value of $v(t)$, or its *d-c component*, as measured by an averaging voltmeter, is thus the same as the *first moment*, or mean, of the probability distribution of $v(t)$, found by averaging a large number of samples.

We could similarly find the second moment m_2 of the distribution by connecting a mean-squared meter (with long time constant) across the output and measuring m_2 directly. This follows from our original interpretation of m_2 as the weighted average of the squared values of the samples available [Eq. (7-37)]. Since the samples of $v(t)$ are actually its values with increasing time, we can let the meter perform the mean-squared evaluation for us. An average power meter would suffice here and would give the same result as would have been obtained by using Eq. (7-37) to find av v^2 from the samples available. The *second moment* m_2 is thus just the *average power* of the time function $v(t)$.

$$\text{av } v^2 = m_2 = \lim_{T\to\infty} \frac{1}{T} \int_0^T v^2(t)\, dt \tag{7-68}$$

This average power is obviously made up of two parts—d-c power due to the average voltage level, and a-c power due to fluctuations about the nonzero average value. These two average-power components are independent and add directly. The average power due to the d-c signal is just m_1^2, or (av $v)^2$ (assuming again a 1-ohm resistor). The average a-c power, or average power due to fluctuations about an average value, is just the difference between the total average power m_2 and the d-c power m_1^2. For fluctuation noise this mean noise power is just the mean-squared output noise discussed in great detail in Chap. 5. Using the symbol N for the mean-squared noise fluctuations about the average value, as in Chap. 6, we have

$$N = m_2 - m_1^2 \equiv \sigma^2 \tag{7-69}$$

from the relation between variance and first and second moments. The *variance* of the probability distribution is thus just the *mean noise power* (1-ohm resistor). A long-time-constant rms voltmeter could be used to find σ directly. The distinction between m_2 and σ^2 is indicated in Fig. 7-19 for a random voltage $v(t)$ with average value V.

For fluctuation noise with zero average value and mean-squared voltage or mean power (1-ohm resistor) N, the probability density of the instantaneous noise voltage is thus

$$p(v) = \frac{1}{\sqrt{2\pi N}} e^{-v^2/2N} \tag{7-70}$$

where the units of both v^2 and N are assumed to be volts squared. The rms noise voltage $\sqrt{N}$ thus determines the width of the gaussian curve. Knowing this rms noise voltage, we can determine the probability that the instantaneous voltage will exceed some specified value, will take on values between two given levels, etc.

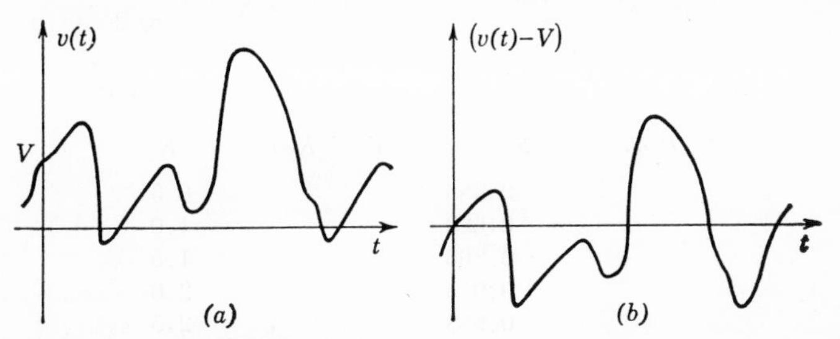

FIG. 7-19. Comparison between m_2 and σ^2. (a) Av $v^2 = m_2$ is average power of wave; (b) av $(v - V)^2 = \sigma^2$ is average power of wave.

If a d-c signal of amplitude V volts is added to the noise, the density function for the instantaneous sum of signal plus noise will be

$$p(v) = \frac{1}{\sqrt{2\pi N}} e^{-(v-V)^2/2N} \tag{7-71}$$

The constant-amplitude signal just serves to shift the noise level from an average of 0 volts to an average of V volts. The rms fluctuation about the average is $\sqrt{N}$ volts in either case.

The numerical results of the previous section can now be applied directly. We showed there that the probability that a gaussian-distributed variable would take on values within $\pm\sigma$ of the average value was 0.68, while within $\pm 2\sigma$ the probability was 0.95. Applied here, the probability that the instantaneous noise voltage will lie within $\sqrt{N}$ volts of its average value is 0.68; within $2\sqrt{N}$ it is 0.95.

The instantaneous noise voltage in a system may theoretically take on any range of positive or negative values. The chance of its doing so diminishes rapidly, however, as the value exceeds the rms noise voltage. For example, if the rms noise voltage is 10 μv at a point in a system, the instantaneous voltage will be less than ± 10 μv 68 per cent of the time on the average. It will be less than ± 20 μv 95 per cent of the time on the average. If this noise is superimposed on top of a 100-μv d-c signal, the total instantaneous voltage will appear between $100 + 10$ μv and $100 - 10$ μv 68 per cent of the time on the average.

Again by using the results of the previous section, the probability that the noise voltage will be found within $\pm K\sigma$ of its average value can be written in terms of the error function defined by

$$\operatorname{erf} x \equiv \frac{2}{\sqrt{\pi}} \int_0^x e^{-v^2}\, dv$$

In particular the probability that $v(t)$ will lie within $\pm K\sigma$ or $\pm K\sqrt{N}$ of its average value is

$$\text{Prob}\,(V - K\sigma < v < V + K\sigma) = \operatorname{erf} \frac{K}{\sqrt{2}} \tag{7-72}$$

This probability is tabulated below for various values of K.

Prob $(V - K\sigma < v < V + K\sigma)$	K
0.383	0.5
0.683	1.0
0.866	1.5
0.955	2.0
0.988	2.5
0.997	3.0
0.9995	3.5
0.99994	4.0

Note that the chance of $v(t)$ deviating very much beyond $V \pm \sigma$ volts becomes very small quite rapidly. For example, if the average value V is zero, the probability that $v(t)$ will exceed 3σ volts is 0.003, while the probability that it will exceed 4σ volts is 0.00006.

We have been stressing thus far in this section the gaussian distribution of noise. Gaussian noise remains gaussian when passed through

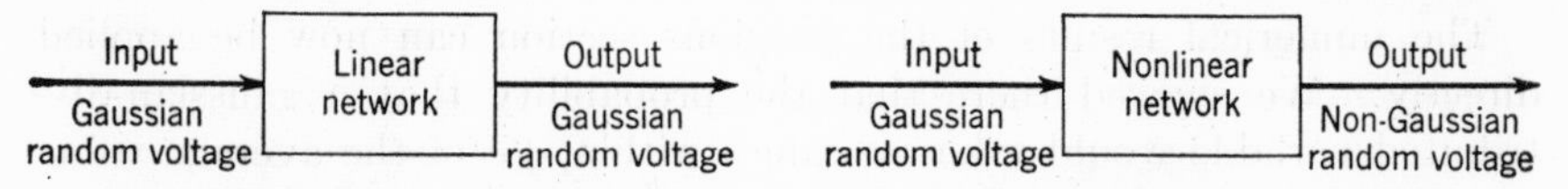

FIG. 7-20. Random voltage passed through linear and nonlinear networks.

linear networks. Once gaussian noise voltage is applied to a nonlinear network, the distribution of the output can no longer be considered gaussian (Fig. 7-20). We shall demonstrate shortly a simple procedure for determining the distribution of noise voltage (or a continuous random variable in general) at the output of a given nonlinear device. Such a procedure will be necessary to determine, for example, the distribution of noise at the output of an envelope detector, square-law detector, or others of the nonlinear devices considered in previous chapters.

In discussing a possible experimental procedure for determining the distribution of $v(t)$ and the different statistical parameters m_1, m_2, and

σ^2 we implicitly assumed that neither the distribution nor the parameters changed over the interval of measurement. We also implicitly assumed that the experimental results were independent of the particular time at which they were obtained. An identical experiment repeated a day later would be expected to give the same results. This implies that all elements of the system under test, whether a temperature-limited diode, a resistor, a vacuum tube, a transistor, etc., do not change with time. We assume negligible aging of tubes; we assume temperatures remaining constant, power-supply voltages unchanging, etc.

Such statistical processes in which the probability distributions, and the moments associated with these, are the same, independent of the time at which they are measured, are said to be *stationary* processes.

In setting up an experimental procedure for measuring the probability distribution of a noise voltage $v(t)$ we chose to utilize a long time record of $v(t)$. This served as one method of generating the *large* numbers of samples of $v(t)$ required. Another possible approach might have been to line up a *large* number of identical noise sources and simultaneously to sample the output of each of these. We could then again determine the relative frequency of occurrence of different values of the voltage v and, from this, its probability density. We could arithmetically average the values of the samples to find m_1, m_2, and σ^2. This method of determining the statistics of a random variable by simultaneously measuring the output of a large number of identical systems producing the random variable is called the *ensemble* method. (An ensemble is a collection or set of similar things.) Here too we can say the process is *stationary* if the statistics measured are the same at different measuring times.

The distinction between time averaging and ensemble averaging and the concept of a *stationary* process are indicated in Fig. 7-21. v_1, v_2, v_3 represent the output voltages of three identical systems. We can determine the probability distribution of any one of these, say v_1, by measuring in time. If such a measurement, begun at time t_1, produces identical results to a measurement begun at time t_2, and then repeated at t_3, etc., the process is said to be stationary in time.

Alternatively we can measure v_1, v_2, v_3 simultaneously at time t_1, for example, and from this determine the statistical properties of the sources. (We would actually need many more than three sources, of course.) This gives rise to ensemble statistics. If the density function for the ensemble at time t_1 is then found to be the same as that measured in a similar manner at times t_2, t_3, etc., the process is stationary.

We gave another example of these two different schemes for determining the statistics of a random variable in Sec. 7-1. There, in discussing the statistics of a language, we pointed out that we could determine the desired parameters by either watching one person writing, and picking out the first letter in each paragraph written (this is the *time* approach), or by setting up 1,000 blackboards and asking 1,000 persons of similar background to start writing simultaneously (the *ensemble* approach).

We shall have occasion later to refer to both methods of determining the statistics of some random process. Do the methods always give identical results? This is important, for later we shall give one example in discussing correlation functions in which the ensemble approach provides information as to the power spectrum and hence time variation of a particular random signal.

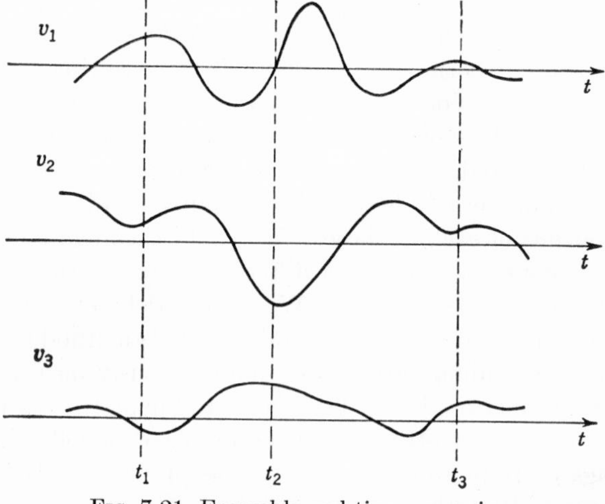

FIG. 7-21. Ensemble and time averaging.

Most physical processes provide identical results under these two methods of measurement. Such processes, in which the statistics of one system over a long period of time are the same as the statistics of an ensemble of systems at one instant of time, are defined to be *ergodic* processes. An ergodic process will always be stationary, but a stationary process is not necessarily ergodic. A trivial example of a stationary, but nonergodic, process would be that of an ensemble of constant-voltage sources. Each source maintains its output absolutely constant with time. Each source provides, however, a different output. Choosing one source at random and performing a time measurement, we would of course get a delta-function probability density centered at the source voltage. This density is stationary with time. Measuring all sources simultaneously, however, we would get a distribution corresponding to the particular source outputs. This too would be stationary. All the random processes considered in this book, whether due to fluctuation noise or to random signal inputs, will be *assumed ergodic.*

A detailed discussion of both stationary and ergodic processes will be found in the books by Laning and Battin[1] and Lawson and Uhlenbeck.[2]

7-6. Error Probability and Threshold Level in PCM. Before going on to further discussions of probability theory and its application to the statistics of noise we pause to apply some of the material already developed to a more quantitative analysis of PCM and signal threshold levels in a PCM system.

We recall from Chap. 6 that all wideband transmission systems were stated to have a signal threshold level below which the noise-improvement properties of the system rapidly deteriorated. This level is experimentally determined for frequency modulation (FM), for example. For PCM the meaning and existence of such a threshold level can be demonstrated mathematically in a simple manner.

We assume first a binary-type off-on PCM system, in which pulses represent 1's in the binary code, the absence of pulses represent 0's (see Chap. 6). Fluctuation noise is added to the incoming group of pulses in the receiver, and there is a possibility that the noise will cause an error in the decoding of the signal. The error will occur if noise in the absence of a signal happens to have an instantaneous amplitude comparable to that of a pulse when present or if noise in the presence of a signal happens to have a large enough negative amplitude to destroy the pulse. In the first case the noise will be mistaken for a pulse signal; in the second case the pulse will be reduced to a 0 signal, as seen by the decoder.

How often will such errors occur on the average? Without any knowledge of noise statistics there is no way of solving this problem. Simply knowing the rms noise and the pulse amplitude, when it appears, is not enough. These do not provide us with any quantitative information as to how many errors we can expect, how large the ratio of pulse to rms noise must be to decrease the rate of errors below a tolerable number, etc. The *S/N* approach of Chap. 6 does not provide us with the answers to these questions, for the errors depend on the chance of the instantaneous noise voltage exceeding a certain specified level. This depends on a knowledge of the statistical distribution of the noise, and not just on a mean-squared parameter.

We can solve the problem quite readily, however, with the aid of the theory developed in the previous section. Assume that the pulse amplitudes are all A_c volts, as in Chap. 6. The decoder then assumes that a pulse is present if the instantaneous voltage (signal plus noise) exceeds $A_c/2$ volts and that a pulse is absent if the instantaneous voltage is less than $A_c/2$ volts. An example of a possible signal sequence and the two

[1] *Op. cit.*

[2] J. L. Lawson and G. E. Uhlenbeck, "Threshold Symbols," McGraw-Hill Book Company, Inc., New York, 1950.

possible types of error is shown in Fig. 7-22. The signal pulses are shown triangular for simplicity's sake. The pulses and noise are shown dashed; the resultant voltage is represented by the solid line. The system decoder responds to the amplitude of the resultant (at the center of the pulse, for example).

How do we determine the probability of error from our knowledge of noise statistics? Assume first that a *zero* is sent, so that no pulse is present at the time of decoding. The probability of an error in this case

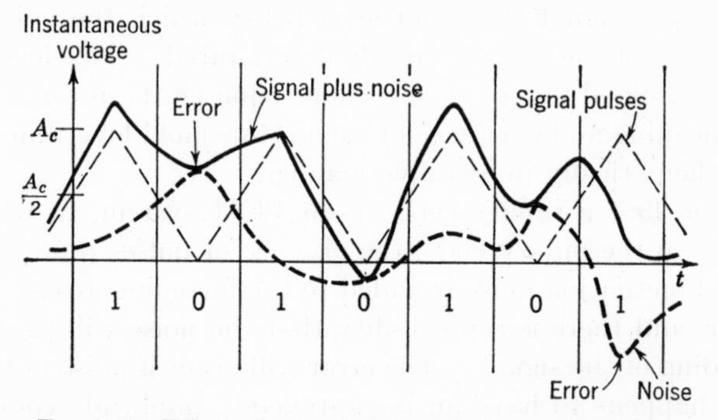

FIG. 7-22. Effect of noise in binary pulse transmission.

is just the probability that noise will exceed $A_c/2$ volts in amplitude and be mistaken for a pulse or a 1 in the binary code. This is just the probability that $v(t)$ will appear somewhere between $A_c/2$ and ∞. When noise alone is present,

$$p(v) = \frac{1}{\sqrt{2\pi\sigma^2}} e^{-v^2/2\sigma} \tag{7-73}$$

and the probability of an error is the area under the $p(v)$ curve from $A_c/2$ to ∞.

$$\text{Prob}\left(v > \frac{A_c}{2}\right) = \int_{A_c/2}^{\infty} \frac{e^{-v^2/2\sigma^2}}{\sqrt{2\pi\sigma^2}} \, dv \tag{7-74}$$

$p(v)$ for this case is shown sketched in Fig. 7-23*a*, with the probability of error indicated by the shaded area.

Assume now that a 1 is transmitted by the encoder. This appears at the decoder as a pulse of amplitude A_c volts plus superimposed noise. At the instant of decoding $v(t)$ is a signal plus noise voltage of average value A_c and with probability density

$$p(v) = \frac{e^{-(v-A_c)^2/2\sigma^2}}{\sqrt{2\pi\sigma^2}} \tag{7-75}$$

The probability of error now corresponds to the chance that signal plus noise will drop below $A_c/2$ volts and be mistaken for noise only (or be judged a 0). This is just the area under the $p(v)$ curve from $-\infty$ to $A_c/2$ and is given by

$$\text{Prob}\left(v < \frac{A_c}{2}\right) = \int_{-\infty}^{A_c/2} \frac{e^{-(v-A_c)^2/2\sigma^2}}{\sqrt{2\pi\sigma^2}}\, dv \tag{7-76}$$

(Alternatively it is also given by the probability that noise alone will be less than $-A_c/2$ volts in amplitude, so that the sum of signal plus noise drops below $A_c/2$ volts.) $p(v)$ for this case is shown sketched in Fig. 7-23*b*, while the probability of error is again indicated by the shaded area.

It is apparent from Fig. 7-23 and from the symmetry of the gaussian curve that the two areas to be calculated are equal. The probability of

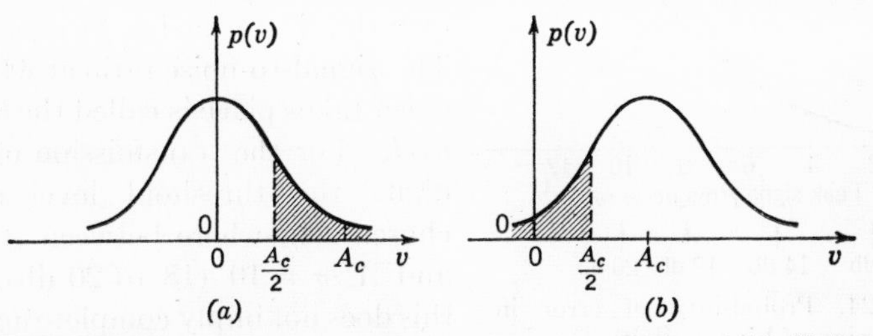

FIG. 7-23. Probability densities in binary pulse transmission. (*a*) Noise only (0 transmitted); (*b*) pulse plus noise (1 transmitted).

error is thus the same in either case. [This may also be shown mathematically by a linear translation of coordinates, letting $x = v - A_c$ in Eq. (7-76), or by noting that the probability that noise alone will be less than $-A_c/2$ is the same as the probability that noise will exceed $A_c/2$.] It is left to the reader as an exercise to show that the probability of error in either case may be written in terms of the error function as follows:

$$\text{Prob error} = \frac{1}{2}\left(1 - \text{erf}\,\frac{A_c}{2\sqrt{2}\,\sigma}\right) \qquad \text{erf}\, x = \frac{2}{\sqrt{\pi}}\int_0^x e^{-y^2}\, dy \tag{7-77}$$

This represents the probability of mistaking a binary 1 for a binary 0, and vice versa. Assuming that the 1's and 0's are equally likely in a long message, Eq. (7-77) gives the probability of an error in the decoding of any digit.

The probability of error is shown plotted vs. peak signal to rms noise (A_c/σ) in Fig. 7-24. Note that for $A_c/\sigma < 8$ (18 db) the probability of error increases rapidly, approaching an error probability of 0.5 for $A_c = 0$. (When the pulse heights are so small as to be practically zero, the decoder will still be right half the time on the average.) For $A_c/\sigma = 8.2$ the error probability is 10^{-4}. This means that 1 digit in 10^4 digits transmitted will be judged incorrectly. If 10^5 digits per second are being transmitted, this means a mistake every 0.1 sec, on the average, and is obviously not too good. If the signal is increased to $A_c/\sigma = 11.6$, however, the error probability decreases to 10^{-8}. For 10^5 digits per second this means a mistake every 1,000 sec, or every 16 min, on the average, and is much more tolerable.

Above $A_c/\sigma = 8$ (approximately), the probability of error decreases very rapidly with small changes in signal. In the example just cited increasing the signal by a factor of 4 db ($A_c/\sigma = 8$ to $A_c/\sigma = 11.6$) reduces the error rate by 10^4. The existence of a narrow range of signal-to-noise ratios above which the error rate is tolerable, below which errors occur quite frequently, is termed a *threshold effect.* The signal-to-noise ratio at which this effect takes place is called the *threshold level.* For the transmission of binary digits the threshold level may be chosen somewhere between $A_c/\sigma = 8$ and $A_c/\sigma = 10$ (18 to 20 db). Note this does not imply complete noise suppression above the threshold level. It merely indicates that for the pulse amplitudes greater than ten times the rms noise, say, errors in the transmission of binary digits will occur at a tolerable rate.

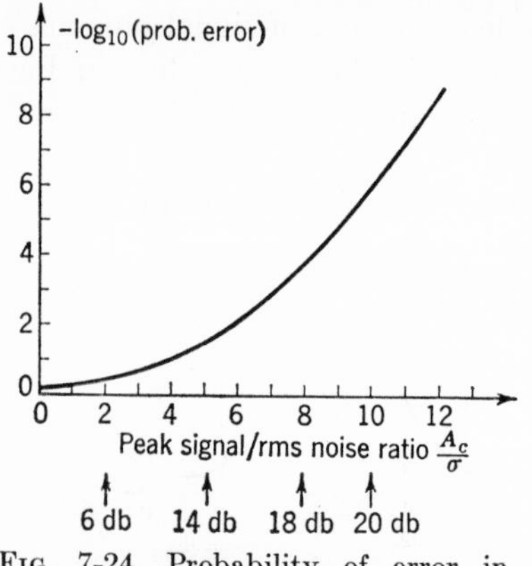

FIG. 7-24. Probability of error in transmission of binary digits.

That the above error analysis for the transmission of on-off binary pulses holds true for bipolarity pulses (positive and negative) is shown by Fig. 7-25. We recall from Chap. 6 that the positive and negative pulses need only be transmitted at $A_c/2$ or $-A_c/2$ volts, respectively.

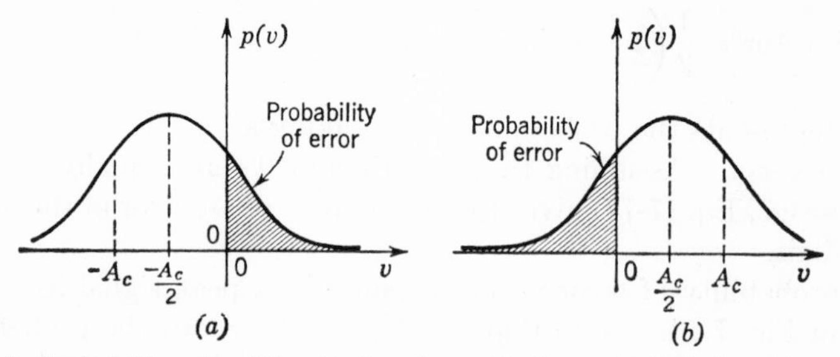

FIG. 7-25. Probability densities in the transmission of bipolarity binary pulses. (*a*) Negative pulse transmitted; (*b*) positive pulse.

The decoder then determines which pulse is present from the polarity of the total instantaneous voltage (signal plus noise). Figure 7-25*a* shows the probability-density function for the negative pulse of $-A_c/2$ volts plus noise. Figure 7-25*b* shows the corresponding curve for the positive pulse plus noise. The error probability is in each case the same, and, comparing with Fig. 7-23, the same as for the case of on-off pulses. The error curve of Fig. 7-24 thus applies to either type of binary-digit transmission.

Figure 7-24 was utilized in the discussion of PCM channel capacity in Sec. 6-6.

7-7. Functional Transformations of Random Variables. Up to this point in our discussion of random variables we have been assuming the probability density known. In the case of random noise this has been shown to be the gaussian distribution.

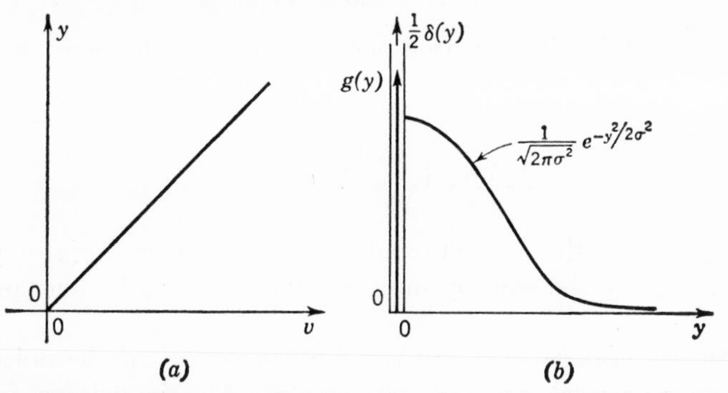

FIG. 7-26. Piecewise-linear rectification of noise. (*a*) Piecewise-linear rectifier; (*b*) probability density, output noise.

We know from our discussion of modulation systems in Chaps. 3 and 4 that many operations, both linear and nonlinear, may be performed on a signal. Noise passing through a system is also operated on by modulators, rectifiers, amplifiers, filters, etc. It is of interest to investigate the effect of the system operation on the probability distribution. We shall restrict ourselves in this section primarily to nonlinear operations, with the output voltage y of a device related to the input v by the relation

$$y = F(v)$$

If v is a random variable with known probability density $p(v)$ (fluctuation noise of zero d-c level, for example), what is the probability density $g(y)$ at the output?

As an example, assume that random noise is passed through a piecewise-linear rectifier of the type analyzed as a modulator and demodulator in Chap. 3. We assume that the characteristics are given by

$$\begin{aligned} y &= v \qquad v \geq 0 \\ y &= 0 \qquad v < 0 \end{aligned} \tag{7-78}$$

What is the probability density $g(y)$ of the noise at the output (see Fig. 7-26*a*)?

If the input noise happens to be of positive amplitude, it will be passed undisturbed through the rectifier. The probability that $y > 0$ must be the same as the probability that $v > 0$. For $v > 0$, then,

$$g(y) = p(v) = \frac{1}{\sqrt{2\pi\sigma^2}} e^{-y^2/2\sigma^2} \qquad v > 0 \tag{7-79}$$

But for $v < 0$ the rectifier produces zero output ($y = 0$). The probability that $v < 0$ is 0.5, and this must correspond to the probability that $y = 0$. Thus

$$\text{Prob } (v < 0) = 0.5 = \text{Prob } (y = 0) \tag{7-80}$$

The probability-density function corresponding to this must be a delta function of area ½ centered at $y = 0$. The total probability density for y is then

$$g(y) = \tfrac{1}{2}\delta(y) + \frac{1}{\sqrt{2\pi\sigma^2}} e^{-y^2/2\sigma^2} \qquad y \geq 0 \tag{7-81}$$

Note that y has both a discrete and a continuous part. $g(y)$ is properly normalized, as can be seen by integrating $g(y)$ over all values of y (Fig. 7-26*b*).

We can use $g(y)$ to calculate the d-c component of the noise at the output (now nonzero), the rms voltage, etc. The d-c voltage, for example, is given by

$$\begin{aligned} m_1 = \text{av } y &= \int_0^\infty \frac{ye^{-y^2/2\sigma^2}}{\sqrt{2\pi\sigma^2}}\,dy + \int_{0^-}^\infty y\delta(y)\,dy \\ &= \frac{\sigma}{\sqrt{2\pi}} \end{aligned} \tag{7-82}$$

where σ is the rms voltage of the input noise.

If the transformation $y = F(v)$ can be expressed algebraically and the inverse $v = f(y)$ readily found, a simple relation between $g(y)$ and $p(v)$ can be developed.

Let v vary between v_1 and v_2. y varies correspondingly between $y_1 = F(v_1)$ and $y_2 = F(v_2)$. The probability that v will range between v_1 and v_2 is $\int_{v_1}^{v_2} p(v)\,dv$, and this must be just the probability that y will vary between y_1 and y_2. Thus

$$\int_{v_1}^{v_2} p(v)\,dv = \int_{y_1}^{y_2} g(y)\,dy \tag{7-83}$$

Now let $v = f(y)$ in the left-hand integral. Assuming that $f(y)$ is a *single-valued function* of y, we get, after transforming the integrand and changing the limits of integration,

$$\int_{v_1}^{v_2} p(v)\,dv = \int_{y_1}^{y_2} p[f(y)]f'(y)\,dy = \int_{y_1}^{y_2} g(y)\,dy \tag{7-84}$$

Comparing the two integrals on the right, we get the relation

$$g(y) = p[f(y)]f'(y) \tag{7-85}$$

Geometrically Eq. (7-83) corresponds to equating the two areas shown in Fig. 7-27. In particular, as $v_1 \to v_2$, we must have $g(y)\,dy = p(v)\,dv$, which is just the relation given by Eq. (7-85).

As an example, assume that v is uniformly distributed in the range $0 \leq v \leq 1$, with $p(v) = 1$. What is the distribution at the output of a square-law detector with the characteristic $y = v^2$?

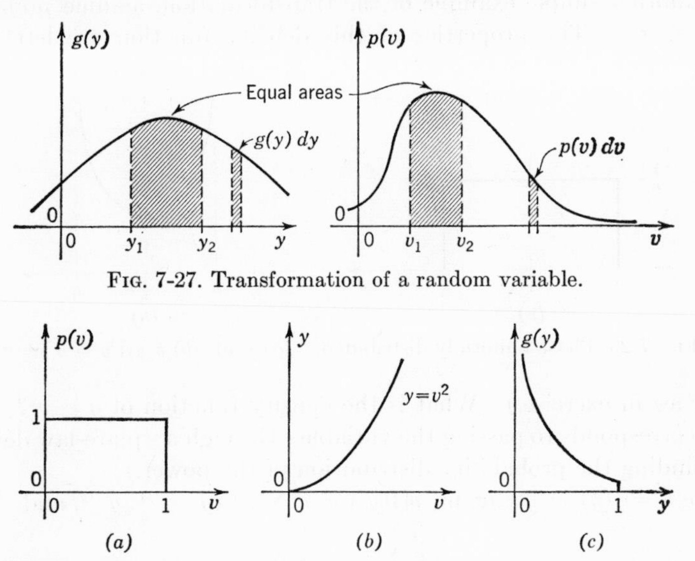

FIG. 7-27. Transformation of a random variable.

FIG. 7-28. Example of a transformation. (a) Input variable; (b) characteristic; (c) output variable.

Here $f(y) = \sqrt{y}$ (since v is positive, the positive square root must be used); $f'(y) = \frac{1}{2}y^{-\frac{1}{2}}$, and the density function at the output is

$$g(y) = \frac{y^{-\frac{1}{2}}}{2} \qquad 0 \leq y \leq 1 \tag{7-86}$$

This is shown sketched in Fig. 7-28*c*. We can check to see whether or not $g(y)$ is properly normalized by calculating the area under the curve.

$$\int_0^1 g(y)\,dy = \frac{1}{2}\int_0^1 y^{-\frac{1}{2}}\,dy = 1$$

as expected.

The cumulative distribution function is given by

$$P(y) = \int_0^y g(y)\,dy = y^{\frac{1}{2}} \tag{7-87}$$

In particular the probability that the output will be less than $\frac{1}{2}$ is $P(\frac{1}{2}) = 0.707$.

The square-law transformation is also interesting because it gives us the density function of the instantaneous *power* if the input function v happens to be a voltage or a current applied to a 1-ohm resistor. For example, in the example just given, the probability that the voltage will be less than 0.707 is just 0.707 (uniform or rectangular distribution). This must correspond to the probability that the power will be less than $\frac{1}{2}$, checking the answer obtained.

As another simple example of the transformation, assume $p(v) = e^{-v}$, $0 \leq v < \infty$. (The properties of this density function are left to the

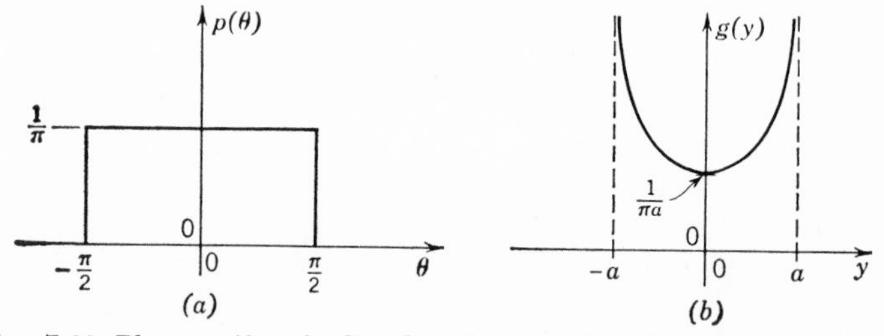

FIG. 7-29. Phase uniformly distributed. (a) $p(\theta)$; (b) $g(y)$: $y = a \sin \theta$.

reader as an exercise.) What is the density function of $y = v^2$? (This again corresponds to passing the variable v through a square-law detector, or to finding the probability distribution of the power.)

Here $v = f(y) = y^{1/2}$ again, $p[f(y)] = e^{-\sqrt{y}}$, $f'(y) = \frac{1}{2}y^{-1/2}$, and

$$g(y) = \frac{e^{-\sqrt{y}}}{2\sqrt{y}} \qquad 0 \leq y < \infty \tag{7-88}$$

As a third example, assume that an angular variable θ is uniformly distributed between the values $-\pi/2 \leq \theta \leq \pi/2$. Then $p(\theta) = 1/\pi$ in that range. We would like to find the distribution of $y = a \sin \theta$. (This corresponds to finding the density function of a sine wave whose angle is uniformly distributed.)

Here $f(y) = \sin^{-1}(y/a)$, $f'(y) = 1/\sqrt{a^2 - y^2}$, and

$$g(y) = \frac{1}{\pi\sqrt{a^2 - y^2}} \qquad -a \leq y \leq a \tag{7-89}$$

$g(y)$ is shown sketched in Fig. 7-29*b*. This result is as might be intuitively expected, for the sine function spends most of its time in the region of $\theta = \pi/2$ or $-\pi/2$ (where its derivative or rate of change has the smallest value). y would thus be expected to have the largest probability density in the vicinity of a and $-a$.

In all three examples cited thus far $v = f(y)$ has been single-valued because of the range of v chosen.

As a final example, consider the case of gaussian-distributed noise passed through a square-law detector. Alternatively we may ask for the density function of the instantaneous power corresponding to a gaussian-distributed noise voltage. Thus with

$$p(v) = \frac{e^{-v^2/2\sigma^2}}{\sqrt{2\pi\sigma^2}} \qquad -\infty < v < \infty$$

and

$$y = v^2$$

find $g(y)$.

Here we have to be very careful. Both positive and negative v contribute to y, and $v = f(y) = \pm\sqrt{y}$ is no longer single-valued. To treat

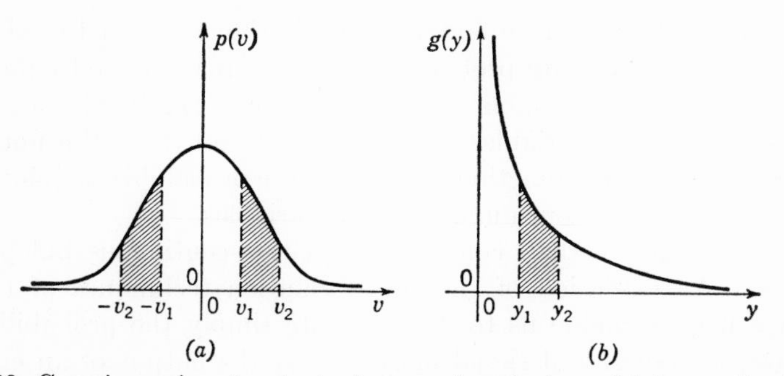

FIG. 7-30. Gaussian noise at output of square-law device. (*a*) Input distribution; (*b*) output distribution.

this case, assume that we are interested in the probability that y lies between two values y_1 and y_2. Since *two* sets of values of v give rise to these values of y and the values of v are *mutually exclusive*, we must sum the probabilities that v lies in the two different regions, to find Prob $(y_1 \le y \le y_2)$. Calling the two sets of values of v, v_1, v_2 and v_1', v_2',

$$\text{Prob }(y_1 \le y \le y_2) = \text{Prob }(v_1 \le v \le v_2) + \text{Prob }(v_1' \le v \le v_2')$$

In terms of the density functions we get

$$\int_{y_1}^{y_2} g(y)\,dy = \int_{v_1}^{v_2} p(v)\,dv + \int_{v_1'}^{v_2'} p(v)\,dv \tag{7-90}$$

for a double-valued function.

The gaussian function happens to be symmetrical about $v = 0$, so that $p(v)$ is the same for the positive and negative values of v that produce the same y. This is shown in Fig. 7-30*a*. In this case we get

$$g(y) = 2p[f(y)]f'(y) \tag{7-91}$$

from Eq. (7-90).

In particular, for $y = v^2$, $f'(y) = 1/2\sqrt{y}$, and

$$g(y) = \frac{e^{-y/2\sigma^2}}{\sqrt{2\pi\sigma^2 y}} \qquad 0 \leq y < \infty \tag{7-92}$$

is the distribution of the noise power, or the distribution at the output of a square-law device.

As a check, it is left to the reader to show that the average value of y is $m_1 = \sigma^2$. Since the input noise voltage has zero average value, its second moment, or total mean power, is just σ^2. (For the voltage, $m_2 = m_1 + \sigma^2 = \sigma^2$ in this case.) The second moment of the voltage is thus just the first moment of the power, as might be expected: the average value of the instantaneous power corresponds to the mean-squared voltage across a 1-ohm resistor.

7-8. Distribution of Two Independent Variables. Up to this point we have been considering probability-density functions and cumulative distributions for one variable [for example, $p(x)$ and $P(x)$]. Just as in the case of discrete variables it is of interest to extend the notions of continuous probability functions to include the probability of joint occurrence of two or more continuous random variables.

In this section we shall concentrate on two continuous independent variables. An extension of the transformation techniques of the last section will then enable us to discuss quite simply the probability distribution of noise and of signal plus noise at the output of an envelope detector. In later sections we shall discuss the probability distribution of the sum of many independent variables, then treat the case of two dependent random variables. This will enable us to determine the effect of linear filtering on the statistical properties of noise and of signal plus noise.

We recall that in Sec. 7-2 we introduced the concept of joint probability for discrete variables by defining a probability $P(AB)$ that both event A *and* event B occur. For example, considering playing cards, if A represents a heart, B a king, $P(AB)$ represents the probability of the king of hearts being drawn. If A represents a spade on the first of two card draws and B a spade on the second draw, $P(AB)$ is the probability of drawing two spades in succession.

If the event B is dependent on the event A, as is true in the two-spade case,

$$P(AB) = P(A)P(B/A)$$

where $P(B/A)$ is the conditional probability that event B will occur, it being known that A has occurred.

In the two-spade case, for example,

$$P(A) = 13/52 = 1/4 \qquad P(B/A) = 12/51 \qquad P(AB) = 1/17$$

We also showed, in Sec. 7-2, that if B is independent of event A, and vice versa,

$$P(B/A) = P(B)$$
$$P(A/B) = P(A)$$
$$P(AB) = P(A)P(B)$$

In the example given this would correspond to replacing the first card once drawn.

By extension to the continuous-probability case we can express the probability that two variables x and y will jointly take on values between

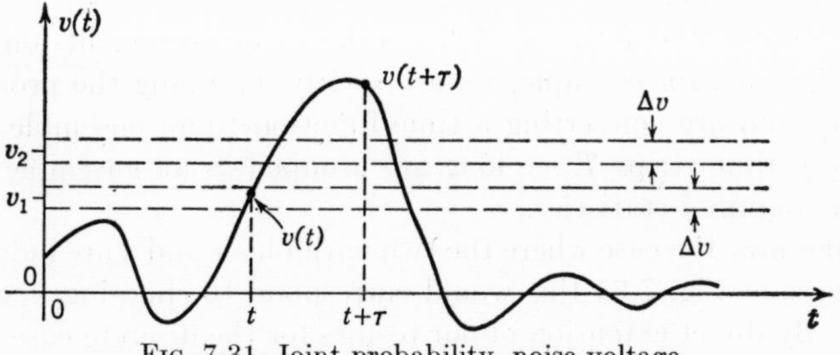

FIG. 7-31. Joint probability, noise voltage.

x_1 and x_2, y_1 and y_2, respectively, by the expression

$$\text{Prob}\ (x_1 \le x \le x_2,\ y_1 \le y \le y_2) = \int_{x_1}^{x_2} \int_{y_1}^{y_2} p(x,y)\ dx\ dy \qquad (7\text{-}93)$$

$p(x,y)$ is a *two-dimensional* probability density, and the joint probability is the *volume* enclosed under the $p(x,y)$ curve in the region bounded by x_1, x_2, y_1, y_2. This compares with the one-dimensional density function $p(x)$ for a single continuous variable, with the probability given by an area under the curve. $p(x,y)\ dx\ dy$ represents the probability that x and y will lie jointly in the region

$$x \le x \le x + dx$$
$$y \le y \le y + dy$$

As an example of the need for the joint-probability formulation occurring in our work, we may ask for the probability that a noise voltage $v(t)$ will at time t appear between v_1 and $v_1 + dv$ volts and, τ sec later, between v_2 and $v_2 + dv$ volts. $v(t)$ then corresponds to x, $v(t + \tau)$ to y (Fig. 7-31). We shall discuss this specific problem in a later section.

The two-dimensional cumulative distribution also becomes a volume integral and is given by

$$P(x_1,y_1) = \int_{-\infty}^{x_1} \int_{-\infty}^{y_1} p(x,y)\ dx\ dy \qquad (7\text{-}94)$$

This represents the probability that x will be less than x_1, y less than y_1.

$p(x,y)$ can be found from the limiting case of a relative-frequency expression, just as in the case of a single variable. For example, we could cut up the noise-voltage curve of Fig. 7-31 into many strips T sec long ($T \gg 1$/bandwidth), divide the voltage scale into many levels Δv volts wide, and sample the voltage at fixed times t sec and $(t + \tau)$ sec from the beginning of each strip. The fraction of times that the voltages $v_1 \pm \Delta v/2$ at t and $v_2 \pm \Delta v/2$ at $t + \tau$ appeared would give us an expression approximating $p(v_1,v_2)\, dv_1\, dv_2$. This procedure is of course identical with the method used in Sec. 7-2 to find joint-probability expressions from relative-frequency counts and is just an extension of the histogram idea to two variables.

Incidentally, in performing such a series of measurements on the voltage of Fig. 7-31, for example, we are tacitly assuming the process to be stationary and are converting a time function to an ensemble function. (The many time strips T sec long are grouped as an ensemble in calculating the required statistics.)

Consider now the case where the two variables x and y are independent. (In the case of Fig. 7-31 this would correspond to choosing $\tau \gg 1$/bandwidth.) By direct extension of our results for the discrete case we define the condition of independence to be

$$p(x,y) = p(x)p(y) \tag{7-95}$$

The joint-probability density of two independent variables is then just the product of the individual probability-density functions, and the individual probabilities multiply. The probability that x will range between x_1 and x_2 and y between y_1 and y_2 is

$$\begin{aligned} \text{Prob}\,(x_1 \le x \le x_2,\, y_1 \le y \le y_2) &= \int_{x_1}^{x_2} \int_{y_1}^{y_2} p(x)p(y)\, dx\, dy \\ &= \int_{x_1}^{x_2} p(x)\, dx \int_{y_1}^{y_2} p(y)\, dy \end{aligned} \tag{7-96}$$

For example, assume that the instantaneous noise voltage across each of two resistors R_A and R_B is measured. Since the voltage across each resistor is gaussian-distributed and the two voltages are independent of each other,

$$p(v_A,v_B) = p(v_A)p(v_B) = \frac{e^{-(v_A{}^2/2\sigma_A{}^2 + v_B{}^2/2\sigma_B{}^2)}}{\sqrt{2\pi\sigma_A{}^2 \times 2\pi\sigma_B{}^2}} \tag{7-97}$$

where σ_A and σ_B are the rms noise voltages of resistors A and B, respectively. The probability that voltmeter A across R_A will read between 2 and 3 volts and voltmeter B across R_B between 1 and 3 volts, for example, is found by integrating Eq. (7-97) between these sets of limits or by finding the individual probabilities and multiplying them together.

7-9. Narrowband Noise and Envelope Detection. We can utilize the fact that the probability density of two independent variables x and y is given by $p(x)p(y)$ to solve some interesting problems in narrowband noise and envelope detection. We recall that the envelope detector was required for the demodulation of amplitude-modulation (AM) signals.

Of particular interest to us are such questions as the probability density of noise and signal plus noise at the output of such a detector, the d-c noise level and rms noise voltage at the detector output, etc. We shall attempt to answer these questions in this section and then shall give some further applications of this material to radar and navigational systems in the next section.

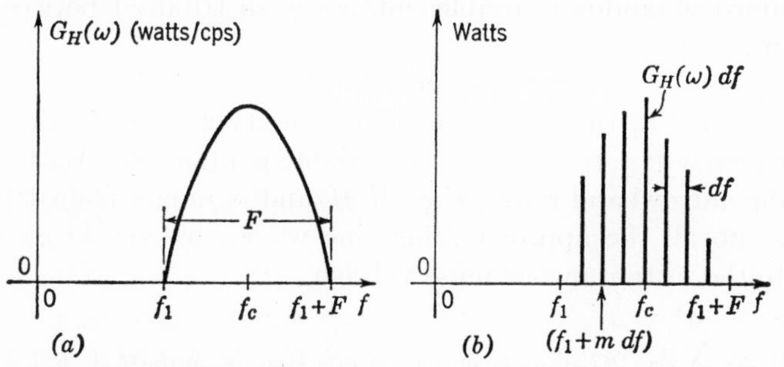

FIG. 7-32. Narrowband noise and its spectrum approximation. (a) Continuous spectrum; (b) discrete approximation.

Assume that white noise generated in a particular system has been passed through a narrowband network of transfer function $H(j\omega)$ centered at frequency ω_c. The spectral density of the white noise is η watts/cps, while at the network output the spectral density is

$$G_H(\omega) = \eta|H(j\omega)|^2 \qquad \text{watts/cps} \tag{7-98}$$

The total noise power at the network output is

$$N = \int_0^\infty G_H(\omega)\,df \tag{7-99}$$

These equations are repeated here as originally written in Sec. 6-1.

All the systems considered in Chaps. 3 and 4, in which a radio-frequency (r-f) signal at the receiver was heterodyned down in frequency and passed through a narrowband intermediate-frequency (i-f) channel, are examples of systems to which the narrowband-noise discussion applies.

In seeking a simple representation of the noise voltages in Sec. 6-3, Signal-to-Noise Ratios in FM and AM, we were led to represent the noise by a sum of sinusoids, with the total mean power in the sinusoids that of the actual noise. We shall extend this approach somewhat in this section.

We again approximate the continuous power-density spectrum of the noise at the network output by a discrete spectrum of many narrow intervals df cps wide ($df \ll$ bandwidth of network; Fig. 7-32). The noise within the range df cps about f cps is now represented by a single sinusoid of the same average power. Since the power within this range is $G_H(\omega)\,df$, the single sinusoid must be of the form

$$\sqrt{2G_H(\omega)\,df}\cos(\omega t + \theta)$$

In Sec. 6-3 we assumed a rectangular narrowband spectrum with $G_H(\omega) = \eta$ within the bandwidth. We also ignored the phase angle θ because we were primarily interested in power at that point. Here we are interested in *instantaneous voltage* and must retain the phase angle. θ is assumed a random variable, uniformly distributed between 0 and 2π radians.

If we assume the narrow band of frequencies to range from f_1 to $f_1 + F$, with $f_c = f_1 + F/2$ the center frequency, the typical single sinusoid will be at frequency $f = f_1 + m\,df$, m a variable parameter. With M intervals in the narrowband range, $F = M\,df$, and m ranges from 1 to M.

Adding up all the approximating sine waves, we get as an approximation to the instantaneous noise voltage

$$v(t) \doteq \sum_{m=1}^{M} \sqrt{2G_H(\omega_1 + m\,d\omega)\,df}\cos[(\omega_1 + m\,d\omega)t + \theta_m] \qquad \text{(7-100)}$$[1]

The θ_m's are uniformly and *independently* distributed.

As df becomes very small and M very large, $v(t)$ is the sum of a large number of independent random variables. (The randomness here is due to the statistical distribution of the phase angles.) By the central-limit theorem, then, $v(t)$ must be normally, or gaussian-, distributed. The representation of the noise voltage $v(t)$ by Eq. (7-100) thus gives both the proper power spectrum and the correct probability distribution for the noise. We shall actually show in Sec. 7-11 that the distribution of the sum of M sinusoids with uniformly distributed and independent phase angles approaches the gaussian distribution.

To emphasize the narrowband characteristics of Eq. (7-100) and to enable us to define the envelope of $v(t)$, we add and subtract ω_c in the expression for frequency in Eq. (7-100). This gives us

$$\cos[(\omega_1 + m\,d\omega - \omega_c)t + \theta_m + \omega_c t]$$

Recalling that $\cos(a + b) = \cos a \cos b - \sin a \sin b$, and writing ω_m for $\omega_1 + m\,d\omega$, we get for the cosine term

$$\cos[(\omega_m - \omega_c) + \theta_m]\cos\omega_c t - \sin[(\omega_m - \omega_c)t + \theta_m]\sin\omega_c t$$

The entire expression for $v(t)$ may then be written in the form

$$v(t) \doteq x(t)\cos\omega_c t - y(t)\sin\omega_c t \qquad \text{(7-101)}$$

[1] Bennett, *op. cit.*

where $$x(t) = \sum_{m=1}^{M} \sqrt{2G_H(\omega_m)\,df} \cos [(\omega_m - \omega_c)t + \theta_m]$$

and $$y(t) = \sum_{m=1}^{M} \sqrt{2G_H(\omega_m)\,df} \sin [(\omega_m - \omega_c)t + \theta_m]$$

$x(t)$ and $y(t)$ are *slowly varying* random variables, since ω_m is close to ω_c for the narrowband system assumed. The central-limit theorem may also be invoked for $x(t)$ and $y(t)$ separately to show that, with $M \to \infty$

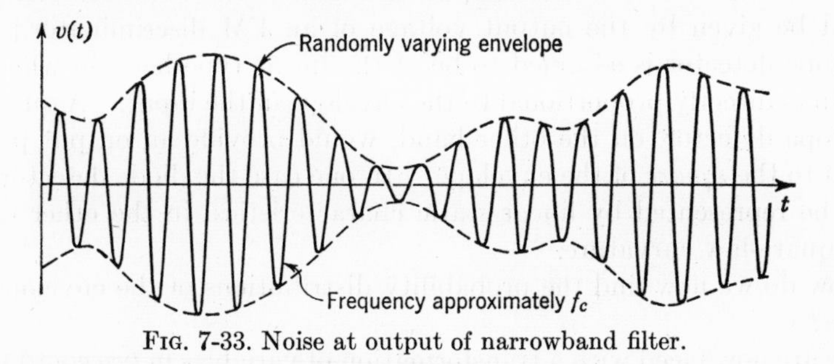

FIG. 7-33. Noise at output of narrowband filter.

and $df \to 0$, both x and y are *normally* (gaussian-) distributed. Each has zero average value,

$$\text{av } x = \text{av } y = 0 \tag{7-102}$$

and each has the same second moment, or mean-squared value, given by

$$\text{av } x^2 = \text{av } y^2 = \sum_{m=1}^{M} G_H(\omega_m)\,df = N \tag{7-103}$$

The second moment for each is just the total noise power (1-ohm resistor) at the network output.

As shown by Bennett,[1] $x(t)$ and $y(t)$ are *independent* random variables. This means that the joint distribution of x and y evaluated at a given instant of time is given by

$$p(x,y) = p(x)p(y) = \frac{e^{-(x^2+y^2)/2N}}{2\pi N} \tag{7-104}$$

with $\sigma_x{}^2 = \sigma_y{}^2 = N$.

Equation (7-104) will be used to determine the statistical properties of the envelope of $v(t)$.

The envelope of $v(t)$ is easily obtained from Eq. (7-101). Because of our assumption of a narrowband filter, $v(t)$ at the output of the filter may be considered a sine wave of frequency ω_c with slowly varying amplitude and phase. An example is shown in Fig. 7-33. As was done with Eq.

[1] *Ibid.*

(6-75) the expressions for envelope and phase may be found from Eq. (7-101) by writing it in the equivalent form

$$v(t) = r(t) \cos [\omega_c t + \theta(t)] \tag{7-105}$$

with $r^2 = x^2 + y^2$ and $\theta = \tan^{-1} (y/x)$. $r(t)$ thus represents the slowly varying envelope (shown as a dashed line in Fig. 7-33) and $\theta(t)$ the slowly varying phase. $r(t)$ would be the voltage at the output of an envelope detector, such as is used in AM receivers and as discussed in Chap. 3. $\theta(t)$ would be found at the output of a phase-sensitive detector. [$\dot{\theta}(t)$ would be given by the output voltage of an FM discriminator.] The envelope detector is assumed to be of the linear type here, in which the output is directly proportional to the envelope of the input. A quadratic envelope detector, on the other hand, would provide an output proportional to the *square* of the envelope. In one case the diode detector used may be represented by linear static characteristics; in the other case it has square-law curvature.

How do we now find the probability distributions of the envelope and phase?

We are now faced with a transformation of variables in *two* coordinates, rather than the one-coordinate transformation of Sec. 7-7. The procedure is essentially the same, however. Given the distributions of two variables x and y, how do we find the distributions of two other variables r and θ, with the transformation given by $x^2 + y^2 = r^2$, $y/x = \tan \theta$? Alternatively we can write $x = r \cos \theta$, $y = r \sin \theta$ as the transformation equations.

In the one-variable case we equated areas under the probability-density curves (Fig. 7-27). Here too we equate probabilities:

$$\text{Prob}\ (x_1 < x < x_2,\ y_1 < y < y_2) = \text{Prob}\ (r_1 < r < r_2,\ \theta_1 < \theta < \theta_2) \tag{7-106}$$

This corresponds, however, to equating volumes under the joint probability-density curves. In this case we are effectively converting from rectangular (x,y) coordinates to polar (r,θ) coordinates. With $q(r,\theta)$ the probability-density function for the polar coordinates we must have

$$p(x,y)\, dx\, dy = q(r,\theta)\, dr\, d\theta \tag{7-107}$$

From Eq. (7-104)

$$p(x,y) = \frac{e^{-(x^2+y^2)/2N}}{2\pi N} = \frac{e^{-r^2/2N}}{2\pi N} \tag{7-108}$$

Transforming differential areas, we have

$$dx\, dy = r\, dr\, d\theta \tag{7-109}$$

(Fig. 7-34).

From Eq. (7-107), then, with Eqs. (7-108) and (7-109),

$$q(r,\theta)\,dr\,d\theta = \frac{re^{-r^2/2N}}{2\pi N}\,dr\,d\theta \tag{7-110}$$

and

$$q(r,\theta) = \frac{re^{-r^2/2N}}{2\pi N} \tag{7-111}$$

To find the distribution $q(r)$ for the envelope alone, we simply average Eq. (7-111) over all possible phases. Since θ varies between 0 and 2π, we get

$$q(r) = \int_0^{2\pi} q(r,\theta)\,d\theta = \frac{re^{-r^2/2N}}{N} \tag{7-112}$$

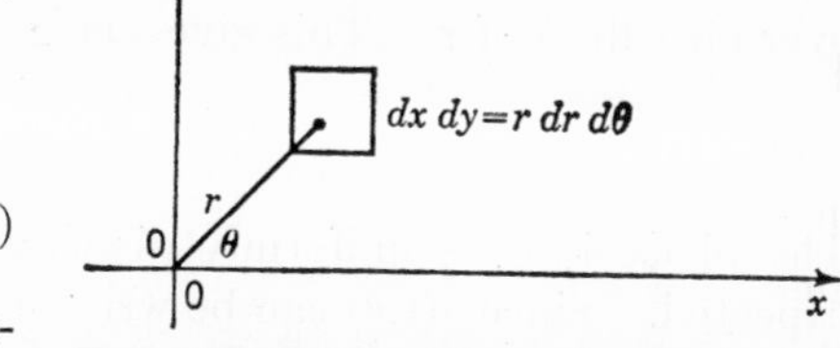

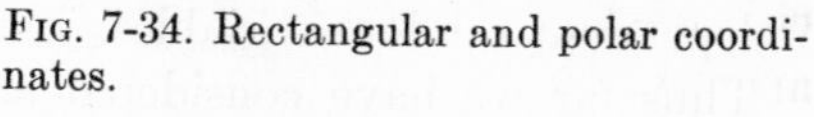
FIG. 7-34. Rectangular and polar coordinates.

This is called the *Rayleigh distribution* and is shown in Fig. 7-35. The peak of this distribution occurs at $r = \sqrt{N}$ and is equal to $e^{-1/2}/\sqrt{N}$. As $\sqrt{N}$, the rms input noise, increases, the distribution flattens out, the peak decreasing and moving to the right. It is easily seen that $q(r)$ is properly normalized, so that $\int_0^\infty q(r)\,dr = 1$. Note that the normalization is from 0 to ∞ here, instead of from $-\infty$ to ∞ for the gaussian distribution. The envelope can have only *positive* values.

The Rayleigh distribution appears in many other applications of statistics. One simple example involves the firing of bullets at a target.

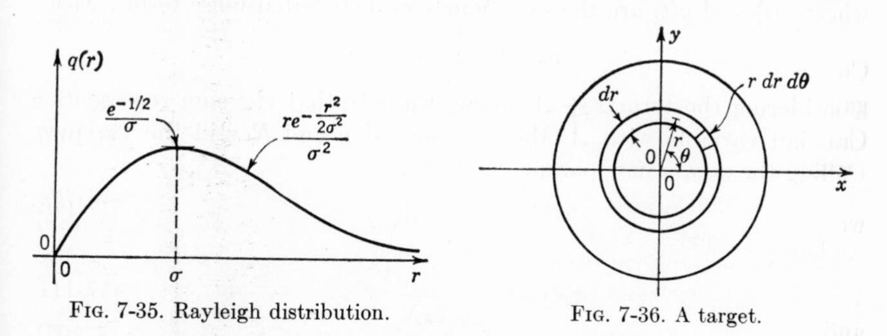

FIG. 7-35. Rayleigh distribution.

FIG. 7-36. A target.

Assume that the distribution of the bullets hitting the target is gaussian along the horizontal, or x, axis of the target and also gaussian along the vertical, or y, axis (i.e., a two-dimensional gaussian distribution) (Fig. 7-36). The average location of the hits is at the origin, and the standard deviation in each direction is σ. The probability that the hits will lie within an annular ring dr units wide and r units from the origin is just $q(r)\,dr$, with $q(r)$ the Rayleigh distribution. The cumulative distribution is

$$P(r) = \int_0^r q(r)\,dr = 1 - e^{-r^2/2\sigma^2} \tag{7-113}$$

[Note from Fig. 7-36 that, if $q(r,\theta)\,dr\,d\theta$ represents the probability that the bullets will lodge within the differential area $r\,dr\,d\theta$, the probability that the bullets will lodge within the concentric annular ring is found by integrating over all values of θ. This is exactly what was done in Eq. (7-112).]

If we are interested in the distribution of phase, we can average $q(r,\theta)$ over all values of r. This gives us

$$q(\theta) = q(r,\theta)\,dr = \frac{1}{2\pi} \tag{7-114}$$

The phase is thus uniformly distributed over 2π radians, as might be expected. Since $q(r,\theta)$ can be written as $q(r)q(\theta)$ in this case, r and θ are independent random variables, just as were x and y.

Thus far we have considered narrowband noise alone applied to an envelope detector. What happens if a sinusoidal signal of amplitude A_c and frequency f_c is added to the noise before detection? This corresponds to the signal-plus-noise case discussed in Sec. 6-3. The signal here represents an unmodulated carrier.

With the signal of the form $A_c \cos \omega_c t$ the signal plus noise at the narrowband filter output may be written

$$v(t) = (x + A_c) \cos \omega_c t - y(t) \sin \omega_c t \tag{7-115}$$

where $x(t)$ and $y(t)$ are the same gaussian-distributed noise terms, with

$$\text{av } x^2 = \text{av } y^2 = N$$

Considering the term $x + A_c$ alone, we note that the sum represents a gaussian variable with A_c the average value and N still the variance. Calling the sum a new parameter x',

$$x'(t) \equiv x(t) + A_c \tag{7-116}$$

we have

$$p(x') = \frac{e^{-(x'-A_c)^2/2N}}{\sqrt{2\pi N}} \tag{7-117}$$

and

$$m_1 = \text{av } x' = A_c$$
$$m_2 = \text{av } x'^2 = A_c^2 + N$$

The envelope of the signal plus noise is now given by

$$r^2 = x'^2 + y^2 = (x + A_c)^2 + y^2 \tag{7-118}$$

and the phase is

$$\theta = \tan^{-1} \frac{y}{x'} = \tan^{-1} \frac{y}{x(t) + A_c} \tag{7-119}$$

As pointed out in Sec. 6-3, the noise added to the unmodulated carrier has produced a resultant carrier which is both amplitude- and phase-modulated. We can again find the probability distributions for both the amplitude (envelope) and phase by a transformation to polar coordinates. This will give us the probability distribution of signal plus noise at the output of an envelope detector, as well as the distribution at the output of a phase detector.

With x' and y independent random variables related to r and θ by the transformations $x' = r\cos\theta$, $y = r\sin\theta$, we have

$$q(r,\theta)\,dr\,d\theta = p(x',y)\,dx'\,dy = \frac{e^{-[(x'-A_c)^2+y^2]/2N}}{2\pi N}\,dx\,dy$$
$$= \frac{e^{-A_c^2/2N} r e^{-(r^2-2rA_c\cos\theta)/2N}}{2\pi N}\,dr\,d\theta \qquad (7\text{-}120)$$

Note that we cannot write $q(r,\theta)$ as a product $q(r)q(\theta)$, since a term in the equation appears with both variables multiplied together as $r\cos\theta$. This indicates that r and θ are *dependent* variables. They are connected together in this case by the term $rA_c\cos\theta$. This is apparent from Eqs. (7-118) and (7-119), as well as Eq. (7-120). If $A_c \to 0$, the two variables again become independent and $q(r,\theta)$ reduces to the product $q(r)q(\theta)$ found for the zero-signal case.

We can find $q(r)$ again by integrating over all values of θ. This gives us

$$q(r) = \frac{e^{-A_c^2/2N} r e^{-r^2/2N}}{2\pi N} \int_0^{2\pi} e^{(rA_c\cos\theta)/N}\,d\theta \qquad (7\text{-}121)$$

The integral in Eq. (7-121) cannot be evaluated in terms of elementary functions. Note, however, its similarity to the defining integral for the Bessel function of the first kind and zero order given by Eq. (3-57). It is in fact related to the Bessel function of the first kind. In particular,

$$I_0(z) \equiv \frac{1}{2\pi}\int_0^{2\pi} e^{z\cos\theta}\,d\theta \qquad (7\text{-}122)$$

is called the *modified* Bessel function of the first kind and zero order. In terms of $I_0(z)$, Eq. (7-121) becomes

$$q(r) = \frac{r}{N} e^{-(r^2+A_c^2)/2N} I_0\left(\frac{rA_c}{N}\right) \qquad (7\text{-}123)$$

The modified Bessel function can be written as an infinite series, just as in the case of the Bessel function of the first kind. This series can be shown to be

$$I_0(z) = \sum_{n=0}^{\infty} \frac{z^{2n}}{2^{2n}(n!)^2} \qquad (7\text{-}124)$$

For $z \ll 1$

$$I_0(z) \doteq 1 + \frac{z^2}{4} + \cdots \doteq e^{z^2/4} \tag{7-125}$$

Letting $A_c \to 0$ in Eq. (7-123), we get the Rayleigh distribution again, checking our previous result for the zero-signal case.

Equation (7-123) contains the term $A_c^2/2N$. Since N is the mean noise power at the input to the detector and $A_c^2/2$ the mean signal power (1-ohm resistor), $A_c^2/2N$ is just the power S/N ratio at the input to the detector, as defined in Chap. 6. If we call this s^2, the probability distribution of the envelope of signal plus noise may be written

$$q(r) = \frac{e^{-s^2} r e^{-r^2/2N}}{N} I_0\left(rs\sqrt{\frac{2}{N}}\right) \qquad s^2 \equiv \frac{A_c^2}{2N} \tag{7-126}$$

We have indicated that, for $s \to 0$, we get the Rayleigh distribution. For large s^2 ($A_c \gg \sqrt{N}$) we obtain, however, the gaussian distribution again. To show this, we make use of a known property of the modified Bessel function that it approaches asymptotically, for large values of the argument, an exponential function. Thus, for $z \gg 1$,

$$I_0(z) \doteq \frac{e^z}{\sqrt{2\pi z}} \tag{7-127}$$

Letting $rs\sqrt{2/N} \gg 1$ (or $rA_c \gg N$) in Eq. (7-126), we make use of Eq. (7-127) to put $q(r)$ in the form

$$\begin{aligned} q(r) &\doteq \frac{r}{N\sqrt{2\pi r A_c/N}} e^{-(r/\sqrt{2N} - s)^2} \\ &= \frac{r}{\sqrt{2\pi r A_c N}} e^{-(r-A_c)^2/2N} \end{aligned} \tag{7-128}$$

This function peaks sharply about the point $r = A_c$, dropping off rapidly as we move away from this point. Most of the contribution to the area under the $q(r)$ curve (or the largest values of the probability of a range of r occurring) comes from points in the vicinity of $r = A_c$. In this range of r, then, we can let $r \doteq A_c$ in the nonexponential (and slowly varying) portions of $q(r)$ and get

$$q(r) \doteq \frac{1}{\sqrt{2\pi N}} e^{-(r-A_c)^2/2N} \qquad rA_c \gg N \tag{7-129}$$

In the vicinity of the point $r = A_c$, which becomes essentially the average value of the envelope r, the distribution approximates a normal (gaussian) distribution. This is of course valid only for $A_c^2 \gg N$, or $s^2 \gg 1$. Note that this normal distribution is identical with that at the input to the envelope detector: it has the same average amplitude A_c and the same variance N.

This might be expected intuitively. For low S/N ratios the envelope will not deviate too far on the average from the $r = 0$ axis. Since r can never become negative by definition of an envelope, we would expect a lopsided probability distribution with most of the contribution coming in the vicinity of $r = 0$. This is just the Rayleigh distribution. As A_c or s^2 increases, however, we would eventually expect the envelope to be symmetrically distributed about A_c. Although variations of the envelope above A_c have theoretically no limit, while below A_c the envelope is constrained never to become negative, the $r = 0$ axis is so remote for $A_c \gg \sqrt{N}$ that this nonzero constraint becomes insignificant and the probability-density curve approaches just the symmetrical bell-shaped characteristic of the gaussian function.

So far as the signal plus noise at the output is concerned, then, the nonlinear operation of the envelope detector has no effect on the distribution for large S/N ratio. The same result is found to hold true for other nonlinear demodulators with high S/N ratio: the output distribution of signal plus noise remains the same as that of the input.

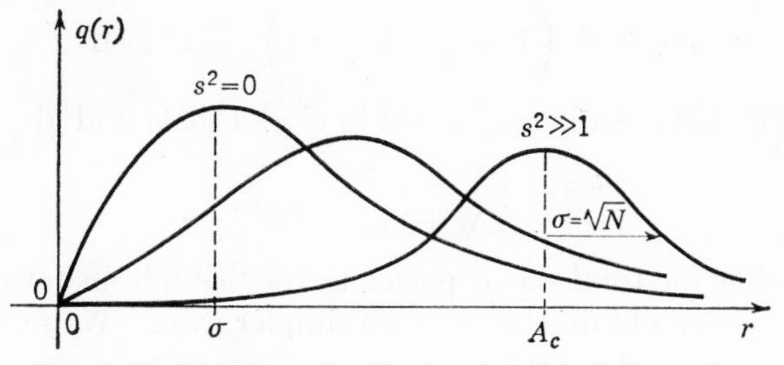

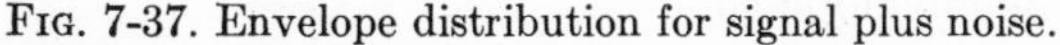

FIG. 7-37. Envelope distribution for signal plus noise.

This is exactly the reason why we have been assuming the noise distribution to remain gaussian as the noise progresses from the r-f stages of a receiver down to the narrowband i-f output. Even with no transmitted signal present the local oscillator injects a large enough signal voltage at the nonlinear mixer to ensure a gaussian noise distribution at the mixer output. The mixer then serves only to translate r-f energy down to the i-f spectrum. The signal and noise properties remain relatively unchanged.

The local carrier injection required for suppressed-carrier demodulation produces the same result: the noise distribution remains gaussian at the demodulator output.

We encountered a similar result in Chap. 6, where we noted, in our discussion of S/N ratio in AM, that the term involving mixing of noise with noise in envelope detectors becomes negligible if a large signal (the unmodulated carrier) is present. The probability density at the output of an envelope detector is shown plotted in Fig. 7-37 for different values of the signal-to-noise ratio s^2.

Mean Values and Output Power. We can utilize our expression for the probability density of the voltage at the output of an envelope detector to find the average (d-c) power and mean a-c power at the detector output. As was indicated previously, the first moment m_1 represents the average (d-c) voltage, the second moment m_2 the total mean power. The variance $\sigma^2 = m_2 - m_1^2$ provides us with a measure of the average a-c, or fluctuation, power.

From Eq. (7-126) and the definition of the different moments the output d-c voltage with signal and noise present is

$$m_1 = \int_0^\infty rq(r)\,dr = e^{-s^2} \int_0^\infty \frac{r^2}{N} e^{-r^2/2N} I_0\left(\frac{rA_c}{N}\right) dr \qquad (7\text{-}130)$$

The total average power for signal plus noise is given by

$$m_2 = \int_0^\infty r^2 q(r)\,dr = e^{-s^2} \int_0^\infty \frac{r^3}{N} e^{-r^2/2N} I_0\left(\frac{rA_c}{N}\right) dr \qquad (7\text{-}131)$$

The integral for m_1 may be evaluated in series form to give

$$m_1 \doteq A_c\left(1 + \frac{1}{4s^2} + \cdots\right) \qquad s^2 \gg 0 \qquad (7\text{-}132)$$

Equation (7-131) can be evaluated in closed form and gives, for m_2,

$$\begin{aligned} m_2 &= 2N(1 + s^2) \\ &= 2N + A_c^2 \qquad s^2 \geq 0 \end{aligned} \qquad (7\text{-}133)$$

This expression for total mean power is very simple in form and could actually have been obtained in a much simpler way. We recall from our definition of the envelope that

$$r^2 = x'^2 + y^2$$

with x' the inphase component of signal plus noise and y the out-of-phase component. Then

$$m_2 \equiv \text{av } r^2 = \text{av } x'^2 + \text{av } y^2$$

But av $x'^2 = N + A_c^2$ [Eq. (7-117)] and av $y^2 = N$. Then $m_2 = 2N + A_c^2$ as found here.

In deriving Eqs. (7-132) and (7-133) we have implicitly assumed a detector constant of unity: the output voltage equals exactly the envelope. Actually we should have written the output voltage $= ar$, with a the detector constant and r the envelope. Then the actual outputs are

$$am_1 \doteq aA_c\left(1 + \frac{1}{4s^2} + \cdots\right) \qquad s^2 \gg 0 \qquad (7\text{-}134)$$

and

$$a^2 m_2 = a^2(2N + A_c^2) \qquad (7\text{-}135)$$

For large S/N the *mean* voltage at the output is just aA_c, or just the detector constant times the amplitude of the input signal. The mean noise power is just the mean-squared variation about the average voltage, or the variance σ^2 multiplied by a^2. From Eqs. (7-134) and (7-135) this mean noise power is

$$a^2\sigma^2 = a^2(m_2 - m_1^2) \doteq a^2N\left(1 - \frac{4}{s^2}\right) \qquad s^2 > 4 \qquad (7\text{-}136)$$

For $s^2 \gg 4$, then, the d-c voltage and rms noise voltage approach aA_c and $a\sqrt{N}$, respectively. This agrees of course with the result found previously that the distribution of the envelope of signal plus noise approaches a gaussian distribution with average value A_c and standard deviation $\sqrt{N}$. This is indicated in Fig. 7-37 for $s^2 \gg 1$.

Equation (7-136) for the output noise power also agrees with the result obtained previously in Chap. 6, as given by Eq. (6-77). There the unmodulated carrier was assumed to be of amplitude A_c. For large S/N ratio at the input the mean noise power at the output of the envelope detector is just the input noise power multiplied by the square of the detector constant.

When noise alone is present at the detector input, the d-c voltage, rms voltage, and total power at the output may be found from the Rayleigh distribution of Eq. (7-112). With the detector constant again denoted by the symbol a the different output parameters become

$$am_1 = a\sqrt{\frac{\pi N}{2}} \qquad (7\text{-}137)$$

$$a^2m_2 = 2a^2N \qquad (7\text{-}138)$$

and

$$a^2\sigma^2 = a^2N\left(2 - \frac{\pi}{2}\right) \qquad (7\text{-}139)$$

Equation (7-139) represents the mean noise power at the output of an envelope detector with the d-c power $(a^2m_1^2)$ filtered out. The derivation of these results is left as an exercise for the reader.

Upon comparing Eqs. (7-136) and (7-139) it is apparent that the output noise power is *greater* with a signal present than for noise alone. The relative increase in noise is $1/(2 - \pi/2) = 2.33$ and accounts in part for the increase in noise noticed in AM receivers when a carrier is tuned in.

7-10. Application to Radar Signal Detection and Phase Detection. We may utilize the results of the previous section to solve some simple problems involving envelope detection of signals in the presence of noise.

We have already applied our knowledge of noise statistics to the calculation of error probabilities in the reception of binary pulses in the presence of noise, with PCM reception as an example. We assumed there a gaussian distribution for the noise, however, so that we were implicitly interested in the *instantaneous* values of a d-c signal pulse plus noise, rather than the *envelope* of a narrowband signal plus noise.

For the PCM analysis to apply to r-f pulsed signals (either on-off or bipolar), we must assume the signals plus noise to be heterodyned down to video frequencies by the injection of a high-level local carrier. This enables us to assume a gaussian noise distribution at the detector output. The demodulator is then the same type as required for suppressed-carrier (double-sideband, DSB) demodulation. This type of demodulation is phase-sensitive, as noted in Chaps. 3 and 4, and requires the r-f signal carrier and injected carrier to be maintained in phase synchronism.

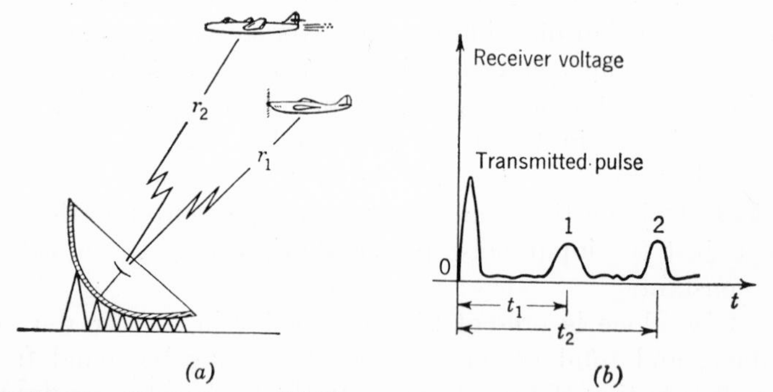

FIG. 7-38. Simple radar system. (a) Transmitter-receiver and targets; (b) transmitted and received signals.

In many communication problems phase-sensitive demodulation by carrier injection is either not possible or not economically feasible. Envelope detection must then be used for the demodulation of narrowband signals. In the absence of a carrier the detected noise has a Rayleigh distribution, and error probabilities must be calculated on this basis.

The normal AM system described in Chap. 3 is one example where envelope detection is used because of its simplicity and relatively low cost. Another example is a telegraph system with messages sent by switching a sine wave on and off.[1]

Most standard radar systems utilize envelope detection also. Radar return signals usually vary randomly in phase because of the nature of the complex targets from which they are reflected. Inphase or coherent carrier injection at the receiver is thus normally not possible.

We shall deal in this section with the problem of detection of radar pulse signals and the calculation of appropriate error probabilities for this case. The reader is referred to the cited article by Bennett for a similar analysis of the envelope detection of telegraph signals.

A simple radar is shown drawn pictorially in Fig. 7-38. As indicated

[1] W. R. Bennett, *Proc. IRE*, vol. 44, pp. 609–638, May, 1956.

by the block diagram of Fig. 7-39 the radar transmitter provides a periodic series of pulsed sine waves. These are normally generated at microwave frequencies in order to obtain a well-defined narrow beam of electromagnetic energy with antennas of reasonable size. Targets in the path of the beam reflect the pulsed high-frequency (h-f) energy. A portion of this reflected energy is then picked up at the antenna, heterodyned down to an intermediate frequency, envelope-detected, and sent on to indicating circuits.

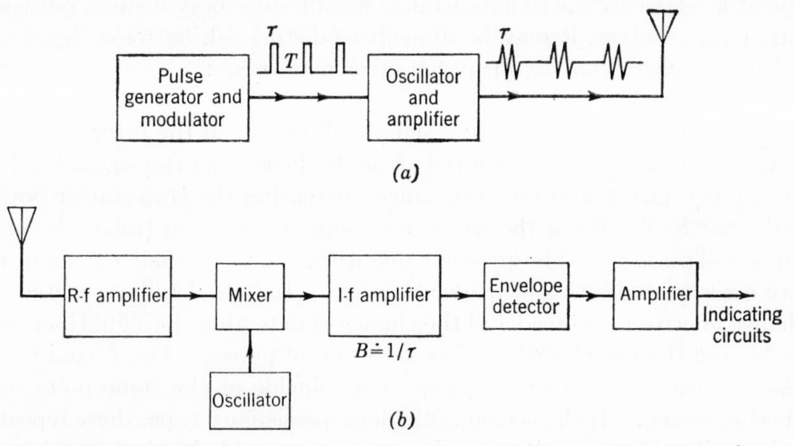

FIG. 7-39. Block diagram, simple search radar. (a) Transmitter; (b) receiver.

The component parts of the radar, excluding necessary synchronizing circuits, are thus essentially the same as those encountered in the usual AM system.

The information carried by the received pulses is primarily range (distance) information. Since electromagnetic energy travels at a speed of $c = 3 \times 10^8$ m/sec in air (actually vacuum), the time taken for the transmitted pulse to travel a distance r_1 m, be reflected, and return to the antenna is

$$t_1 = \frac{2r_1}{c} \quad \text{sec}$$

An indicator presenting transmitted and received pulses in the sequence of time occurrence can thus be calibrated directly in range. Figure 7-38 shows two targets located a radial distance of r_1 and r_2 m, respectively, from the radar. The return pulses appear t_1 and t_2 sec, respectively, after the transmitted pulse. Other information as to target location (azimuth and elevation angle, for example) is obtained from the known direction in which the antenna is pointing at the time of transmission and reception. This is the reason why narrow beams of energy are required.

Search radars, as implied by the name, "search" the skies for the possible appearance of a target. For such radars signal detection consists primarily in determining the presence or absence of a pulse. Pulse shape is secondary. For such radars, then, the system bandwidth is usually chosen as the reciprocal of the pulse width to maximize received signal-to-noise ratio. The matched-filter criterion of Sec. 6-2 thus applies in this case. Tracking radars require information as to the precise time of reception of a pulse, however, and the actual pulse shape used is important.

We shall concentrate on the search radar only. Since a small target or one at a relatively far radial distance will produce only a small pulse signal at the receiver, it may be difficult to distinguish between signal and noise. In particular, two types of error may occur:

1. Noise may be mistaken for signal.
2. There is a chance that the signal will be lost in the noise.

We can obviously decrease the errors by increasing the signal level or, for a given target and given distance, increasing the transmitter power. But what S/N ratio at the receiver is required for given (tolerable) error rates? To answer this question quantitatively, we shall calculate the two error probabilities mentioned above. (In actual radar practice the chance of error is reduced and the chance of detecting the signal increased by hitting the target with a repeated series of pulses. For a fixed target distance the received signal pulses will coincide at the same point on a viewing screen. If the screen is of a long-persistence type, these repeated pulses will add up, eventually rising to a detectable level above the surrounding noise.)

For calculation purposes we assume that the detection process consists in calling a voltage a signal if it exceeds a certain predetermined threshold level. In the binary-pulse case previously discussed this threshold was taken as one-half the expected pulse height. Here there is no one unique signal height expected. Instead we choose the level as one calculated to reduce to a tolerable point the chance of noise, in the absence of a signal, being mistaken for a signal.

With the level chosen there is a chance that a signal, when it does appear, will encounter an instantaneously negative noise voltage. The resulting signal plus noise voltage may drop below the threshold level so that the signal will be lost. To keep the probability of detecting a signal, once it does appear, to as close to a value of 1 as desired will then require a specified minimum signal-to-noise ratio at the input to the envelope detector. With the receiver noise figure and target characteristics known the required transmitter power for a given probability of detection and probability of mistaking noise for signal can be calculated. The probability of detection of a signal is just 1 − (probability of losing a signal).

A typical radar time strip, with threshold level indicated, is shown in Fig. 7-40.

The two probabilities to be calculated depend on the probability distributions found for the envelope of narrowband noise and narrowband signal plus noise. The chance that noise will exceed the level set at

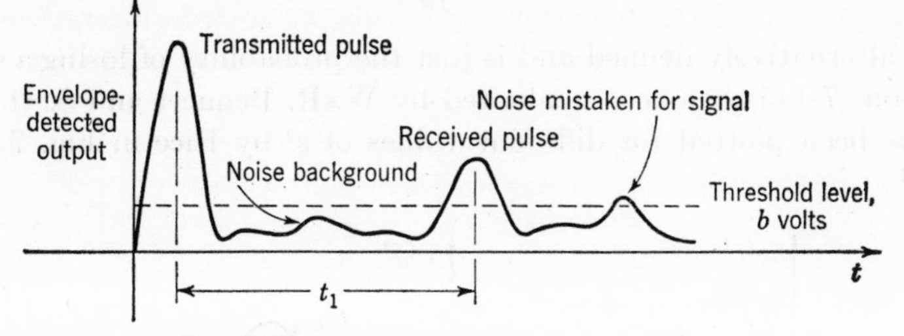

FIG. 7-40. Threshold-level signal detection.

b volts and be erroneously labeled a signal is

$$P_{nb} = \int_b^\infty q_n(r)\,dr \tag{7-140}$$

where

$$q_n(r) = \frac{re^{-r^2/2N}}{N} \tag{7-141}$$

the Rayleigh distribution discussed in the previous section. N is the total average power at the input to the detector. The subscript n is used here to distinguish this envelope distribution from that for signal plus noise.

Integrating Eq. (7-140) directly, we get

$$P_{nb} = e^{-b^2/2N} \tag{7-142}$$

This equation relates the probability of noise being mistaken for signal to the threshold level chosen. A linear-type envelope detector has been assumed and the detector constant normalized to 1. A curve of P_{nb} versus $b/\sqrt{N}$ is shown plotted in Fig. 7-41. P_{nb} is indicated pictorially by the crosshatched area under the $q_n(r)$ curve in Fig. 7-42*a*.

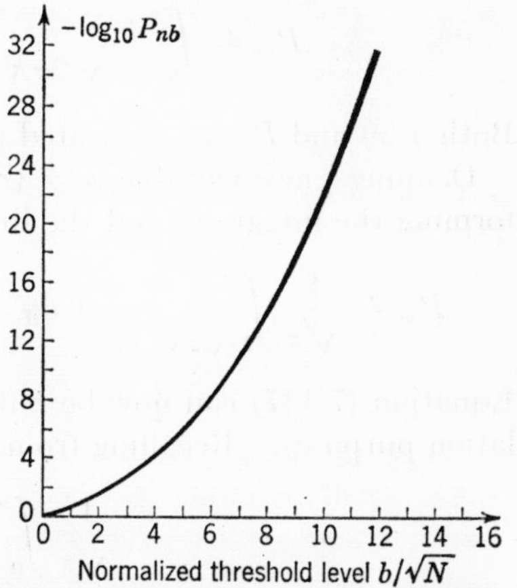

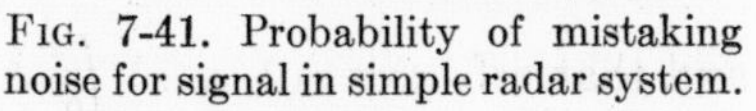

FIG. 7-41. Probability of mistaking noise for signal in simple radar system.

The probability of detecting a signal in the presence of noise is just

$$P_{sb} = \int_b^\infty q_s(r)\,dr \tag{7-143}$$

where

$$q_s(r) = \frac{e^{-s^2}re^{-r^2/2N}}{N} I_0\left(rs\sqrt{\frac{2}{N}}\right) \tag{7-144}$$

the probability density for signal plus noise obtained previously [Eq. (7-126)]. $s^2 = A_c^2/2N$ is the mean power S/N ratio at the detector input.

$$1 - P_{sb} = \int_0^b q_s(r)\, dr \qquad \text{(7-145)}$$

can be alternatively defined and is just the probability of losing a signal. Equation (7-145) has been evaluated by W. R. Bennett and S. O. Rice, and has been plotted for different values of s^2 by Rice in Fig. 7 of his paper.[1]

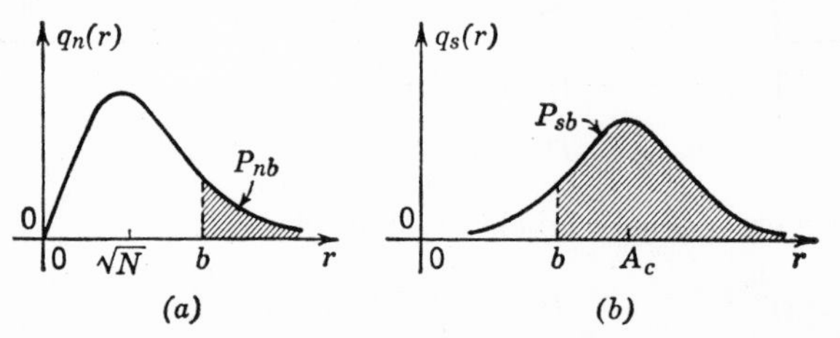

FIG. 7-42. Calculation of error and detection probabilities. (a) Noise only; (b) signal plus noise ($s^2 \gg 1$).

Alternatively we can approximate $q_s(r)$ by the gaussian distribution valid for large s^2. This gives

$$P_{sb} \doteq \int_b^\infty \frac{e^{-(r-A_c)^2/2N}}{\sqrt{2\pi N}}\, dr \qquad b \gg \sqrt{N},\ s^2 \gg 1 \qquad \text{(7-146)}$$

Both $q_s(r)$ and P_{sb} are indicated graphically in Fig. 7-42b.

Defining a new variable, $y = (r - A_c)/\sqrt{2N}$, in Eq. (7-146) and transforming the integrand and the limits accordingly, we get

$$P_{sb} \doteq \frac{1}{\sqrt{\pi}} \int_{b/\sqrt{2N}-s}^\infty e^{-y^2}\, dy \qquad b \gg \sqrt{N},\ s^2 \gg 1,\ s^2 \equiv \frac{A_c^2}{2N} \qquad \text{(7-147)}$$

Equation (7-147) can now be put into the error-function form for calculation purposes. Recalling from our previous work that

$$\frac{1}{\sqrt{\pi}} \int_0^\infty e^{-y^2}\, dy = \tfrac{1}{2}$$

and that $\operatorname{erf}(x) \equiv (2/\sqrt{\pi}) \int_0^x e^{-y^2}\, dy$, we get

$$P_{sb} \doteq \tfrac{1}{2}\left[1 - \operatorname{erf}\left(\frac{b}{\sqrt{2N}} - s\right)\right] \qquad b \gg \sqrt{N},\ s^2 \gg 1 \qquad \text{(7-148)}$$

For small threshold level and small signal-to-noise ratio s^2 we must evaluate P_{sb} using the actual density function for $q_s(r)$ given by Eq.

[1] Rice, *op. cit.*

(7-144). For large s^2, however, Eq. (7-148) approximates the actual result very well. As an example, let $b/\sqrt{N} = \sqrt{2}\,s = 8$ ($s^2 = 32$). Then $P_{sb} \doteq 0.5$, since $\operatorname{erf} 0 = 0$. But $b/\sqrt{N} = 8$ corresponds to $P_{nb} = 10^{-14}$, from Fig. 7-41. So for a noise-error probability of 10^{-14} a power S/N ratio of 32, or 15 db, is required to have signals detected 50 per cent of the time on the average.

The probability of detecting signals may be increased by decreasing the threshold level b. This increases the noise-error probability, however. Alternatively, with b fixed and hence P_{nb} determined (Fig. 7-41),

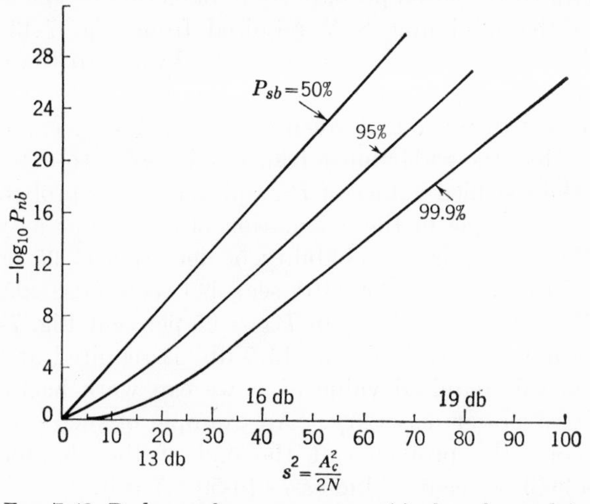

FIG. 7-43. Radar performance curves (single pulses only).

we may increase P_{sb} by increasing s^2. Equations (7-142) and (7-148) [or Eq. (7-143) in the exact case] may be combined to give a set of radar performance curves relating the two probabilities P_{nb} and P_{sb} to the input-power S/N ratio s^2. Such a set of curves is shown plotted in Fig. 7-43. We must emphasize here that these correspond to the simplest type of radar system, in which *individual* signal pulses are required to exceed a threshold level. (In actual systems a group of repetitive pulses are commonly summed or integrated. This is usually done automatically by scanning across a long-persistence viewing screen, as noted previously. The analysis for this case is discussed briefly at the end of the next section.)

How do we utilize the curves of Fig. 7-43? P_{nb} represents the probability that noise, in the absence of signal, will be mistaken for a signal. For a narrowband i-f section, as assumed here, the envelope of the i-f noise voltage will appear roughly as a sequence of pulses of random height. The width of these pulses will be approximately $1/\Delta f$, with Δf the i-f bandwidth. This means that approximately Δf noise pulses per second will appear on the average. If the radar searches for signals at *all* ranges and azimuths, with no particular sections of the volume scanned gated out, each of the Δf noise pulses per second has a chance of being mistaken for signal. On the average, however, only the fraction $P_{nb}\,\Delta f$ will manage to exceed the threshold level and be erroneously labeled signal. The number of errors per second, or false alarms, is thus $P_{nb}\,\Delta f$. It is this number (or its reciprocal, $1/(P_{nb}\,\Delta f)$, the interval between errors on the average) that must be fixed at a tolerable value.

With $P_{nb}\,\Delta f$ given and the system bandwidth known P_{nb} is of course known. With the required probability of detection of signals, P_{sb}, specified we find the minimum S/N required from Fig. 7-43. With the receiver noise figure given we can work backward to the input to the receiver to find the signal power required at that point. For a known target and target distance and given antenna gains we can calculate the signal power that the radar must transmit in order to detect the given target with the specified values of P_{sb} and noise-error probability P_{nb}.

As a simple example of the calculation of s^2, assume a system bandwidth of 1 Mc, a required probability of detection of 95 per cent, and an average interval of 3 hr (10^4 sec) between false alarms. Then $P_{nb}\,\Delta f = 10^4$, or $P_{nb} = 10^{-10}$. For $P_{sb} = 95$ per cent Fig. 7-43 indicates that a minimum S/N ratio of 35 (15.5 db) is required at the detector input. From this required value of s^2 we can work backward to find the transmitted power necessary. An example of such a calculation is included among the problems at the end of the chapter. If P_{sb} is increased to 99.9 per cent, s^2 increases to 50 (17 db).

We shall return to the radar analysis problem briefly at the end of the next section when we discuss the effect of adding n successive pulses reflected from a target in order to increase the probability of detection.

Probability Distribution of Phase. We have discussed at length in the past two sections the probability distribution of the envelope of a narrow-band signal embedded in noise. The probability distribution of the phase of the signal plus noise is frequently also of interest.

We have given some examples, in the chapters on modulation systems, of systems where the phase of a sinusoidal signal carries significant information. Other examples include phase-sensitive navigational systems, such as cycle-matching loran, where the relative phase lag between two sinusoidal signal pulses or the difference in time of arrival of two signals carries positional information.

In all these examples we compare the phase of a received signal to that of a reference signal. (The reference signal may also be received from another transmitting station.) What is the error in determining the desired phase angle because of the presence of fluctuation noise? (Although we have been emphasizing noise generated in the receiver, it could just as well be due to additive noise along the path of signal transmission.)

Assuming a narrowband receiver again, the joint probability density of the envelope and phase of a sinusoidal signal in gaussian noise is given by Eq. (7-120). (The actual phase angle of the signal is assumed to be 0° for convenience.) Repeating that equation here,

$$q(r,\theta) = \frac{e^{-s^2}}{2\pi N} re^{-(r^2-2A_c r \cos\theta)/2N} \tag{7-149}$$

$q(\theta)$, the probability-density function of the phase, is found by integrating over all values of the envelope r.

$$\begin{aligned} q(\theta) &= \int_0^\infty q(r,\theta)\, dr \\ &= \frac{e^{-s^2}}{2\pi N} \int_0^\infty re^{-(r^2-2A_c r\cos\theta)/2N}\, dr \qquad s^2 = \frac{A_c{}^2}{2N} \end{aligned} \tag{7-150}$$

The integral can be evaluated rather simply by completing the square in the exponent. Doing this, and using the symbol I to denote the integral, we get

$$I = e^{s^2\cos^2\theta} \int_0^\infty re^{-(r-A_c\cos\theta)^2/2N}\, dr \tag{7-151}$$

A transformation of variables, $y = (r - A_c \cos\theta)/\sqrt{2N}$, then gives, after some manipulation,

$$I = N + A_c\sqrt{\frac{N\pi}{2}} e^{s^2\cos^2\theta}[1 + \operatorname{erf}(s\cos\theta)] \qquad \operatorname{erf} x \equiv \frac{2}{\sqrt{\pi}}\int_0^x e^{-y^2}\, dy \tag{7-152}$$

The probability-density function for the phase thus becomes the rather formidable-looking expression

$$q(\theta) = \frac{e^{-s^2}}{2\pi} + \frac{1}{2}\sqrt{\frac{s^2}{\pi}} \cos\theta e^{-s^2\sin^2\theta}[1 + \operatorname{erf}(s\cos\theta)] \tag{7-153}$$

For $s^2 = 0$ (no signal) the equation reduces to $q(\theta) = 1/2\pi$, as expected.

$q(\theta)$ is shown sketched in Fig. 7-44. Note that the curve is symmetrical about $\theta = 0$, the assumed phase angle of the signal. (For any other phase angle, say $\theta = \alpha$, the curve is symmetrical about that angle.)

For large signal-to-noise ratio s^2 the curve peaks markedly in the vicinity of $\theta = 0$, with the major contribution to the probability (or area under the curve) coming from that vicinity. As s^2 increases, then, the probability that θ will lie within specified limits about $\theta = 0$ increases as well. For large s^2 and in the vicinity of $\theta = 0$ the curve may be approximated by a gaussian (normal) distribution. Thus, for $s^2 \gg 1$

and $|\theta| < 5°$, $\sin \theta \doteq \theta$, $\cos \theta \doteq 1$, and $\text{erf}\,(s \cos \theta) \doteq 1$. With these approximations we get

$$q(\theta) \doteq \frac{e^{-s^2\theta^2}}{\sqrt{\pi/s^2}} \qquad s^2 \ll 1,\ \theta < 5° \tag{7-154}$$

a gaussian distribution with zero mean value and variance $\sigma^2 = 1/2s^2$. The width of the curve thus decreases inversely as s, the voltage signal-to-noise ratio, approaching an impulse function centered about $\theta = 0$ for $s^2 \to \infty$.

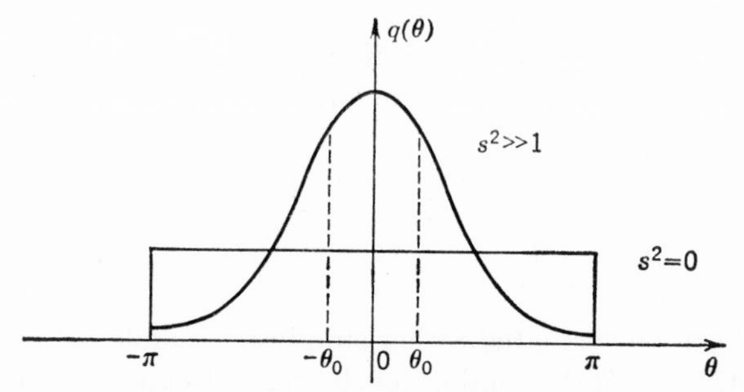

FIG. 7-44. Probability-density function of phase (signal plus noise).

The probability that θ will lie within a range $\pm\theta_0$ radians from 0 radians is given by

$$\begin{aligned}\text{Prob}\,(|\theta| < |\theta_0|) &= \int_{-\theta_0}^{\theta_0} q(\theta)\, d\theta \\ &\doteq \frac{2}{\sqrt{\pi/s^2}} \int_0^{\theta_0} e^{-s^2\theta^2}\, d\theta\end{aligned} \tag{7-155}$$

where $s^2 \gg 1$ and $\theta_0 < 0.1$ radian. Upon using the change of variables, $x = s\theta$, this becomes

$$\text{Prob}\,(|\theta| < |\theta_0|) \doteq \text{erf}\, s\theta_0 \tag{7-156}$$

As an example, assume that the power signal-to-noise ratio is 100 at the output of the narrowband i-f section. The probability that the instantaneous phase angle of the signal pulse will not deviate more than $2\pi/100$ radians (3.6°) from the true phase angle is

$$\text{erf}\,\frac{2\pi}{10} = 0.625$$

The probability that the phase angle will be in error by no more than 0.02 cycle (7.2°) is

$$\text{erf}\ 1.356 = 0.945$$

(In this last calculation we have exceeded the limits of the gaussian approximation somewhat, but the probability found is accurate enough, since the error in the approximation occurs at the tail of the curve, where the contribution to the probability is very small.)

The "jitter" in the signal phase angle due to noise fluctuations will thus be within 3.6° 62.5 per cent of the time and within 7.2° 94.5 per cent of the time on the average. This is for a voltage S/N ratio of 10. If the signal happens to be a timing signal, the signal phase error will constitute a timing error. For example, a 3.6° phase error in a 100-kc wave (as in cycle-matching loran, for example), corresponds to a 0.1-μsec error in timing. The 7.2° phase error corresponds to a 0.2-μsec timing error.

7-11. Sum of n Independent Variables: Characteristic Functions. We have referred in passing, several times, to the central-limit theorem of probability theory that the distribution of the sum of n independent variables approaches the gaussian (normal) distribution. We utilized this theorem in stating that fluctuation noise could be represented by the gaussian distribution. We shall not actually derive the central-limit theorem in this book, but we shall indicate, in this section, the approach usually taken.

In determining the distribution of the sum of n independent random variables we shall begin first by considering the simplest case of the sum of two such variables. Consider then a variable $z = x + y$. With $p_1(x)$ and $p_2(y)$ given and x and y independent how do we find $p(z)$?

The most direct approach is that of performing a transformation of variables just as in the previous sections. We therefore define two new variables given by

$$z = x + y \tag{7-157}$$

and

$$\zeta = x \tag{7-158}$$

The probability that x and y lie within a specified region must equal the probability that z and ζ lie within the corresponding region found from Eqs. (7-157) and (7-158). Thus

$$\int_z \int_\zeta p(z,\zeta)\, dz\, d\zeta = \int_x \int_y p_1(x)p_2(y)\, dx\, dy \tag{7-159}$$

Substituting Eqs. (7-157) and (7-158) into the right-hand side of Eq. (7-159), we obtain

$$\int_z \int_\zeta p(z,\zeta)\, dz\, d\zeta = \int_{z}\int_{\zeta} p_1(\zeta)p_2(z - \zeta)\, dz\, d\zeta \tag{7-160}$$

and

$$p(z,\zeta) = p_1(\zeta)p_2(z - \zeta) \tag{7-161}$$

The distribution for $p(z)$ is then found by integrating $p(z,\zeta)$ over all values of ζ. Since ζ is exactly x,

$$p(z) = \int_{-\infty}^{\infty} p_1(x)p_2(z - x)\, dx \tag{7-162}$$

Note that Eq. (7-162) appears in the form of the convolution integral of Chap. 2. This implies that if we arbitrarily take the Fourier transforms of $p_1(x)$ and $p_2(y)$ the Fourier transform of $p(z)$ must be given by the product of the two transforms. This then gives us another (and frequently simpler) method of finding $p(z)$. Calling $G_x(t)$ the Fourier transform of $p_1(x)$ (t a new parameter), and $G_y(t)$ the corresponding transform of $p_2(y)$, we have

$$G_x(t) = \int_{-\infty}^{\infty} e^{jtx} p_1(x)\, dx \tag{7-163}$$

$$G_y(t) = \int_{-\infty}^{\infty} e^{jty} p_2(y)\, dy \tag{7-164}$$

(We use e^{+jtx} rather than e^{-jtx}, as in Chap. 2, to conform with the notation of probability theory.) These new functions, Fourier transforms of the probability-density functions, are called *characteristic functions.* The characteristic function $G_z(t)$ of the variable z is then

$$G_z(t) = G_x(t) G_y(t) \tag{7-165}$$

and

$$p(z) = \frac{1}{2\pi} \int_{-\infty}^{\infty} e^{-jtz} G_z(t)\, dt \tag{7-166}$$

from Fourier-integral theory. (Note that the $1/2\pi$ now appears in front of the e^{-jtz} term rather than the e^{jtz} term as in Chap. 2.)

Recalling the definition of the average of a function $f(y)$ of a random variable y,

$$\text{av } f(y) = \int_{-\infty}^{\infty} f(y) p(y)\, dy \tag{7-167}$$

we see that the characteristic function is also the average of e^{jty}.

$$G_y(t) = \text{av } e^{jty} \tag{7-168}$$

We can now extend this procedure to the sum of n independent variables. For $z = x_1 + x_2 + \cdots + x_n$ we have

$$\begin{aligned} G_z(t) &= \text{av } e^{jtz} = \text{av } (e^{jt(x_1+x_2+\cdots+x_n)}) \\ &= \text{av } e^{jtx_1} \text{ av } e^{jtx_2} \cdots \text{ av } e^{jtx_n} \\ &= G_{x1}(t) G_{x2}(t) \cdots G_{xn}(t) \end{aligned} \tag{7-169}$$

(The average of the product of n independent quantities is the product of the averages.) The probability density of z is then

$$p(z) = \frac{1}{2\pi} \int_{-\infty}^{\infty} e^{-jzt} G_z(t)\, dt \tag{7-170}$$

with $G_z(t)$ given by Eq. (7-169).

Some examples will demonstrate the utility of the characteristic-function (c-f) method. They will also serve to illustrate some special cases of the central-limit theorem.

1. Sum of n gaussian-distributed variables. Here $z = \sum_{i=1}^{n} x_i$,

$$p_i(x_i) = \frac{1}{\sqrt{2\pi\sigma_i^2}} e^{-(x_i-a_i)^2/2\sigma_i^2} \tag{7-171}$$

The Fourier transform of this gaussian function is itself a gaussian function. In particular it is left for the reader to show that

$$G_i(t) = e^{ja_it}e^{-\sigma_i^2t^2/2} \tag{7-172}$$

Then

$$G_z(t) = \prod_{i=1}^{n} G_i(t)$$

$$= e^{jat}e^{-\sigma^2t^2/2} \tag{7-173}$$

where

$$a = \sum_{i=1}^{n} a_i$$

and

$$\sigma^2 = \sum_{i=1}^{n} \sigma_i^2$$

Comparing Eqs. (7-173) and (7-172),

$$p(z) = \frac{e^{-(z-a)^2/2\sigma^2}}{\sqrt{2\pi\sigma^2}} \tag{7-174}$$

The distribution of the sum of n gaussian-distributed variables is thus also gaussian, with an average value given by the sum of the individual average values and a variance given by the sum of the variances.

As a matter of fact it can be shown, by using the characteristic function, that the average value and variance of a random variable $z = \sum_{i=1}^{n} x_i$, with the x_i's independent and of *any* distribution whatsoever, are given by the sum of the individual average values and variances, respectively. The average fluctuation powers of n independent variables thus add directly. (Here *fluctuation* refers to variations about the average values.)

2. Rectangular distribution (Fig. 7-14a).[1] For simplicity's sake we take the special case of a symmetrical rectangular distribution. Letting $a = -b = x_0/2$ in Fig. 7-14a,

$$p(x_i) = \frac{1}{x_0} \qquad \frac{-x_0}{2} < x_i < \frac{x_0}{2} \tag{7-175}$$

$$p(x_i) = 0 \qquad \text{elsewhere}$$

[1] Bennett, *op. cit.*

This is just the rectangular pulse of Chap. 2, and its Fourier transform is the familiar $(\sin x)/x$ function.

$$G_i(t) = \frac{\sin (tx_0/2)}{tx_0/2} \tag{7-176}$$

For the sum of n such variables, each assumed uniformly distributed over the *same range*,

$$p(z) = \frac{1}{2\pi} \int_{-\infty}^{\infty} \left[\frac{\sin (tx_0/2)}{tx_0/2} \right]^n e^{-itz}\, dt \tag{7-177}$$

Consider now the characteristic function

$$G_z(t) = \left[\frac{\sin (tx_0/2)}{tx_0/2} \right]^n$$

This has the value unity at $t = 0$ and damps out rapidly away from the origin for large n. Most of the contribution to the integral thus comes from small values of t. We can expand this function in a power series about $t = 0$ and get

$$\begin{aligned} G_z(t) &= \left[\frac{\sin (tx_0/2)}{tx_0/2} \right]^n = \frac{[tx_0/2 - (tx_0)^3/48 + \cdots]^n}{(tx_0/2)^n} \\ &= \left[1 - \frac{(tx_0)^2}{24} + \cdots \right]^n \\ &= 1 - \frac{n}{24} (tx_0)^2 + \cdots \end{aligned} \tag{7-178}$$

The first two terms in this power series are the same as those in the series for the exponential

$$e^{-(n/24)(tx_0)^2} = 1 - \frac{n}{24} (tx_0)^2 + \cdots$$

Using the exponential as an approximation to the $[(\sin x)/x]^n$ function in the vicinity of the origin, we have

$$G_z(t) = e^{-(n/24)(tx_0)^2} \qquad n \text{ large, } t \text{ small} \tag{7-179}$$

But this is just a gaussian-type function, and its Fourier transform must also be gaussian. In particular, comparing with Eqs. (7-173) and (7-174), we must have

$$p(z) \doteq \frac{1}{\sqrt{2\pi\sigma^2}} e^{-z^2/2\sigma^2} \tag{7-180}$$

where

$$\sigma^2 = \frac{n(x_0)^2}{12} \tag{7-181}$$

We showed previously that the standard deviation of the rectangular distribution was $(b - a)/\sqrt{12} = x_0/\sqrt{12}$ in the present notation. σ^2

here is then just the *sum* of the individual variances as noted in the previous example.

The gaussian approximation is plainly incorrect for large values of z. z can have no values greater than nx_0; yet the gaussian distribution predicts a finite probability of such values being attained. For large n, however, these values move out to the far tail of the gaussian curve, and the gaussian approximation becomes valid over most of the range of z. In general, just as in the cases of the distribution of the envelope or the phase of signal plus noise, the gaussian approximation is valid only in the vicinity of the peak ($z = 0$ here) and definitely not valid for values of z close to nx_0.

As noted by Bennett[1] this result for the sum of n uniformly distributed variables may be applied to the case of determining the quantizing noise resulting when a number of alternate analogue-to-digital and digital-to-analogue signal conversions are performed.

Both this example and the previous one are special cases of the central-limit theorem.

3. Random-phase distributions. The final illustrative example concerns the sum of n independent sine waves of random phase. Thus, given

$$x_i = a_i \sin \theta_i$$

with θ_i uniformly distributed over 2π radians and a_i an arbitrary constant, we would like to find $p(z)$ for

$$z = \sum_{i=1}^{n} x_i$$

This is just the Fourier-series representation for noise used in Eq. (7-100) of Sec. 7-9.

We recall that, as an example of the calculation of the probability density of a transformed variable, we showed that the density function of x_i was

$$p_i(x_i) = \frac{1}{\pi} \frac{1}{\sqrt{a_i - x_i^2}} \qquad |x_i| < a_i \tag{7-182}$$

The characteristic function $G_i(t)$ is just

$$\begin{aligned} G_i(t) &= \int_{-a_i}^{a_i} \frac{e^{jtx_i}}{\sqrt{a_i^2 - x_i^2}} \frac{dx_i}{\pi} \\ &= J_0(a_i t) \end{aligned} \tag{7-183}$$

with $J_0(a_i t)$ the Bessel function of the first kind and zeroth order. This may be shown by the simple change of variables $x_i = a_i \sin \theta$, from which we obtain the integral definition of the Bessel function given as Eq. (3-60).

[1] *Op. cit.*

Alternatively, and much more simply in this case, we can use the fact that $G_i(t) = \text{av } e^{jtx_i}$ directly. Instead of averaging over x_i we can also write $G_i(t) = \text{av } e^{jta_i \sin \theta_i}$ and average over all values of θ_i. Since θ_i is uniformly distributed, this gives

$$G_i(t) = \frac{1}{2\pi} \int_{-\pi}^{\pi} e^{jta_i \sin \theta_i} \, d\theta_i = J_0(a_i t) \tag{7-184}$$

The characteristic function $G_z(t)$, for the sum of the n variables, is given by

$$G_z(t) = \prod_{i=1}^{n} J_0(a_i t) \tag{7-185}$$

Now assume, as in the previous example, that the amplitudes a_i are all very small and t not too large. For $a_i t \ll 1$ we had, in Chap. 3,

$$J_0(a_i t) \doteq 1 - \tfrac{1}{4}(a_i t)^2 = e^{-\frac{1}{4}a_i^2 t^2} \tag{7-186}$$

using the exponential approximation again. $G_z(t)$ now becomes, from Eq. (7-185),

$$G_z(t) \doteq e^{-\frac{1}{2}\sigma^2 t^2} \tag{7-187}$$

where

$$\sigma^2 = \tfrac{1}{2}(a_1^2 + a_2^2 + \cdots + a_n^2) \tag{7-188}$$

Equation (7-187) represents the characteristic function of a normal distribution with zero average value and variance σ^2.

$$p(z) = \frac{1}{\sqrt{2\pi\sigma^2}} e^{-z^2/2\sigma^2} \tag{7-189}$$

where

$$\sigma^2 = \tfrac{1}{2}(a_1^2 + a_2^2 + \cdots + a_n^2)$$

Note that the term $a_i^2/2$ represents the average power in a sine wave of amplitude a_i. σ^2 is thus the total mean power in the sum of n sine waves of incommensurable frequencies.

Equation (7-189) is again an example of the central-limit theorem and demonstrates the validity of the statement in Sec. 7-9 that a noise voltage, expressed as a sum of a large number of sine waves of differing frequencies and random phases, approaches a normal distribution in instantaneous amplitude. The variance of the normal distribution is just the total mean power (actually the mean-squared voltage) in the wave.

Again care must be exercised in applying Eq. (7-189) to the calculation of probabilities. It is valid only for large n and in the vicinity of $z = 0$. It is again obviously incorrect for $z > \sum_{i=1}^{n} a_i$, since the probability of this happening should be zero, while Eq. (7-189) predicts a finite probability. However, for n large, $p(z)$ falls off extremely rapidly at large values of z, and any errors become negligible if we stay away from the tail of the $p(z)$ curve.

Application to Radar Analysis. The distribution of the sum of n independent variables may be utilized in analyzing radar systems. The discussion of radar signal detection in Sec. 7-10 assumed the simplest type of system, in which individual signal pulses were required to exceed a specified threshold level. In actual systems, however, as noted in Sec. 7-10, there will be a number of pulses, spaced at intervals of the repetition period, reflected from a target. Either these are summed automatically as they are presented on a long-persistence screen, or summing devices (delay lines, storage tubes, etc.) may actually be incorporated in the system. We can assume, as one possible method of signal detection, that the sum of these returned pulses, each embedded in noise, is required to exceed a threshold level to be detected.

Normally the individual returned pulses are envelope-detected before being summed. The envelope of each signal pulse plus its accompanying noise will be statistically distributed according to the signal-plus-noise envelope distribution discussed in Secs. 7-9 and 7-10. The statistical distribution of the sum of n such pulses can be found by using the techniques of this chapter. The probability of detection of a target, P_{sb}, will then be given by the area under the sum distribution curve to the right of the threshold level.

Noise alone, in the absence of a signal, also adds up on the viewing screen or on a summing device purposely incorporated in the system and may be falsely detected as signal. Since the noise samples added are also spaced a repetition period apart, they may be considered independent in their statistical characteristics. The probability P_{nb} that the sum of n successive noise samples will exceed the threshold level and be falsely labeled noise can thus be found by first determining the distribution of the sum of n Rayleigh-distributed independent variables.

The details of the calculation of P_{sb} and P_{nb} for the n-pulse radar system will not be presented here because of the rather tedious computations involved.[1] Instead we include one typical set of radar performance curves found from such an analysis. These are shown in Fig. 7-45 for the one case of $P_{nb} = 10^{-10}$. They assume that the successive signal amplitudes are all of the same known value (this depends on the target characteristics). The S/N power ratio s^2 is the ratio of mean signal power to mean noise power *per pulse* at the input to the envelope detector. (For a signal amplitude of A_c volts and mean-squared noise voltage N this is $s^2 = A_c^2/2N$, as in Fig. 7-43.) The block diagram of the radar receiver assumed is shown in Fig. 7-46. In an actual system the sum-

[1] M. Schwartz, A Statistical Approach to the Automatic Search Problem, Ph.D. dissertation, Harvard University, May, 1951.

ming, threshold, and indicating devices might all be incorporated in one viewing screen.

Although the curves of Fig. 7-45 are for $P_{nb} = 10^{-10}$ only, the variation with P_{nb} is rather small. The values of s^2 and P_{sb} required for a given number n of pulses added do not differ substantially over the range $P_{nb} = 10^{-8}$ to 10^{-12}.

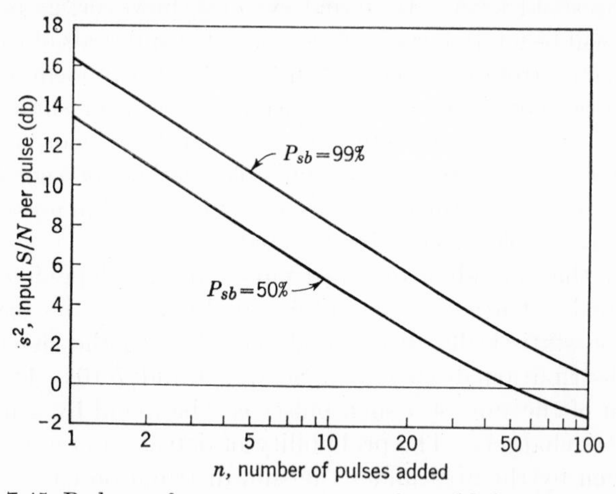

FIG. 7-45. Radar performance curves, n pulses added. $P_{nb} = 10^{-10}$.

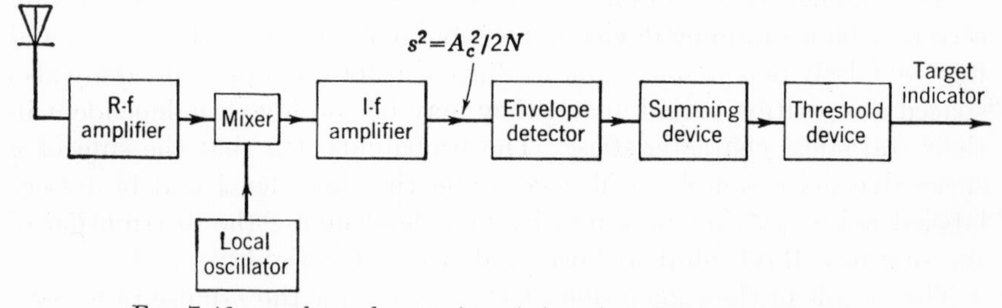

FIG. 7-46. n-pulse radar receiver (triggering circuits not shown).

Note that, as the number of pulses, n, added increases, the signal-to-noise ratio required to maintain a given probability of detection, P_{sb}, and noise-error probability P_{nb} decreases. Initially the decrease is at the rate of about 2.5 db/octave, but this drops to about 2 db/octave for n close to 100. These curves may be used in the same manner as those of Fig. 7-43. For a given P_{sb} and P_{nb} we find the signal-to-noise ratio required at the narrowband i-f section output (detector input). From the system noise figure, target distance and characteristics, etc., we then calculate the transmitter power necessary.

As an example of the application of the curves of Fig. 7-45, consider the radar example cited in the last section. We required an average interval between false alarms (noise mistaken for signal) of 3 hr (10^4 sec) and assumed a system bandwidth of 1 Mc. (The system pulse widths are then approximately 1 μsec.) This gave a required noise-error probability $P_{nb} = 10^{-10}$. For $P_{sb} = 95$ per cent s^2 was then required to be at least 15.5 db (35 numerically), while for $P_{sb} = 99.9$ per cent s^2 was at least 17 db (50). The point $n = 1$ and $P_{sb} = 99$ per cent in Fig. 7-45 gives $s^2 = 16.3$ db, checking the previous numbers.

What is now the effect of adding together a group of pulses (signal plus noise, or noise alone) before requiring them to exceed a given threshold level and be labeled (perhaps erroneously) signal? For $P_{nb} = 10^{-10}$ again and $P_{sb} = 99$ per cent, 10 pulses summed require only 8 db S/N ratio per pulse rather than the 16.3-db figure found for the single-pulse case. The case of 100 pulses received from a target requires only 0.5 db per pulse for the same noise-error probability and signal-detection probability.

The *peak power* of each pulse is thus *reduced* considerably by requiring a group of pulses to be summed. The *average energy* required to detect a given target *increases*, however. For, by directing 10 pulses of fixed pulse width at a given target, ten times as much energy is required if the pulse amplitudes remain unchanged. The energy required would remain the same if the peak power per pulse could be reduced by a factor of 10 db. Since the curves of Fig. 7-45 indicate a peak power reduction of 8 db the net result is a 2-db increase in the energy required to be directed at the target. Similarly, for 100 pulses added, the peak power per pulse would be expected to decrease by 20 db to keep the energy directed at the target unchanged. Figure 7-45 indicates that the peak power is reduced by about 16 db, however.

This apparent increase in total energy over the group of pulses is due specifically to the fact that the pulses were each envelope-detected before being summed. If the signals could be assumed coherent in phase, either the summing of the signals could be carried out in the i-f stages of the receiver, or an inphase local carrier could be injected to heterodyne the signal pulses down to video frequencies. The phase-coherent signals would then add linearly in voltage, the random noise linearly in power. The resultant S/N ratio would decrease linearly with increasing n, and the total energy over the group of pulses would remain fixed.

Return signal-phase coherence is not in general possible because of the complex types of radar targets encountered, atmospheric changes along the path of propagation, etc. This lack of knowledge of the signal phase leads to the requirement of envelope detection of the individual signals, with a resulting loss in the total energy required for detection.

Experimental investigations of the effect of signal-pulse addition on signal detectability, for existing systems with observers locating targets on indicator screens, have shown that the signal-to-noise ratio decreases approximately as $1/\sqrt{n}$, with n the number of pulses added. This is somewhat worse than the results of the threshold analysis. Signal detection by human observers is a very complex process, taking into account many more factors than the simple threshold-level procedure utilized in this book. The threshold analysis serves as a crude first approximation to the process of human signal detection. It applies specifically to an automatic detection system, labeling any voltage above a specified level a signal.

Moment-generating Property of Characteristic Functions. We have cited the radar problem as a specific example of the application of the c-f technique to finding the distribution of the sum of independent random variables. We close this section with a short discussion of an additional valuable property of the characteristic function: its moment-generating property.

Recalling that $G(t)$ is defined as the average value of e^{jtx},

$$G(t) = \text{av } e^{jtx} = \int_{-\infty}^{\infty} e^{jtx} p(x)\, dx \tag{7-190}$$

we may expand the exponential in its power series to obtain

$$\begin{aligned} G(t) &= \text{av } e^{jtx} = \text{av} \sum_{n=0}^{\infty} \frac{(jtx)^n}{n!} \\ &= \sum_{n=0}^{\infty} \frac{(jt)^n}{n!} \text{av } x^n \\ &= \sum_{n=0}^{\infty} \frac{(jt)^n}{n!} m_n \end{aligned} \tag{7-191}$$

by definition of the nth moment, m_n, of the random variable x. We can thus obtain any moment we desire from the appropriate term in the power-series expansion of $G(t)$. We can show this alternatively by considering successive derivatives of $G(t)$ with respect to t. From Eq. (7-190) we have, for example,

$$\frac{dG}{dt} = j \int_{-\infty}^{\infty} e^{jtx} x p(x)\, dx \tag{7-192}$$

Letting $t = 0$,

$$\left(\frac{dG}{dt}\right)_{t=0} = j \int_{-\infty}^{\infty} x p(x)\, dx = jm_1 \tag{7-193}$$

Similarly

$$\left(\frac{d^2G}{dt^2}\right)_{t=0} = -\int_{-\infty}^{\infty} x^2 p(x)\, dx = -m_2 \tag{7-194}$$

We can repeat this differentiation as many times as desired to obtain higher moments.

The successive derivatives of $G(t)$ are the coefficients in its power-series expansion [Eq. (7-191)]. As an example, let

$$G(t) = e^{jat}e^{-\sigma^2 t^2/2} \tag{7-195}$$

We recall from Eqs. (7-171) and (7-172) that this is the characteristic function of the gaussian distribution. Differentiating $G(t)$ with respect to t,

$$\frac{dG}{dt} = jae^{jat}e^{-\sigma^2 t^2/2} - \sigma^2 te^{jat}e^{-\sigma^2 t^2/2} \tag{7-196}$$

Setting $t = 0$,

$$\left(\frac{dG}{dt}\right)_{t=0} = ja \tag{7-197}$$

as expected. The reader can show, in a similar manner, that

$$\left(\frac{d^2G}{dt^2}\right)_{t=0} = -m_2 = -(\sigma^2 + a^2) \tag{7-198}$$

This technique of finding moments of a distribution avoids the frequently tedious procedure of evaluating the integral $\int_{-\infty}^{\infty} x^n p(x)\,dx$. Also, if we are adding independent random variables, we may find the moments of the resultant sum variable from the resultant $G(t)$ without the necessity of finding the Fourier transform of $G(t)$ to give $p(z)$ and then further integrating to find m_n.

7-12. Dependent Random Variables. We have devoted considerable space in the past few sections to a discussion of independent random variables. It is of interest to extend our discussion of probability theory to include the case of dependent variables.

Dependent discrete variables were considered in Sec. 7-2. It was shown there, by example, that the study of dependent variables was important in studying the statistical properties of a language. (This was also alluded to in Chap. 1.) In general, as noted in Chap. 1, there is usually some dependence between successive signals of a message being transmitted. This reduces the rate of transmission of information.

In any study of communication in the presence of noise this dependence of successive voltages on one another must be taken into account. Consider, for example, the noise-voltage plot of Fig. 7-47. We have been interested previously in average properties of such a noise wave: average d-c power, rms voltage, etc. We have also discussed the chance of noise at any *one* instant of time exceeding an arbitrary voltage level and related this to probabilities of error in both PCM and radar systems. We have thus far not discussed the joint statistics of two variables, such as v_1 and

v_2 in Fig. 7-47, separated by a specified time interval, except to say that if they are spaced "far enough apart" they may be considered unrelated or independent.

Yet the band-limiting effect of any system through which noise or signal plus noise is passed will ensure that there is some connection or correlation between two closely spaced voltages. This in turn must be taken into consideration in discussing in any thorough manner the statistics of signals in noise. We shall therefore discuss to some extent the concept of joint statistics of two continuous dependent variables and a

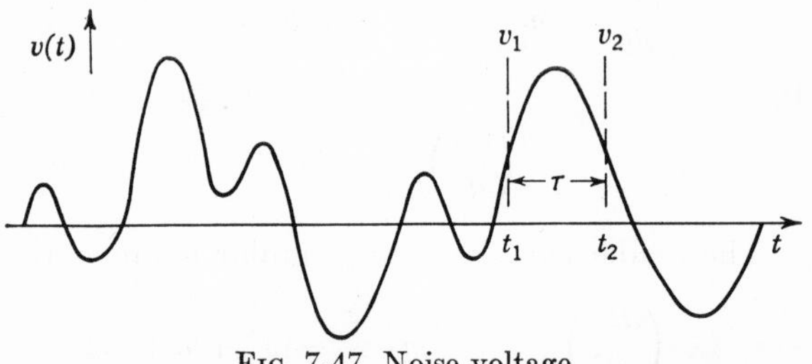

FIG. 7-47. Noise voltage.

particular measure, the correlation function, of this dependency. These concepts can be extended to include dependency between many random variables, as was done with the sum of n independent variables in previous sections. We shall restrict ourselves to two dependent variables, however, in this book.

Consider *two* random variables x and y. By performing repeated measurements on these two variables jointly, as in the case of the discrete variables, we can develop a set of histogram curves relating the frequency of occurrence of different pairs of x and y. (In the example of Fig. 7-47, with $x = v_1$ and $y = v_2$, this would consist of measurements of the different combinations of pairs of voltages occurring.) From such a set of measurements, taken with x broken up into levels Δx units apart and y into levels Δy apart, a joint probability-density function $p(x,y)$ can be constructed. This is the same function introduced in Sec. 7-8 for the discussion of two *independent* variables.

$p(x,y)\,dx\,dy$ represents the probability that x and y will *jointly* be found in the ranges $x \pm dx/2$ and $y \pm dy/2$, respectively. Since some range of x and y must always occur jointly, we must have

$$\int_{-\infty}^{\infty}\int_{-\infty}^{\infty} p(x,y)\,dx\,dy = 1 \tag{7-199}$$

The joint density function $p(x,y)$ is thus normalized so that the *volume* under the curve is 1. As noted in Sec. 7-8 $p(x,y)$ may be written as the product $p_1(x)p_2(y)$ if x and y are independent.

We can define a cumulative-probability function as in the case of one random variable, if we wish, and averages can also be computed. For example, the average of $F(x,y)$ is

$$\text{av } F(x,y) = \int_{-\infty}^{\infty} \int_{-\infty}^{\infty} F(x,y)p(x,y)\, dx\, dy \tag{7-200}$$

In particular the averages of x and y raised to integer powers are again called the moments of x and y and are given by

$$m_{ij} = \text{av } x^i y^j = \int_{-\infty}^{\infty} \int_{-\infty}^{\infty} x^i y^j p(x,y)\, dx\, dy \tag{7-201}$$

These moments play an important role in two-variable statistical theory, just as do the moments in the one-variable case. As special cases, we have

$$\begin{aligned} m_{10} = x_0 = \text{av } x &= \int_{-\infty}^{\infty} \int_{-\infty}^{\infty} xp(x,y)\, dx\, dy \\ &= \int_{-\infty}^{\infty} xp_1(x)\, dx \qquad p_1(x) = \int_{-\infty}^{\infty} p(x,y)\, dy \end{aligned} \tag{7-202}$$

$$\begin{aligned} m_{01} = y_0 = \text{av } y &= \int_{-\infty}^{\infty} \int_{-\infty}^{\infty} yp(x,y)\, dx\, dy \\ &= \int_{-\infty}^{\infty} yp_2(y)\, dy \qquad p_2(y) = \int_{-\infty}^{\infty} p(x,y)\, dx \end{aligned} \tag{7-203}$$

$$m_{11} = \text{av } xy = \int_{-\infty}^{\infty} \int_{-\infty}^{\infty} xyp(x,y)\, dx\, dy \tag{7-204}$$

$$m_{20} = \text{av } x^2 = \int_{-\infty}^{\infty} x^2 p_1(x)\, dx \tag{7-205}$$

$$m_{02} = \text{av } y^2 = \int_{-\infty}^{\infty} y^2 p_2(y)\, dy \tag{7-206}$$

Just as in the one-variable case we can also define central moments or moments about the average values. For example, the central moments of the second order, comparable to μ_2, are

$$\begin{aligned} \mu_{20} &= \text{av } (x - x_0)^2 = \int_{-\infty}^{\infty} (x - x_0)^2 p_1(x)\, dx \\ &= m_{20} - m_{10}^2 = \sigma_1^2 \end{aligned} \tag{7-207}$$

$$\begin{aligned} \mu_{02} &= \text{av } (y - y_0)^2 = \int_{-\infty}^{\infty} (y - y_0)^2 p_2(y)\, dy \\ &= m_{02} - m_{01}^2 = \sigma_2^2 \end{aligned} \tag{7-208}$$

and

$$\begin{aligned} \mu_{11} &= \text{av } [(x - x_0)(y - y_0)] = \text{av } xy - (\text{av } x)(\text{av } y) \\ &= m_{11} - m_{01}m_{10} \end{aligned} \tag{7-209}$$

as may be verified by the reader.

m_{11} and μ_{11} are the two second-order moments which serve as a measure of the dependence of two variables. For, as noted previously, two *independent* variables will have as their joint distribution function the *product* of the individual distribution function, or

$$p(x,y) = p_1(x)p_2(y) \tag{7-210}$$

For this case m_{11} and μ_{11} become, respectively,

$$m_{11} = \text{av } x \text{ av } y = m_{10}m_{01} \tag{7-211}$$

and

$$\mu_{11} = 0 \tag{7-212}$$

μ_{11} is called the *covariance* of the two variables. σ_1^2 and σ_2^2 are again called *variances*. If the two variables are independent, the covariance is zero and m_{11}, the average of the product, becomes the product of the individual averages. (The converse of this statement is not true in general but does hold for the joint gaussian distribution.)

We may define a normalized quantity called the *normalized correlation coefficient* which serves as a numerical measure of the dependence between two variables. Using the symbol ρ for this quantity, we define

$$\rho \equiv \frac{\mu_{11}}{\sqrt{\mu_{20}\mu_{02}}} = \frac{\mu_{11}}{\sigma_1\sigma_2} \tag{7-213}$$

The correlation coefficient can be shown to be less than 1 in magnitude: $-1 \leq \rho \leq 1$. In particular assume first that y is completely determined by x and that a linear relation of the form $y = ax + b$ exists between the two. Then $\text{av } y = a(\text{av } x) + b$, or $y_0 = ax_0 + b$. μ_{11} becomes $\text{av } [(x - x_0)(y - y_0)] = a \text{ av } (x - x_0)^2 = a\mu_{20}$. Also,

$$\mu_{02} = \text{av } (y - y_0)^2 = a^2 \text{ av } (x - x_0)^2 = a^2\mu_{20}$$

Then $\rho = \pm 1$, depending on the sign of a. On the other hand, if x and y are independent, $\mu_{11} = 0$ and $\rho = 0$. So values of ρ close to 1 indicate high correlation; values close to 0 indicate low correlation.

The two-variable gaussian distribution serves as an example of the joint distribution function. It is given by the expression[1]

$$\begin{aligned} p(x,y) &= \frac{1}{2\pi M} \exp\left[-\frac{1}{2M^2}(\mu_{02}x^2 - 2\mu_{11}xy + \mu_{20}y^2)\right] \\ &= \frac{1}{2\pi M} \exp\left[\frac{-1}{2(1-\rho^2)}\left(\frac{x^2}{\sigma_1^2} - \frac{2\rho xy}{\sigma_1\sigma_2} + \frac{y^2}{\sigma_2^2}\right)\right] \end{aligned} \tag{7-214}$$

for zero average values ($x_0 = y_0 = 0$). Here

$$M^2 = \mu_{20}\mu_{02} - \mu_{11}^2 = \sigma_1^2\sigma_2^2(1 - \rho^2)$$

Note that, if $\rho = 0$ ($\mu_{11} = 0$), $p(x,y)$ becomes the product of two single-variable distribution functions, indicating *in this case* that x and y are independent. For nonzero x_0 and y_0, x and y are replaced by $x - x_0$ and $y - y_0$, respectively. The two-dimensional gaussian density function is shown sketched in Fig. 7-48.[2]

[1] Cramér, *op. cit.*

[2] Bennett, *op. cit.*, fig. 3.

The probability that x and y will be found in the ranges x_1 to x_2, y_1 to y_2, respectively, is just the volume under the curve of Fig. 7-48 enclosed by these points. For such a calculation the variances σ_1^2, σ_2^2 and the correlation coefficient ρ must obviously be known from previous information.

That the parameters in Eq. (7-214) satisfy the defining relations for the moments expressed by Eqs. (7-202) to (7-209) may be verified by evaluating the appropriate integral. For example, assume that av x or

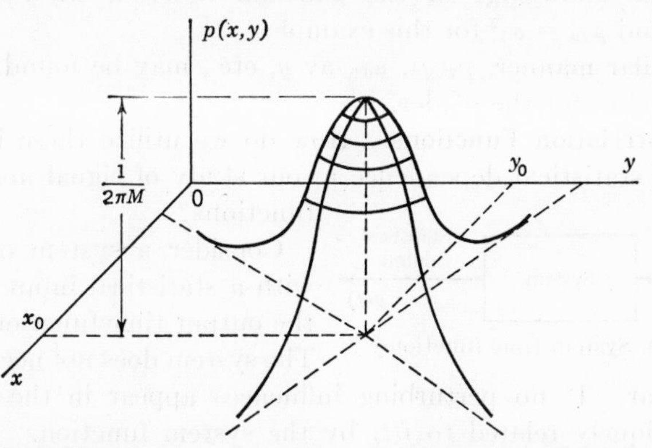

FIG. 7-48. Two-dimensional gaussian probability-density function.

m_{10} and μ_{20} or σ_1^2 are to be found for the gaussian distribution of Eq. (7-214). Since we are interested only in average values of x, independent of variations in y, we first integrate over all values of y to find the distribution in x alone. This is given by

$$p_1(x) = \int_{-\infty}^{\infty} p(x,y)\,dy = \frac{\exp\{-x^2/[2(1-\rho^2)\sigma_1^2]\}}{2\pi M} \int_{-\infty}^{\infty} \exp\left[\frac{-1}{2(1-\rho^2)}\left(\frac{y^2}{\sigma_2^2} - \frac{2\rho xy}{\sigma_1\sigma_2}\right)\right] dy \qquad (7\text{-}215)$$

The integral may be evaluated by first completing the square in the exponent. Thus

$$\frac{y^2}{\sigma_2^2} - \frac{2\rho xy}{\sigma_1\sigma_2} = \left(\frac{y}{\sigma_2} - \frac{\rho x}{\sigma_1}\right)^2 - \frac{\rho^2 x^2}{\sigma_1^2}$$

$p_1(x)$ now becomes

$$p_1(x) = \frac{\exp(-x^2/2\sigma_1^2)}{2\pi M} \int_{-\infty}^{\infty} \exp\left[-\frac{(y/\sigma_2 - \rho x/\sigma_1)^2}{2(1-\rho^2)}\right] dy$$

Using the transformation of variables,

$$z^2 = \frac{(y/\sigma_2 - \rho x/\sigma_1)^2}{2(1-\rho^2)}$$

and recalling that $\int_{-\infty}^{\infty} e^{-z^2}\, dz = \sqrt{\pi}$, we get finally

$$p_1(x) = \frac{e^{-x^2/2\sigma_1^2}}{\sqrt{2\pi\sigma_1^2}} \tag{7-216}$$

as expected from our previous discussion of the one-variable or one-dimensional gaussian function. (Use has also been made here of the defining relation for M.)

From our knowledge of the gaussian function we recognize that av $x = 0$ and $\mu_{20} = \sigma_1^2$ for this example.

In a similar manner, $p_2(y)$, μ_{02}, av y, etc., may be found. These are left as exercises for the reader.

7-13. Correlation Functions. How do we utilize these ideas of correlation or statistical dependence in our study of signal and noise time functions?

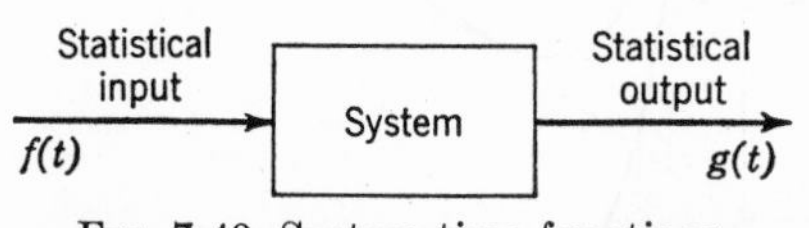

FIG. 7-49. System time functions.

Consider a system of some type with a statistical input $f(t)$ and $g(t)$ the output time function (Fig. 7-49). The system does not necessarily have to be linear. If no perturbing influences appear in the system, $g(t)$ will be uniquely related to $f(t)$ by the system function. If noise and other random disturbances are introduced by the system, however, $g(t)$ and $f(t)$ will be only partially related. The statistical relationship between $f(t)$ and $g(t)$ could be given by the joint distribution function $p(f,g)$ if it were known. The product moment

$$m_{11} = \int_{-\infty}^{\infty} \int_{-\infty}^{\infty} fgp(f,g)\, df\, dg \tag{7-217}$$

serves as a more limited measure of the correlation between $f(t)$ and $g(t)$. In general $p(f,g)$, and therefore m_{11}, may vary with time. If a *stationary* process is assumed, however, the statistics are invariant with time. If the average values of f and g are both zero, m_{11} is the same as μ_{11}.

Equation (7-217) involves an *ensemble average*. We could, however, as described in Sec. 7-5, perform a *time average* as well. Thus let us arbitrarily define a parameter R_{fg} given by

$$R_{fg} = \lim_{T\to\infty} \frac{1}{T} \int_0^T f(t)g(t)\, dt \tag{7-218}$$

R_{fg} is the average of the product of $f(t)$ and $g(t)$ and, in general, may vary with time. For a stationary process, however, as noted in Sec. 7-5, the average will be independent of time. In particular, if we also assume an *ergodic process*, the ensemble average of Eq. (7-217) and the time average of Eq. (7-218) will be equal:

$$m_{11} = R_{fg} \tag{7-219}$$

R_{fg} must thus serve as a measure of the correlation between f and g also. It is frequently called the *cross-correlation function.*

To see why R_{fg} provides a measure of the correlation between $f(t)$ and $g(t)$, consider the related time average

$$R'_{fg} = \lim_{T\to\infty} \frac{1}{T} \int_0^T (f - \bar{f})(g - \bar{g})\, dt = R_{fg} - \bar{f}\bar{g} \qquad (7\text{-}220)$$

with $\bar{f}$ and $\bar{g}$ the average values of $f(t)$ and $g(t)$, respectively. Note that, because of the assumption of ergodicity (which implies a stationary process) and because of the average overall time, R'_{fg} is some number, independent of time. If both functions f and g follow one another very closely, so that they are both simultaneously large (or small), for example, and of the same sign, the average will tend to accumulate positively. Similarly, if they are both large (or small) and always of opposite sign, the average will again accumulate, although negatively.

If the factors vary independently of one another, they would tend to cancel each other on the average. R'_{fg} would thus approach zero.

R'_{fg} thus does appear to provide a measure of correlation. Actually the average of any function of the product $F[(f - \bar{f})(g - \bar{g})]$ would serve as well as a measure of the correlation. R_{fg} or R'_{fg} provides the *simplest* measure of the correlation.

Autocorrelation Function. As noted in the introduction to Sec. 7-12 on Dependent Random Variables the concepts of two-variable probability theory are of particular importance in discussing the statistics of signals in the presence of noise.

The calculation of noise-error probability for the PCM and radar systems was found to be dependent only upon the mean noise power in a system. The frequency band-limiting effect of a system on the noise and signal plus noise did not appear in these statistical calculations. This was strictly fortuitous, however, because in both the PCM and radar cases we were interested in the probability that a noise (or signal-plus-noise) voltage would exceed a given threshold level at any *one particular instant* of time.

The average error rate could then be found by assuming the probabilities of error in successive time intervals to be independent. This required the assumption that successive intervals were spaced "far enough apart in time." In the PCM case this was just the interval between successive binary pulses. In the radar case this was essentially a repetition period.

The assumption as to "far enough apart" can be justified by means of the two-dimensional probability distributions. In particular the material to follow will be devoted to a discussion of the joint statistics of two successive values of a noise (or signal-plus-noise) voltage, spaced

τ sec apart (Fig. 7-47). Since the rate of change of a system voltage depends on the system bandwidth, we shall find the system power spectrum, as defined in Chap. 6, playing a role here.

Consider the noise voltage $v(t)$ of Fig. 7-47, measured at some point in a system. The voltage is assumed to represent a stationary process. Two instantaneous values of $v(t)$ are v_1, measured at time t, and v_2, at time t_2, τ sec later. A possible measure of dependence between the two variables v_1 and v_2 can be found by introducing a correlation function for the two variables.

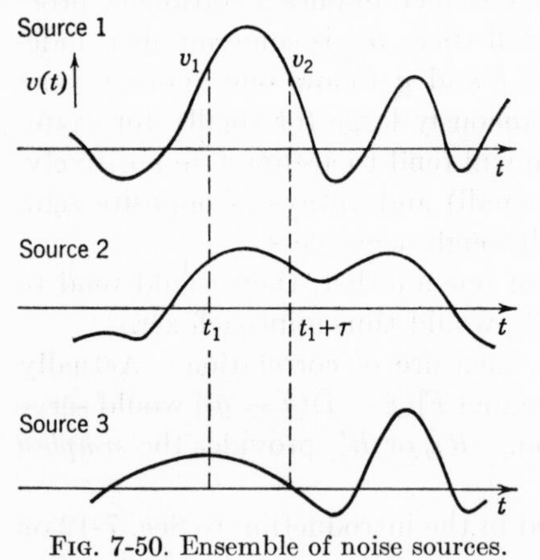

FIG. 7-50. Ensemble of noise sources.

The cross-correlation function of Eq. (7-218) has been shown to serve as a measure of dependence between two statistical variables $f(t)$ and $g(t)$. If we specialize to the case where $f(t)$ is just $v_1(t)$ and

$$g(t) = v_1(t + \tau)$$

(the network of Fig. 7-49 is then just a pure delay device), we get the *autocorrelation* function $R(\tau)$ as a measure of the dependence between $v_1(t)$ and $v_2 = v_1(t + \tau)$. Since the process is assumed to be stationary, this serves as a measure of dependence between *any* two values of the voltage $v(t)$ and $v(t + \tau)$. Specifically the autocorrelation function $R(\tau)$ is defined as

$$R(\tau) = \lim_{T\to\infty} \frac{1}{T} \int_0^T v(t)v(t + \tau)\,dt \qquad (7\text{-}221)$$

Alternatively a measure of correlation between v_1 and v_2 could also be found by measuring the simultaneous outputs of a large number of identical noise sources at times t_1 and $t_2 = t_1 + \tau$. An example of three such sources is shown in Fig. 7-50. The two variables v_1 and v_2 could be described in terms of a joint probability-density function $p(v_1,v_2)$, constructed from the measured pairs of values of v_1 and v_2. For the stationary process assumed in this case $p(v_1,v_2)$ is independent of the particular choice of t_1, and $t_2 = t_1 + \tau$. The product moment m_{11}, found by averaging over the entire ensemble of noise sources, is given by

$$m_{11} = \int_{-\infty}^{\infty} \int_{-\infty}^{\infty} v_1 v_2 p(v_1,v_2)\,dv_1\,dv_2 \qquad (7\text{-}222)$$

If the process is now assumed ergodic, the ensemble average of Eq. (7-222) can be equated to the time average of Eq. (7-221) found by averaging over any one of the noise sources.

For an ergodic process, then, the autocorrelation function $R(\tau)$ found by averaging over any one voltage in time is the same as the product moment m_{11}. If the average value of $v(t)$ over the ensemble is zero, m_{11} is the same as the covariance μ_{11}. The autocorrelation function is then equal to the covariance. μ_{11} for this case is sometimes called the *autocovariance.*[1] The ensemble average m_{11} is frequently referred to as the *autocorrelation function,* while the time average $R(\tau)$ is called the *time autocorrelation function.*[2]

Either Eq. (7-221) or Eq. (7-222) serves as a measure of the correlation between two values of the same noise voltage, measured τ sec apart. A small value of $R(\tau)$ [$R(\tau)$ approaching zero] would indicate that the two values $v(t)$ and $v(t + \tau)$ were almost independent of one another. We would expect this to be true for large τ ($\tau > 1/\text{bandwidth}$, say). The actual variation of $R(\tau)$ with τ will enable us to discuss more quantitatively the relative dependence or independence between $v(t)$ and $v(t + \tau)$.

The calculation of the autocorrelation function is thus of interest in communication problems involving signals and noise. If $p(v_1,v_2)$ is known, m_{11} may be found by the ensemble average of Eq. (7-222). This result will then be the same as $R(\tau)$ for any one voltage strip if the process is ergodic. An example of such a calculation will be given shortly.

Quite commonly the time average of Eq. (7-221) is invoked directly to find $R(\tau)$. This is easily done in many cases because of the simple relation that the *autocorrelation function and power spectrum are Fourier transforms of each other.* This relation is frequently called the *Wiener-Khintchine theorem.* In particular let

$$V(j\omega) = \int_{-\infty}^{\infty} e^{-j\omega t} v(t)\, dt$$

be the Fourier transform of a function $v(t)$ and

$$G'(\omega) = \lim_{T\to\infty} \frac{1}{T} |V(j\omega)|^2$$

its two-sided (positive and negative ω) power spectrum. The theorem states that

$$R(\tau) = \frac{1}{2\pi} \int_{-\infty}^{\infty} e^{j\omega\tau} G'(\omega)\, d\omega = \int_{-\infty}^{\infty} e^{j\omega\tau} G'(\omega)\, df \tag{7-223}$$

and

$$G'(\omega) = \int_{-\infty}^{\infty} e^{-j\omega\tau} R(\tau)\, d\tau \tag{7-224}$$

[1] See, e.g., *ibid.*

[2] See, e.g., Davenport and Root, *op. cit.*

This should not be too unexpected since we have alluded to the fact that correlation between $v(t)$ and $v(t+\tau)$, as measured by $R(\tau)$, depends on how rapidly $v(t)$ changes with time. This of course depends on the system bandwidth and system frequency response.

The Wiener-Khintchine theorem can be proved in a multiplicity of ways. Note that the time-averaged form for $R(\tau)$, Eq. (7-221), is somewhat similar to the convolution integral of Chap. 2. We showed there that if three functions $a(t)$, $b(t)$, and $c(t)$ have their Fourier transforms related by

$$A(j\omega) = B(j\omega)C(j\omega) \tag{7-225}$$

then

$$a(t) = \int_{-\infty}^{\infty} b(\tau)c(t-\tau)\,d\tau \tag{7-226}$$

[Eqs. (2-139) and (2-140)]. The autocorrelation function is given by

$$\begin{aligned} R(\tau) &= \lim_{T\to\infty} \frac{1}{T} \int_0^T v(t)v(t+\tau)\,dt \\ &= \lim_{T\to\infty} \frac{1}{T} \int_{-T/2}^{T/2} v(t)v(t+\tau)\,dt \end{aligned} \tag{7-227}$$

for a stationary process, since $R(\tau)$ is independent of the time origin chosen. Letting $x = -t$ in Eq. (7-227),

$$R(\tau) = \lim_{T\to\infty} \frac{1}{T} \int_{-T/2}^{T/2} v(-x)v(\tau-x)\,dx \tag{7-228}$$

But this is exactly in the form of the convolution integral of Eq. (7-226), with $v(-x)$ corresponding to $b(\tau)$ and $v(\tau - x)$ corresponding to $c(t-\tau)$. If $V(j\omega)$ is the Fourier transform of $v(t)$, $V^*(j\omega) = V(-j\omega)$ is the transform of $v(-t)$. The Fourier transform of $R(\tau)$ must thus be, from Eqs. (7-225) and (7-228),

$$\lim_{T\to\infty} \frac{1}{T} |V(j\omega)|^2 = G'(\omega)$$

by definition of the two-sided spectral density.

The theorem may also be proved directly by taking the Fourier transform of $R(\tau)$ and interchanging the order of integration on the right-hand side of Eq. (7-221).

The Wiener-Khintchine theorem is a valuable tool in noise analysis, for it enables us to find the autocorrelation function of a noise voltage at the output of a linear system directly in terms of the transfer function of the system. Conversely it is frequently utilized to find the power spectrum of noise at the output of a nonlinear device. (In many cases the probability-density function or the correlation function at the output is more easily found than the power spectrum directly.)

As applications of the Wiener-Khintchine theorem consider the following examples.

1. White noise. As noted in Chaps. 5 and 6 white noise is defined to have a flat, or uniform, power spectrum out to all frequencies of interest. Shot noise and thermal noise, when first generated, are examples. For

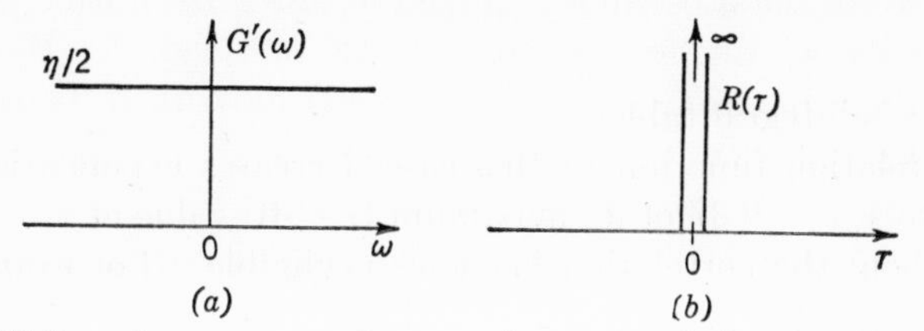

FIG. 7-51. White-noise-power spectrum and autocorrelation function. (a) $G'(\omega)$; (b) $R(\tau)$.

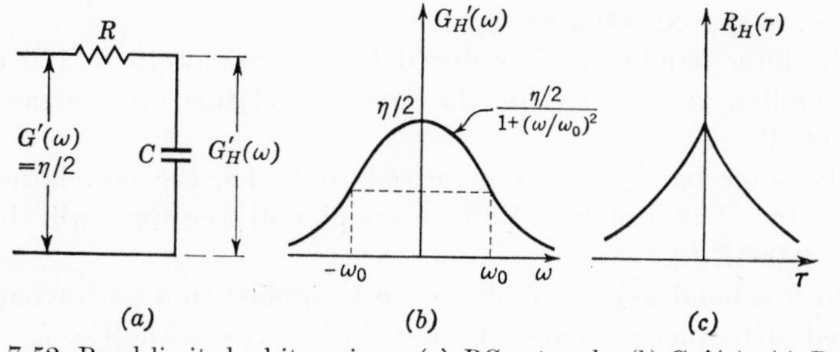

FIG. 7-52. Band-limited white noise. (a) RC network; (b) $G_H'(\omega)$; (c) $R_H(\tau)$.

white noise, then,

$$G'(\omega) = \frac{\eta}{2} \qquad \text{watts/cps} \tag{7-229}$$

and the correlation function is

$$\begin{aligned} R(\tau) &= \frac{1}{2\pi} \int_{-\infty}^{\infty} e^{j\omega\tau} G'(\omega)\, d\omega = \frac{\eta/2}{2\pi} \int_{-\infty}^{\infty} e^{j\omega\tau}\, d\omega \\ &= \frac{\eta}{2}\, \delta(\tau) \end{aligned} \tag{7-230}$$

from the relation for the delta function developed in Chap. 2. White noise, of theoretically infinite bandwidth, can vary infinitely rapidly and so has zero correlation for all nonzero τ (Fig. 7-51).

2. Band-limited noise. Now assume that the white noise of spectral density $\eta/2$ watts/cps is passed through a simple RC filter of transfer function $H(j\omega) = 1/(1 + j\omega RC) = 1/(1 + j\omega/\omega_0)$ (Fig. 7-52a). The spectral density at the output is

$$G'_H(\omega) = \frac{\eta/2}{1 + (\omega/\omega_0)^2} \tag{7-231}$$

The autocorrelation function at the output is

$$R_H(\tau) = \frac{\eta/2}{2\pi} \int_{-\infty}^{\infty} \frac{e^{j\omega\tau}\,d\omega}{1 + (\omega/\omega_0)^2} = \frac{\eta\omega_0^2}{4\pi} \int_{-\infty}^{\infty} \frac{\cos \omega\tau\,d\omega}{\omega^2 + \omega_0^2}$$

$$= \frac{\eta\omega_0}{4} e^{-\omega_0|\tau|} \tag{7-232}$$

using Peirce's integral tables.

The correlation function in this case decreases exponentially with τ, dropping to $1/e = 0.37$ of its maximum ($\tau = 0$) value at $\tau = 1/\omega_0$. For $\tau \gg RC$, then, the correlation becomes negligible. For example, if the time constant of the filter is $RC = 100$ μsec (the frequency bandwidth is 1,600 cps), the correlation between voltage samples 100 μsec apart is 0.37 of the maximum value. It is 0.065 of the maximum value if the samples are spaced 500 μsec apart.

If the filter bandwidth is reduced by a factor of 10 to 160 cps, the corresponding values of τ for the same correlation are increased by a factor of 10.

If the filter bandwidth is increased to 16 kc, the correlation times decrease by a factor of 10. Voltage samples 50 μsec apart will thus have $R(\tau) = 0.065R(0)$.

3. Narrowband noise. White noise is applied to a narrowband filter centered at frequency f_0 and of bandwidth B cps, with $B \ll f_0$. This is exactly the case of white noise passed through a receiver with a narrowband i-f section.

For the sake of simplicity assume the filter to be of the ideal rectangular type,

$$|H(j\omega)| = A \qquad f_0 - \frac{B}{2} < f < f_0 + \frac{B}{2}$$

$$|H(j\omega)| = 0 \qquad \text{elsewhere}$$

for positive frequencies, with the same relation for negative frequencies. With the input spectral density of the white noise again $\eta/2$ watts/cps over all frequencies, the output spectrum in the range of positive frequencies is

$$G'_H(\omega) = \frac{\eta A^2}{2} \qquad f_0 - \frac{B}{2} < f < f_0 + \frac{B}{2} \tag{7-233}$$

$$G'_H(\omega) = 0 \qquad \text{elsewhere}$$

with a similar expression over the negative-frequency range. Note that these are just the relations for the ideal low-pass filter of Chap. 2, shifted up in frequency by f_0 cps.

The autocorrelation function at the filter output is

$$\begin{aligned} R(\tau) &= \int_{-\infty}^{\infty} G'_H(\omega) e^{j\omega\tau}\, df \\ &= \left(\int_{-f_0-B/2}^{-f_0+B/2} + \int_{f_0-B/2}^{f_0+B/2} \right) \frac{\eta A^2}{2} e^{j\omega\tau}\, df \\ &= \eta A^2 B \frac{\sin \pi B\tau}{\pi B\tau} \cos \omega_0\tau \end{aligned} \tag{7-234}$$

after some simple manipulations.

$G'_H(\omega)$ and $R(\tau)$ are shown in Fig. 7-53. $R(\tau)$ resembles an amplitude-modulated carrier. The envelope of $R(\tau)$ follows the familiar $(\sin x)/x$

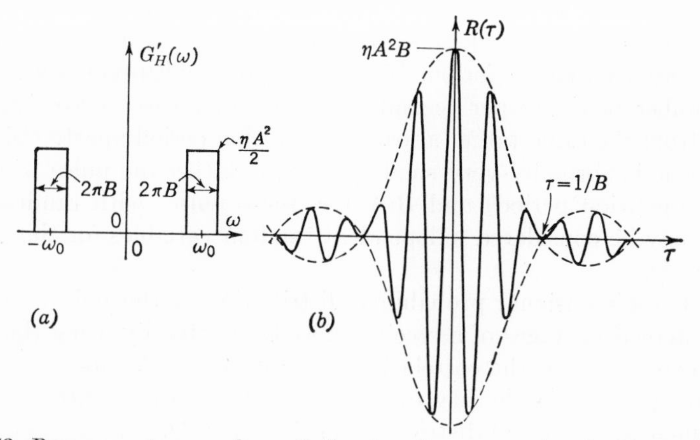

FIG. 7-53. Power spectrum and correlation function, narrowband white noise. (a) Power spectrum; (b) correlation function.

relation, becoming zero at $\tau = 1/B$, and oscillating with decreasing amplitude for larger values of τ. The $(\sin x)/x$ envelope variation is of course due to the choice of a narrowband rectangular filter. Noise applied to an ideal low-pass filter would be expected to have the same $(\sin x)/x$ variation for $R(\tau)$, with the carrier term suppressed.

The low-pass case is left to the reader as an exercise.

The important result brought out by Eq. (7-234) and Fig. 7-53 is the fact that for $\tau > 1/B$ the noise correlation becomes quite small $[< (2/3\pi)R(0)]$. Two samples of noise voltage spaced $1/B$ sec or more apart may thus be assumed effectively independent.

As an example, assume a system with a 1-Mc bandwidth. Voltage samples more than 1 μsec apart are for all practical purposes independent. If 1-μsec signal pulses are transmitted, as in the case of radar or PCM, the signal-plus-noise samples are statistically independent if they are spaced 1 μsec or more apart. This is of course wholly consistent with the inverse time-bandwidth relationship of Chap. 2.

The effect of the narrowband filter is felt over the interval $0 < \tau < 1/B$ and decreases beyond that time. The noise at the output of a narrowband filter centered at f_0 cps would thus be expected to have the appearance of a succession of pulsed sinusoids, each oscillating at approximately f_0 cps, each lasting about $1/B$ sec, and of random amplitude and phase. This is of course in complete agreement with the Fourier-series representation of noise in Sec. 7-9. It was noted there that the noise at the output of a narrowband filter could be written in the form of a sinusoid at frequency f_0 with slowly varying and random amplitude and phase.

This analysis of the correlation function for narrowband white noise confirms the assumption implicitly made in the PCM analysis that the signal plus noise in successive binary-pulse intervals could be treated independently. The average error rate was then found by determining the probability of error for one binary digit and multiplying by the average number of digits per second. In the radar case successive signal pulses from the same target appear a repetition period apart. Since the duty cycle is normally very small ($\tau/T \ll 1$, with τ the pulse width and T the repetition period) and $B \doteq 1/\tau$, these pulses with random noise added may be considered independent random variables for the purpose of analysis.

The two-dimensional probability distribution of the noise voltage in the predetection stages of a receiver may be written by using the appropriate expression for the correlation function $R(\tau)$. As noted previously the joint probability-density function for $v_1(t)$ and $v_2 = v_1(t + \tau)$ is the two-dimensional normal distribution of Eq. (7-214).

$$p(v_1,v_2) = \frac{1}{2\pi M} \exp\left[\frac{-1}{2(1-\rho^2)}\left(\frac{v_1^2}{\sigma_1^2} - \frac{2\rho v_1 v_2}{\sigma_1\sigma_2} + \frac{v_2^2}{\sigma_2^2}\right)\right]$$
$$M^2 = \sigma_1^2\sigma_2^2(1-\rho^2) = \mu_{20}\mu_{02} - \mu_{11}^2$$

For a stationary process av v_1^2 = av $v_2^2 = N$, the total mean-squared noise voltage. Assuming zero average value for the noise voltage $v(t)$, av v_1^2 and av v_2^2 are just the variances μ_{20} or σ_1^2 and μ_{02} or σ_2^2. Thus $\sigma_1^2 = \sigma_2^2 = N$. The joint density function becomes for this case

$$\begin{aligned} p(v_1,v_2) &= \frac{1}{2\pi M} \exp\left[-\frac{1}{2(1-\rho^2)N}(v_1^2 - 2\rho v_1 v_2 + v_2^2)\right] \\ &= \frac{1}{2\pi\sqrt{N^2 - \mu_{11}^2}} \exp\left[-\frac{N(v_1^2 + v_2^2) - 2\mu_{11}v_1v_2}{2(N^2 - \mu_{11}^2)}\right] \end{aligned} \tag{7-235}$$

since $$\rho = \frac{\mu_{11}}{\sigma_1\sigma_2} = \frac{\mu_{11}}{N}$$

[Eq. (7-213)], and

$$M = \sqrt{\mu_{20}\mu_{02} - \mu_{11}^2} = \sqrt{N^2 - \mu_{11}^2}$$

in this case. The distribution thus depends on the mean-squared voltage N and on the covariance μ_{11}. For an ergodic process of zero average value μ_{11} is just the correlation function $R(\tau)$.

Both N and $R(\tau)$ may be written in terms of the power spectral density $G'_H(\omega)$, which in turn depends on the system transfer function $H(j\omega)$. Thus

$$N = \int_{\infty}^{\infty} G'_H(\omega)\, df \tag{7-236}$$

since the integral of the power spectral density over all frequencies gives the mean-squared value of $v(t)$ (the total average power normalized to a 1-ohm resistor). From the Wiener-Khintchine theorem

$$R(\tau) = \int_{-\infty}^{\infty} e^{j\omega\tau} G'_H(\omega)\, df = \mu_{11} \tag{7-237}$$

The two-dimensional probability-density function of an ergodic gaussian process thus depends solely on the power spectral density $G'_H(\omega)$. This in turn depends on the spectral density of the input noise and the system transfer function. In terms of N and $R(\tau)$, $p(v_1,v_2)$ becomes for this case

$$p(v_1,v_2) = \frac{1}{2\pi\sqrt{N^2 - R^2(\tau)}} \exp\left[-\frac{N(v_1^2 + v_2^2) - 2R(\tau)v_1v_2}{2[N^2 - R^2(\tau)]}\right] \tag{7-238}$$

N and $R(\tau)$ are given in terms of the power spectral density by Eqs. (7-236) and (7-237). As noted in the next section and as is apparent from Eq. (7-237) for $R(\tau)$,

$$N = R(0) \qquad \text{also}$$

The expression for $p(v_1,v_2)$ may thus be written in an alternative form:

$$p(v_1,v_2) = \frac{1}{2\pi\sqrt{R^2(0) - R^2(\tau)}} \exp\left[-\frac{R(0)(v_1^2 + v_2^2) - 2R(\tau)v_1v_2}{2[R^2(0) - R^2(\tau)]}\right] \tag{7-239}$$

Either the power spectral density $G'_H(\omega)$ or its transform $R(\tau)$ completely defines the two-dimensional gaussian distribution. It is important to bear in mind the assumptions made in writing $p(v_1,v_2)$ for this case:

1. The process is assumed ergodic.
2. $v(t)$ is the noise voltage in the *predetection* stages of the receiver, where the gaussian distribution holds.

If we integrate over all values of v_2, we obtain the one-dimensional gaussian distribution for $p(v_1)$ or $p(v)$. This appears in terms of $R(0) = N = \sigma^2$, the total mean-squared voltage, and is of course the distribution utilized in the previous sections on noise statistics.

7-14. Properties of the Autocorrelation Function. Some useful properties of the autocorrelation function may be deduced from its time-average definition. Some of these may have already been noted by the reader in studying the examples given.

1. $R(0)$ equals N, the mean-squared value of $v(t)$. This is apparent from the definition of $R(\tau)$.

$$R(\tau) = \lim_{T\to\infty} \frac{1}{T} \int_0^T v(t)v(t+\tau)\,dt \tag{7-240}$$

Then, with $\tau = 0$,

$$R(0) = \lim_{T\to\infty} \frac{1}{T} \int_0^T v^2(t)\,dt = N \tag{7-241}$$

For a 1-ohm resistive load, this is the same as the average power. The Wiener-Khintchine theorem of course checks this result. Since

$$R(\tau) = \int_{-\infty}^{\infty} e^{j\omega\tau} G'(\omega)\,df \tag{7-242}$$

$$R(0) = \int_{-\infty}^{\infty} G'(\omega)\,df = P_{av} = N \tag{7-243}$$

by definition of the power spectral density.

The $\tau = 0$ value of the correlation function thus gives the mean-squared value of the function or its average power (1-ohm resistor).

The previous examples serve to substantiate this result. In the case of white noise, with uniform power spectrum, the total power is infinite. But $R(\tau) = (\eta/2)\delta(\tau)$ was the result for this case, so that $R(0)$ is infinite here. White noise passed through a simple RC network had for its spectral density $G'_H(\omega) = (\eta/2)/[1 + (\omega/\omega_0)^2]$. Integrating this over all positive and negative frequencies gives

$$N = P_{av} = \int_{-\infty}^{\infty} G'_H(\omega)\,df = \frac{\eta\omega_0}{4}$$

This is just the relation found for $R(0)$ in that case.

Similarly, for the rectangular bandpass filter, with $G'_H(\omega) = A^2\eta/2$ over the range of frequencies defined, the total power is $\eta A^2 B$ watts. (Both positive and negative frequencies must be included.) Again this is just $R(0)$ as found from Eq. (7-234).

2. $R(0) \geq R(\tau)$. This is apparent from the examples discussed: in all cases $R(\tau)$ decreases for $\tau > 0$. The proof depends on the fact that the phase factor $e^{j\omega\tau}$ can never increase the value of a function. Thus

$$|R(\tau)| = \left| \int_{-\infty}^{\infty} e^{j\omega\tau} G'(\omega)\,df \right| \leq \int_{-\infty}^{\infty} |G'(\omega)|\,df = R(0) \tag{7-244}$$

since $G'(\omega)$ is always a positive number.

As in the case of the two-variable ensemble average the correlation function may be normalized by dividing by $R(0)$. Then

$$\left| \frac{R(\tau)}{R(0)} \right| \leq 1$$

is a normalized correlation coefficient. For an ergodic process it is the same as the ensemble-average correlation coefficient $\rho = \mu_{11}/\sigma_1\sigma_2$, if av $v = 0$. Since we are dealing with a single function $v(t)$, $\sigma_1 = \sigma_2 = \sigma$. (The ergodic process implies a stationary process.) σ^2 is the mean-squared value of $v(t)$. This is the same as $R(0)$ for an ergodic process. We recall that we also had the relation $|\rho| \leq 1$.

3. $R(\tau) = R(-\tau)$ for a stationary random process. $R(\tau)$ is thus symmetrical in τ. This is of course demonstrated by the previous examples of correlation functions. The proof follows from the definition of the autocorrelation function.

$$\begin{aligned} R(\tau) &= \lim_{T\to\infty} \frac{1}{T} \int_0^T v(t)v(t+\tau)\,dt \\ &= \lim_{T\to\infty} \frac{1}{T} \int_{-\tau}^{T-\tau} v(t)v(t+\tau)\,dt \end{aligned} \tag{7-245}$$

since the time origin can be shifted arbitrarily if the process is stationary. Defining a new variable $x = t + \tau$,

$$R(\tau) = \lim_{T\to\infty} \frac{1}{T} \int_0^T v(x-\tau)v(x)\,dx = R(-\tau) \tag{7-246}$$

4. Correlation function of a periodic function is also periodic. In the discussion of correlation functions up to this point we have tacitly assumed the random variable to have zero d-c or periodic components. In many problems, as, for instance, the PCM and radar examples considered in this chapter, the time function consists of noise plus a periodic or d-c signal. What is the autocorrelation function of the periodic component?

A simple relation holds in this case: if a function $v(t)$ is periodic, $R(\tau)$ is also periodic. As an example, let

$$v(t) = A\cos(\omega t + \theta) \tag{7-247}$$

Then $R(\tau) = \lim_{T\to\infty} \frac{1}{T} \int_0^T A\cos(\omega t + \theta)\, A\cos(\omega t + \theta + \omega\tau)\,dt$

But $\cos A \cos B = \frac{1}{2}[\cos(A+B) + \cos(A-B)]$

Therefore

$$\begin{aligned} R(\tau) &= \lim_{T\to\infty} \frac{A^2}{2T} \int_0^T [\cos(2\omega t + 2\theta + \omega\tau) + \cos\omega\tau]\,dt \\ &= \frac{A^2}{2}\cos\omega\tau + \lim_{T\to\infty} \frac{A^2}{2T} \frac{\sin(2\omega T + 2\theta + \omega\tau) - \sin(\omega\tau + 2\theta)}{2\omega} \\ &= \frac{A^2}{2}\cos\omega\tau \end{aligned} \tag{7-248}$$

As a check, note that $R(0) = A^2/2$ is the mean-squared value of $v(t)$, $R(\tau) = R(-\tau)$, and $R(0) \geq R(\tau)$ in this case (see Fig. 7-54).

$R(\tau)$ retains the periodicity of $v(t)$ but is independent of the phase angle. [This is as expected because of the transform relation between $R(\tau)$ and the power spectral density $G'(\omega)$.]

If $v(t)$ is a d-c voltage $v(t) = A_0$, $R(\tau) = A_0^2$ from the definition of autocorrelation function. This of course agrees with the intuitive concept of correlation. The Fourier transform of a constant is just the impulse function. This checks with the discussion of Chap. 6, in which it was shown that $G'(\omega)$ for a d-c voltage was an impulse function at $\omega = 0$.

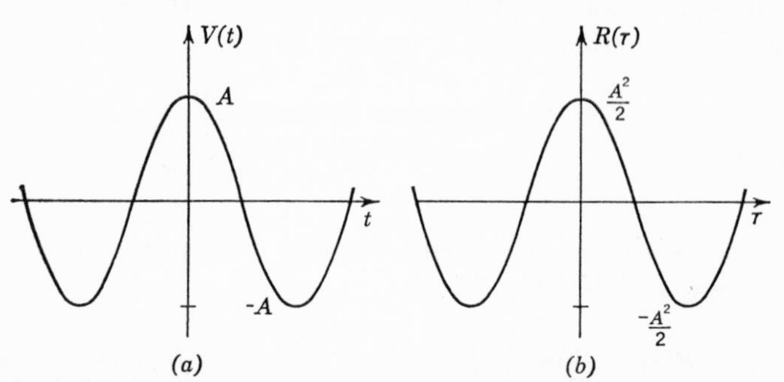

FIG. 7-54. Autocorrelation function of a periodic function. (a) $V(t) = A \cos \omega t$; (b) $R(\tau) = (A^2/2) \cos \omega\tau$.

In general, if

$$v(t) = A_0 + \sum_{k=1}^{n} A_k \sin (\omega_k t + \theta_k) \tag{7-249}$$

with all the frequencies incommensurable ($\omega_m \neq \omega_n$),

$$R(\tau) = A_0^2 + \sum_{k=1}^{n} \frac{A_k^2}{2} \cos \omega_k \tau \tag{7-250}$$

This also agrees with the Wiener-Khintchine theorem, for the Fourier transform of a sinusoid is an impulse function centered at the frequency of the sinusoid (Chap. 2). The spectral density of a group of sinusoids was shown in Chap. 6 to be given by a series of impulse functions at the frequencies of the sine waves.

5. Synchronous detection and autocorrelators. The periodic property of the autocorrelation function of periodic functions has been utilized in detecting the presence of periodic signals in noise.

Assume, for example, that the input to a system consists either of a periodic signal $s(t)$ plus random noise $n(t)$ or of noise alone. To detect the presence of the signal, we arbitrarily multiply the input functions by a sine wave, $\cos \omega_0(t + \tau)$, of the same frequency as the signal and of variable phase angle $\omega_0\tau$. Averaging over a long time interval, we get

$$\frac{1}{T}\int_0^T [s(t) + n(t)] \cos \omega_0(t + \tau)\, dt$$

This is just in the form of the cross-correlation function of Eq. (7-218), with $s + n$ corresponding to $f(t)$ and $\cos \omega_0 t$ corresponding to $g(t)$. Assuming that the noise has negligible power at the frequency f_0, the correlation between $n(t)$ and $\cos \omega_0 t$ vanishes for all τ. Since $s(t)$ is assumed periodic at f_0, the resultant integral approaches the autocorrelation function of $s(t)$, which is of the form $R(0) \cos \omega_0\tau$.

If signal is absent, the cross-correlation term between the noise and $\cos \omega_0 t$ alone appears and averages out to zero.

Devices that perform the indicated multiplication by $\cos \omega_0(t + \tau)$ and then do the time averaging to determine the presence of signals in noise have been constructed and are called *autocorrelators*. The process is identically that of synchronous detection and narrowband filtering which was discussed in Chaps. 3 and 4 and to which reference has already been made in this chapter. Recall that by synchronous or inphase detection was meant the injection of a locally generated sine wave of exactly the frequency of the input signal to heterodyne the signal down to the video-frequency range. The product demodulator of Chaps. 3 and 4 was shown to perform this synchronous-detection process. But the product of $s(t)$ and $\cos \omega_0 t$ is exactly what is called for in the autocorrelator.

The average of this product over a long interval of time corresponds to the use of a narrowband filter to filter out all extraneous frequency components and *associated noise.*

The analysis of synchronous detection in Sec. 4-2 on chopper modulation and demodulation indicated that, if the locally generated sine wave were out of phase with the incoming signal by θ radians, the detector output would be multiplied by the factor $\cos \theta$. Maximum output thus appears for $\theta = 0$, zero output for $\theta = \pi/2$. In the case of the autocorrelator θ is just the term $\omega_0\tau$, and the output is

$$R(0) \cos \theta = R(0) \cos \omega_0\tau$$

Maximum output is thus obtained for $\tau = 0$ and zero output for $\omega_0\tau = \pi/2$. In the case of the autocorrelator the time delay τ is actually varied in steps to obtain a complete curve of the correlation function.

7-15. Autocorrelation Function and Power Spectrum of Random Telegraph Signal.[1] We have placed great emphasis in the past few sections on the two-dimensional probability distribution, and the accompanying autocorrelation function, of band-limited white noise. In particular we

[1] Rice, *op. cit.*, sec. 2.7, p. 44.

have shown how to calculate the correlation function in terms of the power spectral density of the noise voltage.

The autocorrelation technique is frequently useful in a reverse fashion: it is helpful in calculating the power spectrum of various random functions. This depends on being able to determine the ensemble covariance μ_{11} and from this, assuming an ergodic process, the autocorrelation function $R(\tau)$.

The technique has been employed in determining the power spectrum of white noise passed through various nonlinear devices.[1] We shall employ the autocorrelation technique in determining the power spectrum of a particular type of random signal. This is the so-called "random telegraph signal" and has been chosen as illustrative of the technique used. (Other examples may be found in the book by Lawson and Uhlenbeck.[2]) This signal is defined to be a voltage $s(t)$ of binary amplitudes $+a$ or $-a$, as shown in Fig. 7-55.

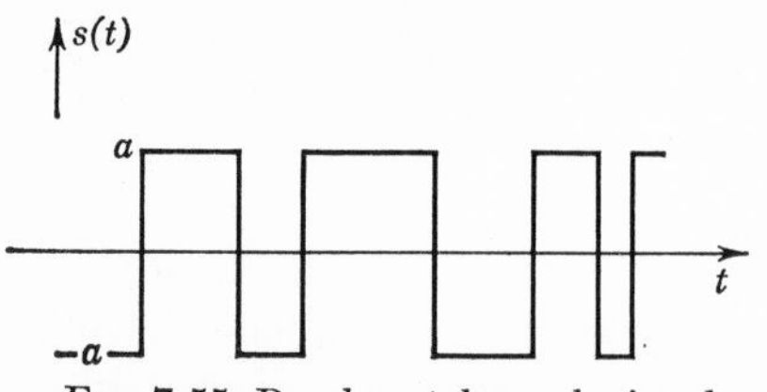

FIG. 7-55. Random telegraph signal.

The length of time for which $s(t)$ remains in either position is random. In particular the number of times the function changes sign (shifting from either amplitude to the other) is given by the so-called "Poisson distribution"

$$P(K) = \frac{(\mu T)^K e^{-\mu T}}{K!} \qquad K \geq 0 \tag{7-251}$$

where $P(K)$ is the probability of exactly K sign changes in T sec and μ is the average number of sign changes (zero crossings) per second.

The power spectrum of such a signal can obviously not be found by using the techniques of Sec. 6-1. The time-averaged autocorrelation function of the past sections can also not be found directly since the random nature of the signal $s(t)$ precludes writing for it a mathematical expression and averaging over all time.

What we shall do here instead will be to determine the ensemble-averaged covariance μ_{11}, assuming that the known statistical distribution is stationary. Assuming as well that the random process is ergodic gives us then the time-averaged autocorrelation function $R(\tau)$, and from this directly the power spectrum.

This method is particularly important because it enables us to discuss for the first time in this book more realistic representations of physical signals.

As has been noted repeatedly throughout this book actual signals to be

[1] See Bennett, *op. cit.*, and Davenport and Root, *op. cit.*, for various examples.
[2] *Op. cit.*

transmitted in practice are always random and unpredictable in form. Otherwise why transmit them? Although the use of a series of test pulses or a sine wave frequently provides us with useful information as to the operation of a particular information-transmission system, such waveforms are artificial representations of actual signals. The random telegraph signal, although still rather crude and specialized in form, is nonetheless a more realistic example of an information-bearing signal than a continuous sine wave.

Once the power spectrum of a particular random signal is known, the filtering effect of various networks through which the signal passes may be determined. Knowing the power spectrum of both the signal and of any noise mixed in with it may enable us to develop schemes for eventually filtering out the signal from the noise. Or we may just as well find that a simple linear filter will not suffice to distinguish between signal and noise.

Knowledge of the signal power spectrum is thus important in the design of information-transmission systems. The calculation of the power spectrum of a random type of signal is the first step in the more realistic approach of designing systems to handle prescribed random inputs rather than arbitrarily assumed pulse and sine-wave inputs.

We shall first discuss briefly the particular statistical distribution, the Poisson distribution, assumed for the random telegraph signal. The calculation of the autocorrelation function, and from that the power spectrum, will then follow.

It is well to repeat at this point that the telegraph signal represents one of many examples of random signals with prescribed statistical properties. This signal happens to have a Poisson distribution. In other examples other distributions would occur. The method to be used for finding the power spectrum would be the same, however.

The Poisson distribution of Eq. (7-251) is an example of a discrete probability distribution, since it is defined only for discrete values of K. That av K is μT may be shown readily from the definition of ensemble average. Thus

$$
\begin{aligned}
\text{av } K &= \sum_{K=0}^{\infty} KP(K) \\
&= e^{-\mu T} \sum_{K=0}^{\infty} \frac{K(\mu T)^K}{K!} \\
&= \mu T e^{-\mu T} \sum_{K=1}^{\infty} \frac{(\mu T)^{K-1}}{(K-1)!}
\end{aligned}
\tag{7-252}
$$

since the $K = 0$ term is zero. But

$$\sum_{K=1}^{\infty} \frac{(\mu T)^{K-1}}{(K-1)!} = 1 + \mu T + \frac{(\mu T)^2}{2!} + \cdots$$

is just the series expansion of $e^{\mu T}$. From Eq. (7-252), then,

$$\text{av } K = \mu T \tag{7-253}$$

and μ represents the average number of sign changes per second.

The Poisson distribution is obtained from the simple assumption for the random telegraph signal that the probability of a sign change in a differential interval t to $t + \Delta t$ is proportional to the length of the interval Δt, independent of occurrences outside this interval.

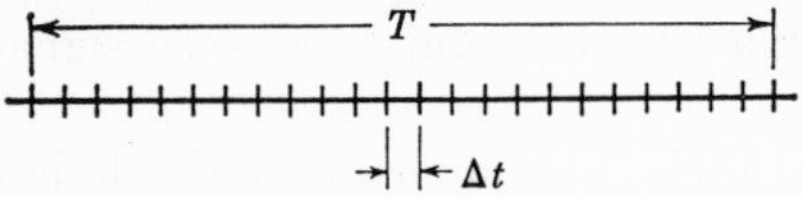

FIG. 7-56. Derivation of Poisson distribution.

To derive the Poisson distribution from this assumption, consider a large interval T sec long divided into M subintervals Δt sec long. Then $M = T/\Delta t \gg 1$ (Fig. 7-56). The probability of a zero crossing (or sign change) in any one interval Δt sec long is $\mu \, \Delta t$ by hypothesis, with μ a proportionality factor ($\mu \, \Delta t \ll 1$). The probability of *no* zero crossing in this small interval must be $1 - \mu \, \Delta t$.

Under the assumption that the probability of an occurrence in one interval is independent of occurrences in the other intervals the probability that there will be *no* zero crossings in any of the M independent intervals is the product of the probabilities. This is just $P(0)$, the probability of no sign changes in T sec, and is given by

$$P(0) = (1 - \mu \, \Delta t)^M = (1 - \mu \, \Delta t)^{T/\Delta t} \tag{7-254}$$

Upon letting $\Delta t \to 0$, $M \to \infty$, and $P(0)$ becomes

$$P(0) = e^{-\mu T} \tag{7-255}$$

in the limit. Recall that

$$\lim_{\epsilon \to 0} (1 - \epsilon)^{1/\epsilon} = \frac{1}{e} \qquad \text{and} \qquad \lim_{\epsilon \to 0} (1 - n\epsilon)^{1/\epsilon} = e^{-n}$$

Similarly the probability of exactly *one* sign change in T sec is

$$\begin{aligned} P(1) &= M(\mu \, \Delta t)(1 - \mu \, \Delta t)^{M-1} \\ &= (\mu T)(1 - \mu \, \Delta t)^{M-1} \end{aligned} \tag{7-256}$$

since there are M possible intervals in which the one sign change can take place. Each of these possibilities is mutually exclusive, and so the probabilities add.

Again taking the limit $\Delta t \to 0$,

$$P(1) = \mu T e^{-\mu T} \tag{7-257}$$

The probability of exactly K sign changes in the M intervals Δt sec long $(K < M)$ is

$$P(K) = \frac{M!}{K!(M-K)!} (\mu \, \Delta t)^K (1 - \mu \, \Delta t)^{M-K} \tag{7-258}$$

for the probability of one sign change in each of K intervals is $(\mu \, \Delta t)^K$ and the concurrent probability of no sign changes in the remaining $M - K$ intervals is $(1 - \mu \, \Delta t)^{M-K}$. The over-all probability is the product of these independent probabilities. But there are $M!/K!(M - K)!$ ways in which K sign changes can occur (the number of combinations of M things, K at a time). These are mutually exclusive, and the resulting probabilities add, giving Eq. (7-258).

The distribution of $P(K)$, given by Eq. (7-258), is another frequently occurring discrete probability distribution called the *binomial distribution*. In the limit, as $\Delta t \to 0$, this distribution approaches the Poisson distribution of Eq. (7-251).

This is easily demonstrated by considering the limit as $\Delta t \to 0$ and $M \to \infty$. For large M, $M!$ may be approximated by Stirling's approximation:[1]

$$M! \doteq \sqrt{2\pi} \, e^{-M} M^{M+\frac{1}{2}} \tag{7-259}$$

(This is even a good approximation for $M = 2$, as may be shown by putting in numbers.) With K fixed, $(M - K)!$ may be similarly represented by

$$(M - K)! \doteq \sqrt{2\pi} \, e^{-(M-K)} (M - K)^{M-K+\frac{1}{2}} \tag{7-260}$$

Substituting these approximations for $M!$ and $(M - K)!$ into Eq. (7-258), we get, for large M,

$$K!P(K) \doteq e^{-K} \left(1 - \frac{K}{M}\right)^{-(M+\frac{1}{2})} \left(1 - \frac{K}{M}\right)^{K} (M\mu \, \Delta t)^K (1 - \mu \, \Delta t)^{M-K} \tag{7-261}$$

By keeping $M \, \Delta t = T$ fixed, as well as K fixed, and taking the limit as $M \to \infty$, Eq. (7-251) is obtained. Again use is made of the relation

$$\lim_{M\to\infty} \left(1 - \frac{K}{M}\right)^{-M} = e^K$$

as well as

$$\lim_{\Delta t\to 0} (1 - \mu \, \Delta t)^{T/\Delta t} = e^{-\mu T}$$

[1] P. Franklin, "A Treatise on Advanced Calculus," John Wiley & Sons, Inc., New York, 1940.

How do we now find the ensemble covariance, μ_{11}, from the known distribution $P(K)$, for the number of sign changes in T sec?

Recall that μ_{11} was defined in Sec. 7-12 as

$$\mu_{11} = \text{av}\,[(x - x_0)(y - y_0)] \tag{7-262}$$

where x and y are two dependent variables and x_0 and y_0 their respective average values. In words, μ_{11} is the average, over all possible values, of the product $(x - x_0)(y - y_0)$.

To apply this definition to the case of the random telegraph signal, assume that a large number of identical sources of such a signal are available. Let x represent the different outputs of the ensemble simultaneously measured at some time t_1. x obviously is either $+a$ or $-a$. Since there is no preferred amplitude, x_0 is just zero. We can measure the simultaneous outputs of the ensemble at time t_2, τ sec later. Let y represent the possible outputs of the ensemble. Again only $+a$ or $-a$ is possible, and y_0 is zero. One member of such an ensemble is shown in Fig. 7-57. The covariance μ_{11} and the product moment m_{11} are the same in this case.

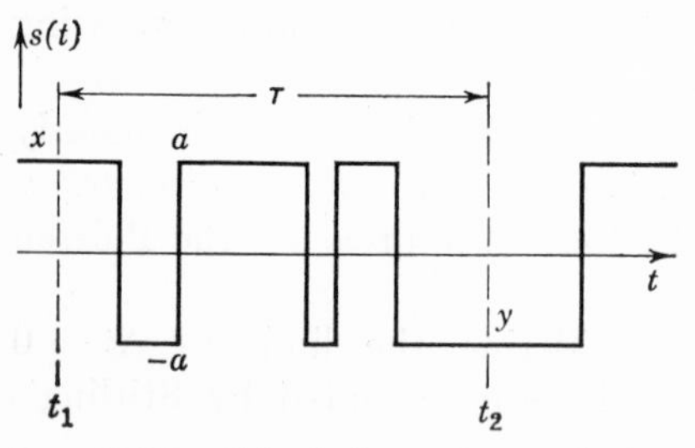

FIG. 7-57. Calculation of correlation function, random telegraph signal.

Since the product $(x - x_0)(y - y_0)$ is either $+a^2$ or $-a^2$, the average of this product is simply $+a^2$ times the number of joint occurrences of this product, plus $-a^2$ times the number of joint occurrences of this product, all divided by the total number of products considered. The ensemble is assumed stationary so that the result should be independent of the initial time t_1 at which it was measured. It depends only on the difference in time τ. If a large number of random telegraph sources were available, a series of such measurements and calculations could be performed for different values of τ.

Alternatively μ_{11} can be calculated from the given Poisson distribution. For the product $+a^2$ will occur if the sign of $s(t)$ changes an even number of times in τ sec, while the product $-a^2$ will be obtained for an odd number of sign changes. In the sample wave of Fig. 7-57, for example, $s(t_1)s(t_1 + \tau)$ is $-a^2$, since the wave has changed sign five times in the τ-sec interval chosen. The ensemble average av $[(x - x_0)(y - y_0)]$ is thus $+a^2$ times the probability of an even number of sign changes of $s(t)$ in τ sec, plus $-a^2$ times the probability of an odd number of sign changes.

The covariance is thus

$$\begin{aligned}\mu_{11} = {} & a^2[P(0) + P(2) + P(4) + \cdots] \\ & - a^2[P(1) + P(3) + P(5) + \cdots]\end{aligned} \tag{7-263}$$

where $P(0)$ is the probability of no sign changes, $P(1)$ the probability of one sign change, etc. The appropriate values for the probabilities are obtained from the Poisson distribution of Eq. (7-251), with T replaced by τ.

$$P(K) = \frac{(\mu\tau)^K}{K!} e^{-\mu\tau} \tag{7-264}$$

The covariance becomes, after interleaving the positive and negative terms,

$$\begin{aligned}\mu_{11} &= a^2 e^{-\mu\tau}\left[1 - \frac{\mu\tau}{1!} + \frac{(\mu\tau)^2}{2!} - \frac{(\mu\tau)^3}{3!} + \cdots\right] \\ &= a^2 e^{-\mu\tau} e^{-\mu\tau} \\ &= a^2 e^{-2\mu\tau}\end{aligned} \tag{7-265}$$

since the sum in brackets is just the power-series expansion for the exponential. Although τ was assumed positive, it could just as well have been

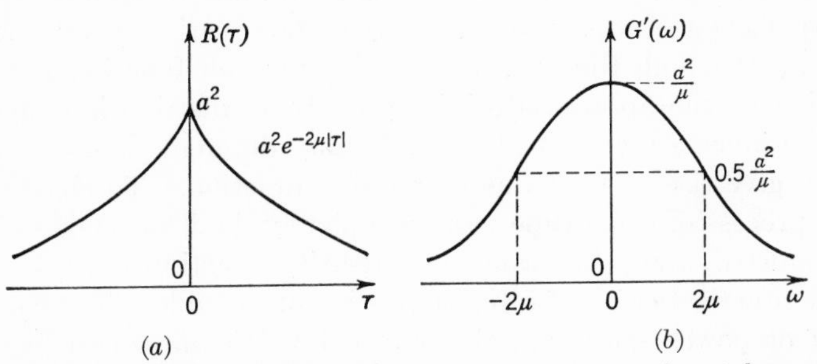

FIG. 7-58. Autocorrelation function and power spectrum, random telegraph signal. (*a*) Correlation function; (*b*) power spectrum.

taken negative (with t_2 and t_1 in Fig. 7-57 interchanged), with the same results. More generally, then, the covariance is given by

$$\mu_{11} = a^2 e^{-2\mu|\tau|} = R(\tau) \tag{7-266}$$

This is the same as the autocorrelation function $R(\tau)$ if an ergodic process is assumed.

Note that $R(0) = a^2$ is just the average power in the signal, checking one of the properties of $R(\tau)$ discussed previously. $R(\tau)$ is an even function of τ, and $R(\tau) < R(0)$, both agreeing with the previous discussion.

Equation (7-266) is shown sketched in Fig. 7-58*a*. An example of an autocorrelation function of this form has already been discussed. In particular the autocorrelation function of white noise passed through a simple RC network was shown in Sec. 7-13 [Eq. (7-232)] to be of exactly this form. The two spectral densities must thus also be of the same form. Using Eq. (7-231), then, the two-sided power spectrum of the random telegraph signal must be given by

$$G'(\omega) = \frac{a^2/\mu}{1 + (\omega/2\mu)^2} \tag{7-267}$$

The power spectrum of the random telegraph signal is thus identical with the spectrum of white noise passed through a single RC network with time constant $RC = 1/2\mu$. (μ represents the average number of sign changes of the signal per second.) The power spectrum is sketched in Fig. 7-58*b*.

This simple example of the calculation of the power spectrum of one type of random signal has also demonstrated the nonunique character of the power spectrum. The random telegraph signal and white noise at the output of an RC network are indistinguishable as far as their frequency spectral behavior is concerned. This is in general true of all power spectra or autocorrelation functions. A given spectrum may represent many different types of random inputs.

The reason for this is easily explained. We have chosen to emphasize one particular set of statistical parameters, the covariance and correlation function. Although the covariance or correlation function is uniquely specified once the appropriate joint-probability-distribution function is given, the inverse is not at all true. Many different distribution functions can give rise to the same correlation function. To characterize a random process of some type more completely, be it noise or a signal to be transmitted, the joint-probability-density function must be known. In many practical cases of interest this is not possible. The correlation function or power spectrum, either calculated or measured experimentally, must thus suffice as a much more limited measure of the statistical properties of a given random function.

7-16. Summary. The elements of the theory of probability have been introduced in this chapter. Starting with a definition of probability in terms of the relative frequency of occurrence of random discrete events, we introduced the ideas of statistical independence, conditional probability, and joint probability. We then went on to consider random continuous variables and the probability-density and -distribution functions utilized in discussing these quantities.

The discussion of random variables enabled us to treat in some detail the statistics of noise and the influence on the noise of physical systems through which it passed. In particular we noted that fluctuation noise could be assumed to follow the gaussian probability-density curve. The one parameter necessary to define the noise, assuming zero average value, was the mean-squared noise voltage, or variance. Passing the noise through a linear system serves only to modify the variance. The probability-density function remains gaussian. Passing the noise through a nonlinear device serves to alter the probability distribution, however.

As an example of the application of noise statistics, we calculated the probability of error due to noise in a binary PCM system. A rather narrow range of S/N ratios was found to exist above which the probability of error dropped rapidly to negligible values, below which the chance of error was high. This was defined to be the *threshold* range of the S/N ratio, a term first introduced in Chap. 6.

The probability distribution of noise at the output of a nonlinear device was then discussed as an example of the calculation of the distribution of a function of a random variable. As a specific important example, we discussed the probability distribution of both narrowband noise and narrowband noise plus a sinusoidal signal at the output of an envelope detector and showed that the noise alone followed the so-called Rayleigh distribution. We also found the probability distribution of the phase both of noise and of signal plus additive noise. Examples of the application of this material included a simple radar detection scheme and a navigational system using phase detection.

The definition of the characteristic function as the Fourier transform of the probability-density function enabled us to determine the probability distribution for the sum of many independent random variables. Using the characteristic function, we were able to demonstrate, in several cases, that the distribution of the sum approaches a gaussian distribution. These examples were all special cases of the very general central-limit theorem of probability theory.

The final sections of the chapter were concerned with the joint probability distribution of two dependent variables. In particular we discussed in detail the joint distribution of pairs of values of a random time function spaced a given interval τ sec apart. Fluctuation noise is one example of such a random time function. Random signals of various types serve as other examples. As a specific measure of the dependence between two random variables we introduced the concept of *covariance*, or the probability average of the product of the two variables. In the case of the random time function we also defined the *autocorrelation function*, the time average of the two values spaced τ sec apart. For an ergodic process with zero average value the covariance and autocorrelation function are equal.

We showed that the autocorrelation function was related to the power spectrum of the random time function. In particular the two turn out to be Fourier transforms of one another. This relationship enables one to calculate the effect of system band limiting on the joint probability distribution of pairs of values of a random time function. Alternatively it supplies us with means for calculating the power spectrum of a given random signal. An example discussed was the so-called random telegraph signal. Other examples appear in the references cited.

The material of this chapter is meant to serve only as an introduction to the study of random signals and noise and to the analysis of information-transmission systems using the concepts developed. The references mentioned throughout this chapter, as also those of previous chapters, should enable the reader to delve further and in more detail into this fascinating field.

PROBLEMS

7-1. An urn contains two white balls and six red ones. What is the probability that one ball drawn at random will be white?

7-2. An analysis of a long message transmitted in binary digits shows 3,000 zeros and 7,000 ones. What is the probability that any one digit in the message is a zero?

7-3. A selected list of words in the English language is to be transmitted by means of a binary code, with each word represented by 12 binary digits or fewer. How many words can there be on the list?

7-4. The numbers 1 through 10 are selected at random. (*a*) What is the probability that the numbers are selected in the order 1, 2, . . . , 10? (*b*) What is the probability of selecting the number 2 right after the number 1?

7-5. (*a*) Find the probability of getting a 7 in the toss of two dice.

(*b*) Find the probability of throwing a 6, 7, or 8 with two dice.

7-6. What is the probability that 4 cards drawn in succession from a deck of 52 will all be aces?

7-7. A box contains five white balls, three red balls, and two black ones. What is the probability that two balls drawn from the box will both be red?

7-8. What is the probability of obtaining four tails if four coins are tossed? What is the probability that at least three heads will appear?

7-9. Calculate the conditional and joint probabilities for the typical message of Shannon's three-letter alphabet at the end of Sec. 7-2. Check with the probability tables shown there.

7-10. Show that the probability of finding a continuous random variable x somewhere in the range x_1 to x_2 is given by $P(x_2) - P(x_1)$, with $P(x)$ the cumulative distribution function [see Eq. (7-22)].

7-11. (*a*) Tabulate the probabilities of getting the numbers 2 through 12 on the toss of two dice. Plot these to scale.

(*b*) What is the probability that a number less than 8 will show? What is the probability of getting a number in the range 7 to 10?

7-12. Consider a discrete variable with the probabilities $P_1, P_2, \ldots, P_n$ corresponding to its n possible values. Show that the relation between the variance, or second central moment, μ_2 and the first and second moments m_1 and m_2, respectively, is given by $\mu_2 = m_2 - m_1^2$.

7-13. A discrete variable x has the two values 0 and 1, with probabilities p and $q = 1 - p$, respectively. Show that the probability that a 0 will occur m times in n repetitions of an experiment involving x is given by the *binomial distribution* $P(m) = C_{n,m}p^m q^{n-m}$, where $C_{n,m}$ is the number of combinations of n things taken m at a time.

[See Eq. (7-258) in Sec. 7-15 for one example of the occurrence of this distribution. It is commonly encountered in statistics. Another example occurs in the study of shot noise, where the variable x represents the emission, yes or no, of an electron in a small time interval. The probability that m electrons will be emitted in n intervals can then be approximated by the binomial distribution. As shown in Sec. 7-15 the binomial distribution approaches the Poisson distribution encountered there for large

n. For still larger numbers the Poisson distribution can in turn be shown to approach the gaussian distribution. This is one method frequently used to establish the gaussian distribution for shot noise.]

7-14. (*a*) Plot the binomial distribution $P(m)$ versus m for $n = 4$ and $p = 0.4$. Repeat for $p = 0.2$. Show, in both cases, that the sum of $P(m)$ for $m = 0$ to 4 is 1. Plot the distribution for $n = 10$ and $p = 0.4$, and show that the sum over all values of m is 1.

(*b*) Find the average value and second moment of m in the three cases of (*a*).

7-15. (*a*) Show that the distribution of the number of heads appearing in the tossing of n coins is given by the binomial distribution with $p = q = \frac{1}{2}$.

(*b*) Show that the first and second moments of the binomial distribution are, respectively, $m_1 = np$ and $m_2 = np[1 + p(n - 1)]$. Check the results of Prob. 7-14*b*. What is the total number of heads expected in 1,000 tosses of three coins?

(*c*) Using the results of Prob. 7-12 and of (*b*) above, show that the variance of the binomial distribution is given by $\mu_2 = npq$.

7-16. Consider the function $p(x) = kxe^{-x^2/2N}$, with k and N positive constants.

(*a*) To what range of values must x be restricted to ensure that the function represents a possible probability-density function?

(*b*) Determine k such that $p(x)$ is properly normalized. The resultant function is called the *Rayleigh distribution* and is discussed in Sec. 7-9. Plot $p(x)$ versus $x/\sqrt{N}$.

(*c*) What is the probability that a variable x obeying the Rayleigh distribution will have values between $x = \sqrt{2N}$ and $x = 2\sqrt{N}$?

(*d*) Find the cumulative distribution $P(\sqrt{2N})$.

7-17. Calculate the mean value m_1 and the standard deviation σ of the Rayleigh distribution of the previous problem. These results should agree with Eqs. (7-137) and (7-139).

7-18. Consider the triangular probability-density function of Fig. P 7-18.

(*a*) Find b in terms of a so that the function is properly normalized.

(*b*) Calculate the mean value and standard deviation of the distribution.

(*c*) Plot the cumulative distribution function $P(x)$.

(*d*) What is the probability that x will be greater than $a/2$?

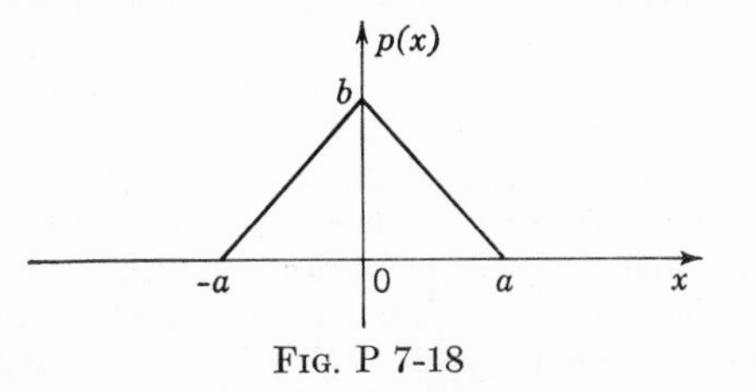

FIG. P 7-18

7-19. Find the variance of the gaussian, or normal, distribution by evaluating the integral of Eq. (7-56).

7-20. Show that the gaussian function of Eq. (7-53) is properly normalized [see Eq. (7-57)].

7-21. Show that the cumulative-probability distribution for the gaussian function is given in terms of the error function by Eq. (7-64). Plot $P(x)$, using any available table of the error function.

7-22. In the manufacture of resistors nominally rated at 100 ohms it is found that the probability distribution of actual resistance values is very closely given by a normal distribution with standard deviation $\sigma = 5$ ohms. What percentage of the resistors manufactured lie within the range 90 to 110 ohms?

7-23. A very sensitive rms voltmeter placed across a resistance network reads 1 μv with the network not connected to any source. What is the probability that the *instantaneous* voltage will not exceed 3 μv at any particular instant?

7-24. Two voltmeters are available for a given experiment, and either one may be chosen at random. Depending upon temperature, humidity, etc., the readings of the voltmeters tend to deviate from the true voltage values. (The additional effect of fluctuation noise is assumed negligible here.) The distribution of the readings about each scale value follows a normal error curve. For one voltmeter the standard deviation is 0.1 volt, for the other 0.2 volt. What is the probability that any voltage read will be within 0.2 volt of its true value?

7-25. The output rms noise voltage of a given linear system is found to be 2 mv. The noise is gaussian fluctuation noise of the type considered in Chap. 5. What is the probability that the instantaneous noise voltage at the output of the system lies between -4 and $+4$ mv?

7-26. Repeat Prob. 7-25 if a d-c voltage of 2 mv is added to the output noise.

7-27. Show that the probability of error in mistaking a binary pulse in noise for noise alone or of mistaking noise for a binary pulse is given by Eq. (7-77). Calculate this error for various values of pulse height to rms noise, and check the curve of Fig. 7-24.

7-28. A binary transmission system transmits 50,000 digits per second. Fluctuation noise is added to the signal in the process of transmission, so that at the decoder, where the digits are converted back to a desired output form, the signal pulses are 1 volt in amplitude, with the rms noise voltage 0.2 volt. What is the average time between mistakes of this system? How is this average time changed if the signal pulses are doubled in amplitude?

7-29. A particular probability-density function is given by $p(x) = e^{-x}, 0 \leq x < \infty$. Sketch both the density and cumulative-distribution functions, and show that $P(\infty) = 1$ (that is, the density function is properly normalized). Find the first and second moments and the variance of this distribution.

7-30. A density function is given by $p(x) = 1, 0 \leq x \leq 1$. Show that the density function of $y = -ln x$ is given by the function of Prob. 7-29.

7-31. Show that the density function of Eq. (7-88) is properly normalized.

7-32. Show that the average value of the distribution of Eq. (7-92) is σ^2.

7-33. The random variable x follows the Rayleigh distribution of Prob. 7-16. Find the distribution of the square of x.

7-34. The receiver of a binary transmission system consists of the two-stage amplifier of Fig. 5-26. The amplifier output is applied directly to the system decoder. Rate of transmission is 100,000 on or off pulses per second. Tuning capacitors (not in Fig. 5-26) are used in each stage of the amplifier to adjust the bandwidth to the optimum required, to maximize the peak S/N ratio at the output (see Fig. 6-9).

Find the signal pulse amplitude required at the amplifier input if the average time between errors in the transmission of the binary digits is to be 1 hr.

7-35. A binary transmission system transmits 10^6 plus or minus pulses per second. The output of the system receiver is fed directly to a decoder. The noise figure of the receiver is 10 db. Its noise equivalent bandwidth is that necessary to ensure maximum peak S/N ratio at the decoder input. Find the average signal power required at the input to the receiver if the average error rate is to be 1 binary digit mistaken every 15 min. Repeat if the digits are represented by on-off pulses.

7-36. What is the probability that the noise voltage at the output of a linear envelope detector will exceed three times the rms noise voltage at the detector input? (Assume that the detector constant is unity.)

7-37. Narrowband fluctuation noise with mean-squared value N is detected by a *quadratic* (or square-law) *envelope detector*, whose output is proportional to the square of the instantaneous envelope voltage. Thus the detector output voltage is cr^2, with c the constant of proportionality and r the envelope voltage.

Find the probability density of the noise at the detector output. Compare with the density function of Prob. 7-29. Calculate the voltages at the output of the detector that would be read by a long-time-constant d-c meter, a long-time-constant rms meter, and a long-time-constant rms meter preceded by a blocking capacitor.

7-38. A non-phase-coherent communication receiver consists of a narrowband tuned amplifier and a quadratic envelope detector. The receiver accepts signal pulses of fixed amplitude. To distinguish between incoming signals and noise present in the receiver, a specific voltage level at the output of the detector is chosen such that all voltages exceeding this level are called signal.

(*a*) What is the probability that noise in the absence of signal will be mistaken for signal if the level is set at $2N$, with N the mean-squared noise voltage at the detector input? (Assume that the detector constant of proportionality is 1 volt/volts^2.)

(*b*) Plot the probability of error due to noise if the voltage level is varied from 0 to $20N$.

7-39. A simple radar system is to be designed, using a threshold detection criterion. The probability that noise alone will be mistaken for signal is specified at 10^{-10}. What must the average S/N ratio at the input to the linear envelope detector be to keep the probability of missing the signal pulse, when it appears, to 0.1? Assume that the S/N ratio and threshold level are high enough so that the gaussian-density-function approximation to the distribution of signal plus noise may be used. Verify this.

7-40. The receiver of the radar system of Prob. 7-39 has a noise figure of 10 db measured from the antenna to the input to the detector. The transmitted radar pulses are 1 μsec wide. (The pulse width is normally fixed by the required resolution of targets in space.) Calculate the peak signal power required at the antenna to attain the specifications of Prob. 7-39. (This may in turn be used to calculate the peak transmitter power required if the system antenna gain and the target range and characteristics are specified.)

7-41. Show that the Fourier transform of a gaussian function is itself a gaussian function. In particular show that, if a probability-density function is the gaussian function of Eq. (7-171), its characteristic function is given by Eq. (7-172).

7-42. A signal pulse has a gaussian-function shape. Find the relationship between the pulse width τ and the spread constant σ in the expression for the gaussian function if τ is the width measured between the half-power points in time. Find the frequency spectrum of the gaussian pulse, and relate the half-power frequency bandwidth to the pulse width τ. (See Prob. 6-12.) Does this result agree with the results of Chap. 2?

7-43. Find the characteristic function for the probability-density function of Prob. 7-29. Using this result, find the probability density for the sum of n such independent random variables.

[HINT: Note that $p(x)$ in Prob. 7-29 corresponds in form to the impulse response of a low-pass RC network. The probability density of the sum of the n variables should correspond to the impulse response of n isolated and cascaded RC networks.]

7-44. Using the moment-generating property of the characteristic function, find the first and second moments and standard deviation of the probability-density function of Prob. 7-43. Compare with the corresponding parameters of the density function of Prob. 7-29.

7-45. From the results of Prob. 7-43 find the probability that the sum of n independent samples of noise, each measured at the output of a quadratic envelope detector, will exceed kN volts. N is the mean-squared voltage of each of the noise samples measured at the *input* to a quadratic envelope detector. Assume that the detector constant is 1. (Note that the results of Probs. 7-37 and 7-38 are a special case of the results of this problem, with $n = 1$.)

Plot the probability vs. the parameter k for $n = 1, 2$, and 5. This gives the probability of error due to noise in the n-pulse radar system using threshold-level detection that is discussed in Sec. 7-11. It applies to the special case of a quadratic envelope detector. Further analysis, including the case where signal plus noise is present, shows that the final radar performance curves of Fig. 7-45 are very nearly independent, however, of the type of envelope detector chosen.

7-46. Show that the two-dimensional gaussian distribution of Eq. (7-214) corresponds to zero average value of y. Show also that the parameters $\mu_{02} = \sigma_2^2$ represent the variance of the one-dimensional density function $p_2(y)$.

7-47. Extend the two-dimensional normal distribution of Eq. (7-214) to the case where av $x = x_0$ and av $y = y_0$. Find $p_2(y)$ for this case, and evaluate the three moments m_{01}, m_{02}, and μ_{02}.

7-48. Show from the time-averaged definition of the autocorrelation function that the autocorrelation function of a periodic sequence of rectangular pulses of amplitude A and width t_0 is given by a periodic sequence of triangular pulses of amplitude A^2t_0/T and base width $2t_0$. T is the period of both sets of functions.

7-49. Show that the result of Prob. 7-48 agrees with the relations given by Eqs. (7-249) and (7-250).

7-50. An autocorrelation function that frequently arises in practical problems is given by

$$R(\tau) = R(0)e^{-\alpha|\tau|} \cos \beta\tau$$

(*a*) Calculate both the one-sided power spectrum $G(\omega)$ and the two-sided spectrum $G'(\omega)$.

(*b*) Typical values for α and β are $\alpha = 1$, $\beta = 0.6$. Plot $R(\tau)/R(0)$ and $G'(\omega)$.

(*c*) Check the results of (*a*) by considering the two limiting cases (1) $\alpha = 0$ and (2) $\beta = 0$.

7-51. Prove the Wiener-Khintchine theorem by actually taking the Fourier transform of $R(\tau)$ as noted in the text.

7-52. White noise of one-sided spectral density $G(\omega) = \eta$ watts/cps is applied to an ideal low-pass filter of cutoff frequency ω_c radians/sec and transfer amplitude A. Find the correlation function of noise at the output. Calculate the total average power at the filter output from the spectral density directly, and compare with $R(0)$.

7-53. White noise of spectral density $G(\omega) = 10\ \mu v^2$/cps is passed through a noiseless narrowband amplifier centered at 400 cps. The amplifier may be represented by an ideal bandpass filter of 50 cps bandwidth about the 400-cps center frequency and amplification factor of 1,000.

(*a*) Write an expression for the autocorrelation function $R(\tau)$ at the amplifier output.

(*b*) The output noise voltage is to be sampled at intervals far enough apart so as to ensure almost independent samples. How far apart should the samples be taken?

(*c*) Using Eqs. (7-238) and (7-239), write an expression for the two-dimensional probability density $p(v_1,v_2)$. v_1 represents an instantaneous sample of the output noise voltage $v(t)$, and v_2 a sample τ sec later.

(*d*) Find the one-dimensional density function $p(v)$ by integrating over-all values of v_2 in the density function of (*c*).

(*e*) What are the moments μ_{11} and μ_{20} of the distribution of (*c*)?

INDEX